Cultural Intersections in Music Therapy:
Music, Health, and the Person

Edited by:
Annette Whitehead-Pleaux
& Xueli Tan

Barcelona PUBLISHERS

Cultural Intersections in Music Therapy:
Music, Health, and the Person

Copyright © 2017

Print ISBN: 9781937440978
E-ISBN: 9781937440985

Distributed throughout the world by:
Barcelona Publishers
10231 Plano Road
Dallas TX 75238

All orders are placed online as follows:

North American Orders: www.barcelonapublishers.com
Other International Orders: www.eurospanbookstore.com/barcelona

Dedication

I speak softly, so you'll have to come closer to hear me.
I speak in English, so you'll have to come closer to interpret my affect and not my words.
I speak of a different world, so you'll have to transcend time and space.
I spoke of you, so you'll know I always remember.

Xueli

I dedicate this book to those who endure oppression,
        to those who resist oppression,
        and to the allies who stand strong at our side.
             Together, we bring truth and justice.

Annette

ACKNOWLEDGMENTS

This book is the result of the work of many people who have sparked our ideas, shared their experiences and thoughts, offered us guidance, and believed in our vision. We are extremely grateful to Sandi Curtis, for it was her foresight to create space for the multicultural institute at the 2012 that became the spark that started this book. We want to extend our sincerest thank you to the original presenters from that institute: Nicole Hahna, Karen Estrella, Feilin Hsiao, Karen Jean Reed, Therese West, Paige A. Robbins Elwafi, Rebecca J. Froman, Spencer Hardy, Marcia Humpal, and Beth York, as well as the additional authors who joined in to write this book — Susan Hadley, Sangeeta Swamy, Aksana Kavaliova-Moussi, Darlene Brooks, Debra Jelinek Gombert, Carolyn Kenny, Roia Rafieyan, Sandi Curtis, Dawn McDougal Miller, Deforia Lane, Leah Oswanski, Amy Donnenwerth, and Stephanie Brink. Finally, we want to acknowledge and offer our deepest thanks to the many clients and families each of us have worked with over our careers. It was in those sessions where we began to question "where is the intersection of music, health, and the individual in this person's culture?"

Xueli & Annette

Personally, I want to thank my wife and daughter for being understanding those many days and nights when I was working on the book. Finally, I want to thank my best friend for her unending encouragement.

Annette

Cultural Intersections in Music Therapy:
Music, Health, and the Person

Edited by:
Annette Whitehead-Pleaux
& Xueli Tan

Barcelona
PUBLISHERS

Cultural Intersections in Music Therapy:
Music, Health, and the Person

Copyright © 2017

Print ISBN: 9781937440978
E-ISBN: 9781937440985

Distributed throughout the world by:
Barcelona Publishers
10231 Plano Road
Dallas TX 75238

All orders are placed online as follows:

North American Orders: www.barcelonapublishers.com
Other International Orders: www.eurospanbookstore.com/barcelona

CONTENTS

CONTRIBUTORS

Stephanie L. Brink, MS, CCLS, MT-BC
Shriners Hospitals for Children
Boston, MA

Darlene Brooks, PhD, MT-BC
Temple University
Philadelphia, PA

Amy M. Donnenwerth, MA, MT-BC
Beckett Springs Behavioral Health Hospital
West Chester, OH

Sandra L. Curtis, PhD, MT-BC
Concordia University
Montreal, Canada

Paige Robbins Elwafi, MMT, MT-BC
Cincinnati Association for the Blind and Visually Impaired
Cincinnati, OH

Karen Estrella, PhD, MT-BC
Lesley University
Cambridge, MA

Rebecca J. Froman, MA, MT-BC
Private practice
Chicago, IL

Debra Jelinek Gombert, MA, MT-BC
Eastern Michigan University
Ypsilanti, MI

Susan Hadley, PhD, MT-BC
Slippery Rock University
Slippery Rock, PA

Nicole D. Hahna, PhD, MT-BC
Slippery Rock University
Slippery Rock, PA

Spencer Hardy, MT-BC
Primary Children's Hospital
Salt Lake City, UT

Feilin Hsiao, PhD, MT-BC
University of the Pacific
Stockton, CA

Marcia Humpal, MEd, MT-BC
Cleveland State University
Cleveland, OH

Aksana Kavaliova-Moussi, MMT, MTA
Private practice
Kingdom of Bahrain

Deforia Lane, PhD, MT-BC
University Hospitals Cleveland Medical Center/Seidman
Cancer Center
Cleveland, OH

Dawn McDougal Miller, MME, MT-BC
Park Nicollet Methodist Hospital
St. Louis Park, MN

Leah G. Oswanski, LPC, MT-BC
Carol G. Simon Cancer Center, Morristown Medical Center,
Morristown, NJ

Roia Rafieyan, MA, MT-BC
Hunterdon Developmental Center
Clinton, NJ

Karen Jean Reed, MA, RMT
Department of State Hospitals – Coalinga
Coalinga, CA

Carolyn Kenny, PhD, MT-BC
Professor Emerita Antioch University
Santa Barbara, CA

Sangeeta Swamy, PhD, MT-BC
Sound Mind School of Music & Wellness Center
Carrboro, NC

Xueli Tan, PhD, MT-BC
Lesley University
Cambridge, MA

Therese M. West, PhD, MT-BC
GIM Private practice
Portland, OR

Annette Whitehead-Pleaux, MA, MT-BC
Saint Mary-of-the-Woods College
Saint Mary of the Woods, IN

PREFACE

Annette Whitehead-Pleaux & Xueli Tan

The Beginning

On February 11, 2014, we sent our proposal for this book to Ken Bruscia at Barcelona Publishers. We had been working on this proposal for several months, honing the language to express our ideas to explore culturally competent music therapy. While we knew our ideas were not new, we knew the field of music therapy did not have a book on the topic at that time. We shared how our book would explore multicultural music therapy in a way that differs from previous books about multicultural music therapy. It was our idea to bring new focus, the voices of first-person music therapists sharing their experiences as minorities, as well as our experience working with individuals from cultures other than our own. Our proposed book would explore the intersections of music, health, and the individual within a variety of cultures, examining how music therapy is relevant within an individual's cultural context. We were excited and nervous to submit our proposal. By our estimation, we expected an answer in about two weeks. However, we were shocked when we received a reply within two hours that Barcelona Publishers had accepted our book. In his email to us, Ken stated that he had been waiting for this book.

We had often discussed how our field has looked at the intersection of culture and music therapy, albeit one culture at a time. In addition, many discussions of culture have been limited to ways to interact with people from other cultures based on rules that differ from the majority culture. But we live in a pluralistic society where cultures interact and intertwine daily. At that time, music therapy did not have a book that had investigated the intersectionality of cultures and music therapy. Our idea for a book was different.

The ideas for this book grew from both of our clinical practices in burn care. We first met in 2006 at an American Burn Association conference, where we were both presenting on music therapy in burn care. Our friendship grew from that initial meeting. Both of us worked with people from a variety of cultures who had been injured and were being treated at the institutions at which we worked. Over the years, we had many of the same questions about cultural competency in music therapy. We worked toward understanding the intersections of culture and music therapy. Xueli had explored and presented on culturally competent educational practices for educating students from Asia, while Annette had written about working with children and families from cultures other than her own as well and worked with Team Rainbow to create its LGBTQ best practices.

In early 2012, Annette was asked to chair an institute focusing on culture at the American Music Therapy Association's (AMTA) conference. The first task was to recruit Xueli to cochair the institute. Together, we sought out music therapists from across the continent who were highly recommended by their peers to be the most prolific writers and experts in the areas of multiculturalism, health, and music therapy. Together, we created the *Multicultural Music Therapy Institute: The Intersections of Music, Health, and the Individuals* that was held at the AMTA 2012 Annual Conference: *Changing Winds: Innovation in Music Therapy* in St. Charles, IL. The institute featured this distinguished panel of music therapists who specialize in specific cultures as well as a 150-page manual that contained chapters on each of the cultures. Collectively, the 12 individuals wrote an 11-chapter manual to complement the institute. All of the authors/ presenters are well versed in minority cultures, and we had purposefully sought out several who can attest to the authenticity of their firsthand experience as members of those cultural groups. This manual allowed the panel of music therapists to provide a deeper education for the attendees.

After the conference presentation, we felt that this work was relevant to the field of music therapy in North America and wanted to share it with a wider audience. It was our desire to augment the existing manual with additional chapters, create greater depth within the existing chapters, and publish it as a book. We consulted with the institute presenters/authors and came to a collective decision to make this manual into a book. Once we got the acceptance from Barcelona Publishers, we began to bring this idea into reality. We recruited additional authors to expand the book's exploration of culture.

The Book Design

The purpose of this book is to bring to the forefront of our consciousness the notion that the world is becoming more culturally pluralistic, that it is becoming increasingly challenging to define and pigeonhole any one individual into a cultural corner fenced in by myths, assumptions, and stereotypes.

Prior to hearing the voices of minority music therapists, we want to provide an understanding of the systems that limit the voices of minorities. The first section of the book draws from the ethos of models of discrimination, oppression, and overlapping cultures expounded in the fields of psychology, multicultural counseling, and critical race theory. These first three chapters focus on oppression and discrimination, microaggression, and bias.

The voice of the majority is easy to detect due to its sheer volume. This includes the White, Christian, male, and cisgender cultures. Given that these cultures are omnipresent, we do not include them within this edition. Instead, we bring focus to cultures that are in the minority in North America. In the second section of the book, we pass the literary microphone to individuals who find their belongings and identities in cultures of heritage, religion, sexual orientation, gender, disability, and survivorship. This section starts with chapters that explore cultures of heritage, including the Hispanic and Latino, East and Southeast Asian, South Asian, Arabic, African-American/Black, and Native American and First Peoples. In addition, we explore the unique cultures and challenges of those who are biracial and biethnic. The next two chapters examine cultures of religion, specifically the Islamic and Jewish cultures. Following these are chapters that explore sexual orientation and gender-based cultures. One chapter focuses on the LGBTQI+ cultures, while the other focuses on the culture of women. The final cultures within this section examine the cultures of survivorship and disability.

To sharpen the focus on the intersections of culture, health, music, and the individual, we developed 10 themes for each of the culture chapters. These themes are: Personal reflection or epoch; Introduction; Worldview of the culture(s); Historical realities versus popular myths; Diversity within the culture(s); Acculturation and assimilation; Minority stress, minority discrimination, and microaggressions; Meaning of medicine and well-being in the culture(s); Meaning and function of music in the culture(s); and Conclusion.

Within the "Personal reflection or epoch," each author was asked to include some of their personal story that they were comfortable sharing. This is to bring forth each author's experience and show how it is related to the chapter topic. This practice is continued through all the chapters in the book. From these personal thoughts and experiences, we hope the reader will see that the authors are not experts sitting upon some pedestal but instead people who are on the same journey toward cultural competence.

While the "Introduction" is self-explanatory, the "Worldview" is less easily understood. Each culture views the world in different ways. This view is not often apparent or understood by the majority culture. In addition, these differing views are often squelched by the majority cultures.

The "Historical realities versus popular myths" section of the chapter brings to light the history of the culture within the historical constructs of the majority cultures. Often, there are historic realities that are the root of popular myths or from which stereotypes are created. The authors were instructed to explore these myths and bring light to the truths behind them.

No culture has one unifying voice; there are many differences and subcultures within each culture. "Diversity within the culture(s)" is a section within the chapters that explores the diversity in the populations, beliefs, and experiences. The authors explore these differences, highlighting how we cannot view one culture as a finite set of people with the same beliefs and experiences.

The "Acculturation and assimilation" section of the chapter explores these forces upon each culture. This is most relevant to the cultures of heritage and religion. However, these forces can impact those who are not "born into" a culture (e.g., LGBTQI+ and disability). You will find that the authors of each chapter explore acculturation and assimilation in a variety of ways.

"Minority stress, minority discrimination, and microaggressions" impact all minorities. The discrimination each culture experiences is different, although it stems from the same root: oppression. The microaggression each faces is different as well. The result of those discriminatory actions is often called minority stress, and the evidence of that stress varies from population to population. Each author explores these in relation to her/his/zer culture(s).

The "Meaning of medicine and well-being" varies from culture to culture. The authors bring forth these meanings for the reader to understand how beliefs about health and wellness vary from the dominant views of these concepts.

With regard to "Meaning and function of music in the culture(s)," as music therapists, we are aware that music has many different meanings and functions within cultures. The authors discuss music in all its forms within the culture(s). This is to bring forth the ways in which music therapy is relevant within the cultural constructs of each culture.

Each chapter ends with a "Conclusion" that draws together final thoughts on these major themes.

The third and final section of the book contains chapters dedicated to practical solutions for use by music therapists to begin to bridge these cultural divides. The section starts with a chapter that focuses on the unique experiences of minorities in teaching and supervisory roles. Next, social justice ally theories and models are investigated with an eye on how this addition to our education will impact our field. Third, both a theory and practical applications of a culturally competent music therapy assessment are proposed.

Cultural identity throughout one's life is rarely stagnant and often multidimensional. We do not attempt to provide all the answers with this book. Instead, we conclude the book with a chapter of questions for readers and propositions for further explorations about culture and identity. For the authors, writing this book compelled us to pay attention to the myriad minority voices and to continue a cultural dialogue with our readers. It is our sincere hope that our book will inspire continued conversations about cultural identities and belongings long after the reader has read the last word.

About the Authors

It is important to know that we, each of the authors, do not come to you as experts in the cultures or concepts about which we write. Instead, we are all seekers of knowledge. We bring to this book our experiences, our passions, and our desire to make the world a better place. Many times, when we first asked the authors to be a part of our book, we heard, "But I am not an expert on this topic; there must be someone else." But actually, all the authors were chosen because of who they are and their unique viewpoints. We brought together authors who range from those who are well published and known for their work to authors for whom this is their first time writing; from bachelor-level to doctoral-level music therapists; from the United States, Canada, and beyond. Each author has spent hours researching and bringing information from our sister fields to this forum for us to learn and grow from; to inform music therapists about the intersections of culture, music, and the individual as well as the microcosm of culture, bias, and beliefs that is within each of us.

We worked to bring first-person voices to the book, meaning that most authors are writing about cultures of which they are a part. We were mostly successful in this endeavor. We were unable to find music therapists to write in the first person about Arabic, disability, and biracial cultures. It was with great care that we expanded our search to potential authors who are not members of those cultures. With Arabic and disability cultures, we turned to music therapists who specialize in working with people within these cultures. In regard to the biracial and biethnic chapter, the author of that chapter is bi-ethnic but not biracial. Although these authors may not be from these cultures, we believe that each author has presented these cultures free of bias and as thoroughly as they could within the confines of each chapter. We were actually thrilled with the extent to which each author worked to present these cultures.

The World in Which We Live

Most books like this strive to avoid historical cultural references that date it, especially in the introduction. However, we felt strongly that we must break from this tradition. Over the past few months, the world we live in has become one that has been shattered with violence that stems from oppression and accentuated stereotypes. Hate crimes, racially motivated violence, and mass killings punctuated the beginnings of Summer 2016. Several authors amended their chapters to include information about these horrific events as well as changed language to state even more firmly how very damaging these systems of oppression are to each and every one of us. Whether we are Black, LGBTQ+, Muslim, or not, we are all part of these systems, even if we do not subscribe to the beliefs and oppression that motivate these actions. If we choose to be silent, to stand on the sidelines, to be a spectator, we have already vicariously contributed to the systems of oppression. Nonaction perpetrates indignities. It is up to each of us, as individuals, to change this world. If we wait for organizations or governments to make these changes, we condone the oppression. We condemn violence.

It is interesting to see just how much these events have influenced each of us. As lesbians, the hate crime in Orlando where over 100 Latinx LGBTQ+ individuals were shot; the event has left us feeling even less safe in a world that has never been safe for us. Then, to see the video footage of the police killing Black and Latino men; the mass killing of police in Dallas; the attack on people in Nice, France, during Bastille Day

celebrations; and the violent uprising in Turkey has left us even more frightened for our safety as well as the safety of those we care about. We are even more committed to enacting change in the world around us. Part of that change is to bring the words and experiences of each author to the reader.

It is our sincerest hope that this is not a book you read and put away on your shelf. We hope that understanding and ideas are planted within you, bringing forth transformations within each reader that you spread to your communities. We hope that the dialogue started here continues on and that it informs each of us with ways in which we can work to validate the experiences of those with whom we work, advocate for those with whom we are allies, and work to transform this world into a place of understanding instead of violence.

The Journey Begins

This book, designed to be a journey for the reader, has actually led to journeys for each author involved and both editors. Each of us has learned from the research we have conducted. And this learning was not just with our brains but also with our hearts. We do not believe that any of us could say we view the world just as we had prior to starting work on this book. It is our hope that you are also changed. This is just a starting point for your journey within yourself and within your practice of music therapy or music therapy education.

Cultural Intersections in Music Therapy:
Music, Health, and the Person

Chapter 1

DISCRIMINATION AND OPPRESSION

Annette M. Whitehead-Pleaux

I remember clearly that when I was a child of maybe three or four, my parents gave me a two-piece bathing suit. At first, I was excited for a new swimsuit, but then I noticed that neither of my brothers had to wear a top. They were still allowed to be topless when we played in the sprinklers, but I could not. It made no sense because up until that day, I was able to play topless in the water. I hadn't changed overnight. It was the swimsuit and the rules of society (I was told that it was not proper for girls to be topless) that changed my freedom. I was outraged that I was different because I was a girl. Soon, at this young age, I started to notice that all boys, not just my brothers, as well as all men, did not have to wear a top. Yet I did, as did all the girls and women I saw. I was hurt to see that I, as well as all women, were subject to different rules than men. I saw these different rules for women as limiting (at least limiting my desire to continue to play in the water topless), and I was outraged. It was not fair, in my young mind. To this day, I am still outraged by the rules that limit women and benefit men. It is still not fair.

Since that early day in my life, I have experienced oppression in several ways, with the main ones being sexism, classism, heterosexism, and ableism. Some of these I experience every day, while others happen with less frequency. The effects of the discrimination and oppression I have experienced have impacted my well-being, physically and emotionally. Some days, it has been hard to stand up proud under the weight of the messages that I am less than others.

Several years ago, I started volunteering with an LGBTQ youth center. It was required that all volunteers go through diversity training with the center staff. These trainings were conducted with the youth and volunteers. Having firsthand knowledge and experience of being oppressed as well as being a generally kind individual who cares about the well-being of others, I believed I was fairly enlightened about the systems of oppression. In addition, I had gone through several pretty good diversity trainings at different jobs. I had done work to understand my power as a White, middle-class, educated individual from a Christian upbringing, so I thought this training would be a piece of cake. I couldn't have been more wrong. I remember very well the moment I finally understood the depth of the roles I played in racism as a White person. It was a soul-crushing realization that I played a role in the domination of and oppression of people of color, as well as many other minority groups. I was engaging in my own Race to Innocence as well; through my silence about injustices I saw every day, I was complacent and in essence giving my thumbs-up to the oppression of those around me. I was horrified by what I saw in myself and my actions/inactions. From that day forward, I

have worked to make myself a better person. I don't always succeed, but I keep trying. I have a long way to go, but I continue to move forward.

I share this at the start of the chapter to let you, the readers, know that this is a process that is evolving through our lives. I am not standing here saying I have this right. I don't. I try each day, sometimes doing good, sometimes falling on my face. I know each of us is on our journey. Our progress does not align with the progress of others and that is OK; we are all on our own path. The knowledge that each of us has combined with our personal experiences shapes how we are in the world and what we know about the systems of oppression and discrimination. As music therapists who are generally nice people who want to do good in the world, we have chances daily to make a difference in our work or in our personal lives. We can be a part of the system of oppression or an agent of change. But to be an agent of change, we must understand oppression and the roles we play in it, as oppressed, oppressor, and resister.

We are all on this path. To be open to knowledge and open to seeing ourselves clearly is essential as we travel together.

Introduction and Definitions

"Discrimination" and "oppression" are common terms in our North American societies. We use them and hear them on the news, read them in books, and use them to describe the experiences of ourselves and others. But how much do we really know about the terms, the root of oppression, how different types of oppression work, and the impact of them upon our societies and the individuals who are oppressed? To understand oppression and discrimination and their impact upon humans, it is best to start with an understanding of the terms. To move forward into the systems of oppression and discrimination, it is important to have a clear understanding of the words I will use, which include power, discrimination, prejudice, injustice, and oppression.

To start, let's look at "power." Within the context of this chapter, the best definition of power comes from GLSEN. Power is simply "the ability to get what you want" (2016, p. 7). Power is at the root of discrimination and oppression, both attaining power within society and the use of power to demean and oppress others and to keep them from gaining any power. Power is a powerful motivator for many human beings.

The next word, "discriminate," according to the *Merriam-Webster Dictionary* (2016), is "the practice of unfairly treating a person or group of people differently from other people or groups of people." Discrimination is often used in conjunction with the word prejudice. Prejudice is:

> the prejudgment or unjustifiable, and usually negative, attitude of one type of individual or groups toward another group and its members. Such negative attitudes are typically based on unsupported generalizations (or stereotypes) that deny the right of individual members of certain groups to be recognized and treated as individuals with individual characteristics. (Institute for Democratic Renewal and Project Change Anti-Racism Initiative, n.d., p. 33.)

When discussing discrimination and prejudice, one often hears the term "injustice" used; for example, "This discriminatory action is an injustice." Gil (1994) defined injustice as the "discriminatory, dehumanizing, and development-inhibiting conditions of living (e.g., unemployment, poverty, homelessless, and lack of health care), imposed by oppressors upon dominated and exploited individuals, social groups, classes, and peoples" (p. 233).

Injustice is a term that is applied within a contextual conception of a situation. For example, prior to the federal law that brought marriage equality to all of the states in the union, many LGBTQ individuals felt that to be denied marriage rights was an injustice. However, individuals who are members of the religious communities that do not approve of same-sex unions did not see denial of marriage rights as an injustice; instead, to these individuals, withholding this right was following the beliefs of their religions and was instead a righteous act. That which is an injustice to one person is acceptable and correct to another person. Injustice comes from the cultural context in which a person identifies.

"Oppression" is defined by the *Merriam-Webster Dictionary* (2016) as the "unjust or cruel exercise of authority or power, especially by the imposition of burdens; the condition of being weighed down; an act of pressing down; a sense of heaviness or obstruction in the body or mind." It is important to note that oppression in this definition is not only an action toward others but also an emotional state. In a definition for social workers, Gil (1994) described oppression as a term that refers to "relations of domination and exploitation—economic, social, and psychological—between individuals; between social groups and classes within and beyond societies; and, globally, between entire societies" (p. 233).

According to this definition, oppression can occur on micro, meso, and macro levels and can target specific individuals, groups of people, and societies. Gil (1994) continues to explore oppression, stating that:

> oppression seems motivated by an intent to exploit (i.e., benefit disproportionately from the resources, capacities, and productivity of others), and it results typically in disadvantageous, unjust conditions of living for its victims. It serves as a means to enforce exploitation toward the goal of securing advantageous conditions of living for its perpetrators. (p. 233)

This expanded view that explores how to oppress others is motivated not only by prejudice against another person/group of people but also by a desire to deny others power and resources *and* to keep power and resources for oneself/one's group. Now that the terms are defined, we can look at a theoretical model to conceptualize and understand the systems of oppression and discrimination and their effects on individual people.

The Matrix of Domination/Interlocking Systems of Oppression Theory

Within the social justice organizations where I have worked and volunteered, one theory has frequently been employed to educate and open discussions about oppression and discrimination. The Matrix of Domination theory was developed by Patricia Collins, a Black feminist writer. The theoretical model not only helps us to conceptualize oppression and discrimination but also can be used as a framework for self-examination.

Patricia Collins first wrote about the Matrix of Domination as she explored prejudice and sexism in her book *Black Feminist Thought: Knowledge, Consciousness, and the Politics of Empowerment* (Collins, 1990). She (1990) stated that the theory was influenced by the work of Angela Davis, the Combahee River Collective, and Audre Lourde. Not only does her theory explain discrimination and oppression, but also it explores the dynamic relationships between oppressing, being oppressed, and resistance. Years later, her theory was renamed the Interlocking Systems of Oppression, and other feminist theorists have continued to explore how this model helps us to understand the impact of discrimination and oppression on all of us. Since Collins first conceived of this theory, other theories that explore discrimination and oppression have been created by social psychologists, sociologists, feminists, and so on, yet, for me, none captures so well and so simply the complexities of oppression within our societies.

Collins's theory differed significantly from previous theories about oppression and discrimination. Prior to the Matrix of Domination, the theories of oppression and discrimination were comparative and focused on single types of oppression. These models were unable to capture the dynamic reality of our world, where many types of discrimination and oppression of many different groups of people occur at the same time, sometimes to the same individual. Instead of this single oppression view, she saw that the oppression and prejudice of all peoples was related and needed to be viewed in its entirety. Collins (1990) stated that "experiences were shaped not just by race, but by gender, social class, and sexuality" (p. 18). By focusing on only one form of oppression, the entirety of many individuals' experiences could not be understood, for there are many people in our societies who are members of two or more minorities. For example, a woman experiences sexism, a form of oppression, because she is a female. But if she is also a Latina Jewish lesbian, it is likely that she will experience racism, anti-Semitism, and heterosexism in addition to sexism. Collins (1990) described this macro view of individuals' experiences as the "interconnections among systems of oppression." She named this phenomenon "intersectionality," a term to describe the interaction of the various forms of oppression. Describing the interwoven nature of systems of oppression, Crenshaw (1989) stated that the term "intersectionality" embraced how all types of oppression can strengthen or weaken each other. Prior to the Matrix of Domination, no model existed that was able to present a multidimensional picture of oppressed individuals' experiences.

Collins developed the Matrix of Domination so that it could encompass the forms of oppression which included race, social class, gender, and sexuality. Later versions included other forms of oppression, including Protestantism, colonialism, ableism, and so forth. In doing so, Collins was careful to acknowledge that not all oppressions are similar in appearance or function or experience, yet the unifying factor is that the basic root of all oppression is that one group believes that it is superior to another. When first describing her theory, she stated:

> The Matrix of Domination is grounded in the belief that all forms of oppression have the same foundation: a belief in domination, that some groups are superior to other groups, and that the superior groups have the right to rule over the inferior groups. (Collins, 1990, p. 226)

These superior groups employ a variety of methods to perpetuate the oppression of groups seen as inferior. The superior group's "intersecting oppressions of race, class, gender, and sexuality could not continue without powerful ideological justifications for their existence" (Collins, 1990, p. 70). With these justifications, the superior group works to maintain its power over other groups through the manipulation of ideas, exploitation of existing symbols, and creation of "controlling images" that are "designed to make racism, sexism, poverty, and other forms of social injustice appear natural, normal, and inevitable parts of life" (p. 70). These images, symbols, and ideas are so pervasive in our society that those who are subordinate do not see these overt attempts to demean and objectify minorities. Instead, it is just the way life is. Members of those oppressed groups may buy into these ideas and perpetuate them against others in their group as well as themselves without knowledge that they are actually participating in the oppression and domination of people in their lives.

This system of oppression creates "binary thinking" that "categorizes people, things, and ideas in terms of their differences from one another" (Keller, 1985, p. 8). Collins (1990) wrote that binary thinking leads to objectification,

which is key to the domination of others, stating, "[D]omination always involves attempts to objectify the subordinate group" (p. 71). If the subordinate group of people is objectified, their humanity is decreased in the eyes of the superior group. When individuals are identified as others, they/them, by diagnosis, by a quality, they are objects, and unworthy of being treated with dignity, kindness, or humanity, and what once was a person becomes a thing or an object. When people are no longer people but things, acts that marginalize, abuse, and degrade are palatable and acceptable behavior in society. An example of this is the rape culture within the United States. Women are objectified and seen as things with which men can do what they will. If a woman were seen as a human, not a thing, rape would not be possible. Continuing to view women as objects to be used or owned perpetuates this heinous behavior and, in some circles, condones it.

According to Collins (1990), even though all oppression comes from the same core belief that one group is superior to others, there are vast differences in the way oppression is enacted and experienced. For example, the oppression experienced by a woman is different than the oppression experienced by an African-American man, even though both are based in the belief that one group (men or Caucasians) is better than another (women or African-Americans). The manifestations of sexism and racism in society are different, as are each individual's or group's perception of each type of discrimination. While a woman shopping in a guitar store may be subjected to objectifying stares, lewd comments, and get "mansplained," an African-American male may be followed and watched for theft by the store staff as he shops. For other examples of how oppression differs between groups, look at the manifestations of ableism and Protestantism. The ways ableism is manifested includes restaurants that have doorways that are too narrow to allow for a wheelchair, menus that are not in Braille, and entryways without ramps. Religious sectarianism in North America is manifested in food items prepared only within Christian rules and holiday closures based on Christian religious holidays. While each type of oppression is devastating to the individuals and groups who experience it, the experiences of one group are different from the next group. This all-encompassing model of oppression allows for all oppressed groups to find commonality of the root, the belief that one group is superior to others, while acknowledging the differences in each group's experience of oppression.

Oppression occurs on a variety of levels. Collins (1990) recognized this and described three types of oppression: institutional, interpersonal, and internalized. Institutional oppression is oppression that occurs in the society at large and can include federal laws, employers' policies, city ordinances, customs, and religious doctrine. An example of institutional heterosexism was the Defense of Marriage Act in the United States, a heterosexist law which stated that marriage was limited to heterosexual couples only.

Interpersonal oppression is oppression between individuals. An example of interpersonal oppression is an individual telling a coworker who is of Puerto Rican descent, "Your fiery temper must come from your Latin blood." Finally, internalized oppression is when the individual believes and has incorporated into her/his/our identity the oppressive messages from society, family, friends, and so forth. An example of this is an impoverished youth, who believes that he will never succeed because he is "White trash." Whether oppression is institutional, interpersonal, or intrapersonal, the effects upon the individual and group are damaging.

As the lens that examines oppression within our societies pans out, it becomes apparent that these systems of oppression do not affect just those who are oppressed. Anderson and Collins (1992) state that the stratification of power shapes the experiences of not only those who are victimized but also everyone in our societies. Zinn and Dill (1994) explain that the "structures of discrimination create disadvantages to minorities and provide unacknowledged benefits to those who are at the top the hierarchies" (p. 5). The experiences of power within society create benefits that many of us who are White, middle- to high-income, and educated enjoy without awareness of these benefits. And these benefits, this power held by the majority groups, remains dependent upon the continued oppression of others. Without that oppression, the power is shared equally and privileges disappear. Zinn and Dill (1994) continue this exploration of the macro effects of oppression. They find that the assaults on minority cultures are systematic and necessary to maintain and expand a group's control of power. These attacks are essentially ways for the dominant group to maintain control and manage groups of people. This control ranges from oppression on the interpersonal level to the institutional level. The practices "denigrate the cultural patterns of the (subordinate) groups while elevating the values and practices of the dominant groups" (Zinn & Dill, 1994, p. 5). In essence, the dominant group gains power and maintains control through oppressing others and promoting the dominant culture.

Not all oppression is to devalue the cultural aspects of minority cultures. Feminist author and activist bell hooks (1992) describes a process called the commodification of difference. Within this process, elements of diverse cultures are seen as exotica and used as items to make boring White existence more interesting. But coopting and fawning over interesting elements of a minority's culture is not valuing a culture but instead is engaging in microaggressions.

Collins (1990) named this theory the Matrix of Domination because it is best displayed as a grid or matrix (see Figure 1). The x-axis contains the different types of oppression. These can include but are not limited to sexism (oppression of women), racism (oppression of people of color), classism (oppression of people in lower socioeconomic classes), heterosexism (oppression of those who are in same-sex relationships), Protestantism (oppression of people who are not of the Protestant faith), and ableism (oppression of people who are

differently abled). The y-axis focuses on the three types of oppression: institutional, interpersonal, and internalized.

Figure 1. *Matrix of Domination/Interlocking Systems of Oppression Theory*

	Institutional	Interpersonal	Internalized
Sexism			
Racism			
Classism			
Heterosexism			
Ableism			
Ageism			
Genderism			
Imperialism			
Protestantism			

By plotting the experiences of a fictitious music therapist (an African-American, Christian, middle-class woman), we will explore this process. First, as a woman, she has experienced sexism institutionally (inequity in pay with male colleagues despite equal work) and interpersonally (men objectify her). As a person of color, she has experienced institutional oppression (despite having superior skills, she has repeatedly been passed up for promotions in favor of White colleagues), interpersonal oppression (having racial slurs shouted at her), and intrapersonal oppression (the negative messages about African-Americans are internalized as part of her self-talk). By mapping out her experiences of oppression on the matrix, we get a picture of the myriad of ways an individual experiences oppression and the intersections of those oppressions.

Differing from earlier theories that explore oppression, this theory allows for the complexity of life and the different roles people hold. The matrix allows for further exploration, discovering where people have oppressed others. According to Collins, the "individual may be an oppressor, a member of an oppressed group, or simultaneously oppressor and oppressed" (Collins, 1990, p. 225). Through this exploration, the matrix illuminates the many ways oppression exists in each of our lives, either as the oppressed or the oppressor.

If we return to our fictitious music therapist, we can map out where she has oppressed others. She engages in interpersonal religious sectarianism (oppression of non-Christian clients by frequently using songs only from the Christian tradition in her sessions). In addition, she exhibits classism both institutionally (she donates to an organization that is working to halt the building of a homeless shelter in her community) and interpersonally (frequently saying that people who panhandle need to take a shower and get a job). These are all acts that oppress others, no matter how well-intentioned she is. The matrix grows in complexity, reflecting how we as human beings are complex creatures.

Yet, this is not the end of the explorations of oppression through the Matrix of Domination. Through further examination of the matrix, people can identify places where they actively resist or enable oppression. Zinn and Dill (1996) state that every spot on the matrix can be a place of oppression and a place of resistance. They emphasize that each person can be an active agent in that spot, not just the person who is oppressed. To actively resist oppression, individuals stand up and not only defend their oppressed group but also defend other groups to which they do not belong. Conversely, by not acting in the defense of others, people enable and perpetuate oppression. Albert Einstein stated, "If I were to remain silent, I'd be guilty of complicity." By not speaking up in protest of the oppression of others, our silence is a tacit approval of the oppression.

Let's go back to the fictional music therapist. She has places where she actively resists oppression and places where she is complacent with it. She resists ableism on the institutional level (part of a disability task force working on state legislation) and interpersonally (educating her son and his peers to not use the slur "retard"). However, she was silent in her church when a gay couple was ostracized. Her personal belief is that that marriage equality is morally correct, but her silence on the matter enabled the institutional heterosexism of her fellow parishioners.

Through this examination of the fictitious music therapist, we have explored how the Matrix of Domination can be used to examine ourselves, exploring how we are oppressed, how we oppress others, how we resist oppression, and how we enable oppression. This exploration allows for a comprehensive picture of all that we are on many levels. From this personalized view, we can see where we are doing well and where we may need to focus attention. The matrix can give us insight that can help us build therapeutic client relationships that are based on a true connection, not on disguised prejudices or stereotypes. In addition, it can be a tool for knowing with whom we can work and who we need to refer to other music therapists. Finally, it can give us insight into potential or actual transference and countertransference within our sessions. The complexity of each of us, our actions, inactions, and beliefs, is captured within this simple matrix.

Such self-examination is difficult to endure. It forces us to look at the parts of ourselves that we prefer not to see. However, not engaging in self-examination can not only impact our music therapy sessions but also lead to what Fellows and Razack (1998) call the "Race to Innocence." The Race to Innocence begins with an individual believing that she/he/ze does not play a role in the oppression of other groups of people. It is the belief that if one does not actively participate in spitting upon or shouting foul epithets at oppressed groups, then one is not an oppressor. But, if that person is complacent while spitting and racial slurs are hurled, is that person still subordinating others? Just as Collins said, "Yes, this is complacency," Fellows and Razack (1998) also say yes. They continue delving deeper into this question, even though many people believe that the answer is no. These people flee from self-examination to a false sense of innocence which they term the "Race to Innocence."

In essence, individuals run toward the false idea that they

are innocent in the oppression of others. The person looks at her/his/zer actions and says, "I have not engaged in the enslaving of African-American people, denied anyone a job based on skin color, or told racial jokes to my friends, so I am not engaging in racism." This person is racing toward a stance of innocence instead of looking at how she/he/ze has benefited from being White. Further, this person does not see how her/his/zer inaction is in fact complacency and implicates her/him/zer in the subordination or oppression of people of color. In this system, our society, dominant group members are not innocent even if we do not actively oppress others. Fellows and Razack (1998) continue by stating that the belief that we are innocent limits our ability to acknowledge the differences in power that operate between groups. And by not acknowledging those differences, members of dominant groups are truly unable to see the full effects of oppression on others as well as their role in that oppression.

As music therapists, if we are engaged in this "Race to Innocence," we are treading on very thin ice when working with clients who have experienced oppression. We cannot honestly witness the pain and suffering our clients have experienced and continue to experience from being oppressed nor can we help them to enact change nor can we understand what our clients' experiences are as gay men, Latinas, differently abled individuals, older adults, or Hindis. If we are blinded by the unwillingness to see and understand our role in the oppression of others, can we create a truly healthy therapeutic relationship? No, we cannot. But by acknowledging our power and role in the oppression of others, we can begin to have a better understanding of a client's experiences and create an even deeper therapeutic relationship.

Another pitfall which Fellows and Razack (1998) warn of is the idea of competing marginalities, an individual's or group's belief that that how she/he/ze/ they have been oppressed is the most awful of all. Yes, others have also been oppressed, but no one is as oppressed or has suffered so much as my group. This phenomenon of competing marginalities brings attention to the experience of the individual, for it is far worse for them than anyone else. When an individual or group focuses only on her/his/zer/their own pain and maintains the belief that no one suffers more than her/him/zer/them, this individual or group can never see clearly the suffering of others and cannot see their role in the oppression of others.

An example of this is the music therapist who believes that the sexist oppression she has endured in her life is far more horrible than any discrimination any other group has faced. This music therapist is essentially unable to see the oppression that these other groups suffer and its deleterious effects upon the members of those oppressed groups. Moreover, she is further limited because she is unable to acknowledge or even see the role she may be playing in the oppression of the elderly, people of color, non-Christians, people with disabilities, and so forth. However, if she fought against the Race to Innocence, worked to see that the oppression suffered by other groups is as horrible as the oppression she suffers, and acknowledged that the oppression her clients endure is experienced differently but is no less painful or damaging, then the music therapist would be open to seeing what others are experiencing, who they truly are, and the possible role that she may play in the oppression of others. This self-exploration allows her to then build deeper therapeutic relationships filled with clarity of vision and compassion for her clients' experiences.

The Effects of Oppression on Individuals

Oppression and discrimination are social ills within our societies. They deny people basic human rights. They keep the best and brightest from succeeding. It keeps the powerful in power. The stress of being oppressed deeply affects individuals. It leaves the people within subordinate groups (a majority of all peoples in our societies) coping with additional stressors from the near constant barrage of discriminatory experiences. They are left fearing for their well-being, whether financial, educational, social, physical, or psychological.

Psychologists and sociologists have investigated and theorized about the effects of oppression and discrimination on individuals and groups of people. A variety of models and theories exist (Meyer, 2003). Most focus on one category of discrimination (e.g., racism, sexism, sexual orientation); there are a few that look at the broader category of racism. Finally, a handful of models look at the impact of several factors (e.g., sexual orientation and race and sexism and socioeconomic status). Nearly all describe a connection between discrimination and health outcomes, both mental and physical. And all describe the stress that individuals experience from discrimination as additional to the normal life stressors that everyone experiences (Meyer, 2003). It is this additional stress that causes numerous health and psychological problems in those experiencing it.

Racism is prevalent in our societies and affects individuals from racial and ethnic groups who are not White (Pascoe, 2009; Williams, 2006; Yin, 2006). Even the perception of racism will lead to an increased stress response (Pascoe, 2009). In investigating the effects of racism on the health of Asian-Americans, Gee (2002) found institutional and individual types of discrimination to be associated with health issues. Similarly, researchers have found discrimination associated with chronic health conditions, especially heart disease, pain, and respiratory illness, in people of Asian descent (Gee, Spencer, Chen, & Takeuchi, 2007; Yip, Gee, & Takeuchi, 2008; Yoo & Richards, 2008). Among African-Americans, experiences of institutional and interpersonal discrimination as well as the stigma of inferiority are connected to both psychological and physiological health concerns (Utsey et al., 2008; Williams, 2006). Native Americans/First Peoples have a long history of experiencing discrimination and oppression and have documented mental and physical effects from it (Nelson, 2011).

There are mitigating elements that can offset or increase the damaging effects of racism. Psychological resources and social resources can help to decrease the effect of stress from racism.

Yoo and Richards (2008) explored ethnic identity in Asian-Americans as a buffer against the effects of racial discrimination and found overall that racial incidents did increase negative affect. In addition, they discovered that those with high racial identity experienced greater amounts of negative affect, while those with lower amounts of racial identity experienced a smaller negative affect. Similarly, Yip, Gee, and Takeuchi (2008) found ethnic identity to buffer the effects of racism and mental health issues in Asian-Americans. Depending on the individual's existing coping ability, the outcomes will be positive or negative (Meyer, 2003). The experience of discrimination can be mitigated by adaptive coping processes. Environmental and social stress can cause adaptation, yet significant stress can cause damage to physical and psychological health.

Racism is not the only discrimination that impacts the health and well-being of individuals. Green et al. (2005) found that people who experienced ableism had negative psychosocial consequences. Women suffer from sexism (Belle Doucent, 2003; Landrine et al., 1995; Pavalko, Mossakowski, & Hamilton, 2003; Swim et al., 2001).

From the study of the effects of heterosexism and genderism on LGBTQ individuals has come a concept called "minority stress." Minority stress is the excessive stress that an individual from a stigmatized group experiences as a result of the discrimination they face (Meyer, 2003). Research into minority stress has revealed that heterosexism and genderism have strong effects upon the mental health of LGBTQ individuals (Cochran, Sullivan, & Mays, 2003; Conran, Mimiaga, & Landers, 2010; Frost, Lehavat, & Meyer, 2012; Gilman et al., 2001; Herrell et al., 1999; Meyer, 2003; Stanford et al., 2001). The depth of suffering experienced by people who experience discrimination continues on for their lifetimes in the forms of psychological and physical ailments.

Conclusion

Humans are complex beings influenced by society, upbringing, and experiences. Oppression and discrimination have roots early in our human existence. People gather power and subjugate others to maintain that power. As we enter into therapeutic relationships with clients, we must be aware of the causes, forms of, and effects of oppression and discrimination. We need to also understand our roles, as oppressee and oppressor, and we need to willingly engage in practices that will help us to move from oppressor to ally. Susan Hadley will expand upon the ideas shared here as she investigates microaggressions. In the chapter by Nicole Hahna, we explore bias and look inside ourselves to see where we maintain biases. Finally, in the chapter by Leah Oswanski and Amy Donnenwerth, we learn how to move from complacency to becoming a social justice ally. Without a full understanding of ourselves in these systems of oppression, how can we fully understand what someone from another culture is saying about her/his experiences? This is especially true if that individual has suffered oppression by a group to which the music therapist belongs. To truly know and be present to help others, music therapists must truly know themselves.

References

Andersen, M. L., & Collins, P. H. (1992). *Race, class, & gender: An anthology.* Belmont, CA: Wadsworth Publishing.

Belle Doucet, D. J. (2003). Poverty, inequality, and discrimination as sources of depression among U.S. women. *Psychology of Women Quarterly, 27*(2), 101–113.

Carter, R. T. (2007). Racism and psychological and emotional injury: Recognizing and assessing race-based traumatic stress. *The Counseling Psychologist, 35*(1), 13–105.

Cochran, S. D., Sullivan, J. G., & Mays, V. M. (2003). Prevalence of mental disorders, psychological distress, and mental health services use among lesbian, gay, and bisexual adults in the United States. *Journal of Consulting and Clinical Psychology, 71*(1), 53–61.

Collins, P. H. (1990). *Black feminist thought: Knowledge, consciousness, and the politics of empowerment.* Boston, MA: Unwin Hyman.

Conran, K. J., Mimiaga, M. J., & Landers, S. J. (2010). A population-based study of sexual orientation, identity, and gender differences in adult health. *American Journal of Public Health, 100,* 1953–1960.

Fellows, M. L., & Razack, S. (1997). The race to innocence: Confronting hierarchical relations among women. *Journal of Gender, Race & Justice, 1,* 335.

Frost, D. M., Lehavat, K., Meyer, & I. H. (2012). Minority stress and physical health among sexual minority individuals. *Journal of Behavioral Medicine, 38*(1), 1–8.

Gee, G. C. (2002). A multilevel analysis of the relationship between institutional and individual racial discrimination and health status. *American Journal of Public Health, 92*(4), 615–623.

Gee, G. C., Spencer, M. S., Chen, J., & Takeuchi, D. (2007). A nationwide study of discrimination and chronic health conditions among Asian-Americans. *American Journal of Public Health, 97*(7), 1275–1282.

Gil, D. G. (1994). Confronting social injustice and oppression. In F. G. Reamer (Ed.), *The foundations of social work knowledge* (pp. 231–263). New York, NY: Columbia University Press.

Gilman, S. F., Cochran, S. D., Mays, V. M., Hughs, M., Ostrow, D., & Kessler, R. C. (2001). Risk of psychiatric disorders among individuals reporting same-sex sexual partners in a national comorbidity study. *American Journal of Public Health, 91*(6), 933–939.

GLSEN. (2016). The GLSEN Jump-Start Guide. Retrieved from https://www.glsen.org/sites/default/files/Jump%20Start%20Guide%20Part%205_1.pdf

Green, S., Davis, C., Karshmer, E., Marsh, P., & Straight, B. (2005). Living stigma: The impact of labeling, stereotyping, separation, status loss, and discrimination in the lives of individuals with disabilities and their families. *Sociological Inquiry, 75,* 197–215.

Herrell, R., Goldberg, J., True, W. R., Ramakrishnan, V., Lyons, M., Eisen, S., & Tsuang, M. T. (1999). Sexual orientation and suicidality: A co-twin control study in adult men. *Archives of General Psychiatry, 56*(10), 867–874.

hooks, b. (1992). *Black looks: Race and representation.* Boston, MA: South End Press.

Institute for Democratic Renewal and Project Change Anti-Racism Initiative. (n.d.). *A Community Builder's Tool Kit.* Claremont, CA: Claremont Graduate University.

Keller, E. F. (1985). *Reflections on gender and science.* New Haven, CT: Yale University Press.

Landrine, H., Klonoff, E. A., Gibbs, J., Manning, V., & Lund, M. (1995). Physical and psychiatric correlates of gender discrimination. *Psychology of Women Quarterly, 19,* 473–492.

Merriam-Webster. (2016). *Merriam-Webster Dictionary.* Retrieved from http://www.merriam-webster.com/

Nelson, T. (2011). Historical and contemporary American Indian injustices: The ensuing psychological effects. *Commonwealth Honors College Theses and Projects,* Paper 6. Retrieved from http://scholarworks.umass.edu/chc_theses/6

Pascoe, E. A., & Smart Richman, L. (2009). Perceived discrimination and health: A meta-analytic review. *Psychological Bulletin, 135*(4), 531–554.

Pavalko, E., Mossakowski, K., & Hamilton, V. (2003). Does perceived discrimination affect health? Longitudinal relationships between work discrimination and women's physical and emotional health. *Journal of Health and Social Behavior, 44*(1), 18–33.

Sandford, T. G., de Graaf, R., Bijl, R. U., & Schragel, P. (2001). Same-sex sexual behavior and psychiatric disorders: Findings from the Netherlands Mental Health Survey and Incidence Study (NEMESIS). *Archives of General Psychiatry, 58*(1), 85–91.

Swim, J. K., Hyers, L. L., Cohen, L. L., & Ferguson, M. J. (2001). Everyday sexism: Evidence for its incidence, nature, and psychological impact from three daily diary studies. *Journal of Social Issues, 57,* 31–53.

Utsey, S. O., Giesbrecht, N., Hook, J., & Stanard, P. M. (2008). Cultural sociofamilial and psychological resources that inhibit psychological distress in African-Americans exposed to stressful life events and race-related stress. *Counseling Psychology, 55*(1), 49.

Yin, P. (2006). A systematic review of empirical research on self-reported racism and health. *International Journal Epidemiology, 35*(4), 888–901.

Yip, T., Gee, G. C., & Takeuchi, D. T. (2008). Racial discrimination and psychological distress: The impact of ethnic identity and age among immigrant and United States–born Asian adults. *Developmental Psychology, 44*(3), 787–800.

Yoo, H. C., & Richard, M. (2008). Does ethnic identity buffer or exacerbate the effects of frequent racial discrimination on the situational well-being of Asian-Americans? *Journal of Counseling Psychology, 55*(1), 63–74.

Zinn, M. B., & Dill, B. T. (1994). Difference and domination. In M. B. Zinn & B. T. Dill (Eds.), *Women of color in U.S. society* (pp. 3–12). Philadelphia, PA: Temple University Press.

Zinn, M. B., & Dill, B. T. (1996). Theorizing difference from multiracial feminism. *Feminist Studies, 22*(2), 321–331.

Chapter 2

I DON'T SEE YOU AS BLACK/GAY/DISABLED/ MUSLIM/ETC.: MICROAGGRESSIONS IN EVERYDAY ENCOUNTERS

Susan Hadley

Personal Context

Throughout this chapter, I will provide examples from my personal life narrative in italics.

I am a White 49-year-old woman. Born in Princeton, New Jersey, of White Australian parents, I grew up in Perth, Western Australia. When I was 25, I returned to the United States to study . My initial intention was to stay for only between two and four years, but I have now lived in Pennsylvania for almost half of my life. Growing up, I was cocooned by privilege. I attended a private Christian school for girls, both residential and nonresidential. We lived on the school property because my father was the principal. Although some of my friends were Chinese, Japanese, or Indian, with even fewer who were Malaysian, Singaporean, Korean, or Indonesian, most of my peers were White. There were very few Black students. I remember only a couple of Indigenous Australians and one person who had the phenotypical features of someone of African descent, although she had complete absence of pigment in her skin, hair, and eyes, a condition known as albinism. I also remember that she had decreased visual acuity and nystagmus as a result and thus used a magnifying glass to read materials.

Most of my peers were from the middle to upper socioeconomic classes in Perth. I knew very few people who were poor. We had a woman who was foreign and a single mother who was employed to clean our house and do our laundry. The school paid for these services because my father was the principal. I remember my father providing our cleaner's daughter with a scholarship to attend our school. I had another friend whose parents rented a small apartment in a high-rise and thus must not have had much money. However, their daughter did attend this private school, so I'm skeptical about classifying them as poor. Most of my peers were not disabled. I remember two students who wore braces and my best friend's sister, who had spina bifida used a cane and a wheelchair. I do not remember anyone with an intellectual disability or with a diagnosis on the autism spectrum. I remember one student with an eating disorder. All of my peers were female. Most of my peers were heterosexual, and those who were not were certainly ostracized in many ways. Most of my peers were Christian, although some were Jewish and some were Hindu. I had one close friend who was Jewish, and I remember their family traditions as being different and in some ways "strange." I felt special to be invited to share in their family celebrations.

We had a small number of Middle Eastern teachers, an older Egyptian man and a Lebanese woman, and a couple of Jewish teachers. We also had two male teachers of Indian heritage. To my knowledge, I had one gay male teacher and one lesbian teacher. All of my peers were English-speaking; there were no accommodations for people whose first language was not English. We were given opportunities to interact with males from neighboring private Christian schools, but the demographics of these males mirrored the demographics of our school and our sister schools. These demographics were in evidence not only in my school, but also at my church, in my neighborhood, at my local shopping center, at my local beaches, and in my experience in out-of-school (classical) musical experiences, such as youth orchestras.

Overview of Microaggressions

Origins

It is widely acknowledged that the term "microaggressions" was first coined by African-American psychiatrist and Harvard University professor Chester M. Pierce in 1970. In 1974, Pierce wrote:

> … the major vehicle for racism in this country is offenses done to Blacks by Whites in this sort of gratuitous never-ending way. These offenses are microaggressions. Almost all Black–White racial interactions are characterized by White put-downs, done in automatic, preconscious, or unconscious fashion. These minidisasters accumulate. It is the sum total of multiple microaggressions by Whites to Blacks that has a pervasive effect on the stability and peace of this world. (Pierce, 1974, p. 515)

Elaborating on this concept in terms of racism in the United States, Pierce and his colleagues wrote:

> The chief vehicles for proracist behaviors are microaggressions. These are subtle, stunning, often automatic, and nonverbal exchanges which are 'put-downs' of Blacks by offenders. The offensive mechanisms used against Blacks often

are innocuous. The cumulative weight of their never-ending burden is the major ingredient in Black–White interactions. (Pierce, Carew, Pierce-Gonzalez, & Willis, 1978, p. 66)

Broadening Its Scope

While microaggressions were originally discussed in terms of race and racism, cross-cultural counselor Derald Wing Sue has expanded the definition to encompass the experiences of marginalized groups more generally. Based on work with his colleagues (Sue et al., 2007), Sue (2010b) defines microaggressions as "[t]he everyday verbal, nonverbal, and environmental slights, snubs, or insults, whether intentional or unintentional, that communicate hostile, derogatory, or negative messages to target persons based solely upon their marginalized group membership" (p. 3). That is, these comments, tones of voice, looks, gestures, actions, and inactions leave the recipient feeling invalidated, demeaned, overlooked, devalued, excluded, undesirable, inferior, dangerous, or even abnormal, because of his/her race, class, gender, sexuality, disability, religion, ethnicity, and so forth. Such actions imply that all people of that group are the same and also that they do not belong to the "normative" group.

Overt discrimination and hate crimes, in contrast, would be seen as "macroaggressions." These overt messages and behaviors are deliberate. While they are no doubt threatening and harmful, the intentions behind them are more openly expressed and thus easier to navigate. Microaggressions, however, are most often unconscious, unintentional, and automatic. The invisibility to the perpetrator is what gives microaggressions so much power. Because microaggressions are so widespread, they are often not recognized or dismissed as innocent and harmless. However, because they are so widespread, the impact on the recipients can be very damaging psychologically in terms of self-esteem, emotionally in terms of the anger and frustration they foster, and physically in terms of health and well-being.

In the kind of social context in which I grew up, how does a person become aware of microaggressions? I was committed to issues of social justice but was unaware of the ways in which I engaged in microaggressions. In looking back, over time I have been very fortunate to have had relationships and experiences that have made me more aware of how seemingly small actions and comments can be very damaging to the person addressed. When we are in the dominant group, we are often unaware of our daily microaggressions. However, when we spend time with those not in dominant groups and allow ourselves to be open to their experiences, we can begin to see these "innocent" encounters as invalidating, insulting, and even assaultive.

Perpetrators of Microaggressions

Most "decent" people can easily identify instances of blatant

ableism, classism, ethnocentrism, heterosexism, racism, sexism, and religious intolerance. Encountering such overt bigotry, we become outraged and distance ourselves from the "likes of those" performing the injustice. It may be difficult for fair-minded people in dominant groups to accept that for people in marginalized groups, it is not the bigots who pose the greatest threat. This is because their prejudice is out in the open, so there is no guesswork involved. The greater threat comes from those who are well-intentioned, who hold to egalitarian values, who believe they are good, moral people, and who see themselves as fair and just and would not consciously discriminate against others. Because microaggressions are often fueled by unconscious biases, they are most often committed by, among others, "well-intentioned, moral, and decent family members, friends, neighbors, coworkers, students, teachers, clerks, waiters and waitresses, employers, health care professionals, and educators" (Sue, 2010a, xv).

In the Western world, we are shaped by the subjugating or oppressive systems of Eurocentricity, patriarchy, heterosexism, and capitalism. We are also shaped by hegemonic Western assumptions embedded within such areas as psychiatry/ psychology and medicine. Thus, what we hear and what we see is fundamentally shaped by such systems (Hadley, 2013). Perpetrators of microaggressions are members of groups that historically have had power and privilege over those not in these dominant groups, they are part of the oppressive system. Recipients of microaggressions are members of groups that historically have been subjugated or oppressed. Being born into these systems, members of the dominant groups are socialized to believe that they are "superior," that they "naturally" belong to the normative group, that they are the "standard" by which all should be measured. This form of socialization is reinforced through mass media, in educational curricula, in family structures, in peer groupings, in neighborhood communities in which we live, in political and financial institutions, and so on. This social conditioning shapes how we think, feel, and act. It leads to implicit biases of which most people remain unaware. And because we believe that having prejudices and biases belies being good, moral people, it is extremely difficult to acknowledge these biases (Hadley, 2013).

Although members of the dominant group benefit greatly from power and privilege, there are many detrimental cognitive, affective, behavioral, and moral costs associated with this social conditioning (Sue, 2010a). Being unaware of prejudices and biases allows people to live with the distorted view of reality that they are superior and that other groups are inferior. Living with this distorted reality may lead people in dominant groups to avoid and even fear people of other groups. It may also lead to either a lack of empathy toward people in marginalized groups or feelings of guilt about being in the oppressor group. Inevitably, living with this distorted sense of reality curtails the genuine scope of our humanity.

Manifestations of Microaggressions

Microaggressions can occur at multiple levels: the individual (from one person to another), the institutional (in terms of policies, practices, procedures, and structures that are in place in different institutions), and the cultural (where one group sees itself as superior and has the power to impose its values and standards on other groups) (Sue, 2010a). Furthermore, microaggressions can be expressed verbally (as direct or indirect comments to targets), nonverbally/behaviorally (through the use of body language or other more direct physical actions), or environmentally (the physical surroundings, including physical structures, numerical imbalance of one's own group, inaccurate media portrayals, inclusion or exclusion in educational curricula, signs, symbols, and even mascots).

Forms and Process of Microaggressions

Sue and his colleagues (Sue, 2010a, 2010b; Sue et al., 2007; Sue et al., 2008) describe microaggressions as falling into three major categories: microassaults, microinsults, and micro-invalidations.

Microassaults are conscious-biased attitudes, beliefs, or behaviors that are communicated to marginalized groups. These can include verbalizations, behaviors, or environmental cues. They are intended to threaten or intimidate the target person/group or make the target person/group feel unwelcome or unwanted. Microassaults include name-calling, jokes, avoidant behavior, and a wide array of discriminatory actions. Unlike in the past when this kind of behavior was commonly accepted, this kind of overt display of discrimination is widely condemned today. Nonetheless, there are certain conditions under which perpetrators feel safe to engage in this type of microaggression. For example, perpetrators feel freer when there is a degree of anonymity, such as through graffiti art, online posts, and so forth or when they are among like-minded people. At other times, these microassaults come shooting out of the person as if by their own volition. Yancy (2008) describes this phenomenon, which can happen even to the most self-aware individuals, as the person being *ambushed* by their unconscious biases, perhaps in moments of stress or when usual defenses are down, such as when a person is intoxicated.

Microinsults are likely to be much more subtle than microassaults. A perpetrator is not usually conscious of the bias she/he/ze is communicating. Microinsults demean a person's identity. They can come in the form of a positive statement/compliment, which is really communicating a larger biased/stereotyped attitude. When I was growing up, we referred to this kind of statement as a backhanded compliment. By "praising" the individual while simultaneously insulting the group to which they belong, the perpetrator is clearly communicating their biases/prejudices, although unconsciously, and can remain guilt-free in their ignorance.

Microinvalidations are also largely unconscious and are very damaging to the recipient. These communications "exclude, negate, or nullify the psychological thoughts, feelings, or experiential reality of certain groups" (Sue, 2010a, p. 37). When perpetrators do this, they are imposing their reality on those in the marginalized group. For those in the dominant group to be open to the experiential reality of those in a marginalized group requires a level of vulnerability and humility that has the potential of exposing their own distorted view of reality as a myth. Rather than risking such exposure, perpetrators instead cling to the belief that what they are hearing cannot be true. Mills (2007) refers to this phenomenon as an *epistemology of ignorance*—that is, when ignorance is actively produced by dominant groups to misrepresent/distort reality for the purposes of sustaining power, privilege, and oppression. An example of this kind of myth in the United States is the Horatio Alger myth, or the myth of meritocracy—that all people, no matter to what social group they belong, have equal opportunities to succeed. Holding this view, it is easy to attribute blame to those who do not succeed—they must not have tried hard enough.

There is a fairly typical process that surrounds microaggressions (Sue, 2010a). However, there are many possible ways of experiencing each phase, which is influenced by the context, severity and consistency of the message being communicated, and so on. First, the comment, gesture, or environmental cue is experienced by the person. Second, the person attempts to establish whether the incident is motivated from conscious or unconscious biases. The person then responds to the incident cognitively, behaviorally, or emotionally. The person then explores the possible meaning of the incident. Finally, the consequence for the individual comes in the form of behavioral, emotive, or thought processes which develop over time as a result.

In order to trace my relationship with the topic of microaggressions, I have looked back on which of my relationships have made me more aware of everyday comments, actions, and environmental factors that are invalidating, insulting, or assaultive to various groups in society. There are so many instances of microaggressions in my past and present: I am painfully aware of some and painfully oblivious of others. Throughout this chapter, I will share a few significant instances that relate to race/ethnicity, gender, sexual orientation, and disability.

When I think back now on some of the microaggressions in which I was complicit, I feel very saddened and wish I could go back in time and make up for them. For example, I remember that we used to have competitions to see how far we could carry one of our friends on our back. She was the heaviest student in our class because she was quite overweight. We did not see it as demeaning to her, and she did not show signs of being hurt by it. But we all knew why it was that our physical strength was being judged based on the distance we could carry her. I also remember how we failed to include one person in our teams at recess because she wore braces and we knew she would "handicap" the team that included her. Later, I witnessed similar treatment toward the sister of one of my best friends and witnessed the indignant responses (from my friend, her sister, and her parents) to her being treated in any way as less than anyone else. These were very important influences in my life.

Another early experience for me was that my younger brother was adopted. He was in so many ways different from the rest of us in the family. There was a very strong family resemblance between my other siblings and me. But my brother was as tall as we were short, had very pale skin while ours was quite brown, had freckles where our skin had few markings, and had blue eyes while we all were brown-eyed. I cannot count how many times people tried to find similarities where there were none. I remember comments such as "You have your father's eyes," to which he would respond, "I wouldn't know." Or, "These three are all peas in a pod. What happened to you?" It was a continual reminder for him that not only was he different, but he didn't fit. This had a profound impact on him growing up.

Now that I am married to an African-American man and we have four biracial sons, I am aware of racial microaggressions on a daily basis. As a woman, I am aware of gender microaggressions on a daily basis. Having had such close relationships with disabled people, I am aware of microaggressions toward disabled people on a daily basis. As I have become friends with people from various marginalized groups, my awareness has continued to grow. These experiences and my readings on issues of diversity, power, privilege, and social justice have made this topic one that is incredibly significant to me. And yet I still perpetuate microaggressions without realizing it and continue to work hard to recognize and guard against such actions.

Increasing Awareness: Making the Invisible Visible

As the most damaging microaggressions are not in the conscious awareness of the perpetrators, and as the majority of perpetrators are well-meaning, moral, decent people who would not knowingly demean or degrade, it is imperative that we work diligently to become more aware of microaggressions when they occur. Microaggressions are easier to see when we are the recipient. As perpetrators, our unintentional biases are most often invisible to us. Furthermore, as mentioned above, there can be fundamentally different perceptions of reality between the group that holds power and those who are disempowered. However, when those who are disempowered point out the offensiveness of a microaggression, they are accused of being mistaken, overly sensitive, playing some card or other, or paranoid (Sue, 2010b). In the event that the perpetrator acknowledges that the communication may have unintentionally been offensive, it is then usually downplayed and rendered harmless. However, it is not harmless to the person who is the recipient of multiple microaggressions on a daily basis. Study after study shows that microaggressions have major physical, emotional, behavioral, and cognitive effects on

marginalized groups (see several examples at Sue, 2010a, 2010b). Given all of this, the importance of gaining greater awareness regarding the occurrence of microaggressions becomes all the more significant. It is only when we have more awareness that we can act with greater responsibility.

Thus, in this section with the aim of increasing awareness, I will describe some common microaggressions experienced by various marginalized groups. (For a large number of examples from people outside music therapy, visit The Microaggressions Project blog at http://www.microaggressions.com/.) I will include examples experienced in my life and within the music therapy context by clients, therapists, students, and professors.

Race/Ethnicity

There are shared and unique experiences of microaggressions for different "racial"/ethnic groups. Shared experiences include being seen as inferior to White people, racialized residential segregation, social segregation, and being underrepresented and stereotypically represented in the mass media, educational curricula, and government. Such groups also experience being invisible and yet at the same time hypervisible. The unique experiences are based on the different stereotypes associated with each racial group. For example, "Black" and "Brown" people are more likely to be assumed to be criminal, violent, dangerous, loud, less intelligent, and poor, whereas Asian people are more likely to be assumed to be law-abiding, hardworking, intelligent, and quiet. People of African heritage are more likely to be assumed to be athletic, strong, and musical. Indigenous people are assumed to be primitive, superstitious, and alcoholics (Hill, Kim, & Williams, 2010); perceived as historical relics, their cultural artifacts and practices are appropriated in a demeaning fashion for tourism and mascots. Latinas/os are assumed to be illegal aliens (Rivera, Forquer, & Rangel, 2010). In the United States, Asian-Americans and Latinas/os are assumed not to speak English. People of color are also seen as representative of the entire group, whereas White people are assumed to be individuals. Multiracial people are perceived as exotic, not Black/Latina/o/Asian/Native enough, trying to act/be White, a mistake, and so on (Johnston & Nadal, 2010).

When I arrived in the United States, many things that had lurked beneath the surface of my awareness became much more visible. Living in North Philadelphia, I could not hide from racial, cultural, religious, and class injustices. I was surrounded by so much more diversity. As I have written elsewhere, when I moved to Philadelphia, I felt my whiteness more vividly than I had before. I began to see many ways in which I had been socialized to see myself as superior. I made comments like "You are being Jewish with your money" without thinking it was offensive. I had grown up with the phrase, without anyone problematizing it. At one point, I went back home to Perth to visit and heard a young cousin of mine chanting the "Eeny, Meeny, Miny, Moe" rhyme. I was horrified when she used the N-word, and I told her not to use it and explained why it was so wrong. I realized that I, too, had been taught that playground chant with that term included. Growing up, I did not realize that word was not referring to some exotic animal. Adults in my life, even in Australia, so far away from the United States, must have known how derogatory the term was, yet we as children were never privy to that. We just sang it out without any knowledge, without any conscience—it was just how it was. We were unconsciously learning that to be White is to be superior and to hurt others with impunity.

Recently, my 15-year-old biracial son came home upset. That day, when he stood up to get off the bus, an older White woman had pulled her possessions close to her. He was visibly upset by the experience. He told me that he had looked her directly in the eyes to see whether she felt any remorse. He could not see any. He said that at first he had tried to believe it was because he was a tall teenage male. When I asked him whether he believed that was what it was, he said, "No, it was because she saw me as Black and therefore as dangerous!" We talked about how if he had been a White male teenager and she had pulled her possessions close, he wouldn't have had to wonder whether it was because of his race. He went on to say that we had always explained that this is how he would be seen, no matter how light-skinned and mild-mannered he is. He said that until that moment, it had not really sunk in. At the moment that she pulled her possessions close, he experienced firsthand and to his core what it was to be treated as "Other" and dangerous because he wasn't White.

During my time in the United States, I have often received the comment that I speak English well when people discover that I am Australian. While I can brush this off as ignorance, I often wonder how this compliment is felt by people for whom English is not their primary language. I have also had student evaluations from non–music majors who complain that they cannot understand the lectures because of my lack of fluency in English. This is a microaggression communicating that I do not speak "proper" English and hence do not belong in this country. Because English is and always has been the only language that I speak, I am not too offended, but again this would hit me very differently if English were not my native tongue.

Within the music therapy context there are a multitude of examples of microaggressions. I will mention a few examples from my experience:

Most of the people of color whom I interviewed for *Experiencing Race as a Music Therapist: Personal Narratives* (Hadley, 2013) described the experience, as music therapy students, of being the only minority or one of few people of color in the dominant group. Also described was the lack of representation in the curricula and in the musical styles learned. The hidden messages being communicated were that White is normal, that White people developed music therapy, and that White music is universally accessible.

An African-American student auditioned for a music therapy program as a voice major. She sang two classical pieces, as she was trained in a Western classical vocal tradition. At the conclusion of her audition, the voice professor commented, "I

just wanted to be clear, we don't teach jazz here." The student looked confused and replied, "OK." The implicit message was that African-American people only want to sing jazz, or "You are all alike."

In his narrative about his experiences of race in music therapy, Dennis Kahui discussed the pressure he felt to represent his culture as the only Maori student in his music therapy class (Kahui & Hadley, 2013). The microaggression came when he sat and listened to his "culture being shared in an academic environment and by a non-Maori" (p. 104). He felt the urge to take over the teaching because the information was being taught incorrectly and because he knew that how it was taught was how it would be transmitted further. With White people in power and transmitting his culture incorrectly, the hidden message was that he was a second-class citizen and, since he had not been consulted, that his expertise was devalued.

An Indigenous Australian music therapist had racial slurs directed toward him from White skinhead clients (Bann & Hadley, 2013).

A Japanese music therapist related to me two incidents of microaggression (the first environmental, the second verbal) during his internship in the Bronx in a setting in which the clients were mostly African-American and Latina/o. When he arrived, he thought, "Oh, my goodness, I am so visible. I do not blend in at all in this setting" (Hadley & Anonymous, 2013, p. 175). This was an environmental microinvalidation that was reinforced when clients would call out to him, "Hey, Jet Li."

A White music therapist working in a mental health facility had created a songbook from which clients could select songs to be sung in the group. When he asked a young African-American female for her choice, she responded, "You don't have any Black girl music in here." Later, when a White music therapy intern who agreed that there were no culturally relevant songs for young African-Americans asked the music therapist what he thought about what she had said, the therapist trivialized her response by attributing her diagnosis as the reason she had refused to make a selection. In both cases, the message was that White is superior and music of White people is the standard.

An African-American patient requested a gospel tune (or spiritual), one that wasn't super popular but was well-known among African-Americans. An African-American music therapy student was trying to re-create the song with the patient. The music therapy student wondered at the time why his supervisor, a middle-age White guy, didn't participate in their attempt to re-create it. After the session, the White music therapist expressed to the student that Gospel music was popular among patients on the unit floor, but that he hadn't learned the style. The African-American student felt very put off by this disclosure. This White therapist had worked at this site for about 10 years, and to not have incorporated into his practice a style of music that was popular among the patients there, in particular the Black patients, was very offensive not only to the African-American student, but to the clients as well. Looking back at the incident, the African-American student considered what the therapist might have meant by not learning the style. The White therapist certainly knew "Amazing Grace" and other popular Gospel tunes, so the style he was really talking about was Black Gospel songs. Given the ready access to a variety of music styles on the Internet and other resources, there was really no excuse, especially after 10 years in the field.

Seung-A Kim shared various experiences of microaggressions aimed toward her as a music therapist (Kim & Hadley, 2013). When working with an older adult woman, Kim was made to feel very uncomfortable and demeaned by the woman's husband, who had fought in the Korean War and had made it clear that he did not like Korean people and did not want her to work with his wife. At another facility in which she worked, Kim noticed that in the cafeteria there were tables where White people sat together and tables where African-American people sat together, but as one of only two Asian staff members, there was no table for her. The message being communicated was that she did not belong. Kim also shared how alienating it is when people do not take the time to learn her name or to learn how to pronounce her name.

Puerto Rican music therapist Magdaliz Roura and African-American music therapist Frances Goldberg both have shared experiences of when they have been perceived as exceptions to their race (Roura & Hadley, 2013; Goldberg & Hadley, 2013). The message communicated in these encounters is that they are members of groups that are devalued.

Roia Rafiayan, a Jewish Iranian music therapist, experienced an environmental microassault shortly after 9/11 when she saw a Confederate flag painted on the vehicle of one of her White coworkers with the words "Kill the Ragheads" (Rafiayan & Hadley, 2013, p. 186).

A microaggression that I perpetuated as a White music therapy professor was to single out the only person of color in the class to speak to an issue about race that was raised. In response, she challenged me to explore why I was asking *her* to speak on it. This was a moment of realization. The message to her was that White was the norm and that she did not have a place in the whiteness club in which the rest of us belonged. There was also my assumption that she was capable of speaking on behalf of her entire group, a position in which individual Whites are not asked to be and a function that they are not expected to perform.

Gender

In a so-called postfeminist era, there are still multiple manifestations of gender microaggressions. Gender microaggressions come in many forms, including objectifying looks, being whistled at, sexist jokes, mass media representations, unrealistic standards of beauty, name-calling, degrading comments, being infantilized, being interrupted, differential pay scales, role expectations, denial of sexism, underrepresentation in educational curricula, under-representation in political and financial institutions, sexual harassment, sexual assault, and physical assault.

As a result of gender microaggressions, females are perceived, in Simone de Beauvoir's term, as "the second sex." Compared to their male counterparts, females are perceived as physically weaker, less tolerant of pain, less agile, less coordinated, less intelligent, less qualified for certain jobs, emotionally less stable, less logical, less capable of dealing with financial concerns, less independent, less able, and so on. (Although I am talking about males and females here as though they are fixed categories, these concepts of weakness, intolerance of pain, and so on, get complicated when viewed through the lenses of race, sexuality, and disability.) Conversely, women are perceived as more caring, softer, more submissive, more emotionally expressive, and more domestic than their male counterparts. They are also perceived as always available to men and yet in some ways innocent and pure. If women stray from these stereotypes, they are labeled as pushy, aggressive, loose, aloof, conceited, unfeminine, a raving feminist, and so on. There is an assumption that if a woman is married, she will have the same last name as her spouse. When this assumption is made, it communicates that women have an inferior or secondary status to men, who are not expected to change their names. The practice of giving a woman away when she is married assumes that she is property of her father and then property of her husband.

When I began working as a music therapy professor in a university setting, I was faced with many instances of gender microaggressions. In my interview with the provost, for example, I was called "Sweety," "Honey," and "Love," all of which are microaggressions. When I was one of only three faculty members in our department with a doctorate (and the only one with a PhD), I was frequently referred to as Ms. Hadley. At first, I thought that this was just out of habit, given that so few of the faculty had doctorates. However, when a fellow faculty member, who is male and who did not have a doctorate, was frequently referred to as Dr. So-and-so, I brought it to the students as a gender microassault. One female student denied it was a problem, saying, "It is not because he is a man that we call him Dr. So-and-so, it is because we respect him." Bam! A double whammy. What was really striking is that she did not even realize that by saying that, she was insulting me even further.

Females are taught from a young age that their value comes from their attractiveness, and the media standards for this are unattainable or "attainable" at great risk to females as they try to fit the social stereotype for "female attractiveness." Females are also dissected into their various body parts, and these dismembered bodies are used to sell products that are tailored to fragment female bodies further. Moreover, narrow conceptions of femaleness render low-pitched voices, muscular body types, and certain fashion choices as deviant, abnormal, unpalatable.

I vividly remember one night during my high school years waking at 2:00 a.m. to the sound of some people trying to get into my room through my floor-to-ceiling window. I could hear a lot of whispering. Feeling very scared, I ran up and told my dad, who scared them off. The next morning, I found a doll outside my window with its legs spread apart and in the air and its clothes pulled up above its waist. This vivid image haunted me for years. Every night, I woke in a panic at 2:00 a.m. The message was clear: As a young woman, my body was one for the taking. Later, during my undergraduate years, I recall one guy announcing to a group of friends that he would never consider dating a girl who didn't wear makeup and didn't shave. Again, the message was clear: Females are not valued for their intelligence or their personality, but only for their looks—objects to be admired and used for sex.

Within the music therapy context, there are several examples of gender microaggressions:

From information gathered by the American Music Therapy Association, we learn that women continue to earn around $10,000 less annually than their male counterparts at every degree level. This communicates that women's work is less valued than men's.

There are proportionally more males in academic music therapy positions than females. This communicates that women are not as academically successful as men.

Female pioneers in music therapy in the United States (such as Eva Augusta Vescelius, Isa Maud Ilsen, Harriet Ayer Seymour) are less referenced and less revered than their male counterparts (Willem van de Wall, E. Thayer Gaston). This communicates that the contributions of these women are less important.

Female professors frequently have been called by their first name or by Ms./Mrs. instead of Dr., whereas their male counterparts are frequently referred to as Dr. even when they have not earned a doctorate. This communicates less respect for women in academia.

A qualified female music therapist was insulted that her workplace employed an unqualified male "music therapist," treated him as if he were equally qualified, and at times talked about him as if he was her superior. This communicates that even with her qualifications, her status was less than the male's.

At music therapy conferences on the East Coast of the United States, it is not uncommon to have an open mic night. The band of music therapists is most often made up of male musicians, and the music therapists who come up to sing are most often females. I remember an instance when a female music therapist who is a drumset player went up to play one song with the band. They questioned whether she could really play before letting her play. Having played with famous musicians in the past, she was offended. She played on the one piece but, being so insulted by the initial assumption of her incompetence (women do not play the drumset well), has never played at a conference again.

Messages in songs reinforce gender role socialization. Songs often communicate females as dependent on a male's love and attention ("can't live without him"), as sexual objects ("ho"), as nameless ("woman," "bitch," "lady in red," etc.), as infantilized ("baby," "girl"), and so on, and men as wanderers, adventurers, dominators, protectors, and so forth.

Music videos of most genres oversexualize women and glamorize the dehumanization of women by men (see Sut Jhally's *Dreamworlds 3,* 2007).

Androgynous voices, such as Tracy Chapman's, are seen as abnormal. I have heard students respond when learning that the person singing is a woman: "Ooh, that's just wrong! That sounds like a dude!" Such a narrow conceptualization of the diversity of female voices communicates deviance and denial of group membership.

A female client who desired to sing commented, "My voice is too low! I can't reach the high notes … girls are supposed to have high voices" (Rolvsjord & Halstead, 2013). Again, the gendering of voices becomes very limiting and alienating to those whose voices do not fit within the normative range.

Female music therapists have experienced not having their voices heard in team meetings and have come to understand this as a function of having their voices policed.

Female music therapists have experienced sexual advances from male colleagues and male clients.

Female clients have been inappropriately touched by male workers (see Linton, 2006).

Sexual Orientation

A wide array of microaggressions are perpetrated on LGBTQI individuals. From a young age, bullies call their targets gay, lesbian, or queer. In the recent past, the term "gay" has become very common to refer to something as being pointless, weird, and ridiculous. This pejorative use of the term "gay" communicates that being gay is something to be avoided, something unacceptable. There is an assumption that heterosexuality is "normal" and that therefore other sexual orientations are abnormal, deviant, and inferior. Because there has been an inordinate weight placed on homosexuality as a sin by some religious groups, there is a lot of guilt associated with being LGBTQI. There is also fear of rejection by family, friends, and coworkers as well as fear of being the victim of hate crimes, given the frequency and severity of such crimes toward LGBTQI individuals. In the not-too-distant past (1970s), homosexuality was classified as a mental illness, and conversion therapy was a treatment option. In fact, conversion therapy is still practiced in many places and currently is only outlawed in very few states.

Many people associate being gay with being sexually promiscuous and even as being synonymous with pedophilia or having proclivities toward child molestation. Thus, children are kept away from LGBTQI individuals for fear that they will try to "convert" the child to "that lifestyle" (another microaggression) or that they will "contaminate" them with some disease (such as AIDS). This fear of contagion or conversion has also led to LGBTQI individuals being excluded in many contexts, such as changing rooms, residence halls, military barracks, and so on. Sexual orientation is associated solely with sexual activity and thus such deemed unnecessary to be open about; this should be something that remains private. This denies the full personhood of LGBTQI.

The mass media still overwhelmingly portrays romantic relationships as between a man and a woman, marriage has traditionally been defined as between a man and a woman, and forms that ask for family information have the terms "mother" and "father" on them, thus alienating nontraditional families and rendering them "abnormal." And narrow conceptions of masculinity and femininity can be so alienating for those who do not conform that they can result in self-inflicted tragedy.

I remember sitting beside a friend on the first day back at high school after the summer break. I patted her knee and asked how her summer had been. I remember her caustic response, "Take your hands off me, you lesbian!" I looked at her with utter disbelief. I was upset that she thought that this was actually an insult. It reinforced that being heterosexual was deemed to be superior. Interestingly, I have recently learned that this girl is now openly lesbian, so perhaps at the time she was having difficulty with conflicting feelings. But at the time, I had no sense of this being the case.

There are many microaggressions that LGBTQI individuals experience within the therapy environment. Shelton and Delgado-Romero (2013) delineate seven themes that represent microaggressions commonly experienced by LGBTQI individuals in the therapy setting: (1) assumptions by the therapist that the sexual orientation of LGBTQI individuals is the cause of all their presenting issues, (2) avoidance or minimization by the therapist of issues pertaining to the sexual orientation of the individual, (3) attempts by the therapist to overidentify with LGBTQI individuals, (4) making stereotypical assumptions about LGBTQI clients, (5) expressions by the therapist of heteronormative bias (in the environment or verbally), (6) assumptions that LGBTQI individuals are flawed and need psychotherapy, and (7) warnings from the therapist about the dangers of identifying as LGBTQI.

A gay male music therapy student of mine was very concerned about a preschool child running up and hugging him at the end of the session. The children also did this to other female music therapists. His concern was how this would be viewed by the staff. He was not sure whether they knew that he was gay, but he knew that if they did, they might assume that he was a child predator. This response was because of environmental communications that gay men prey on young boys.

Messages in songs reinforce heteronormativity and alienate those in the LGBTQI community.

LGBTQI music therapists feel that they have to hide pictures of their significant others in fear of alienation of colleagues or clients. Heterosexual therapists display photos of their partner or family openly.

LGBTQI music therapists feel that they have to hide the pronoun of their partners out of fear of alienation of colleagues or clients. The therapist asks the client about his girlfriend.

Forms that ask for family information in which categories of "mother" and "father" are the only options alienate children of same-sex parents.

When talking about an issue not related to sexual orientation, the therapist asks, "What do you think this issue has to do with your sexuality?"

A lesbian music therapist was once told by a music therapist after receiving a GIM session that her imagery indicated that her sexual orientation would change to straight, suggesting that heterosexuality is the only true sexual orientation.

A gay music therapist was "praised" by a more senior music therapist in the team for not sounding and acting gay, like other gay males she knew. This "compliment" communicated that being gay in more noticeable ways was distasteful. Passing as heterosexual was a socially palatable way for him to be gay. The communication was that there are acceptable and less offensive ways of expressing masculinity and, by implication, femininity.

The therapist avoids using LGBTQI terminology, indicating either that they don't think that discussing issues having to do with the individual's sexual orientation is important or that the individual should not talk about these issues.

The therapist makes a point of mentioning LGBTQI friends or family members, trying to indicate a lack of homophobia.

The environment in the therapist's office has pictures only of heterosexual couples.

The therapist asks if the individual has really thought through their sexual orientation and talks about the difficulties associated with "this lifestyle."

The communication is that this is an identity that the individual has chosen, and thus the problems that the individual is encountering are really the individual's problems of his own making because of this choice.

A music therapy advisor told a music therapy student, after she came out to him, that her career would be affected by her sexual orientation. She might not be able to work in several areas, especially with children.

A music therapy intern working in a skilled nursing facility was conducting a music therapy group on Valentine's Day. In the session, she asked each group member what song was played at their wedding. When asked, one client stated, "I was never married." Immediately, the intern realized that she had assumed all clients in the group were married and heterosexual.

When thanking a coworker, who is married to a woman, for his advocacy, a lesbian music therapist stated that she was thankful this coworker was a great ally to the LGBTQAI community. The coworker confronted the music therapist's assumption that he is straight and corrected her by coming out as pansexual.

Disability

People with disabilities have been historically treated as outcasts, alienated, and isolated physically and socially. The physical environment has been designed for nondisabled people. Until relatively recently, they have had segregated housing (sent to live in residential facilities) and education (ironically called "special," although no one nondisabled is rushing to be admitted to such "special" schools). Behaviorally, nondisabled people often avoid eye contact when they see a disabled person. Touch is either avoided or, alternatively, deemed inappropriate.

Terms to describe people with disabilities are used to describe nondisabled people disparagingly, such as retarded, spastic, dumb, lame, crazy (Charlton, 2006). Nondisabled people are described as "blind" if they are biased or unaware, "crippled" by something if they are hindered in some way, and having a "fit" if their rage or frustration becomes uncontrollable. The use of terminology in this way communicates that having a disability means that you are deviant, inferior, undesirable. Terminology used to describe disabled people similarly communicates negative messages. An example of this is describing someone as "suffering" from a certain condition or being a "victim" of some disease/disorder (Linton, 1998/2006). I recall attending a talk given by disability studies theorist Simi Linton in which she referred to people who used such terms as being "confined" or "bound" to a wheelchair. She debunked that myth by saying that she is not confined to a wheelchair; instead, using one affords her greater freedom than not using one. Even praising someone for "overcoming" their disability communicates that in their original state they were inferior. Disabled people are described not only as abnormal, but also as deformed. Even the term "invalid," when pronounced differently (that is, where the term is not about logical inconsistency, but instead means to be "enfeebled" or "sick"), denies a disabled person's full humanity. Disabled people often hear that they are inspirational (Rousso, 2013). This kind of comment is patronizing because they are just living their everyday lives like everyone else.

After completing my undergraduate degree, I was employed part time at a residential facility for people with physical disabilities. I worked there in many different capacities. I was a nursing assistant, a physical therapy assistant in the pool, and a part-time music therapist. Later, I worked as a personal care provider for some former residents who had moved away from the facility to live in a house in the community. My conversations and experiences with the people I met here shaped me in significant ways.

I will share a few stories. I recall a conversation I had with a group of residents when one man shared his feelings about the decision of his sister to have an abortion upon finding out that her child would have muscular dystrophy. Each of the residents felt angry about this decision because it communicated to them that their lives were not worth living, not valid—invalid. Each of them shared how important being alive was to them and that even though there were things that they couldn't do, they had rich lives. I also recall the humor with which each of them spoke about their impairments or some of the funny situations in which they found themselves. I also quickly learned that as with other forms of humor, the context of who is telling the joke and to whom is very important.

I also remember being driven to a pub by a guy with no legs to play pool. He would often get drunk, which in Australia is

referred to as being "legless." At different times, he would play with this language, but in hindsight the use of this term was demeaning to him and others who had no legs.

Also, when I was working at this facility, two of the residents married each other. There were some staff who were not supportive of this marriage and were vocal about it. The assumption was that these two individuals did not have the same rights as most human beings. After they were married, they requested staff assistance in positioning them in ways that they could enjoy sexual intercourse. While this may have been awkward for some, it was so important for all parties in realizing the needs of this couple and, by extension, all disabled people.

I remember the day at this same facility when I was first asked to work with Caroline as if it was only yesterday. Everyone at this facility was assigned someone to work with them each day—except Caroline. Caroline selected her personal care aides. This was an unspoken practice, but one of which we were all aware. I was approached by Sharon, who was her main personal care aide. It was made clear to me that this was, in fact, an honor and meant that I had gained her trust. I recall the responsibility I then felt. It is strange that this feeling was so pronounced, when I had worked with so many of the other residents. What message were we sending the residents by randomly assigning people to work with them, rather than having them decide who they wanted to care for them each day? Was this practice invalidating, a way of silencing their voices? What I learned from Caroline was that you should not take this work for granted, that you are in some ways an extension of the people with whom you are working. You have to treat their bodies as you would your own. She made me think about the respect you need to bring to the people with whom you are working. This was no longer a job, but an intimate partnership. And Caroline taught me how important trust was in this relationship. She was trusting me to touch her and move her in ways that she could not do without this help. She took time to get to know people and to decide whom she would let into her circle. She took this circle with her when she moved into the community. We were not only her personal care aides but also her friends. Ours was one of the deepest friendships I have had. I believe that this is because it was founded on trust. And when she died, this was one of the biggest losses I had ever experienced. My experiences in restaurants, on trains, at the movies, shopping, and in other regular activities opened my eyes to the microaggressions of well-meaning people and the constructed physical environment itself toward disabled people. It also opened my eyes to my own limited perspectives and my own microaggressive practices.

People with disabilities are often infantilized, seen as helpless, and therefore helped even when they are capable of completing the task themselves. They are also rarely asked to help or take responsibility for others. Denying their right to privacy, nondisabled people will often ask disabled people personal questions about their impairments. Disabled people are often reduced to their impairments, rather than appreciated as a whole person, fulfilled and enjoying life.

Nondisabled people are often incredulous when they hear of disabled people being in relationships, driving cars, having a healthy sex life, and so forth. It is as if no part of their lives can be "normal." Their lives are deemed so inferior that women are tested during pregnancy for the likelihood of having a child with a disability, given the option to terminate the pregnancy if tested positive, and counseled about parenting a child with a disability.

Disabled people are reduced to their impairments and invalidated as whole persons when the assumption is that the goals to work on in therapy are directly related to the impairment.

When disabled people are placed in a group only with other people with their diagnosis, the communication is that all of them will be dealing with the same or similar issues due to their impairment.

Grouping disabled people only with other disabled people can communicate that the important defining feature of each individual is his/her/zir diagnosis impairment.

Often, disabled clients are not involved in developing goals in therapy or in the decisions regarding the direction and scope of "treatment." This communicates that the therapist is the expert in what the disabled client needs and the client has less knowledge.

When we praise disabled people for every small accomplishment, what is being communicated is that we do not believe they are capable of more.

Disabled individuals have been inappropriately touched and sexually harassed (see Linton, 2005).

Music therapy students with disabilities have been told that they are "exploiting" their disabilities to their advantage by "using" their disabilities to get them out of doing hard work. This assumption serves to invalidate the effort they are putting into all of their classes. They are complimented when they do not use needed accommodations. This communicates to them that they are more accepted when they appear more "normal."

There are few messages in popular songs which depict disabled people in positive ways. Analogies such as "blind" meaning ignorant, "seeing clearly" meaning not being confused, or being "crazy" meaning not in control of one's emotions are commonly used. Each of these associations communicate that this mode of being (being blind, having impaired vision, having a mental illness) is undesirable.

There are virtually no music videos with disabled people in them in the mainstream music industry. (For alternatives, see D-PAN, the Deaf Professional Arts Network, www.disabilityartsonline.org.uk; Disability Arts Online, www.disabilityartsonline.org.uk; National Arts and Disability, www.semel.ucla.edu/nadc; Disability Arts International, http://www.disabilityartsinternational.org/.)

When a therapist talks to people with physical impairments as if they are younger than they are or in a loud voice as if they are hard of hearing or talks to the non-disabled person who is with them as if they cannot speak for themselves, he/she/ze is communicating a sense of superiority over disabled people and

a sense that all disabled people are alike.

I have observed therapists asking nonverbal clients questions that require a verbal response. This communicates that verbal communication is the superior form of communication and that nonverbal people are inadequate at communicating.

Potential music therapy students have been kept out of the profession because their impairments have meant that there are certain specific competencies that they cannot perform. In some cases, no adaptations have been made to accommodate these individuals. One particular disabled student has questioned how a profession that professes to care about disabled people can be so restrictive in terms of accommodating the needs of disabled people who want to become music therapy clinicians.

A music therapist with dyslexia is repeatedly "teased" for her frequent misspellings by her boss who is aware of her disability.

Intersectionality

It is important to keep in mind that different people may belong to more than one marginalized group. While the experiences of microaggressions for each marginalized group are different, so are the experiences of those within each marginalized group, depending on how that identity intersects with another marginalized identity. So, the experiences of microaggressions for an Asian male amputee will be very different from those for an African-American lesbian.

Developing and Maintaining Anti-Oppressive Practices: Habit Formation and Vigilance

Once we begin to notice the invisible oppressive systems that parade as normal and neutral and that shape how we think, feel, and act, we need to be vigilant and ever mindful of their presence all around us. We need to learn to listen differently and to see differently and, ultimately, to develop profoundly different forms of relationality that respect the humanity of all persons. We need to establish what Sue Baines refers to as anti-oppressive practices in music therapy (Baines, 2012). Anti-oppressive practice, as outlined by Baines, recognizes that "the power imbalances in our society affect us all" (p. 4). Anti-oppressive practice is "a way of addressing the 'problems' that our clients present within the context of their sociopolitical reality and resourcing both ourselves and persons we serve to address social inequity toward the goal of creating a socially just future" (p. 4).

In order to develop anti-oppressive practices in our lives and work, we need to increase our awareness of oppressive systems and help others to increase their awareness of oppressive systems. In addition, it is important that we have meaningful relationships with people from a variety of marginalized groups. It is essential that we develop new habits of communicating in order to substantially reduce (or even eliminate) microaggressions, as well as develop new habits in response to being confronted with the microaggressions that we commit. Finally, we must remain ever vigilant to the ways in which oppressive systems shape our thoughts, feelings, and actions.

It is not only important to increase our own awareness, but also to help others become aware of the ways in which oppressive systems are invisible to all of us and how such systems parade as normal and neutral. The development of such an awareness is not an easy process because it is very difficult for people to accept that their perspective of reality is distorted. People in dominant groups have a vested interest in maintaining the status quo. It seems counterintuitive to dismantle a system that has been stacked in our favor (Myers, 2007).

In order to develop anti-oppressive practices, we need to develop and nurture different habits. This requires critical attention to the words we use and what they communicate, our bodily responses in relation to others, the messages that are conveyed in the mass media, the curricula covered in our educational programs, the music we use in our sessions, our responses to being called out on the various microaggressions we perpetuate unintentionally, and so on.

A common response when beginning this process is, "I feel like I am walking on eggshells now. I just can't say anything anymore without worrying about what it is communicating." While it does take a conscious effort, as the formation of any new habit does, with time it will become much easier and more automatic. In other words, generative and anti-oppressive habits will come to replace habits which tend to dehumanize and oppress others.

Finally, we need to "dwell near" (Yancy, 2012) those in marginalized, disadvantaged groups when we are members of advantaged groups. We may be able to see the ways in which we are disadvantaged and recognize microaggressions when we are on the receiving end but may find it more difficult to recognize microaggressions that we perpetuate. By having rich and meaningful relationships with those in marginalized groups and being personally committed to eradicating forms of social injustice that are different from the normative groups to which we belong, we are more likely to become aware of our biases and prejudices and thereby reduce them. We are also more likely to become attuned to the ways in which members of those groups are invalidated, demeaned, and devalued. It is important that we honor the experiences of those who are not in the advantaged groups. And when we hear about the complexity of their lived experiences, rather than deny them, invalidate them, or diminish them, we need to bear witness to them and, if necessary, be moved to action by them.

The insidious nature of oppressive/subjugating systems in our society is that they have a way of rebuilding themselves constantly even when we attempt to dismantle them. Thus, it is a never-ending process. There is no point of arrival per se (Yancy, 2008). But we must continue to work at it. Some people will argue that it seems pointless to try if we never get there. Yet, we remain hopeful. Perhaps hope is all that we have. This is not to be bemoaned, but celebrated, because the structure of hope points in the direction of the future, and it is the future that holds the possibility for a more collective and inclusive sense of humanity and shared fellowship.

References

Baines, S. (2012). Music therapy as an anti-oppressive practice. *The Arts in Psychotherapy, 40,* 1–5. doi:10.1016/j.aip.2012.09.003

Bann, G., & Hadley, S. (2013). The view from the floor. In *Experiencing race as a music therapist: Personal narratives.* Gilsum, NH: Barcelona Publishers.

Charlton, J. I. (2006). The dimensions of disability oppression: An overview. In L. J. Davis (Ed.), *The disability studies reader* (2nd ed.). New York, NY: Routledge.

Disability Arts Online. Retrieved from www.disabilityartsonline.org.uk

Disability Arts International. Retrieved from http://www.disabilityartsinternational.org/

D-PAN, the Deaf Professional ArtsNetwork. Retrieved from www.disabilityartsonline.org.uk

Hadley, S. & Anonymous (2013). Seeing through both lenses. In *Experiencing race as a music therapist: Personal narratives.* Gilsum, NH: Barcelona Publishers.

Hadley, S. (2013). Dominant narratives: Complicity and the need for vigilance in the creative arts therapies. *The Arts in Psychotherapy, 40*(3), 373–381.

Hill, J. S., Kim, S., & Williams, C. D. (2010). The context of racial microaggressions against Indigenous peoples: Same old racism or something new? In D. W. Sue (Ed.), *Microaggressions and marginality: Manifestation, dynamics, and impact.* Hoboken, NJ: John Wiley & Sons, Inc.

Jhally, S. (Producer). (2007). *Dreamworlds 3: Desire, sex & power in music video* [Motion picture]. Northampton, MA: Media Education Foundation.

Johnston, M. P., & Nadal, K. L. (2010). Multiracial microaggressions: Exposing monoracism in everyday life and clinical practice. In D. W. Sue (Ed.), *Microaggressions and marginality: Manifestation, dynamics, and impact.* Hoboken, NJ: John Wiley & Sons, Inc.

Kahui, D., & Hadley, S. (2013). He Hikoi (The Journey). In *Experiencing race as a music therapist: Personal narratives.* Gilsum, NH: Barcelona Publishers.

Kim, S., & Hadley, S. (2013). Bringing my Asian identity to light through acculturation. In *Experiencing race as a music therapist: Personal narratives.* Gilsum, NH: Barcelona Publishers.

Linton, S. (1998). *Claiming disability: Knowledge and identity.* New York, NY, & London, UK: New York University Press.

Linton, S. (2005). *My body politic: A memoir.* Ann Arbor, MI: University of Michigan Press.

Media Education Foundation, & Jhally, S. (2007). *Dreamworlds 3: Desire, sex, & power in music video.* Northampton, MA: Media Education Foundation.

Mills, C. (1997). *The racial contract.* New York, NY: Cornell University Press.

Myers, V. (2007). Understanding unearned advantage. Retrieved from http://www.vernamyersconsulting.com/Articles/Understanding%20Unearned%20Advantage%20by%20Verna%20Myers.pdf

National Arts and Disability. Retrieved from www.semel.ucla.edu/nadc

Pierce, C. (1974). Psychiatric problems of the Black minority. In S. Arieti (Ed.), *American handbook of psychiatry.* New York, NY: Basic Books.

Pierce, C. M., Carew, J., Pierce-Gonzalez, D., & Willis, D. (1978). An experiment in racism: TV commercials. In *Television and education.* Beverly Hills, CA: SAGE.

Rafiayan, R., & Hadley, S. (2013). Does your family drive camels? In *Experiencing race as a music therapist: Personal narratives.* Gilsum, NH: Barcelona Publishers.

Rivera, D. P., Forquer, E. E., & Rangel, R. (2010). Microaggressions and the life Experience of Latina/o Americans. In D. W. Sue (Ed.). *Microaggressions and marginality: Manifestation, dynamics, and impact.* Hoboken, NJ: John Wiley & Sons, Inc.

Rolvsjord, R., & Halstead, J. (2013). A woman's voice: The politics of gender identity in music therapy and everyday life. *The Arts in Psychotherapy, 40*(4), 420–427.

Roura, M., & Hadley, S. (2013). "You don't look/sound/act Puerto Rican": Experiencing myself as an exception. In *Experiencing race as a music therapist: Personal narratives.* Gilsum, NH: Barcelona Publishers.

Rousso, H. (2013). *Don't call me inspirational: A disabled feminist talks back.* Philadelphia, PA: Temple University Press.

Shelton, K., & Delgado-Romero, E. A. (2013). Sexual orientation microaggressions: The experience of lesbian, gay, bisexual, and queer clients in psychotherapy. *Psychology of Sexual Orientation and Gender Diversity, 1*(S), 59–70.

Smith Goldberg, F., & Hadley, S. (2013). Creating a path in the middle. In *Experiencing race as a music therapist: Personal narratives.* Gilsum, NH: Barcelona Publishers.

Sue, D. W. (2010a). *Microaggressions in everyday life: Race, gender, and sexual orientation.* Hoboken, NJ: John Wiley & Sons, Inc.

Sue, D. W. (2010b). Microaggressions, marginality, and oppression: An introduction. In D. W. Sue (Ed.), *Microaggressions and marginality: Manifestation, dynamics, and impact.* Hoboken, NJ: John Wiley & Sons, Inc.

Sue, D. W., & Capodilupo, C. M. (2008). Racial, gender, and sexual orientation microaggressions: Implications for counseling and psychotherapy. In D. W. Sue & D. Sue (Eds.), *Counseling the culturally diverse: Theory and practice* (5th ed.). Hoboken, NJ: John Wiley & Sons, Inc.

Sue, D. W., Capodilupo, C. M., Torino, G. C., Bucceri, J. M., Holder, A. M. B., Nadal, K. L., & Esquilin, M. (2007). Racial microaggressions in everyday life: Implications for clinical practice. *American Psychologist, 62,* 271–286.

Yancy, G. (2008). *Black bodies, White gazes: The continuing significance of race.* New York, NY: Rowman & Littlefield.

Yancy, G. (2012). *Look, a White! Philosophical essays on whiteness.* Philadelphia, PA: Temple University Press.

Chapter 3

REFLECTING ON PERSONAL BIAS

Nicole D. Hahna

When I was asked if I wanted to write a chapter for a book on multicultural issues, I considered it for a long time before agreeing to do so. "What would I have to contribute? I am the least qualified person to be talking about multiculturalism that I know," I thought to myself. I am a White, heterosexual, able-bodied woman. I am educated and was raised in a working-class household with Protestant values. I was born in the United States, and English is my first language. I work in an institution based upon power and privilege—sometimes referred to as the ivory tower, no less. How can I write about multicultural issues and personal bias? I had to search deep for an answer. Perhaps, as a part of the majority culture, I may be positioned in a place where other people from the majority culture can hear me on a different level. Perhaps this is one way I can help to create social change within the system of music therapy, as part of a grassroots collective effort.

In terms of personal bias, well, I knew that I would have plenty to share about that—we all do. In no way did I approach this topic as someone who has "mastered" how to eliminate personal bias. As a feminist music therapist, I incorporate reflexivity into my practice and try to examine ways in which my actions (or lack thereof) perpetuate systems of oppression. Reflexivity can be defined as "dwelling with it (in this case, personal bias)," where "dwelling means thinking about, pondering, considering, and processing the reality of the profound experience of meeting with a client, student, or patient" (Skovoholt & Trotter-Mathison, 2011, p. 43). Feminists often take a critical stance, or critical awareness, in terms of reflexivity, in examining themselves and society, looking to decenter and reconceptualize patriarchal constructs in a system of power and privilege.

I am learning every day how my own personal bias impacts the students and clients with whom I am privileged to work, as well as how it impacts my personal life. So, with a humble heart, I invite you to explore with me ways in which we all experience personal biases and how this affects our ability to work with clients, coworkers, and students in music therapy. As you read this section on personal bias, I ask that you have an open mind (and heart), especially when confronting things that are hard to hold in your consciousness. Consciousness-raising refers to impacts my personal life. So, with a humble heart, I invite you to explore with me ways in which we all experience personal biases and how biases experienced personally by women impacts our ability to work.

As we all raise our consciousness levels and begin to see the cultural constructs that we assume are truths, we can help each other to break them down. I believe that the first step on the journey toward dismantling systems of power, privilege, and oppression is to look deep within. It is only then that we can take meaningful action toward social change.

Overview: Implications of Personal Bias

The need to address cultural competency has increasingly become more urgent in many aspects of music therapy practice (Bradt, 1997; Kim & Whitehead-Pleaux, 2015; Shapiro, 2005), supervision (Estrella, 2001; Forinash, 2006), and training (Darrow & Molloy, 1998; Toppozada, 1995; Valentino, 2006). Relevant literature highlights the importance of music therapists taking personal responsibility for addressing cultural complexities, including the need for music therapists to become aware of how their personal biases and worldviews affect their clinical practices (Bradt, 1997; Chase, 2003; Hadley, 2013; Hadley & Norris, 2015). In this chapter, I will explore the implications of personal bias within the therapeutic relationship. Additionally, I will highlight the systemic issue of oppression, the field of feminist therapy, and ways in which music therapists can work to decrease the impact of these biases in their clinical work.

What Is Personal Bias?

As music therapists, we may have a false sense of immunity to concepts such as bias, stereotyping, classism, racism, heterosexism, ageism, ableism, sizeism, and so forth. We may rationalize that we are in the helping profession and therefore always treat the client in an objective and fair manner. Depending on our theoretical orientation, we may even be encouraged to practice in a manner that views the therapist as a blank slate or perhaps views the therapist as being able to clearly separate the personal from the professional in the clinical setting. These are enticing lenses through which to view the therapeutic relationship, but is this how our clients experience their interactions with us? And, is this in fact the best way to practice? I would argue that it is impossible to practice in a purely objective manner. Instead of hoping that we can maintain a value-neutral stance, I encourage music therapists to increase their awareness of their personal biases and work to diminish the negative effects of these biases (Sue & Sue, 2003). For me, it is not a matter of *whether* personal biases will affect the therapeutic relationship, but *how*.

Personal bias can be defined as "a tendency to think, act, or feel in a particular way" (Hays, 2008, p. 24). These tendencies often occur without us thinking about them, and this is what can be potentially dangerous. This has likely detrimental effects on our clients when these second-nature tendencies are congruent with the majority culture (Sue & Sue, 2003). If left unchecked, we may assume that these biases are accurate. In a culture that values personal independence and assertiveness, such as in the United States, we may mistakenly assume that a client's silence regarding one of our personal biases is equivalent with their agreement with us or perhaps that they are not offended by something we said or did (Robinson-Wood, 2013). Taking this approach does not consider the various identity markers or cultures of which our clients may be a part, in which questioning authority and assertiveness may not be valued as highly as it is in other cultures. Silence does not equal consent, so we should not wait for a client to tell us that they are offended by our comments, actions, or lack of actions—we need to be proactive and vigilant in examining our own personal bias (Pedersen, Crethar, & Carlson, 2008).

Additionally, our ideas of biases are often dichotomous. That is, we tend to think that we are biased or that we are not biased, and we do not see our own personal bias on a continuum. Culture is complex (McAuliffe, 2013a; Stige, 2002), and there are many layers of our cultured identities. These multiple identities have a profound impact on the lived experience of each person. This effect is often referred to as intersectionality, or "the way sexism, racism, classism, ageism (and any -ism) intersect in lived experience, bringing awareness to the varying degrees of oppression in layered structures of power" (Villaverde, 2008, p. 55). The effect can also be referred to as "compound discrimination" (McAuliffe, 2013b, p. 29). Often, when the majority culture values certain identity markers over others (such as race, gender, sexual orientation, socioeconomic class, age, ability, size, and so forth.), a person whose identity markers differ from those that are valued may feel marginalized (Robinson-Wood, 2009).

Being marginalized and oppressed can lead to the expression or suppression of feelings and behaviors often associated with behavioral health issues. The danger in viewing behaviors dichotomously is that health care professionals may assess and diagnose a person's experience of marginalization as a behavioral health issue instead of the systemic issue of oppression that it is (Caldwell, 2013). It is important that we look at ways in which we have been/are being marginalized, as well as ways in which we oppress others (Robinson-Wood, 2013). Let's look at classism as an example.

In terms of recognizing our own experiences of marginalization, Liu (2011) recommended helping professionals to examine "experiences of being marginalized because of clothing, where one lived, having to ride a bus to school, or even bringing lunch to school or eating meals targeted for low-income children—essentially anything that marked the individual as different" (p. 110). Liu described his own experience of "lateral classism" when moving to a more affluent neighborhood as an adult and realizing that he was not able to "keep up with the Joneses," so to speak, because he did not understand the middle-class norms of the neighborhood to which he had recently moved (p. 111). It was not until Liu made this move that he became aware of bias related to class because of personal bias's tendency to be an automatic thought.

In processing our own experiences of bias, marginalization, and privilege, we are able to recognize ways in which we might unintentionally be overcompensating for our own experiences of oppression or undervaluing the experience of oppression by our clients. Failure to critically examine our own personal bias could in turn lead to the further oppression of others, even if unintentional. Neither guilt nor denial regarding our own personal bias is helpful, and in fact both can create barriers to the therapeutic relationship.

My experience as a music therapist working in several women's shelters has taught me that we should not blame the victim, and the same concept applies to systematic oppression. We should not blame clients for experiencing marginalization and the symptoms that may accompany their lived experience of oppression. We need to realize the systemic oppression that exists—which creates unnecessary suffering for some and unearned privilege for others. I remember a conversation I had with a male music therapist when he questioned women's experience of oppression. I asked him, "Did you think about the parking spot you chose when you came in to work today?" He replied, "No, I parked in the first available spot." I then told him my experience of parking my car that day. Knowing that I would be working late and that the parking lot would be deserted when I left for the day, I had to circle the parking lot to find a parking space near a streetlight. In that moment, he understood. When he left for the day, he only had to remember where he parked his car. When I left for the day, I had to worry about my safety. It is important to avoid making assumptions that our experience is the same as another person's experience, on an individual or collective level.

We also need to be aware of ways in which we may represent the majority culture when working with clients, which may exacerbate their experiences of "symptoms." In writing this, I am reminded of an African-American woman with whom I worked who lived in what she described as "the projects." The first time we met, she announced that coming to therapy was "bogus." Her words will remain with me forever—"I'm not the one that needs therapy." It must have been difficult for her to say this to an educated, White woman living in a middle-class neighborhood and to confront the racist culture that I represent due to my unearned privilege. Looking back, I now see that her words did not describe a cultural belief about therapy. Instead, she was expressing her experience of systemic oppression. Given the systemic nature of oppression, misogyny, and violence against women, her words ring true.

The first step toward growth is to have awareness of our own personal biases. This often begins with personal work, so that we can become conscious of our own culture and identity markers. If we are part of the majority culture, we may take for granted our identity markers, as these may already be identified as normative by the majority culture (Hadley & Hahna, 2010). This can occur because "culture is often rendered invisible, largely because of its pervasiveness" by those in the majority culture (Robinson-Wood, 2009, p. 5). This creates a potentially unethical situation where the therapist may not be aware of their own race, gender, socioeconomic class, religion, sexual orientation, and so on, which can lead the therapist to assume that their experience is the same as the experience of their clients.

Unpacking White Privilege

Since a majority of music therapists in the United States identify as White (American Music Therapy Association, 2013a), it is important to understand, and unpack, White privilege (Robinson-Wood, 2013). I realize that some people reading this statement may say that they "do not see race" or that we are all part of the "human race." It is tempting to think that we can see beyond color, but the historical oppression of persons based upon identity markers, such as race, cannot be easily erased (Neville & Awad, 2014; Sue & Sue 2003; Toppozada, 1995). We must remember that "we are taught to not recognize White privilege" and that by not recognizing this we "are taking part in oppression, albeit unpremeditated in nature" (Pedersen, Crethar, & Carlson, 2008, p. 82). McAuliffe, Grothaus, and Gómez (2013) described "color-blind racism" as "people denying the lingering effects and continuing presence of racism in the 21st century" (p. 101). We do not live in a "postracial" society, or a "postfeminist" society, for that matter (Neville & Awad, 2014), and these terms discount the pain experienced by persons who are marginalized by an attempt to bring comfort to those who are part of the oppressive, majority culture. While laws may have been passed to grant increasing freedoms to oppressed persons, this does not mean that unconscious bias has changed. And the denial of the problem "often exacerbates racial tensions and disparities" (Neville & Awad, p. 313). As Williams, a law professor, wrote, "the rules may be color-blind, but people are not" (1991, p. 120). It is important that we take ownership in music therapy of our personal bias and work to change it. Toppozada (1995) found that "many of the comments [from music therapists participating in a multiculturalism] … indicated support for a 'color-blind' approach to working with people" (p. 79). The author discussed ways in which these types of assumptions, which diminish or deny multicultural issues, "may hinder rather than help the therapy process" (p. 80). The issue of color-blind racism is an one that many music therapists need to address as we confront our own personal biases.

In addition to the need for music therapists to understand their own culture and personal identity makers, it is also important to make sure that this understanding moves beyond a simplistic or dichotomous understanding of culture and toward a more complex and diverse understanding of culture. Using the example of race, Williams (1991) discussed the limitations of dualistic thinking in terms of values and identity markers:

> If White is good and Black is good and White and Black are different, then goodness must be different for each—or goodness becomes a limited property that is the subject of intense competition, as if it were a physical thing, a commodity or object whose possession can know only one location. (p. 122)

This highlights the inherent danger in dualistic thinking compounded with a lack of reflexivity.

It is vital that music therapists adopt a reflexive practice as part of this broadening of awareness and understanding of diversity and culture (Dileo, 2000, 2006). Mobley (1999) encouraged counselors to "explore their level of awareness about their own 'emic'—that is, their own culture-specific assumptions, values, biases, and limitations—and engage in active self-reflection using existing racial identity development models" (p. 91). If a music therapist comes from the dominant culture, an important part of reflexive practice is to confront any denial that the therapist may have regarding personal and institutional/systemic racism.

Denial of White privilege and/or racism may be based upon several factors. D'Andrea and Daniels (1999) described one reason that racism persists in the United States as stemming from a "moral contradiction" between the value of democracy and the experience of discrimination by persons who do not represent the majority culture. Another rationale that D'Andrea and Daniels provided for why White people may deny the existence of racism and/or their own racism is due to feelings of being overwhelmed when confronted by the enormity of the problem. It may be easier for therapists to deny that racism continues to exist, they theorize, because it is difficult to know where to begin to dismantle this complex system of oppression. Finally, McIntosh (1989) identified a barrier that many White people experience in dismantling racism and systems of oppression due to the unearned privilege they receive. She described this as an "invisible weightless backpack" (p. 1). Later, she added an additional metaphor to describe White privilege and the need for social change:

> White privilege [can be seen] as a *bank account* which I was given at birth, and did not ask for, but which I can spend down in the service of social justice. And because it is White privilege, it will automatically refill even after I spend it down. In other words, I do not have much to lose within my own life circumstances, by working against injustice. (2012, p. 196)

Her charge for the dominant culture to use their privilege to dismantle systems of oppression is inspiring and hopefully one that will be adopted by music therapists.

Psychologically, it may be easier for we White music therapists to say to ourselves that we have earned our positions of power and privilege due to hard work (Euro-centric values) and merit. It is important that we examine the circumstances of our lives to see how we have benefited from the system of racism, so that we can take steps to dismantle it and work toward positive social change (Sanjnani, 2012). This unearned privilege is invisible to those in the majority culture until we raise our consciousness and decide to unpack it from our invisible backpack. It is our responsibility to make the invisible visible and to examine power differentials that exist within the culture.

In the United States, education on multiculturalism is often inaccurate (Fawcett & Evans, 2013). History is often rewritten from the perspective of the victor, in this case, White European men. Children are taught these revised histories at quite a young age in primary and secondary school. By the time therapists enter the university setting, they may not be aware of the "societal reinforcement of racial ignorance ... public schools teach history by using texts that promote White supremacy and perpetuate the belief that minority groups in America are unimportant" (pp. 69–70). People who have received higher education may feel that they could not possibly be ignorant, biased, or racist, due to their further studies. And, higher education is not exempt from the systemic dissemination of patriarchal values—in fact, it was created to promote them (Bowen & Hobson, 1974; Karabel, 2005; McClelland, 1992; Nye, 1988). As music therapy educators, we must be aware of personal and systemic bias that exists in higher education and work to dismantle it (Hahna, 2013). However, whether we are aware of it or not, the classroom is a political space.

Personally, I had to (and still do) critically examine my own German values regarding having a strong work ethic when working with clients in a crisis shelter. I had been brought up to believe that if I worked hard enough, anything was possible. If I did not continually examine my personal bias surrounding my work ethic, I may not have been able to be as empathetic as I needed to be with the clients with whom I worked. It is imperative in my work that I do not feed into the culture of victim blaming as part of an assumption that hard work can get you out of a difficult situation. Socially condoned, misogynistic concepts such as "Why didn't she leave her abuser?" and "Why didn't she fight her rapist?," which are perpetuated by patriarchy, play into the bias of assuming that hardworking people can "pull themselves up by their bootstraps."

This type of thinking can be dangerous when applied to intimate partner violence and sexual assault—which is about power and control. Often, the most dangerous time for a woman who experiences intimate partner violence is right after she decides to leave her abuser, so her choice to stay in a violent situation may be what she feels is the best option for her at the time and does not indicate that she is not hardworking and/or that she does not have agency. On the contrary—without examining my own personal biases, toward glorification of a strong work ethic for instance, I might inaccurately assess the client's decision-making skills or progress in music therapy. A biased assessment can have long-term effects for clients. Doing my own personal work and seeking supervision allows me to honor both the context and the values of the client, from their perspective, and to be aware

of my own values and biases. This in turn helps to deepen the therapeutic relationship because I am better able to authentically connect with my clients and to see clients for who they truly are (and not my preconceived notions of them).

The Systemic Issue of Oppression

Groups that have been marginalized by the majority culture often experience oppression, discrimination, and stereotyping (Schwarzbaum & Thomas, 2008). The oppression of people based upon identity markers ...

> "... is based on systemic and structural constraints that do not stem from the actions of an individual tyrannical ruler, but rather are the result of rules and practices related to the power afforded by the privilege and domination of some groups with severe consequences for the subordinate groups with less power." (Schwarzbaum & Thomas, p. 14)

This is not to say that individual actions of violence and oppression do not occur. This quote does, however, highlight the broader social system that condones, and is established upon, a system of power and privilege. It is also important to note that creating a policy does not in and of itself end racism.

In looking at institutional racism, Ridley and Thompson (1999) suggested that "rather than perceiving these problems [institutional racism] as being influenced by societal attitudes and therefore structurally embedded in the ethos of institutional conduct, leaders of these institutions have established piecemeal solutions that are often targeted at preparing the student to cope with or manage the environment" (p. 12). Coping skills are not the answer to systemic oppression. Social change is not just policy change. The examination of systemic oppression, power, and privilege has been explored in various critical approaches, including feminist theory and critical race theory, with the hope of dismantling these patriarchal systems and replacing them with an egalitarian, grassroots system that values diversity. In the next section, I will highlight concepts from feminist theory, as they relate to personal bias, which is one of the lenses through which I see the world and thus my own personal bias.

Feminist Theory

Feminist therapists have highlighted the importance of viewing issues through a systemic lens, with a sensitivity to understanding that "problems and symptoms often arise as methods of coping with and surviving in oppressive circumstances" (Enns, 2004, p. 10). This shift away from a symptom-based approach, with its roots in narrow and marginalizing patriarchal constructs, has led many feminist-informed therapists to examine the context in which their client's live, or their "lived experience" (Rolvsjord, 2010). Lived experience can be defined as "holding clients' stories (their understanding of their experiences) as valid, and indeed central to therapy" (Ballou, Hill, & West, 2008, p. 2). Feminist therapists see lived experiences as valuable "by recognizing the multiplicity and complexity of influences and experiences for any individual" (Ballou et al., 2008, p. 51). This dissatisfaction with traditional psychological theory has led feminist therapists to reconceptualize behavioral health theories through consciousness raising and decentering from normative models of behavioral health (Villaverde, 2008). In addition, feminist therapists value the establishment of egalitarian relationships as well as the empowerment of clients as goals of therapy (Worell & Remer, 2003). Other goals of feminist therapy include demystification of the therapeutic relationship, acknowledging that the personal is political, and valuing women's perspectives (Curtis, 2006; Worell & Remer, 2003).

Feminist therapists use a variety of techniques to work toward dismantling oppressive systems and addressing client needs. These include reframing, or redefining, as coping skills what traditional theories consider to be symptoms. The idea that the client has strength, resilience, and agency is central to a feminist-informed approach (Rolvsjord, 2004; Worell & Remer, 2003). It is not enough to work on change within the therapeutic relationship—changing society is equally important from a feminist perspective (Ballou, Hill, & West, 2008; Enns, 2004). Other techniques in feminist therapy include power analysis and gender role analysis (Curtis, 2006; Worell & Remer, 2003).

A movement within music therapy, as well as other creative arts therapies, toward the incorporation of feminist perspectives and critical race theories highlights the increasing awareness of systems perspectives in understanding how oppression, power, privilege, and patriarchy affect everyone within society and culture (Edwards & Hadley, 2007; Hadley, 2006; Hadley & Hahna, 2016; Mayor, 2012; Sajnani, 2012). Patriarchy is defined as *male-dominated* structures and social arrangements (Hadley, 2006, p. 11). Additionally, culture-centered music therapy (Stige, 2002) is helping music therapists to broaden their understanding of culture. This new awareness sees clients within the context of their lived experiences. It also acknowledges the unstated artifacts of history that influence the values and norms of a culture. The goal of making the invisible visible, therefore, is an important way in which feminist therapy can help to inform music therapists wishing to work on decreasing the effects of personal bias in music therapy (Hadley, 2006).

Personal Bias and Music Therapy

According to the *AMTA Standards of Clinical Practice* (AMTA, 2012), "music therapy assessment will explore the client's culture. This can include but is not limited to race, ethnicity, language, religion/spirituality, social class, family experiences, sexual orientation, gender identity, and social organizations" (2.2). In thinking about personal bias, I wonder if subtle (or not so subtle) forms of oppression might be part of our assessment process. While the *AMTA Standards of Clinical Practice* mention multiculturalism only in the area of assessment, it is important

to remember to be mindful of the impact of these identity markers (our own and our clients) in all aspects of therapy, supervision, teaching, and research.

It is significant to note that the language in the *AMTA Standards of Clinical Practice* has evolved from earlier versions—"considerations may be given to a client's spirituality and cultural background" (AMTA, 2006, 2.1)—to the most recent standard, stating that assessment "will explore" these issues (AMTA, 2012). The need to consider issues of multiculturalism and personal bias is also examined in documents from the Certification Board for Music Therapists (CBMT). The *Scope of Practice* (CBMT, 2010) does not require action, such as personal work, for issues such as personal bias, but does require the music therapist to "assess areas for personal growth and set goals" (4.A.1). According to the *Scope of Practice*, music therapists should "acknowledge [the music] therapist's bias and limitations in interpreting assessment information (e.g., cultural differences, clinical orientation)" (I.B.4, p. 1). While the *Scope of Practice* is also focused on assessment, this standard highlights the role of interpretation within the assessment process, which could possibly be extended to all aspects of the therapeutic process. It is imperative that as a profession we move beyond awareness, exploration, and goal setting, and move toward action when it comes to addressing concerns such as personal bias. As with change in psychological theories, the adage that insight is not sufficient would be important for music therapists to consider as we take action in reducing the negative impact of our personal bias. This next section will examine ways in which personal bias can affect assessment, diagnosis, treatment, and evaluation of client progress in music therapy.

Assessment, Diagnosis, and Evaluation

Conducting culture-centered music therapy assessments is an important part of practice. Depending on the type of assessment tool the music therapist is using, standardized or therapist-derived, there are different issues regarding personal bias in assessment (Shuttleworth, 2006). Standardized assessments have been critiqued for their lack of sensitivity to cultural diversity and comparison of client development based upon norms that are biased toward the values of the dominant culture (Perry, Steele, & Hilliard, 2003; Suzuki, Onoue, & Hill, 2013). On the one hand failure to create assessment measures that are sensitive to cultural diversity can "further perpetuate inadequate training models and subsequent counseling services" due to the lack of reliability and validity of the instrument for diverse groups (Robinson-Wood, 2009, p. 33). On the other hand, a therapist-derived assessment runs the risk of embedding personal biases within the instrument itself. One way this can occur is in the language on the form. For instance, an intake form may use the words "mother" and "father," perpetuating a heteronormative stance. Also, a form may have only two options for gender, marginalizing a transgender, genderqueer, or intersex client (Shuttleworth, 2006; Whitehead-

Pleaux et al., 2012). Additionally, failing to view the client's experience within a broader social context, a music therapist might describe a client's presenting needs without taking into consideration the oppressive system in which the person lives (Shuttleworth, 2006). The compounding effects of such personal bias at this stage of therapy cannot be overstressed, as the assessment often serves as the baseline measurement for the client and involves the establishment of treatment goals (Ballou, Hill, & West, 2008; Robinson-Wood, 2009).

While music therapists do not diagnose clients, we do work within a system that is increasingly reliant upon the *Diagnostic & Statistical Manual* (*DSM*, American Psychiatric Association, 2013). Often our assessments and progress reports at treatment team meetings are used to inform diagnostic classification for clients or to help to make differential diagnosis. With this in mind, having an understanding of how personal bias can affect diagnosis is important for music therapists, especially as members of an interdisciplinary treatment team, so that they can advocate for their clients as needed. Just as with assessment, critique regarding the bias within the diagnostic categories of the *DSM* is important to consider, especially when examining issues such as personal bias (Ballou, Hill, & West, 2008; Frances, 2013). Failure to take a systems perspective can potentially lead to inaccurate diagnosis, as seen in the following passages regarding counseling LGBT (lesbian, gay, bisexual, and transgender) clients:

> It sometimes becomes difficult to separate psychological issues from political ones. The struggle to remove homosexuality as a pathology and to practice gay- and lesbian-affirmative counseling has led some counselors away from diagnosis (Gonsiorek, 1982).

> Sometimes a client manifests pathology that results from difficulty in accepting a gay or lesbian identity. Sometimes the issue is severe pathology and not a reaction to coming out and oppression. Sometimes it is a combination of both (Dworkin & Gutiérrez, 1992, p. 328).

As seen in these passages, the complexities of diagnosis are such that understanding the broader social context of the client is important, as well as understanding the limitations of language and diagnostic categories in the *DSM*. For this reason, some feminist therapists either do not provide diagnoses for their clients based upon the *DSM* (in health care fields where the therapist can diagnose), or they collaboratively discuss the diagnosis with the client and choose language that is culturally sensitive and that fully supports the client's lived experience and context (Ballou, Hill, & West, 2008; Worell & Remer, 2003).

During the treatment phase of therapy, it is important that the music therapist work to decrease the impact of personal bias on the therapeutic relationship with the client through seeking supervision and doing their own personal work. Dworkin and Gutiérrez (1992) discussed the importance of therapists working in the LGBT community to work on "the therapist's own internalized or latent homophobia causing mutual client and counselor blind spots that could affect the therapist's capacity for beneficence" (p. 331). This same concept applies not only to working with persons in the LGBT community, but also to working with clients with diverse personal identity markers such as race, gender, ability, class, age, size, socioeconomic status, and so forth. (Robinson-Wood, 2009). In order to establish trust and rapport, we must have unconditional positive regard and congruence when working with a client to decrease the impact of our personal bias—this involves confronting our own internalized oppression as well.

Finally, it is important that the music therapist ensures that her evaluations of client progress do not include discriminatory or demeaning language. Feminist therapists have critiqued the use of language and labeling within the dominant culture, both within the therapy room and in society as a whole. Ballou, Hill, and West (2008) emphasized the importance of language in therapeutic evaluations due to "the way language is always embedded in the system of meanings that form the fabric of the social environment. It is impossible to isolate and avoid those social constructions that help create and maintain inequities and injustice" (pp. 19–20). In music therapy, Darrow and White (1998) encouraged music therapists to be aware of "handicapping language" and its effects on clients (p. 81). At the same time, some people coming from a disability studies perspective reject person-first language and instead advocate for identity first language (LaCom & Reed, 2014; Linton, 1998). We must be mindful of what we are communicating when evaluating client progress, making sure that we are not perpetuating social norms and/or stereotypes and that we accurately represent the client.

Just as it is important to examine the language we use as music therapists, we must also be conscious of what we are not saying in our clinical evaluations. We must be mindful that we do not overlook or downplay a client's experience of oppression, especially if it is a topic that is personally difficult to confront ourselves, such as racism, heterosexism, misogyny, and so on. We might ask ourselves whether our questions, observations, or assessments contain "spread"—"the tendency for people without disabilities to act as if the individual's disability has a more pervasive impact than it does" (Getch & Johnson, 2013, p. 520). Has our personal bias caused "interaction strain"—"[an interaction which] occurs when individuals without disabilities interact with persons with disabilities and experience anxiety as a result of not being confident in how they should interact" (Getch & Johnson, p. 521). To address issues such as these, Caldwell (2013), a dance therapist, recommended that "observation, assessment, and diagnosis can be coconstructed by therapist and client" (p. 185). Collaborating with a client in all aspects of the music therapy process is incredibly important so that we do not "end up reconstructing the client in an ableist fashion according to standards of normality, seeking the value of clients solely through their abilities" (Rolvsjord, 2014, para 39).

Personal Responsibility of Therapist

Building upon the ideas of feminism, critical race theory, culture-centered music therapy, disability studies, and multiculturalism, it becomes imperative that music therapists understand the complexities of cultural issues that impact their perspectives and personal bias in the therapeutic setting. Taking an honest and reflexive look at our own biases, assumptions, and values is a critical first step and an important part of daily practice (Sue & Sue, 2003). Hays (2008) stated that therapists should use humility, compassion, and critical thinking when assessing their own biases, giving attention to the impact of power imbalances and well-meaning intentions. It is important that our worldviews and actions allow clients to feel safe and heard within the therapeutic space. To this end, therapists are encouraged to engage in their own personal work to increase their awareness of their personal values and belief systems (Bradt, 1997; Chase, 2003). The reader is also encouraged to explore Whitehead-Pleaux (2009) and Stige's interview with Forinash (2000; as cited in Stige, 2002) for more detailed examples of two music therapists' processes while working with persons from different cultures.

In addition to becoming aware of our own values and biases, it is important for therapists wishing to practice with cultural empathy to understand their own culture (Sue & Sue, 2003). Learning about the history and cultural heritage of our own cultures is a critical step in learning about the broader, systemic, cultural values that may be considered to be normative and thus often unnamed. It is also important to understand this cultural history (for me, this involves acknowledging the persecution, colonization, and genocide that my cultural group inflicted upon minority groups) and how this cultural heritage may be oppressive to other cultural groups. Additionally, it is important to understand our own cultural heritage even if it seems on the surface that the issues of oppression occurred a long time ago. This also pertains to the music we use in a session. Stige (2002) reminded us that "classical music is not different from any other tradition of music; it is embedded in culture(s) and it carries certain cultural values" (p. 93). We must also become more aware of how our own cultural heritage might impact things such as song selection, especially when a client tells the music therapist to "play anything you like—I like all kinds of music." Using a song from the Christian tradition, such as "This Little Light of Mine," does not overtly reference a deity; however, one is implied, and this religious reference might suppress a client's interactions with us, especially if they do not follow this faith tradition. As a supervisor, I find myself going back and forth between checking in with my own personal bias and then trying to facilitate my supervisee's ability to do the same. For me, consciousness raising is a gradual process, and unpacking our privilege takes time and concerted effort. As a teacher or supervisor, I find myself often needing to explain reasons why a student or supervisee cannot use a particular song without further assessment of musical preference and/or faith practice.

Regardless of the level of our personal participation in systems of oppression, or how long ago they took place, music is a cultural artifact, and we should be mindful of the unspoken messages we are passing along when using different genres of music. This occurs outside of the music portion of the music therapy session. Surprisingly, a survey of music therapists found that "only 11% of participants believed that music therapists needed to be aware of the role of music in a client's culture for therapy to be beneficial" (Valentino, 2006, p. 113). Personally, I imagine that my last name (of Austrian heritage) can be a difficult barrier for a client coming from Jewish heritage. My cultural history enters the therapeutic space, regardless of whether I realize it, as part of the history of Austria's involvement in WWII and the Holocaust. It is, therefore, important for me to explore this. This becomes further compounded when considering the implications of music used within a music therapy session when the client and therapist have different cultural identities. The impact of me using Wagner's music, for instance, in a session would carry embedded cultural messages. If I was unaware of this composer's anti-Semitic views or my own Austrian heritage, I might not understand why a client became upset or offended when it was played. This is especially important for me as a Fellow in the Bonny Method of Guided Imagery and Music (GIM). I need to analyze not only the music/score, but also the cultural context of the piece and composer. Otherwise, I may be passing on cultural messages that perpetuate systems of privilege and oppression. Understanding our own cultural history, and its relationship to other cultures, is especially important when a therapist is from a majority culture to avoid being "ethnocentric … believing in the superiority of his or her group's cultural heritage (arts, crafts, traditions, language), [and] there is respect for cultural differences" (Sue & Sue, p. 19).

Just as learning about our own culture is essential, it is also critical that music therapists look to deepen our understanding of the culture of others. Again, it is important to avoid a dichotomous view of cultures and instead to cultivate an understanding of cultural difference based upon individual experience with rich variation of expression. As we deepen our knowledge of various cultures, we should also learn about the cultural heritage of our clients by both researching this ourselves and asking our clients. Identity markers are highly personal and complex, especially when we identify with several cultures and groups, and I have found that it is best to ask the experts in their lived experience—the clients—so that I can understand the context of their identities using thick description and language that holds personal meaning for them. Involving clients in the process of therapy, including the creation of goals and the viewing of progress notes, can allow for member-checking (to borrow another qualitative idea) and create a more egalitarian relationship. I am also mindful that clients' preferences regarding labels and/or language may shift over time, especially as consciousness raising occurs, so I check in with them about language I use, both verbally and in my written reports, over time. For example, in working with survivors of intimate partner violence, I find that clients may identify with a variety of terms, including "victim," "survivor," "thriver," and "advocate." If I assume that a woman identifies as a survivor, this could minimize her experience of the trauma and abuse she experienced. To assume that a woman identifies as a victim could be disempowering and patronizing. I must also remember that how a woman identifies on a continuum can vary from week to week (or day to day), depending on her lived experience.

As music therapists, we know that understanding our client's culture also involves a need to understand the music of the client's culture (Jones, 2006). Chase (2003) encouraged music therapists practicing from a multicultural stance to "be musically flexible" in terms of song choice, genre, instrumentation, and so forth. (p. 87). She also urged music therapists to understand the role of music and healing in various cultures so that the music therapist does not engage in experiences that are contraindicated or culturally insensitive. As music is central to music therapy practice, Chase's recommendations are profoundly important to consider for all aspects of music used in a session. As Forinash (2000, as cited in Stige, 2002) and Whitehead-Pleaux (2009) remind us, it is important to follow the client's lead and practice in a compassionate and culturally empathetic manner when working with persons from diverse cultures.

Advocating for Social Change

Music therpists are encouraged to be advocates. The Certification Board for Music Therapists' *Scope of Practice* (2010), in the area of "Professional Responsibilities," indicates that a music therapist should "serve as a representative, spokesperson, ambassador, or advocate for the profession of music therapy" (4.B.17). The American Music Therapy Association's *Code of Ethics* (2013b), under the section "Responsibility to the Community/Public," states that music therapists should "strive to increase public awareness of music therapy." As part of my own reflexive practice (for full disclosure: I am cochair of a music therapy state task force), I wonder why music therapists interpret advocacy as relating only to the profession of music therapy. What if we felt a professional responsibility (Baines, 2012; Hadley, 2013) to our community to advocate for social change (Estrella, 2011)? In recognizing my own bias and the systemic oppression of groups in our culture, I do not feel comfortable working with a client only at the microlevel of the therapeutic setting when the macrolevel continues to perpetuate oppression. I yearn for the time when the profession of music therapy embraces concepts of social change—as do some of our sister professions in counseling (Hays & Erford, 2014), social work (National Association of Social Workers, 2008), and expressive arts therapy (Levine & Levine, 2011; Rogers, 2011)—as part of our

professional responsibilities. As Forinish (2006) described in her discussion of feminist supervision and bias, "we need to go beyond simply recognizing the biases and actually challenge them" (p. 420). Chang, Crethar, and Ratts (2010) describe the counseling profession's support of social advocacy as "unequivocal" and list the following examples of ways in which the counseling profession has embraced social change:

> (a) the formation of the ACES [Association for Counselor Education and Supervision] Human Rights and Social Justice Committee in 2006; (b) its endorsement of the ACA (American Counseling Association) Advocacy Competencies …; (c) sponsorship of the ACES Social Justice Summit in 2007 and 2009; and (d) the election of social justice–oriented counseling scholars. (p. 82)

The National Association for Social Workers also addressed social action in its *Code of Ethics* (2008). Section 6.04.d of the ethics code states:

> [S]ocial workers should act to prevent and eliminate domination of, exploitation of, and discrimination against any person, group, or class on the basis of race, ethnicity, national origin, color, sex, sexual orientation, gender identity or expression, age, marital status, political belief, religion, immigration status, or mental or physical disability. (para. 4)

How refreshing it is for me to see that professions such as counseling and social work not only embrace the professional responsibility of therapists to advocate for social change, but also make this an integral part of their curriculum. Grothaus, McAuliffe, Danner, and Doyle (2013) described the movement of social change in counseling as "beyond the provision of remedial services in order to attend to the conditions that cause or contribute to mental and social disorder" (p. 46). In expressive arts therapy, Estrella (2011) advocated for the inclusion of social action into the curriculum due to the field's "use of the arts for change" (p. 43). Rogers (2011) talked about the "urgency for social change" with the expressive arts (p. 17). In my own research with a colleague on music therapy education (Hahna & Schwantes, 2006), several music therapy educators reported not using feminist pedagogy, including topics such as social change, in their curriculum due to lack of time because they thought that the personal and the political should be kept separate from the classroom space. It is my hope that music therapists will see the importance of teaching social justice concepts as integral to the curriculum and as a way to work toward social change, just as counselors and social workers do in both the clinic and classroom.

My own bias on the topic of advocacy is that we should not only advocate for social change in our communities, but also take it upon ourselves to be responsible for the change that needs to occur. It seems selfish to me that our profession requires us to advocate only for music therapy or client access to music therapy. I am in no way suggesting that we stop doing this, because access to services is important (again, I am cochair of a music therapy state task force). However, when it comes to the education of future generations of music therapists and the continuing education of current music therapists, we can no longer blame full curricula, or the fear of bias, for our lack of action on this matter. We need to teach our students about the need for change at the macro level and not just at the micro level with things such as goal- and objective-writing.

I am all too aware of ways in which my own biases, and those of the majority culture, serve as impenetrable barriers for many of the clients I serve. It is time that the profession of music therapy expand its mandate for advocacy to that of social change. There is no easy fix for this complex issue so a paradigm shift is necessary, as well as a grassroots movement based upon egalitarianism. What stands in our way? Is the field of music therapy too pre-occupied with trying to be viewed as a legitimate profession, from the standpoint of traditional counseling and/or the medical model, that we have distanced ourselves from other disciplines, such as expressive arts therapy, that more readily embrace social change (Estrella, 2011)? Perhaps, as we can confront our own biases and any shame we may feel (Johnson, 1994), we can begin to take a step toward social change by expanding our *Scope of Practice* and *Code of Ethics* and step toward a more equitable system for everyone.

Conclusion

This chapter highlights the profound impact that personal bias can have on the therapeutic relationship, often without the therapist's awareness of the issue. It is important, therefore, that music therapists engage in supervision and personal work to diminish the negative impact that the personal biases of each of us will have on the therapeutic process. Additionally, training in multiculturalism and culture-centered music therapy is recommended for music therapists to raise their consciousness about issues of diversity as well as to encourage them to make meaningful changes to their clinical practice that demonstrate culture empathy. Music therapists should be mindful of the complexities and individual nature of culture and be "musically flexible" as Chase (2003, p. 87) recommends. Finally, adapting a reflexive practice can assist music therapists in critically examining their own thoughts, feelings, biases, and behaviors over time. With courageous, humble, and honest self-assessment, music therapy as a profession can make the necessary changes needed to broaden our definition of advocacy to include the necessity for social change. Perhaps shifting from a "rule-based" code of ethics to an "aspirational" ethics, as proposed by Dileo (2006, p. 487), could assist music therapists in moving toward positive social change to dismantle systems of oppression. The time for change is long overdue.

References

American Music Therapy Association. (2006). AMTA standards of clinical practice. *Music therapy sourcebook.* Silver Spring, MD: Author.

American Music Therapy Association. (2012). *AMTA standards of clinical practice.* Retrieved from http://www.musictherapy.org/about/standards/

American Music Therapy Association. (2013a). *2013 AMTA member survey and workforce analysis.* Retrieved from http://www.musictherapy.org/documents/

American Music Therapy Association. (2013b). *Code of ethics.* Retrieved from http://www.musictherapy.org/about/ethics/

American Psychiatric Association. (2013). *Diagnostic and statistical manual of mental disorders* (5th ed.). Washington, DC: Author.

Baines, S. (2012). Music therapy as an anti-oppressive practice. *The Arts in Psychotherapy, 40,* 1–5. doi:10.1016/j.aip.2012.09.003

Ballou, M., Hill, M., & West, C. (2008). *Feminist therapy theory and practice: A contemporary perspective.* New York, NY: Springer.

Bradt, J. (1997). Ethical issues in multicultural counseling: Implications for music therapy. *The Arts in Psychotherapy, 24*(2), 137–143. doi:10.1016/S0197-4556(97)00017-8

Bowen, J., & Hobson, P. R. (1974). *Theories of education: Studies of significant innovation in western educational thought.* Sydney, Australia: John Wiley and Sons Australia.

Caldwell, C. (2013). Diversity issues in movement observation and assessment. *American Journal of Dance Therapy, 35,* 183–200. doi:10.1007/s10465-013-9159-9

Certification Board for Music Therapists. (2010). *Scope of practice.* Retrieved from http://www.cbmt.org

Chang, C. Y., Crethar, H. C., & Ratts, M. J. (2010). Social justice: A national imperative for counselor education and supervision. *Counselor Education and Supervision, 50,* 82–87.

Chase, K. M. (2003). Multicultural music therapy: A review of literature. *Music Therapy Perspectives, 21,* 84–88. doi:10.1093/mtp/21.2.84

Curtis, S. L. (2006). Feminist music therapy: Transforming theory, transforming lives. In S. Hadley (Ed.), *Feminist perspectives in music therapy* (pp. 227–244). Gilsum, NH: Barcelona Publishers.

D'Andrea, M. D., & Daniels, J. (1999). Understanding the different psychological dispositions of white racism: A comprehensive model for counselor educators and practitioners. In M. S. Kiselica (Ed.), *Confronting prejudice and racism during multicultural training* (pp. 59–87). Alexandria, VA: American Counseling Association.

Darrow, A-A., & Molloy, D. (1998). Multicultural perspectives in music therapy: An examination of the literature, educational curricula, and clinical practices in culturally diverse cities of the United States. *Music Therapy Perspectives, 16,* 27–32. doi:10.1093/mtp/16.1.27

Darrow, A-A., & White, G. W. (1998). Sticks and stones … and words CAN hurt: Eliminating handicapping language. *Music Therapy Perspectives, 16,* 81–93. doi:10.1093/mtp/16.2.81

Dileo, C. (2000). *Ethical thinking in music therapy.* Cherry Hill, NJ: Jeffrey Books.

Dileo, C. (2006). Feminist therapy ethics: Implications for music therapy. In S. Hadley (Ed.), *Feminist perspectives in music therapy* (pp. 475–491). Gilsum, NH: Barcelona Publishers.

Dworkin, S. H., & Gutiérrez, F. J. (1992). *Counseling gay men & lesbians: Journey to the end of the rainbow.* Alexandria, VA: American Counseling Association.

Edwards, J., & Hadley, S. (2007). Expanding music therapy practice: Incorporating the feminist frame. *The Arts in Psychotherapy, 34*(3), 199–207. doi:10.1016/j.aip.2007.01.001

Enns, C. Z. (2004). *Feminist theories and feminist psychotherapies: Origins, themes, and diversity* (2nd ed.). Binghamton, NY: Haworth Press.

Estrella, K. (2001). Multicultural approach to music therapy supervision. In M. Forinash (Ed.), *Music therapy supervision* (pp. 39–66). Gilsum, NH: Barcelona Publishers.

Estrella, K. (2011). Social activism within expressive arts "therapy": What's in a name? In E. G. Levine & S. K. Levine (Eds.), *Arts in action: Expressive arts therapy and social change* (pp. 42–52). London, UK: Jessica Kingsley.

Fawcett, M. L., & Evans, K. M. (2013). *Experimental approach for developing multicultural counseling competence.* Thousand Oaks, CA: SAGE.

Forinash, M. (2006). Feminist music therapy supervision. In S. Hadley (Ed.), *Feminist perspectives in music therapy* (pp. 415–427). Gilsum, NH: Barcelona Publishers.

Frances, A. (2013). *Saving normal.* New York, NY: Harper Collins.

Getch, Y. Q., & Johnson, A. L. (2013). Counseling individuals with disabilities. In G. McAuliffe (Ed.), *Culturally alert counseling: A comprehensive introduction* (2nd ed., pp. 505–539). Thousand Oaks, CA: SAGE.

Gonsiorek, J. C. (1982). The use of diagnostic concepts in working with gay and lesbian populations. In J. C. Goniorek (Ed.), *A guide to psychotherapy with gay and lesbian clients* (pp. 9–20). New York, NY: Haworth.

Grothaus, T., McAuliffe, G., Danner, M., & Doyle, L. (2013). Equity, advocacy, and social justice. In G. McAuliffe (Ed.), *Culturally alert counseling: A comprehensive introduction* (2nd ed., pp. 45–73). Thousand Oaks, CA: SAGE.

Hadley, S. (Ed.). (2006). *Feminist perspectives in music therapy.* Gilsum, NH: Barcelona Publishers.

Hadley, S. (2013). Dominant narratives: Complicity and the need for vigilance in the creative arts therapies. *The Arts in Psychotherapy, 40*(4), 373–381. doi:10.1016/j.aip.2013.05.007

Hadley, S., & Hahna, N. D. (2010, November 18). *Unpacking sites of privilege: Expanding the therapist's self-awareness.* Continuing Music Therapy Education (CMTE) presentation at the American Music Therapy Association Conference, Cleveland, OH.

Hadley, S., & Hahna, N. D. (2016). Feminist perspectives in music therapy. In J. Edwards (Ed.), *The Oxford handbook of music therapy.* Oxford, UK: Oxford University Press.

Hadley, S., & Norris, M. S. (2015). Musical multicultural competency in music therapy: The first step. *Music Therapy Perspectives.* Advanced online publication. doi:10.1093/mtp/miv045

Hahna, N. D. (2013). Towards an emancipatory practice: Incorporating feminist pedagogy in creative arts therapies. *The Arts in Psychotherapy, 40*(4), 436–440. doi:10.1016/j.aip.2013.05.002

Hays, D. G., & Erford, B. T. (2014). *Developing multicultural counseling competence: A systems approach.* Boston, MA: Pearson.

Hays, P. A. (2008). *Addressing cultural complexities in practice* (2nd ed.). Washington, DC: American Psychological Association.

Johnson, D. R. (1994). Shame dynamics among creative arts therapists. *The Arts in Psychotherapy, 21*(3), 173–178. doi:10/1016/0197-4556(94)90046-9

Jones, L. (2006). Critical reflections on song selection for women's empowerment in music therapy. In S. Hadley (Ed.), *Feminist perspectives in music therapy* (pp. 324–354). Gilsum, NH: Barcelona Publishers.

Karabel, J. (2005). *The chosen: The hidden history of admission and exclusion at Harvard, Yale, and Princeton.* Boston, MA: Houghton Mifflin.

Kim, S., & Whitehead-Pleaux, A. (2015). Music therapy and cultural diversity. In B. L. Wheeler (Ed.), *Music therapy handbook* (pp. 51–63). New York, NY: The Guilford Press.

LaCom, C., & Reed, R. (2014). Destabilizing bodies, destabilizing disciplines: Practicing liminality in music therapy. *Voices: A World Forum for Music Therapy, 14*(3), doi:10.15845/voices.v14i3.797

Levine, E. G., & Levine, S. K. (Eds.). (2011). *Art in action: Expressive arts therapy and social change.* London, UK: Jessica Kingsley.

Linton, S. (1998). *Claiming disabilities: Knowledge and identity.* New York, NY: NYU Press.

Liu, W. M. (2011). *Social class and classism in the helping professions: Research, theory, and practice.* Thousand Oaks, CA: SAGE.

Mayor, C. (2012). Playing with race: A theoretical framework and approach for creative arts therapists. *The Arts in Psychotherapy, 39,* 214–219. doi:10.1016/j.aip.2011.12.008

McAuliffe, G. (2013a). Culture and diversity defined. In G. McAuliffe (Ed.), *Culturally alert counseling: A comprehensive introduction* (2nd ed., pp. 3–23). Thousand Oaks, CA: SAGE.

McAuliffe, G. (2013b). Culture: Clarifications and complications. In G. McAuliffe (Ed.), *Culturally alert counseling: A comprehensive introduction* (2nd ed., pp. 25–43). Thousand Oaks, CA: SAGE.

McAuliffe, G., Grothaus, T., & Gómez, E. (2013). Conceptualizing race and racism. In G. McAuliffe (Ed.). *Culturally alert counseling: A comprehensive introduction* (2nd ed., pp. 89–121). Thousand Oaks, SAGE.

McClelland, A. E. (1992). *The education of women in the United States*. New York, NY: Garland.

McIntosh, P. (1989). White privilege: Unpacking the invisible backpack. *Peace and Freedom, July/August,* 8–10.

McIntosh, P. (2012). Reflections and future directions for privilege studies. *Journal of Sociial Issues, 68*(1), 194–206.

Mobley, M., & Cheatham, H. (1999). R.A.C.E.—racial affirmation and counselor education. In M. S. Kiselica (Ed.), *Confronting prejudice and racism during multicultural training.* Alexandria, VA: American Counseling Association.

National Association of Social Workers. (2008). *Code of ethics of the National Association of Social Workers.* Retrieved from http://www.socialworkers.org/pubs/code/code.asp

Neville, H. A., & Awad, G. H. (2014). Why racial color-blindness is myopic. *American Psychologist, 69*(3), 313–314.

Nye, A. (1988). *Feminist theory and the philosophies of man.* New York, NY: Routledge.

Pedersen, P. B., Crethar, H. C., & Carlson, J. (2008). *Inclusive cultural empathy: Making relationships central in counseling and psychotherapy.* Washington, DC: American Psychological Association.

Perry, T., Steele, C., & Hillard, A. (2003). *Young, gifted, and black: Promoting high achievement among African-American students.* Boston, MA: Beacon Books.

Ridley, C. R., & Thompson, C. E. (1999). Managing resistance to diversity training: A social systems perspective. In M. S. Kiselica (Ed.), *Confronting prejudice and racism during multicultural training* (pp. 3–24). Alexandria, VA: American Counseling Association.

Robinson-Wood, T. L. (2009). *The convergence of race, ethnicity, and gender: Multiple identities in counseling* (3rd ed.). Columbus, OH: Pearson.

Robinson-Wood, T. L. (2013). *The convergence of race, ethnicity, and gender: Multiple identities in counseling.* Upper Saddle River, NJ: Pearson.

Rogers, N. (2012). *The creative connection for groups: Person-centered expressive arts for healing and social change.* Palo Alto, CA: Science & Behavioral Books.

Rolvsjord, R. (2004). Therapy as empowerment: Clinical and political implications of empowerment philosophy in mental health practices of music therapy. *Nordic Journal of Music Therapy, 13,* 99–111.

Rolvsjord, R. (2010). *Resource-oriented music therapy in mental health care.* Gilsum, NH: Barcelona Publishers.

Rolvsjord, R. (2014). The competent client and the complexity of disability. *Voices: A World Forum for Music Therapy, 14*(3). doi:10.15845/voices.v14i3.787

Sajnani, N. (2012). Response/ability: Imagining a critical race feminist paradigm for the creative arts therapies. *The Arts in Psychotherapy, 39,* 186–191. doi:10.1016/j.aip.2011.12.009

Schwarzbaum, S. E., & Thomas, A. J. (2008). *Dimensions of multicultural counseling: A life story approach.* Thousand Oaks, CA: SAGE.

Shapiro, N. (2005). Sounds in the world: Multicultural influences in music therapy in clinical practice and training. *Music Therapy Perspectives, 23,* 29–35. doi:10.1093/mtp/23.1.29

Shuttleworth, S. A. (2006). Viewing music therapy assessment through a feminist therapy lens. In S. Hadley (Ed.), *Feminist perspectives in music therapy* (pp. 429–450). Gilsum, NH: Barcelona Publishers.

Skovholt, T. M., & Trotter-Mathison, M. (2011). *The resilient practitioner: Burnout prevention and self-care strategies for counselors, therapists, teachers, and health professionals* (2nd ed.). New York, NY: Routledge.

Stige, B. (2002). *Culture-centered music therapy.* Gilsum, NH: Barcelona Publishers.

Sue, D. W., & Sue, D. (2003). *Counseling the culturally diverse: Theory and practice* (4th ed.). New York, NY: John Wiley & Sons.

Suzuki, L. A., Onoue, M. A., & Hill, J. S. (2013). Clinical assessment: A multicultural perspective. In K. F. Geisinger (Ed.), *APA handbook of testing and assessment in psychology* (vol. 2, pp. 193–212). Washington, DC: American Psychological Association.

Toppozada, M. R. (1995). Multicultural training for music therapists: An examination of current issues based on a national survey of professional music therapists. *Journal of Music Therapy, 32,* 65–90. doi:10.1093/mtp/24.2.108

Valentino, R. E. (2006). Attitudes towards cross-cultural empathy in music therapy. *Music Therapy Perspectives, 24,* 108–114. doi:10.1093/mtp/24.2.108

Villaverde, L. E. (2008). *Feminist theories and education.* New York, NY: Peter Lang.

Whitehead-Pleaux, A. (2009, October). Ismaeeilmusika—Listen to the music. *Voices: A World Forum for Music Therapy, 9.* Retrieved from https://normt.uib.no/index.php/voices/article/view/49/250

Whitehead-Pleaux, A., Donnenwerth, A., Robinson, B., Hardy, S., Oswanski, L., Forinash, M., … & York, E. (2012). Gay, bisexual, transgender, and questioning: Best practices in music therapy. *Music TherapyPerspectives, 30,* 158–166. doi:10.1093/mtp/30.2.158

Williams, P. J. (1991). *The alchemy of race and rights: Diary of a law professor.* Cambridge, MA: Harvard University Press.

Worell, J., & Remer, P. (2003). *Feminist perspectives in therapy: Empowering diverse women* (2nd ed.). Hoboken, NJ: John Wiley & Sons.

Chapter 4

MUSIC THERAPY WITH HISPANIC/LATINO CLIENTS

Karen Estrella

My Story

My grandmother was born the daughter of sugarcane field hands. She lived in a shack on the outskirts of a city on a postcolonial island that still stands as a protectorate, a possession, of the United States—Puerto Rico, la isla verde, the green island. Several years ago, when I asked her about her childhood, her upbringing, her parents' history, in Spanish she said, "What do you want to know that shit for?" "I'm writing about my family, abuela. I want to know where I came from … what it was like for you …." Then, thinking somehow that I could justify the intrusion, I said, "It's for a school project." But books, school, opportunities for advancement, self-reflection, and pride were not something she knew about as a girl. Why would you want to remember poverty, hunger, dirt, and hard, backbreaking work? This was not a history that one could read about; There was no written word, no oral tradition, no history. This was not a story meant to live on by the remembering. For my grandmother and the immigrants of her generation, there was only the hope of a better life for her children and her children's children. There was the American Dream.

The family story is that she did not see a clock until she stepped foot off the boat that brought her to New York Harbor at the age of 18, a passage bought by an older brother who hustled to bring his mother and sisters to a better life. They settled in Spanish Harlem in 1933, my grandmother and her sister and mother, eager to make a better life. At 18, by island standards, my grandmother was almost too old to marry. But as a young island girl with no English, no education, no money, and only domestic skills, what else was she supposed to do? So she ended up with an older man, a man who had left his wife and sons ("uncles" that I would never know more about)—an entrepreneur, perhaps a bookie, a gangster, let's just say a businessman—"he owned a cigar store for a while." [Reprinted with permission from SAGE Publications. These two paragraphs were previously published in Estrella, K., & Forinash, M. (2007). Narrative inquiry and arts-based inquiry: Multinarrative perspectives. Journal of Humanistic Psychology, 47(3), 376–383.]

You see, these were not stories that I was supposed to know. I never really knew whether they happened this way. As Blacksher (2002) says, anyone can feel inadequacy, vulnerability, or shame, but for poor people, these feelings are "chronic. Like barnacles, these feelings 'attach,' becoming a permanent part of their host" (p. 459). And so these stories of history, past, and roots are dripping with shame. They expose the lack of education and middle-class skills that my grandmother had. They expose the underclass and what my family had come to think of as our lack. There was always the

desire to wash the old shit away. No one talked about what it was like. Instead, I was left to piece together the bits I remembered overhearing, to sew up the fragments in my narrative the way my grandmother had taken the old drapes and made dresses out of them for me and my dolls.

She married and had five children—five children, a cold-water flat, violence, and more poverty and hunger. She worked sewing—lamp shades, clothes, any piecework she could get. There were many nights when my father went to bed without food. I don't mean to make it sound dramatic—it was just the way things were (and still are for many). But again, these are not the stories that one is supposed to speak out loud.

My father was the oldest, so when his father died, there was no question but that he would quit school to work, to pick up any odd jobs he could get around the neighborhood. The fact that he was 12 or 14 didn't matter. He was hardworking, and he was smart. I'm told that an old Jewish man who sold women's underwear on the Avenue hired him. I always wondered why it was important in this story that the man was Jewish. Was this the man who gave my father the ambition to leave the ghetto and "become somebody?" Were the hardworking values of education and entrepreneurialism something my dad learned from this man?

In reading about class identity for my dissertation, I read that often working-class boys struggled to find a "real and presentable self" that could be reflected back in the eyes of their friends at school (Wexler, 1992). For my father and his brothers, this arena was "the streets." For these boys, their main activity was attempting to establish an image of an identity. According to Wexler (1992), "'Becoming somebody' is action in the public sphere, and this is what life in high school is about" (p. 155). The public sphere for my father was the Avenue. And the rule of becoming was chutzpah and hustle.

He and his brothers hustled. They used every scrap. There were no extra clothes, shoes; there were certainly no toys or birthday parties. They struggled to pay for food, water, housing, and basic necessities in postwar New York. At 17, my father joined the Army, leaving behind a pregnant girl and a history-less past.

My father always spoke of his time in the Army as his "college years." As a "White" man with green eyes, he could pass for Italian—"You look just like Frankie," they said, and who wouldn't want to be compared to Sinatra, the idol of swing. It was 1955, and my father was a GI in Germany. In those black and white photos, with his Harris Tweed jacket and cigarette dangling from his mouth, he looks like any other young American from Connecticut or Chicago or Kentucky. He was doing it, living the American Dream—from rags to riches. With three squares, money to send home, and an opportunity to use the mind he'd never had a chance to exercise in "school," he became a computer analyst. Those were the days when a computer took up three rooms, and a program was made with flowcharts and a truckload of punch cards. But most importantly, working with computers was not manual labor—this was a profession. This was a real job, and he was living the high life!

When he returned in 1959, he knew he would never go back to the neighborhood. He married the girl he had met at the street dance four years earlier, signed up as a career Army man, moved into the enlisted men's housing on Governors Island, and prepared to get to know his four-year-old son and newborn baby daughter. When the opportunity to move his mother, sister, and brother into new public housing in the South Bronx came along in 1960, he jumped at the chance. With three sons in the armed services, my grandmother felt entitled to public assistance. Who could have predicted then that those rows of new high-rise modern apartments would become the notoriously segregated concrete jungle of violence, drugs, hopelessness, and despair that they became by 1970?

But that reality was a world away for my family and me. With the Army under his belt, money to send home to Mom, and his own All-American family, my dad eagerly accepted the chance to move to Hawaii for his next tour of duty.

Honolulu, 1963. Who ever could have guessed that a girl who had been taken away from her mother by the state to live in a "home" for 6 years would have ended up on the set of Elvis's Blue Hawaii? For my mom, this was heaven—banana cream pie, fried bologna sandwiches on Wonder bread, ring molds of Jell-O with canned fruit cocktail—it was the '60s, on an Army base in the middle of Paradise, with Don Ho crooning in the background and two scabby-kneed kids riding around on their bikes on the street in the sun.

My mother was also a child of Spanish Harlem, a Nuyorican, a product of the postagricultural bust of Puerto Rico, her mother and father also fleeing the island as teens in hope of opportunity and promise. My mother's parents were preachers, traveling holy rollers, speaking in tongues that began in Spanish and ended in singing and rapture. When money didn't stretch, they did yardwork and eldercare. They traveled to California, staying with families who fed them and clothed them in exchange for inspired divination. But within only a few years, my grandfather would run off, leaving my grandmother with four children and no real means of support. My grandmother returned to Spanish Harlem, to her brothers, father, and stepmother. She began working odd jobs, at one time caring for rich older women on Park Avenue. But under the pressure, she cracked, and her children were sent off to live in a "home" for children in need of care. A horrible place that left my mother forever wounded. My mother's schooling, self-esteem, and health were as fractured and fragmented as her mother's English.

Pregnant and alone at 17, my mother mustered the courage to write the Army, to have them track down my father. She wanted him to pay child support for the son he had not yet known. When he returned and offered her a life of travel and financial stability, how could she not say yes?

So, I grew up in a military family with two Puerto Rican parents who were trying to adapt to middle-class, mainstream culture. Although both parents had grown up in Spanish Harlem, very poor, speaking Spanish as their first language, and dropping out of school quite young, by the time I was born into our family, we were regular Americans. My brother and I were second-generation kids, trying to live the vestiges of the Leave It to Beaver life of the 1950s. We did not speak Spanish at home. We did not live with other Puerto Ricans. We were White. Sure, we ate rice and beans, and my grandmother came for 3-month visits, and my brother's tan left him darker than your average kid, but life on an Army base is first and foremost American.

While my grandmother, aunts, uncles, and cousins lived on the streets and in the "projects," continuing to suffer the consequences of poverty and racism and unable to cross the color line, we moved around the country and lived, by my parents' standards, a rich life. Sure, most of my relatives lived on welfare, but not us. I had all the things my parents had never had and my cousins would barely have, even as adults—food on the table, a roof over my head, birthday parties, and bicycles. Heck, we even had a car! My mom was a stay-at-home housewife with a 250 bowling average, and my dad was a sought-after programmer, at his prime on the cusp of the Silicon Valley boom—except that he wasn't healthy enough to stay working. He had been diagnosed with rheumatoid arthritis at the age of 25, and after many severe bouts of illness, his dreams of being a career Army man were over. He was forced to retire from the Army when I was 11. By then, we were living in San Francisco.

San Francisco Bay Area, the 1970s, home of Jefferson Airplane, Tower of Power, and Patty Hearst. I was truly a city kid. I would ride the bus all over town. I would take myself to many interesting places, places my parents knew nothing about—museums, libraries, the ballet, the symphony. I was an artist. I played flute seriously throughout junior high and high school, performing in chamber groups, the school orchestra and band. I wanted to be a classical musician. And in spite of my parents' divorce, my brother's drug addiction, and my family's struggle with domestic violence and perpetual crises, I was going to make it. I was going to go to college. My father's entrée into computer programming had convinced him that an education was critical for advancement, and his brother's tours in Vietnam had convinced him that the military was not necessarily the best path there. So he pushed me to go to college.

My brother was not as lucky as I – as a boy, as a more visibly Hispanic person, as the victim of years of child abuse, he was unable to break the cycle of violence, poverty, or racism. He dropped out of high school, and quickly his life descended into drug abuse and homelessness. There is a complicated web of circumstances and forces that allowed me to escape what my brother did not. Certainly gender, skin color, birth order, and family dynamics played their role in framing my life chances and choices.

There is a name for the black sheep of the family, but what

is the name of the sheep that wanders into greener pastures and leaves the darker sheep behind? It would be an interesting metaphor, as I later struggled with folks assuming that I was "White," and as I struggled to hold on to my "Brown" identity. But for now, in 1977, I was the one on my way to San Francisco State University, and within a year to the Music Therapy program at the University of the Pacific.

As an undergraduate, I studied music therapy. Pursuing a master's degree in expressive arts therapy (a field which uses an interdisciplinary approach to the arts in therapy), I discovered a path to develop myself as an artist and satisfy my desire to be of service to others. In 1996, I decided to pursue a doctorate in clinical psychology in response to a strong desire to provide further depth to and precision in my teaching, supervision, and clinical work. Initially, I struggled with my identity as a border-crosser. I felt that that I struggled not only with my identity as a "White" person with a "Brown" background, but also as a working-class person in a now solidly middle-class position. I've wrestled under the discomfort of "fitting in" with the largely upper–middle class, White, Boston suburb where I live as an adult, struggling, mostly feeling a sense of embarrassment—embarrassment at living in such contrast to my own family of origin, embarrassment at being a doctoral graduate, embarrassment at having so much when I know so many who don't have enough—and of feeling dislocated. Despite my personal struggles, for 30 years as a mental health counselor, music therapist, and expressive arts therapist, I have provided clients the opportunity to make meaning of and find dignity in their lives through art and music-making, psychotherapy, and therapeutic community, and my work in community mental health has allowed me to continue to experience a sense of "home."

Introduction

The Hispanic/Latino culture is rich with ambiguity, complexity, and diversity. Even the Latin music industry has seen a recent recognition of both the diversity of the genre, reflective of its people, and the "exciting and assertive" new music that has emerged during the past few years alone because of that diversity (Cabo, 2012). Given that music therapists are likely to work with Hispanic/Latinos at some point in their careers (Hispanic/Latinos are the largest minority group in the United States)—whether as clients, coworkers, or administrative colleagues—this chapter sets out to outline some of the major considerations in working with Hispanic/Latino clients. At present, there are only a handful of articles devoted to the use of music therapy with this population (Kennedy & Scott, 2005; Kenny, 2011; Rilinger, 2011; Schwantes, 2009; Schwantes, Wigram, McKinney, Lipscomb & Richards, 2011). There is a need for music therapists to further develop their scholarship and understanding of the cultural needs of this diverse group and to develop and determine the unique and effective uses of music therapy with this population.

Rooted in a history of conquest and colonization, civil wars and repressive regimes, liberation movements and outstanding resilience, displacement, migration, immigration, and cultures of remittance, the Hispanic/Latino people represent "descendants of both oppressive European cultures and oppressed Indigenous peoples" (de las Fuentes, Barón, & Vásquez, 2003, p. 207). The vibrancy of Latin music—salsa, merengue, bachata, tango, mambo, samba, mariachi, ranchero, tejano, cumbia, reggaeton, flamenco—reflects the passion, intensity, and resilience of its people. In its broadest definition, the Hispanic/Latino population is panethnic and multiracial, representing a variety of socioeconomic positions and spanning residents of North, South, and Central America and the Caribbean of Spanish or Latin descent. The many faces of this community within the United States can be represented by a wide variety of individuals: for example, a wealthy second-generation Cuban-American businessman in Miami, an undocumented Mexican migrant farmworker in California, a second-generation Mexican state senator in New Mexico, a third-generation Nuyorican poet in the Bronx, a Jewish-Argentinian international graduate student in Massachusetts, a Salvadoran restaurant owner in Chicago, or a Mayan Guatemalan community activist in Houston, Texas.

According to the 2010 United States (U.S.) Census, 50.5 million people who identify as Hispanic/Latinos (H/L) reside in the United States. Estimates in 2013 raised that number to 54 million and 17% of the total U.S. population (U.S. Census Bureau, 2014). As the largest minority group in the United States, Hispanic/Latinos made up 16% of the total U.S. population in 2010, an increase from 13% (or 35.3 million) in 2000 (Ennis, Rios-Vargas, & Albert, 2011), and from 9% in 1990 and 6% in 1980 (U.S. Census Bureau, 1992). In the state of New Mexico alone, Hispanic/Latinos make up 46% of the state's total population, while in California and Texas, they make up 37% of each state's total, and in Florida, they make up 23%, constituting large segments of the total populations (Ennis, Rios-Vargas, & Albert, 2011).

The terms *Hispanic* and *Latino* are used interchangeably to refer to a large, economically diverse, racially mixed, gender-inclusive group that is unified by some cultural characteristics and by language, yet includes millions of people coming from 22 countries representing significant cultural differences based on race, gender, immigration status, geopolitical histories, and socioeconomic realities. H/L refers to people from Central and South America, the Spanish-speaking Caribbean, Mexico, Puerto Rico, the Dominican Republic, Cuba, and other Latin American countries. [It should be noted that while some authors also include Brazilians in the category of "Latin Americans" (Melville, 1994; Sánchez Prado, 2012), historically, only 4% of Brazilians self-identify as "Hispanic" on the U.S. Census (Passel & Taylor, 2009).]

People of Mexican heritage make up 63% of the total Hispanic/Latino population in the United States, while Puerto Ricans make up 9% and Cubans make up 4%. Some specific countries have had significant increases in emigration during the past 10 years; for example, the Salvadoran population in the United States saw a 152% increase from 2000–2010, while

Guatemalans saw a 180% increase in that time period, with both communities now topping 1 million people in the United States (Ennis, Rios-Vargas, & Albert, 2011). Hispanic/Latinos categorize themselves along a wide racial continuum: Some are White, some are Black, some Asian (for example, the president of Peru from 1990–2000 was Alberto Fujimori, of Japanese ancestry) or Indigenous, and most are multiracial or of mixed raced *(mestizo)* backgrounds (de las Fuentes, Barón, & Vásquez, 2003).

The term *Hispanic* is often replaced by the more politically progressive term *Latino,* yet both terms "can be seen as emphasizing White European (Spain and Portugal) heritage at the expense of Indigenous, slave, mixed *(mestizo),* and non-European heritage" and defining a group of people by the oppressing and colonizing civilizations (Spain and Portugal) that "founded" them (Delgado-Romero, 2001, pp. 207–208). As Romero (2009) points out, many individuals and groups reject the term *Hispanic* and prefer *Latino* or *Chicano,* while others prefer to self-identify based on their country of origin or ancestry, for example, Puerto Rican, Mexican, Guatemalan, Peruvian, or Salvadoran. Sanchez (2012) notes that these terms were originally "designed as marks of otherness" (para. 2). In a national survey conducted in 2011, 55% of Hispanic/Latinos were found to have no preference between the terms *Hispanic* or *Latino,* while 33% who do have a preference prefer the term *Hispanic* (Taylor, Lopez, Martinez, & Velasco, 2012). Given the data, the term "Hispanic/Latino (H/L)" will be used in this chapter. While many H/L do not think of themselves as members of this large, inclusive group except in the context of exclusion or discrimination, some view terms such as *Hispanic* and *Latino* negatively, as a politically salient way of ascribing minority status to themselves as a large group within the United States, while others see this ascription positively, as an opportunity for coalition building and the acquisition of political power (Delgado-Romero, 2001).

Worldview: Diversity Within the Culture

In order to understand the worldview of Hispanic/Latinos, one must appreciate the complexity and diversity of within-group differences among this ever-growing panethnic group. As a music therapist working with H/Ls, one must be willing to both coinvestigate further with one's clients the particular cultural experiences that have shaped their identity and refrain from indiscriminate application of cultural stereotypes (Andrés-Hyman, Ortiz, Añez, Paris, & Davidson, 2006). Although United States–born H/Ls make up over half of all H/Ls (Motel & Patten, 2012), many still identify with their family's country of origin, and most of the H/Ls who are recent immigrants also identify with their country of origin. According to a Pew Hispanic Center survey conducted in 2011, most H/Ls do not think of the H/L culture as monolithic within the United States, but rather identify their attitudes and values as originating from many cultural influences, including influences of race, immigration status, and experiences passed down from their countries of origin (Taylor, Lopez, Martinez, & Velasco, 2012). One must

understand "an overview of the unique social and political histories of the countries of origin and of the immigration patterns of the different groups of Latinos living in the United States" (de las Fuentes, Barón, & Vásquez, 2003, p. 208).

Hispanics and Latinos in the United States are made up of English and Spanish speakers (as well as speakers of numerous Indigenous languages), people who have recently arrived in the United States, and those who have family roots dating back to before the founding of the nation (some Mexican-American families living in the Southwest can trace their family trees back to the late 1500s [Weaver, 1994]). There are those who are closely identified with their ethnic heritage and those who feel they are primarily identified as "American" (as assimilated into the U.S. culture) (Ginorio, Gutiérrez, Cauce, & Acosta, 1995). In order to truly understand the experience and identity of Hispanic/Latinos in the United States, one must explore the many ways their experience is shaped by relevant cultural, familial, sociopolitical, and individual issues. One must examine ways that experiences of those H/Ls living in the United States may differ from "that of Latinos living in their countries of origin and from that of mainstream White Americans, African-Americans, and Americans of other ethnic origins" (Quiñones, 2007, p. 154).

Other major contributions to the H/L worldview include the legacy of colonialism in North, South, and Central America; the history of U.S. intervention in Latin American countries; and the impact of emigration and immigration into the United States, creating cultures of diaspora. In describing the impact of colonization and colonial racism on H/L's worldview, Quiñones (2007) points out that living under colonial rule for generations, one's individual and collective sense of autonomy and agency are greatly affected. She notes,

> It is difficult to see oneself as the master of one's own destiny when one's own or prior generations have been shaped by a history of oppressive political and economic systems. This legacy stands in sharp contrast to the American ideal of independence and autonomy. (p. 155)

Hispanic/Latino cultures have strong identities linked with fatalism—one has only to hear the phrase *"si Dios quiere"* ("if it be God's will") or *"que será será"* ("what will be will be"), ubiquitous in the Spanish vernacular, to see its role. That said, many Hispanic/Latinos whose families have lived in the United States for generations or who have experienced themselves as having considerable resources have adopted the American ideal of an internal locus of control.

In addition to histories of colonization, the history of U.S. intervention in Latin America is marked by military, diplomatic, and political maneuvers (Grandin, 2007), often under the guise of a war on drugs or terror, that have mostly not been in the best interests of our Latin American neighbors, but rather served to have subordinated "many of the hemisphere's nations to the strategic, geopolitical, and geoeconomic interests of the United States" (Suárez Salazar, 2007, p. 105). H/Ls coming from countries with recent or past histories of civil war, internal displacement, violence, or political upheaval (one needs only to think of Argentina, Cuba, Colombia, El Salvador, or Guatemala) will bring specific experiences of immigration, often experiences linked to a loss of trust, safety, or optimism (Farias, 1994).

While the issues involved in illegal immigration are beyond the scope of this chapter, the recent increase in unaccompanied minors entering the United States at its southern border highlighted some of the dire consequences at the heart of the issue of undocumented migration. This influx resulted in a humanitarian crisis as the fiscal year 2014 came to a close (Zezima & O'Keefe, 2014) and as President Obama sought immigration reform. While Mexicans make up about half of all undocumented immigrants (Krogstad & Passel, 2014), in this crisis they represented only about a quarter of the children detained while entering the United States during the FY 2014 (Krogstad, Gonzalez-Barrera, & Lopez, 2014). During this period, over 56,000 unaccompanied minors were detained upon entering the United States via Mexico, and three quarters of these children came from El Salvador, Honduras, and Guatemala, where people are fleeing unprecedented levels of poverty and violence [e.g., at present, Honduras's murder rate is the highest in the world (Kahn, 2013)]. The degree of violence promoted by gangs, drug trafficking, and governmental corruption has complicated roots in the geopolitical, economic, and strategic history of the Americas. That families would be willing to risk so much as a means of seeking a better life for their children speaks only to the height of the stakes at the heart of these issues.

The role of emigration, immigration, transnationalism (being part of two societies at the same time), and cultural diaspora affects the H/L worldview. It is important for music therapists to understand the reasons for their clients' (or their clients' parents' or grandparents') emigration. Leading causes for immigration include political asylum, escape from natural disaster, economic and educational opportunities, and family ties (Taylor, Lopez, Martinez, & Velasco, 2012). Some emigrate as refugees; some as workers, businessmen, or students; some pay a "coyote" to smuggle them into the country, intending to stay only as long as needed to make money to send home; some come to the United States from affluent backgrounds, already having considerable resources; while others come as citizens from Puerto Rico, looking to relocate to another area of the country, as many mainland Americans do. [The term "coyote" refers to someone who assists undocumented migrants in border crossing. Sometimes referred to as "guides," "smugglers," or "human traffickers," these men present themselves along a continuum, acting at times as protectors, exploiters, and/or abusers (see Cave & Robles, 2014; Guillén, 2001; Ortmeyer & Guinn, 2012; Spener, 1999).] Currently, nearly half (21.2 million) of the H/Ls in the United States were born in Latin America or the Caribbean (Acosta & de la Cruz, 2011).

Generational/Migration Differences Within the H/L Culture: The Role of Acculturation/Assimilation and Bicultural Identities

As with the diversity within the H/L community, there is a rich diversity of experiences with migration, immigration, and emigration that exists within the Latino population. One needs merely to look at the experiences within the five largest H/L groups in the United States—Mexicans, Puerto Ricans, Cubans, Dominicans, and Salvadorans— to grasp the complexities of generational/migration differences and the role of acculturation, assimilation, and biculturalism within this largely heterogeneous group.

Mexican-Americans

At nearly 32 million (Taylor, Lopez, Martinez, & Velasco, 2012), Mexican-Americans and Mexican immigrants make up the largest group (two out of three, or 63%) within the H/L population in the United States. Gonzalez (2000) refers to the influx of Mexicans within the United States as a "diaspora" that lies at the "core of our country's Latino heritage" (p. 96). Mexicans represent not only the largest group of new immigrants to the United States, but also some of the earliest settlers on our nation's land (Gonzalez, 2000). In addition to the many waves of Mexican immigration and the constant influx of Mexican migrants to the United States, there is a group of Mexican-Americans who can date their place within the United States back to the late 1500s. These earliest Mexican landowners, pioneers, and ranchers did not migrate to the United States, but instead found themselves conquered during the Mexican-American War of 1846–1848 (Giornio et al., 1995). Over the next 70 years, Mexican-Americans found themselves the majority in places like the Rio Grande Valley (where Texas borders Mexico), yet without land rights, business holdings, or political power. Instead, the small White minority systematically gained control over the years of both the land and the politics (Gonzalez, 2000). This became true of much of the Southwest. This troubled history has led to a paradox that despite some Mexican-Americans being able to trace their ancestry back centuries, they are still struggling for legitimacy, recognition, or respect as contributing citizens. Centuries of colonial domination in the form of "school segregation, housing discrimination, political gerrymandering, job discrimination, and other direct forms of oppression" have led to a large Mexican-American population with relatively little political or economic power (Giornio et al., 1995, p. 243).

Alongside this settled group of Mexican-Americans, there also exists a large group of Mexicans who migrate back and forth over the 2,000-mile-long border between Mexico and the United States. The steady contact between both sides reinforces the culture and a strong sense of ethnic identity (de las Fuentes, Barón, & Vásquez, 2003), both for those who become permanent residents and for those whose stay is dictated by economic opportunities. These opportunities allow these migrants to work for a time in the United States and then return, with money often necessary to combat dire poverty. It is estimated that there are an additional 6.5 million undocumented Mexicans in the United States [the estimated total number of undocumented H/Ls in 2010 was 9.1 million (Passel & Cohn, 2011)]. Between those whose families have been here for centuries and those who have just arrived lie many Mexican-Americans along a wide continuum of immigration and naturalization processes. Some are here legally; some are undocumented; some are first-, second- or third-generation; and some are in the process of becoming citizens. Some have more family in Mexico, while others have more family in the States. In a 2011 Pew Hispanic Center Survey, 38% of H/Ls were found to speak predominantly Spanish, 38% were bilingual, and 24% are English dominant (Taylor, Lopez, Martinez, & Velasco, 2012). Given the extreme gap between fully assimilated and recent, temporary migrant status, music therapists must be cautious in assessing levels of acculturation and ethnic identity.

The process of immigration, acculturation, enculturation, and assimilation always involves loss. Often immigrants (along with their children and grandchildren) experience the loss of a sense of rootedness, social status, history, or sense of mastery. While they come with the hope of a better life, many immigrants face a language barrier, a lack of familiarity with the values of the dominant culture, a lack of familiarity with the labor market, a lack of a sense of entitlement, and a growing sense of social marginalization.

> These changes result in a complexity of feelings, including the pain of a lack of shared experiences with peers; stress and weariness from the effort to acculturate to, and cope with, cultural differences; rejection from the new and dominant culture, which may affect mood and self-worth; confusion in terms of role expectations, values, and identity; and a sense of powerlessness from being unable to function as effectively in the new culture as one did in the home culture. (de las Fuentes, Barón, & Vásquez, 2003, p. 208)

While many individuals do begin an acculturation process that includes adapting to, or even internalizing aspects of, the dominant culture (including beliefs, values, and behaviors) while holding on to aspects of their culture of origin, the need for this kind of acculturation is influenced by the communities into which these individuals transition. At one time, acculturation was thought of as a "replacement model" where one culture would replace another (Padilla, 2000). Now, acculturation is recognized as varying considerably and as influenced by multiple forces, resulting in multiple outcomes along a bicultural continuum. At times, immigrants move to communities where they are able to maintain a strong tie to their cultural identity and heritage, while at other times, they find themselves living in multiple distinct cultural contexts with

the possibility of maintaining and adhering to proficiency in both cultures or feeling marginalized by one or the other (Miller, 2007).

At other times, H/Ls experience their ethnicity as a source of shame, causing them to experience the "need to assimilate and become part of the mainstream at any cost, even if it requires negating their cultural heritage" (Quiñones, 2007, pp. 155–156). Ironically, in a recent study of Mexican-American youth, researchers found that the youth who were more identified with their ethnic values (Mexican cultural values such as *familismo,* religiosity, or respect for elders) were more resilient, with reduced risks of negative mental health symptoms and increases in academic confidence, than youth who were less identified with their Mexican-American roots (Berkel et al., 2010).

Puerto Ricans

As with Mexican-Americans, Puerto Ricans found themselves part of the United States as a result of war in the late 19th century. Puerto Rico was ceded to the United States during the Spanish-American War, and since 1917, islanders have been awarded citizenship, although their rights have been curtailed under the agreement of their status as an unincorporated territory. Islanders do not have representation in Congress, and they cannot vote for president (unless they become a resident of one of the 50 states), yet their status as citizens does allow them the unique opportunity as H/Ls to enter the states legally and without visa or alien status (Suárez-Orozco & Páez, 2002). Islanders remained on the island with relatively few migrations to the mainland from 1917 until World War II (Collazo, Ryan, & Bauman, 2010).

From 1946 to 1960, over a million Puerto Ricans migrated from the island to the mainland, with so many moving to the New York metropolitan area that the names *Nuyorqueños* and *Nuyoricans* were developed (Gonzalez, 2000; Weaver, 1995). Despite the evolution of the island from a plantation and agricultural economy to an economy based on industrial development (particularly by pharmaceutical companies), there continued to be widespread unemployment and poverty on the island, driving many to seek better economic opportunities in the States (Collazo, Ryan, & Bauman, 2010). Some would say this migration had less to do with economic opportunity than it did with U.S. involvement in the use of land for economic tax sheltering and an encouragement to migrate for geopolitical reasons. Between 1960 and 2010, the population of Puerto Ricans in the States grew so significantly that there are now more Puerto Ricans living in the States than on the island (Collazo, Ryan, & Bauman, 2010).

At present, Puerto Ricans make up the second largest group of H/Ls in the United States. Numbers for Puerto Ricans are somewhat ambiguous—only Puerto Rican residents of the 50 states are counted in the U.S. Census and total 4.6 million (Ennis, Rios-Vargas, & Albert, 2011), while another 3.7 million live on the island, uncounted in the official numbers and often overlooked as central to the U.S. experience, simultaneously described as immigrants and citizens. This status of second-class citizenry has often left stateside Puerto Ricans, despite their numbers, continuing to feel marginalized and like "foreigners" or outsiders on the mainland, with little economic or political power (Gonzalez, 2000, p. 81). This has left islanders strongly ambivalent about their citizenship, with some even advocating for independence (Weaver, 1994).

Puerto Ricans are described as deeply transnational, that is, engaged in dual migration (to and from the island) and dual loyalties, with deep ties to the island and to the mainland, maintaining social, cultural, and political involvement in island affairs even when living in the 50 states (Suárez-Orozco & Páez, 2002). Puerto Ricans are also among the poorest H/Ls in the country (along with Mexicans, Hondurans, and Dominicans), with 27% of mainland Puerto Ricans (and 45% of islanders) living in poverty in 2010, compared with 15% of the U.S. general population (Collazo, Ryan, & Bauman, 2010; Motel & Patten, 2012). While Puerto Ricans on the mainland are most likely to speak English at home, some authors propose that they are continuing to suffer the consequences of decades of behaviors perpetuated by an "underclass" lifestyle, behaviors that tended to "perpetuate poverty by de-emphasizing work as a means to getting ahead in life. The Puerto Rican population was concentrated in the New York area, where unskilled jobs were increasingly difficult to find" (Collazo, Ryan, & Bauman, 2010, p. 4). In addition, Puerto Ricans, like Dominicans, are likely to have a more visibly mixed-race heritage, and many Puerto Ricans "may have faced discrimination in jobs and housing that made it difficult for them to advance" (Collazo, Ryan, & Bauman, 2010, p. 4).

Cuban-Americans

Cuban-Americans offer another excellent example of the complexities of generational/migration differences within the H/L culture. As González-Pando (1997) notes, nearly all Cuban émigrés consider themselves reluctant émigrés, political exiles, even asylum seekers or refugees. Aside from the initial wave of Cuban immigrants who emigrated in the late 19th century as tobacco farm owners, most of the largest wave of Cuban refugees arrived from 1959–1980 as a result of Castro's revolution (de las Fuentes, Barón, & Vásquez, 2003). The impact of exile has been so strong that González-Prado (1997, p. 51) has described the waves of immigration among Cuban-Americans as happening within six stages: survival (1959–1962), transition (1962–1965), adjustment (1965–1973), economic miracle (1973–1980), diversification (1980–1990), and post-Soviet era (1990 to the present).

Unlike most H/Ls who emigrated for economic or educational opportunities, many Cuban-Americans were aware that they would lose much with regard to status and socioeconomic standing in the United States (González-Pando, 1997). During the initial wave of Cuban exile, the majority of those immigrating to the United States were considerably overrepresented by the upper- and middle-class nonpolitical elites of Cuba. Not only

were they generally older than most immigrants and thus more settled in their ethnic identity, but also they were more likely to be able to rebuild their lives, given their educational and professional backgrounds and their pride and entrepreneurial drive (González-Prado, 1997). In addition, subsequent waves of Cubans benefited from the ethnic enclave economies developed by the first-wave Cubans (Giornio et al., 1995).

Cuban-Americans began to claim status as the model Latino—the most educated, socioeconomically successful, and most political of Latin Americans (Hay 2009). At present, Cuban-Americans are more likely than the majority of other H/L groups to be older (the median age for Cuban-Americans is 40 compared to 25 for Mexicans), own their own homes, have a bachelor's degree, and be a citizen (Motel & Patten, 2012), all qualities that have translated into higher cultural capital in the United States. Although Cuban-Americans previously had the highest earning power, at present they earn the average salary for the H/L population ($40,000), which is less than Colombians, Ecuadorans, and Peruvians, but greater than the median income of Guatemalans, Mexicans, Hondurans, Puerto Ricans, and Dominicans (Motel & Patten, 2012).

While Cuban-Americans as a whole have had generally more success, there is also a large group of Black Cuban-Americans who have not done as well socioeconomically or culturally as their White counterparts. As time passes from that initial wave of immigration, new Cuban immigrants begin to appear more similar to other H/L groups who are poorer and less assimilated. One hypothesis is that many of these immigrants have not only encountered the same large-scale racism within the United States. that African-Americans and many of their darker-skinned H/L compatriots have encountered, but also experienced discrimination by coethnics. As with many Black immigrants, some Black Cubans have "responded to racism by seeking refuge in their ethnic group and holding on to their traditional values and attitudes, while others respond to racism by becoming 'racial' and feeling allied with African-Americans" (Hays, 2009, p. 5).

A Note About Race

The problem of race for H/Ls is pervasive among all of the various ethnic groups within the H/L population. The White European ideal not only is something which H/L immigrants encounter upon entering the United States, but also is sustained pervasively within Latin American countries and cultures, and perhaps most destructively within H/L families and individuals as internalized racism. Racism and internalized racism remain a legacy of colonization and are maintained by current global sociopolitical dynamics. One group of researchers also noted that because H/Ls entering the United States are assimilating to a society still rife with racism, as one's identification with U.S. culture increases, one's internalized racism is also likely to increase (Hipolito-Delgado, 2010).

For Mexicans within their country (and this is also true for other Central and South American countries), there continues to be overt racism against Indigenous populations in the form of economic, political, and educational segregation; social, cultural, and racial marginalization and discrimination; and larger institutionalized systems of privilege and exclusion that prevent Indigenous peoples from experiencing equality (Fortes De Leff, 2002). In addition, in the Caribbean (and elsewhere), these forms of racism extend to the descendants of slaves as well as the mixed Indigenous peoples, thus creating a racial hierarchy in which those who appear Whiter or more European receive more social and cultural power and possibilities than those who are darker or Black or who appear more African or Indigenous (Quiñones, 2007). Unlike in the United States, where race is often constructed as a binary—Black or White— in many H/L countries, race falls on a hierarchical continuum where there are many intermediate categories defined "not only by skin color, but also by socioeconomic status and cultural elements" (Itzigsohn & Dore-Cabral, 2000, p. 226).

Once in the United States, H/Ls encounter a largely dichotomous reaction to race, and they experience themselves as needing to choose affiliations. Even in those cases where one's race is ambiguous, "race and racial identification present a double bind" (Quiñones, 2007, p. 156):

> On the one hand, White Latinos may pass as White people of European descent, in which case they may deny their racial heritage. On the other hand, they may experience trouble being accepted as mainstream because they are not "White enough." Black Latinos experience both ethnic and racial discrimination, and their race locates them lower in the social power hierarchy. Latinos with mixed skin tones fit more into the mainstream description of what a Latino "looks like," but this may result in their becoming the target of more overt racism by both Black and White people. (Quiñones, 2007, p. 156)

Dominican-Americans

As with Cuban-Americans, the migration of a large group of Dominicans can be seen as the result of refugee flight and geopolitics dating back to the mid-1960s, in this case politics that involved the demise of the Trujillo regime, the consequent invasion by the United States, and the subsequent exportation of the Dominican political opposition (Itzigsohn, 2005). From 1961–1986, more than 400,000 people emigrated legally from the Dominican Republic to the United States, most of them moving to New York City (Gonzalez, 2000). As Cubans did in Miami, Dominicans created a strong ethnic enclave on the Upper West Side of New York City, and by the mid-1980s, when a second wave of immigrants came from the island, this time seeking economic opportunities due to economic devastation there, they received some assistance from fellow countrymen. At present, over 1.5 million legal Dominican-Americans live in the United States (Motel & Patten, 2012).

As Mexicans found themselves taking great risks to enter

the States, Dominicans have also found themselves paying smugglers to enter the United States, this time through Puerto Rico. During the year 1990 alone, more than 13,200 Dominicans were deported after entering Puerto Rico illegally (Gonzalez, 2000). Although initially there was a helpful relationship between Puerto Ricans and Dominicans in New York, where both groups found themselves the targets of discrimination and limited opportunity, as time passed, more tension built between the two groups over race and citizenship status. Interethnic tensions seem to have been generated in the face of societal racism and tension around the "Latino" threat instigated by illegal immigration.

Dominicans, like many H/Ls, find themselves facing two significant identity tasks upon migrating to the United States. First, they find themselves moving from a society in which they are the dominant group to a nation in which they are identified as part of a panethnic minority group of Hispanic/Latinos. Second, they find themselves moving "from a society in which they define themselves as non-Black to a society that defines many of them as Black and almost all of them as non-White" (Itzigsohn, Giorguli, & Vasquez, 2005, p. 58). These tasks of forming a panethnic Latino identity and of responding to the binary racial classification system in America are significant for all Latinos, but particularly for Dominican-Americans, who are overwhelmingly classified by Americans as Black.

At home, Dominicans historically save the classification of Black for Haitian immigrants, with whom they share the island of Hispaniola. Dominicans have a range of racial categories that combine both color and nationality with different terms being used to refer to different shades of skin color, such as *"mulato," "jibao," "trigueño," "indio claro," "indio oscuro"* and *"indio quemado"* (Itzigsohn & Dore-Cabral, 2000, p. 231). While dark-skinned Dominicans can look indistinguishable from their Haitian neighbors, for most Dominicans, Haitians are Black and French-speaking, while they themselves are "indio oscuro" and Spanish-speaking. To find themselves identified as Black and then as part of a larger ethnic group is often disorienting for newly arriving Dominicans and may contribute to the strength with which many Dominicans hold on to their national identity.

Dominicans are highly transnational, sending remittances, saving for property and retirement on the island, and traveling back and forth between the island and the United States. While remittances are second only to tourism as a form of national revenue and constitute a significant aspect of the Dominican economy, there is also tension on the island between those who have not emigrated and those who travel back and forth between the Dominican Republic and the United States (Itzigsohn & Dore-Cabral, p. 231). Transnationalism is so significant that researchers have identified three forms to which Dominicans adhere—*linear transnationalism,* which involves remittances, sustained contact with home, and the development of ethnic institutions in the United States as a means of rebuilding social relationships and customs from home; *resource-dependent transnationalism,* which involves transnational entrepreneurship and the development of business opportunities in both countries; and *reactive transnationalism,* which results from immigrants sustaining their connection with their country of origin in order to experience the prestige and positive identification they have with their homeland, rather than the significant frustration with work and social status and with discrimination and negative perceptions they have received in the United States (Itzigsohn & Giorguli Saucedo, 2002).

Salvadoran-Americans

El Salvador was ravaged by civil war during the 1980s. During and even after the war was officially over, economic, social, and cultural instability and displacement led to large-scale immigration of political refugees and victims of war. However, unlike Cuban refugees, many Salvadoran immigrants found themselves denied refugee status, once again due to geopolitical dynamics (Itzigsohn & Giorguli Saucedo, 2002). U.S. intervention in Central America significantly impacted immigration policy, and many Salvadoran émigrés found themselves unable to enter the country legally.

While the growing number of Salvadorans here as legal citizens is rising (Salvadorans are now the fifth largest H/L group in the United States, numbering over 1.8 million; Motel & Passel, 2012), there continue to be many Salvadorans here as "illegal aliens," causing them to live in a socially marginalized way and to continue to feel limited by low-paying jobs from which remittances are often made. Those unlucky enough to be caught at the border experience even greater hardship. Abrego (2009b) notes that "exorbitant smuggling fees, the treacherous journey through Mexico, the terrible treatment in detention centers, and the vulnerability of being unprotected by any legal system" are all realities experienced by undocumented Salvadoran migrants (p. 30). Again, one needs only to be reminded of the tens of thousands of unaccompanied minors detained at the U.S. border during 2014 to see the huge risks taken by Salvadorans in hope of reuniting families.

Despite the risks, Salvadorans continue to emigrate to the United States. Like Dominicans, Salvadoran-Americans are deeply transnational, so much so that some estimate that four out of 10 children in El Salvador grow up without one or both parents due to migration and the desire for parents to earn money to send back to El Salvador from the United States (Abrego, 2009a). In addition, nearly two-thirds of sixth through ninth graders in 1999 reported that they would consider emigrating to the United States, despite the fact that the civil war was over and the economy in El Salvador was settling, indicating a deeply transformative cultural mindset in which transnationalism was seen as the norm (Mahler, 1999). It is estimated that 20%–35% of Salvadorans emigrate and that remittances make up 18% of the nation of El Salvador's GDP (Abrego, 2009b).

Salvadoran transnationalism appears to offer a glimpse into the role that immigration plays in changing gender dynamics in the H/L community. For Salvadoran women, transnationalism often translates into a double standard by which they are not expected to enter into new relationships despite the long absences endured during separation, yet many Salvadoran men who do feel justified in establishing new relationships often do so at the expense of their families back home (Abrego, 2009a). In addition, women who do migrate for work often continue to send money back to their families in El Salvador, often at great sacrifice to themselves, given that they generally work for less and under harsher conditions. Many immigrant mothers experience "unjust working conditions, miserably low wages, and blocked paths to upward mobility" as well as few legal protections despite their being more likely to be undocumented and less likely to be legal permanent residents than immigrant fathers (Abrego, 2009a, p. 1082). Despite this, they generally remit more than fathers. As Abrego (2009a) reports, "following gendered social expectations that require their self-denial as ideal mothers, women willingly make extreme sacrifices that include uncomfortable living conditions, employment abuse, physical abuse from partners, and self-deprivation—to consistently send their children money" (Abrego, 2009a, p. 1082).

Cultural Values and Health and Wellness

Family plays a central role in the H/L culture and cultural value system, so much so that there is a name for this collectivist tendency in Spanish—*familismo*—a term that connotes the importance of attachments, family loyalty, and the extension of family status to close friends and godparents *(compadres)* (Andrés-Hyman et al., 2006; de las Fuentes, Barón, & Vásquez, 2003). Common American values such as independence and individuality are traditionally deemphasized in favor of collectivist tendencies which promote interdependence and cooperation through sacrifice of one's own ambitions for the greater family's needs and turning to family for strength and resilience. Families tend to live together in the same neighborhood or even household for many generations and tend to be emotionally close, often visiting and talking daily and offering financial, social, and emotional support to one another (Andrés-Hyman et al., 2006). Many of these behaviors and characteristics serve as protective factors and symbols of health and well-being in H/L communities.

The Latino approach to family *(familismo)* is increasingly seen as a source of resilience, strength, and health for H/Ls (Cardoso & Thompson, 2010; Consoli et al., 2011). The cultural characteristics of loyalty, solidarity, obligation, interdependence, and shared responsibility often serve to promote social and economic stability and family connectedness even when nuclear and extended families live at a distance. "Family involvement, supervision of children, and communication are essential resources that lead to resilience among Latino youth in immigrant families" (Cardoso & Thompson, 2010, p. 260). Biculturalism is associated with resilience in the H/L community, and families and parents are known to foster bicultural skills and emphasize positive communication. Given that families often share a common migration story, parents are able to empathize with difficulties their immigrant children may experience, and they often are able to seek religious and professional help both for themselves and their children (Cardoso & Thompson, 2010).

In addition to the concomitant values inherent in *familismo* and traditional gender roles (to be discussed in greater detail later in this chapter), music therapists working with this population must understand other cultural values, such as *personalismo, simpatía, respeto,* and an understanding of the role of religion for many Latinos. *Personalismo* is related to *familismo* in that both represent ways of staying connected to others and of working in familiar, and not unfamiliar, relationships. Understanding this is critical to establishing a therapeutic alliance with this population. Developing *confianza,* or trust, requires the "social lubrication" of "warm, personalized attention," not to be confused with informality or overly casual friendliness, and should include a limited amount of small talk or *plática,* as well as "judicious self-disclosure" (Organista, 2006, p. 81).

Simpatía and *respeto* are related values in that both recognize the importance of deference. *Simpatía* (sympathy) emphasizes politeness and the prevention of conflict through repression of "spoiled" behavior (to be "spoiled" in Spanish translates as one who is "brought up badly" or *malcriado*). And *respeto* (respect) represents the value of deference to authority, whether it be toward someone who is older and possibly wiser or someone who holds a hierarchical relationship to you—so that, "by convention, youth defers to age, children to parents, women to men, employees to employers, laypeople to experts, and so forth. However, *respeto* promotes 'equality, empathy, and connection' in every relationship, even within those perceived as hierarchical" (Andrés-Hyman et al., 2006, p. 696). These relational styles are promoted by cultural values and serve to enhance a greater sense of community and extended family networks. These networks also serve a protective function and promote health and well-being.

The role of religion and spirituality should be considered in working with H/Ls. According to a 2007 Pew Hispanic Center report, nine out of 10 H/Ls identify with a particular religion, with 68% of Latinos identifying as Roman Catholic and an additional 15% identifying as evangelic Protestants (Pew Research Center, 2007). In addition to traditional forms of religion, many H/Ls practice hybridized forms of traditional religion and folk healing practices, such as *curandería* or *santería*. These practices involve folk and medical beliefs and rituals and address psychosocial and spiritual concerns (de las Fuentes, Barón, & Vásquez, 2003). This means that music therapists are likely to encounter religiously inclined Latino clients, and they need to be aware of their own experiences of and relationship to religion and spirituality (Leseho, 2007). H/L clients are likely to find church, religiosity, and spirituality serving as sources of support and continuity. Religious traditions may provide a sense of "familiarity [with] and connection to the country of origin" for immigrant youth, and

youth groups and bible classes may even provide guidance related to issues of substance use, sexuality, parenting, and psychological distress (Cardoso & Thompson, 2010, p. 261).

While religion and spirituality are often a source of health, well-being, and strength for many Latinos, religion and religious beliefs can also serve as a risk factor for multiply identified groups. In particular, it should be noted that religion has a deep impact on the experience of sexuality for many LGBT-identified Latinos. In one study of Latino gay men, several men described growing up as Catholics and believing that their homosexuality was "dirty, sinful, and shameful to their families and loved ones" (Díaz, Bein, & Ayala, 2006). The triple oppression of being gay, poor, and Latino for many of these men resulted in great harm to their physical, mental, sexual, and spiritual health. Many reported "experiencing both verbal and physical abuse, police harassment, and decreased economic opportunities on account of their being gay or effeminate" and also on account of their skin color or immigration status (Díaz, Bein, & Ayala, 2006, p. 212). In addition:

> [S]ome men felt sexually objectified by White boyfriends and lovers, who stereotypically paid more attention to their skin color or Spanish accents than to who they truly are, giving the men a feeling of invisibility and of being used just for fantasy material rather than attempting a more authentic and equitable relationship. (p. 212)

Despite these adverse conditions, Díaz, Bein, and Ayala (2006) suggest that "family acceptance, satisfaction with social and sexual networks, and the presence of gay role models" can all serve as "resiliency factors" for these men (p. 222). Music therapists should work with H/L clients to attend to these social factors, particularly given the importance of relationships in these collectivist cultures.

Gender Diversities

As we've seen, there is great diversity within this cultural group—it would therefore be unadvisable to speak of a singular Latino/a experience. At the core of the Hispanic/Latino identity is the reality of a "mixed race" or "mixed blood" (Indigenous, Spanish, and, for many, African). Arredondo (2002) says, "All Latinos, culturally and historically, are *mestizos/mestizas* or *criollos*. These terms reflect our "mixed blood." For Latinos, *raza* means the essence of the people, our very being" (p. 311). These mixed cultures have resulted in a worldview and consciousness that respects diversity, difference, pluralism, cultural adaptability, and flexibility (Arredondo, 2002). The intersection of race, country of origin, legal status, socioeconomic class, and level of acculturation, coupled with stories of immigration and family cultural legacies, all influence the experience of gender and sexuality. While traditional gender roles are common in H/L communities, these identities become richly complex and require delicate negotiations, particularly when mixed with other markers of identity, with U.S. values, and with slowly transforming U.S. gender roles.

The Spanish language itself is gendered—the term "Latinos" refers both to a group of men and to women or men only, making males the "norm from which females must call attention to differentiate their gender (e.g., Latino/a)" (Gloria & Castellanos, 2013, p. 170), whereas the term "Latina" indicates both gender and race/ethnicity. Latinas are traditionally socialized to subordinate themselves to the males in their lives. Family is a large source of identity and support in the H/L community, and women, generally speaking, are expected to be dedicated wives, mothers, and daughters (Bratini, Ampuero, & Miville, 2013). For modern women, these traditional roles couple with their experiences of discrimination, acculturation, self-determination, and growth to lead to delicate negotiations and self-constructions of gender.

Women are often expected to be similar to the Virgin Mary in their virtuous and maternal qualities, according to the traditional gender role referred to as *marianismo* (de las Fuentes, Barón & Vásquez, 2003). Women are expected to tolerate much *("aguantarse")* from husbands, children, and parents and to be selfless, enduring much suffering, and self-sacrifice, albeit in exchange for reverence and high esteem. I grew up with the common Spanish phrase *"como la madre no hay ninguna"* ("there is no one as worthy as a mother"), and my mother certainly has lived her life in sacrifice to her family, yet with the pride and honor those sacrifices afforded her. Stevens (as cited by Jezzini, Guzmán, & Grayshield, 2008) states, in relation to the cultural value of *marianismo*, "No self-denial is too great for the Latin-American woman ... no limit can be divined to her vast store of patience for the men in her life." The role of mother is one of the most respected roles in Latino/a culture, and women are generally expected to be in charge of the domain of the house *"en la casa,"* while men are expected to be in charge of business outside the home in the world *"en el mundo"* (Bratini, Ampuero, & Miville, 2013). Gil and Vasquez (1996) define *marianismo* by a set of "commandments" to not forget a woman's place; not forsake tradition; not be single, self-supporting, or independent-minded; not put one's own needs first or forget that having sex is not about pleasure but for making babies; not wish to become more than a housewife or be unhappy with one's man; not ask for help; not change; and not discuss one's personal problems outside the home (Arredondo, 2002; Bratini, Ampuero, & Miville, 2013).

Despite the constraints of these traditional roles, many Latina women are working to transform these images and expectations into new gender role constructs (Bratini, Ampuero, & Miville, 2013). Being submissive and remaining chaste and sexually faithful while valued as in a position of honor and spiritual superiority certainly conflicts with the widespread sexuality that H/L teens (and women) encounter in the United States. While the idea of chastity may seem anachronistic to many youth in the United States, the ideal of a feminine woman who is both nurturing and maternal but also sexually attractive and

subservient to men is stereotypic for the Latina woman. Latinas may struggle to differentiate themselves from traditional values, but they may also find those values the source of both pride and socially attenuating expectations.

> The processes of transforming old images into new empowered ones, both individually and collectively, is important for promoting mental health and well-being, since, like other women of color in the United States, Latinas have been marginalized and exoticized in the larger society ... learning to negotiate the traditional roles of promoting family functioning and cultural survival without losing self in the process may be a key aspect of constructing gender roles for Latinas in today's complex society. (Bratini, Ampuero, & Miville, 2013, pp. 135–136)

Latino men are also expected to fulfill traditional gender roles and also participate in transforming old images into new ones. While *machismo* is often described in a negative light, as focused on sexual and physical virility and on power and dominance, the role for men of pride and respectability is also inherent in Latino gender roles (de las Fuentes, Barón, & Vásquez, 2003). The role of *caballero* or gentleman encompasses the values of "family leader and role model, and a primary wage earner, thereby deserving of the respectable title of *Don*" (de las Fuentes, Barón, & Vásquez, 2003, p. 210). Taken together, these roles of *machismo* and *caballerismo* cover many expectations for what it means to be "a man" in H/L culture. The Latin/Hispanic man is expected to be ...

> strong, reliable, virile, intelligent, and wise. They are expected to exhibit valor, dignity, self-confidence, and a high degree of individuality outside the family and be knowledgeable regarding sexual matters ... to be worthy of being good in society, be regarded as being honest, be considered compassionate, have integrity, and be indebted to no one. The ideals of tradition command that men are supposed to be proud, brave, courageous, devoted, loyal, honorable, the head of the family, the unquestioned authority figure, the authoritative caring parent, and the leader and protector of their families. (Solbralske, 2006, p. 384)

This broad definition of Latin masculinity defies the stereotype of the "macho man."

Researchers are increasingly concerned with the complexities within these *machismo/caballerismo* constructs and the ways that these values serve as both "risk-promoting and risk-reducing" (Estrada, Rigali-Oiler, Arciniega, & Tracey, 2011, p. 359). These risk-reducing and risk-promoting aspects of gender role expectations are particularly important for

Latino gay men, who as dual minorities (particularly given that within Latino culture there is a belief that "being gay is the worst thing a man can do") are particularly vulnerable not only to racism and homophobia but also to internalized homophobia (Estrada, Rigali-Oiler, Arciniega, & Tracey, 2011, p. 358). Recognizing and identifying ways that Latino masculinity serves both as a protective factor and as a risk factor for both straight and gay Latinos is critical. While these gender roles are rooted in the cultural values of *familismo* and *respeto,* at times they also lie in contradiction with one another and at still other times they allow for an increased sense of self-esteem and well-being, allowing men to feel they can be "the whole package" (Ojeda & Piña-Watson, 2014, p. 293).

Like Latinas, H/L men also struggle to reconcile these values with U.S. values and culture and with changing roles in the face of acculturation. Diaz, Miville, and Gil (2013) observe that Latino men often experience gender role strain as they navigate and try to live up to the contradictory demands of masculinity. They note (p. 99): "[S]ocietal and cultural expectations of what it means to be a man contradict one another, often leaving men feeling ambiguous about their masculinity … how should Latino men act according to the larger society?" As Latino families reconcile these traditional roles with more egalitarian gender roles in the United States, there is pressure to create family structures based more on mutuality (Diaz, Miville, & Gil, 2013)

Music in Hispanic/Latino Culture

The rich complexities of H/L culture are reflected in its music. In July 2014, Stavans, after eight years of work and solicitation from 63 contributors, published a two-volume, nearly 1,000-page encyclopedic compendium entitled *Latin Music: Musicians, Genres, and Themes.* What is Latin music? Clearly, for Stavans (2014), the scope of Latin music was wide. Within the historical, economic, ethnic, political, and social contexts, the repertoire spans from popular rhythms like cumbia, salsa, Tejano, and vallenato to songs like "Livin' la Vida Loca" and "Ojalá que Llueva Café." The Latin repertoire also includes centuries of Iberian, Hispanic American, and Brazilian music in the United States, and music from the pre-Columbian period to the present (Stavans, 2014).

Stavans has catalogued 48 rhythms and styles in Latin music, including areíto, bachata, banda, bolero, bomba, bossa nova, bugalú (bugaloo), cha-cha-cha, conga, conjunto, corrido, cubop, cumbia, danzón, décima, duranguense, electronic music, fado, flamenco, folk, guajira, heavy metal, hip-hop, house, jíbaro, keyboard, Latin jazz, Latin pop, mambo, mariachi, merengue, MPB *(Música Popular Brasileira),* narcocorrido, nueva trova, opera, punk, reggaetón, rhumba (rumba), rhythm and blues, rock 'n' roll, salsa, sephardic music, serenata, son jarocho, tango, tejano, vallenato, and zarzuela. The variability in Latin music is linked not only to style but also to generational and regional differences.

When I was a child, we listened to salsa and Afro-Cuban jazz in my home—this was partly due to my father's love for jazz, partly due to the music of his time and place, and mostly because we were Nuyoricans in the 1950s. In particular, one of the few albums we had when I was a child was the 1954 album *Tremendo Cumban,* recorded in New York City studios by Machito and his Afro-Cubanos. One of my favorite songs on this album was *Que bonito es Puerto Rico* (see https://www.youtube.com/watch?v=UF5wm1UcyZc), a love song to the island. This song came to symbolize the longing for home for me and held in it bittersweet memories for a generation in diaspora. As a young Latina growing up in the States with parents who had never been to the island, wanting their children to assimilate, this music was one of the few cultural traditions with which there were no restrictions. We may not have spoken Spanish in our home, but we listened to mambo. Had I grown up in a South American home or Mexican-American home, my musical history would probably have been different.

Music therapists working with H/L populations should inquire as to their clients' musical preferences—and in particular may want to inquire as to their clients' parents' musical tastes. We know that music has a special place in our memories, but recent research is highlighting the ways that music in particular becomes a form of cultural legacy for families—"parents actively or passively expose their children to music of their own era, focusing on certain songs, artists, and albums" (Krumhansl & Zupnick, 2013, p. 2067). Krumhansl and Zupnick (2013) suggest that there may be an intergenerational "cascading" of reminiscence because "music heard during childhood, likely reflecting the tastes of previous generations, would make a lasting impression on children's autobiographical memories, preferences, and emotional responses" (p. 2067). Given the many ways families manage immigration and acculturation, biculturalism and assimilation, music may be one way that clients retain, regain, or remember their cultural identities.

Given the growth of the H/L population in the United States, music therapists should develop and expand their musical repertoire to include Latin music—there are many sources today for familiarizing oneself with varied musical styles. iTunes lists several genre song charts under their mega "Latin" music store, including "alternativo y rock Latino, Brazilian, Pop Latino, Latin Urban, Regional Mexicano, and Salsa y Tropical," and with online streaming, there are many Latino radio stations playing a variety of styles of music. The sources for finding Latin music seem to have mushroomed along with the Latin music industry. One need only look at the numbers. In 2013, 9.8 million viewers watched the Latin Grammy awards, now in their 15th year, on the Spanish television network *Univision* (Scherer, 2014). Sources for finding music abound—Spotify, Pandora, Live 365 Internet radio, Batanga radio, YouTube, and Rdio just to name a few, with *Billboard* offering charts for the Top Hot Latin Songs, Latin Airplay, Latin Digital Songs, Latin Streaming Songs, Regional Mexican Songs, Latin Pop Songs, and Tropical Songs. There are many options for familiarizing yourself with Latin music of many genres and styles.

Conclusion

There are no simple stories. Cultural groups are complicated. and the diversity within each group is rich and dynamic. Music therapists must come to know their own stories and must do the hard work of sorting out in collaboration with their clients (and on their own with supervisors and professional communities) the ways that their clients' cultural stories impact their paths to health and well-being. Rilinger (2011) offers us a model for understanding and applying practical considerations of culture to music therapy. She offers us a historical and cultural context for working with Mexican-American children. She offers us a list of common Mexican children's songs, a list of genres, and performers, and a list of resources for working with Mexican-American children in music therapy—websites, literary resources, selected music books, and selected CDs of children's music. This is the type of research we need to do when working with Hispanic and Latino communities in music therapy. My favorite children's song, "Arroz con Leche" (http://www.123teachme.com/learn_spanish/children_songs_arroz_con_leche), is naturally not on the list, but my grandmother was Puerto Rican, not Mexican, and of course, when I went to research the song, I found many versions but none quite the same as my *abuelita*'s. Find the Latin music that speaks to you and that speaks to your clients from *la corazón*, from the heart.

References

Abrego, L. (2009a). Economic well-being in Salvadoran transnational families: How gender affects remittance practices. *Journal of Marriage and Family, 71*(4), 1070–1085.

Abrego, L. J. (2009b). Rethinking El Salvador's transnational families. *NACLA Report on the Americas, 42*(6), 28–32.

Acosta, Y. D., & de La Cruz, G. P. (2011, September). *The foreign-born from Latin America and the Caribbean: 2010* (American Community Survey Briefs: ACSBR/10-15). Retrieved from http://www.census.gov/prod/2011pubs/acsbr10-15.pdf

Andrés-Hyman, R. C., Ortiz, J., Añez, L. M., Paris, M., & Davidson, L. (2006). Culture and clinical practice: Recommendations for working with Puerto Ricans and other Latinas(os) in the United States. *Professional Psychology: Research and Practice, 37*(6), 694–701.

Arredondo, P. (2002). Mujeres Latinas-Santas y marquesas. *Cultural Diversity and Ethnic Minority Psychology, 8*(4), 308–319.

Berkel, C., Knight, G. P., Zeiders, K. H., Tein, J., Roosa, M. W., Gonzales, N. A., & Saenz, D. (2010). Discrimination and adjustment for Mexican-American adolescents: A prospective examination of the benefits of culturally related values. *Journal of Research on Adolescence, 20*(4), 893–915.

Blacksher, E. (2002). On being poor and feeling poor: Low socioeconomic status and the moral self. *Theoretical Medicine, 23,* 455–470.

Bratini, L., Ampuero, M. C., & Miville, M. L. (2013). Latina gender roles. In M. L. Miville (Ed.), *Multicultural gender roles: Applications for mental health and education* (pp. 133–168). Somerset, NJ: John Wiley & Sons Inc.

Cardoso, J. B., & Thompson, S. J. (2010). Common themes of resilience among Latino immigrant families: A systematic review of the literature. *Families in Society: The Journal of Contemporary Social Services, 91*(3), 257–265. doi:10.1606/1044-3894.4003

Cave, D., & Robles, F. (2014, October 6). A smuggled girl's odyssey of false promises and fear. *New York Times.* Retrieved from http://ezproxyles.flo.org/login?url=http://search.proquest.com/docview/1586065064?accountid=12060

Cobo, L. (2012). A business transformed. *Billboard, 124*(14), LM3.

Collazo, S. G., Ryan, C. L., & Bauman, K. J. (2010, April 15). Profile of the Puerto Rican population in the United States and Puerto Rico: 2008 *U.S. Census Bureau, Housing and Household Economic Statistics Division*. Paper presented at the population association of America annual meeting, Dallas, TX, April 15–17, 2010. Retrieved from http://www.census.gov/hhes/socdemo/education/data/acs/paa2010/Collazo_Ryan_Bauman_PAA2010_Paper.pdf

Consoli, M. L. M., López, S. A., Gonzales, N., Cabrera, A. P., Llamas, J., & Ortega, S. (2011). Resilience and thriving in the Latino/a population: Intersections and discrepancies. *Revista Interamericana de Psicología/Interamerican Journal of Psychology, 45*(3), 351–362.

de las Fuentes, C., Barón, A., & Vásquez, M. J. T. (2003). Teaching Latino psychology. In P. Bronstein & K. Quina (Eds.), *Teaching gender and multicultural awareness: Resources for the psychology classroom* (pp. 207–220). Washington, DC: American Psychological Association.

Delgado-Romero, E. A. (2001). Counseling a Hispanic/Latino client—Mr. X. *Journal of Mental Health Counseling, 23*(3), 207–221.

Diaz, M. A., Miville, M. L., & Gil, N. (2013). Latino male gender roles. In M. L. Miville (Ed.), *Multicultural gender roles: Applications for mental health and education* (pp. 97–132). Somerset, NJ: John Wiley & Sons, Inc.

Díaz, R. M., Bein, E., & Ayala, G. (2006). Homophobia, poverty, and racism: Triple oppression and mental health outcomes in Latino gay men. In A. M. Omoto & H. S. Kurtzman (Eds.), *Sexual orientation and mental health: Examining identity and development in lesbian, gay, and bisexual people* (pp. 207–224). Washington, DC: American Psychological Association.

Ennis, S. R., Rios-Vargas, M., & Albert, N. G. (2011, May). *The Hispanic population: 2010* (2010 Census Brief: C2010BR-04). Retrieved from http://www.census.gov/prod/cen2010/briefs/c2010br-04.pdf

Estrada, F., Rigali-Oiler, M., Arciniega, G. M., & Tracey, T. J. G. (2011). Machismo and Mexican-American men: An empirical understanding using a gay sample. *Journal of Counseling Psychology, 58*(3), 358–367.

Farias, P. (1994). Central and South American refugees: Some mental health challenges. In A. J. Marsella, T. Bornemann, S. Ekblad, & J. Orley (Eds.), *Amidst peril and pain: The mental health and well-being of the world's refugees* (pp. 101–113). Washington, DC: American Psychological Association.

Fortes De Leff, J. (2002). Racism in Mexico: Cultural roots and clinical interventions. *Family Process, 41*(4), 619–623.

Ginorio, A. B., Gutiérrez, L., Cauce, A. M., & Acosta, M. (1995). Psychological issues for Latinas. In H. Landrine (Ed.), *Bringing cultural diversity to feminist psychology: Theory, research, and practice* (pp. 241–263). Washington, DC: American Psychological Association.

Gonzalez, J. (2000). *Harvest of empire: A history of Latinos in America.* New York, NY: Viking.

González-Pando, M. (1997). Developmental stages of the "Cuban Exile Country." *Cuba in Transition: Papers and Proceedings of the Seventh Annual Meeting of the Association for the Study of the Cuban Economy (ASCE), 7,* 50–65. Retrieved from http://www.ascecuba.org/publications/proceedings/volume7/

Grandin, G. (2007). Democracy, diplomacy, and intervention in the Americas. *NACLA Report on the Americas. 40*(1), 22–25.

Guillén, A. (2001). Traveling north: A chronicle of an undocumented journey. *NACLA Report on the Americas, 35*(2), 36. Retrieved from http://go.galegroup.com.ezproxyles.flo.org/ps/i.do?id=GALE%7CA79086528&v=2.1&u=les_main&it=r&p=AONE&sw=w&asid=0266f12f38616926915cf69b15f0cd54

Hay, M. A. (2009). *"I've been Black in two countries": Black Cuban views on race in the U.S.* El Paso, TX: LFB Scholarly Publishing LLC.

Hipolito-Delgado, C. P. (2010). Exploring the etiology of ethnic self-hatred: Internalized racism in Chicana/o and Latina/o college students. *Journal of College Student Development, 51*(3), 319–331.

Itzigsohn, J. (2005). The Dominican immigration experience. *Centro Journal, 17*(1), 270–281.

Itzigsohn, J., & Dore-Cabral, C. (2000). Competing identities? Race, ethnicity, and panethnicity among Dominicans in the United States. *Sociological Forum, 15*(2), 225–247.

Itzigsohn, J., & Giorguli Saucedo, S. (2002). Immigrant incorporation and sociocultural transnationalism. *International Migration Review, 36*(3), 766–798.

Itzigsohn, J., Giorguli S., & Vazquez, O. (2005). Immigrant incorporation and racial identity: Racial self-identification among Dominican immigrants. *Ethnic and Racial Studies, 28*(1), 50–78.

Jensen, L., Cohen, J. H., Toribio, A. J., De Jong, G. F., & Rodríguez, L. (2006). Ethnic identities, language, and economic outcomes among Dominicans in a new destination. *Social Science Quarterly, 87*(5), 1088–1099.

Jezzini, A. T., Guzmán, C. E., & Grayshield, L. (2008, March). *Examining the gender role concept of* marianismo *and its relation to acculturation in Mexican-American college women.* Based on a program presented at the ACA Annual Conference & Exhibition, Honolulu, HI. Retrieved from http://counselingoutfitters.com/vistas/vistas08/Jezzini.htm

Kahn, C. (2013, June 12). Honduras claims unwanted title of world's murder capital [Blog post]. *Parallels: Many stories, One world. NPR—National Public Radio.* Retrieved from http://www.npr.org/blogs/parallels/2013/06/13/190683502/honduras-claims-unwanted-title-of-worlds-murder-capital

Kennedy, R., & Scott, A. (2005). A pilot study: The effects of music therapy interventions on middle school students' ESL skills. *Journal of Music Therapy, 42*(2), 244–261.

Kenny, C. (2011). Bridging the cultural divide: Comments on Schwantes, Wigram, McKinney, Lipscomb, and Richards's article. *Australian Journal of Music Therapy, 22,* 21–23.

Krogstad, J. M., & Passel, J. S. (2014, November 18). 5 facts about illegal immigration in the U.S. *Fact Tank: Report of the Pew Research Center.* Retrieved from http://www.pewresearch.org/fact-tank/2014/11/18/5-facts-about-illegal-immigration-in-the-u-s/

Krogstad, J. M., Gonzalez-Barrera, A., & Lopez, M. H. (2014, July 22). Children 12 and under are fastest growing group of unaccompanied minors at U.S. border. *Fact Tank: Report of the Pew Research Center.* Retrieved from http://www.pewresearch.org/fact-tank/2014/07/22/children-12-and-under-are-fastest-growing-group-of-unaccompanied-minors-at-u-s-border/

Krumhansl, C. L., & Zupnick, J. A. (2013). Cascading reminiscence bumps in popular music. *Psychological Science, 24*(10), 2057–2068.

Mahler, S. J. (1999). Engendering transnational migration: A case study of Salvadorans. *American Behavioral Scientist, 42*(4), 690–719.

Melville, M. B. (1994). "Hispanic" ethnicity, race and class. In T. Weaver (Ed.), *Handbook of Hispanic cultures in the United States: Anthropology* (pp. 85–106). Houston, TX: Arte Repulico Press/University of Houston. Retrieved from the Latinoteca website: http://www.latinoteca.com/latcontent/repository/free-content/Anthropology/Hispanic Ethnicity, Race and Class/at_download/file

Miller, M. J. (2007). A bilinear multidimensional measurement model of Asian-American acculturation and enculturation: Implications for counseling interventions. *Journal of Counseling Psychology. 54*(2), 118–131.

Motel, S., & Patten, E. (2012, July). *The 10 largest Hispanic origin groups: Characteristics, rankings, top counties.* Retrieved from the Pew Hispanic Center website:http://

www.pewhispanic.org/files/2012/06/The-10-Largest-Hispanic-Origin-Groups.pdf

Ojeda, L., & Piña-Watson, B. (2014). Caballerismo may protect against the role of machismo on Mexican day laborers' self-esteem. *Psychology of Men & Masculinity, 15*(3), 288–295.

Organista, K. C. (2006). Cognitive-behavioral therapy with Latinos and Latinas. In P. A. Hays & G. Y. Iwamasa (Eds.), *Culturally responsive cognitive-behavioral therapy: Assessment, practice, and supervision* (pp. 73–96). Washington, DC: American Psychological Association.

Ortmeyer, D. L., & Quinn, M. A. (2012). Coyotes, migration duration, and remittances. *The Journal of Developing Areas, 46*(2), 185–203.

Padilla, A. M. (2000). Hispanic psychology. In A. E. Kazdin (Ed.), *Encyclopedia of psychology, Vol. 4* (pp. 126–131). Washington, DC: American Psychological Association.

Passel, J., & Taylor, P. (2009). *Who's Hispanic?* Retrieved from the Pew Hispanic Center website: http://www.pewhispanic.org/files/reports/111.pdf

Passel, J. S., & Cohn, D. (2011). *Unauthorized immigrant population: National and state trends, 2010.* Retrieved from the Pew Hispanic Center website: http://www.pewhispanic.org/files/reports/133.pdf

Pew Research Center. (2007). *Changing faiths: Latinos and the transformation of American religion.* Retrieved from the Pew Hispanic Center website: http://www.pewhispanic.org/files/reports/75.pdf

Quiñones, M. E. (2007). Bridging the gap. In J. C. Muran (Ed.), *Dialogues on difference: Studies of diversity in the therapeutic relationship* (pp. 153–167). Washington, DC: American Psychological Association.

Rilinger, R. (2011). Music therapy for Mexican-American children: Cultural implications and practical considerations. *Music Therapy Perspectives, 29*(1), 78–85.

Romero, M. G. (2009). Mental health counseling with Hispanics/Latinos: The role of culture in practice. In I. Marini & M. A. Stebnicki (Eds.), *The professional counselor's desk reference* (pp. 231–240). New York, NY: Springer Publishing.

Sánchez Prado, I. M. (2012). Latin(o) America: A story of crossroads. In *The American mosaic: The Latino American experience.* Retrieved August 18, 2012, from http://latinoamerican2.abc-clio.com.ezproxyles.flo.org/

Scherer, M. (2014, November 20). The Latin Grammy Awards celebrates Obama's immigration plan. *Time.* Retrieved from http://time.com/3598813/immigration-latin-grammy-awards-barack-obama/

Schwantes, M. (2009). The use of music therapy with children who speak English as a second language: An exploratory study. *Music Therapy Perspectives, 27*(2), 80–87.

Schwantes, M., Wigram, T., McKinney, C., Lipscomb, A., & Richards, C. (2011). The Mexican *corrido* and its use in a music therapy bereavement group. *Australian Journal of Music Therapy, 22*, 2–20.

Sobralske, M. (2006). Machismo sustains health and illness beliefs of Mexican-American men. *Journal of the American Academy of Nurse Practitioners, 18*(8), 348–350.

Spener, D. (1999). This coyote's life. *NACLA Report on the Americas, 33*(3), 22. Retrieved from http://go.galegroup.com.ezproxyles.flo.org/ps/i.do?id=GALE%7CA58177716&v=2.1&u=les_main&it=r&p=AONE&sw=w&asid=b7a820716c718fc0d5ccf23030d7d5a6

Stavans, I. (Ed.). (2014). *Latin music: Musicians, genres, and themes.* Retrieved from http://www.abc-clio.com/ABC-CLIOCorporate/PrintProduct.aspx?pc=B3922C

Suárez-Orozco, M. M., & Páez, M. M. (Eds). (2002). *Latinos: Remaking America.* Berkeley and Los Angeles, CA: University of California Press.

Taylor, P., Lopez, M. H., Martinez, J. H., & Velasco, G. (2012, April). *When labels don't fit: Hispanics and their views of identity.* Retrieved from the Pew Hispanic Center website: http://www.pewhispanic.org/files/2012/04/PHC-Hispanic-Identity.pdf

U.S. Census Bureau. (1992, October). *We asked … you told us: Hispanic Origin* (Census Questionnaire Content, 1990 CQC-7). Retrieved from http://www.census.gov/main/www/cen1990.html

U.S. Census Bureau. (2014, September 8). *Profile America Facts for Feature: Hispanic Heritage Month 2014* (CB14-FF.22). Retrieved from http://www.census.gov/newsroom/facts-for-features/2014/cb14-ff22.html

Weaver, T. (1994). The culture of Latinos in the United States. In T. Weaver (Ed.), *Handbook of Hispanic cultures in the United States: Anthropology* (pp. 15–38). Houston, TX: Arte Repulico Press/University of Houston. Retrieved from http://www.latinoteca.com/latcontent/repository/free-content/Anthropology/The%20Culture%20of%20Latinos%20in%20the%20US/at_download/file

Wexler, P. (1992). *Becoming somebody: Toward a social psychology of school.* London, UK: Falmer Press.

Zezima, K., & O'Keefe, E. (2014, June 2). Obama calls wave of children across U.S.-Mexican border "urgent humanitarian situation." *The Washington Post.* Retrieved from http://www.washingtonpost.com/politics/obama-calls-wave-of-children-across-us-mexican-border-urgent-humanitarian-situation/2014/06/02/4d29df5e-ea8f-11e3-93d2-edd4be1f5d9e_story.html

Chapter 5

EASTERN AND SOUTHEAST ASIAN CULTURE

Xueli Tan & Feilin Hsiao

Xueli: *Why is there a need to have six ink-to-paper depictions of a name to identify one person? In my passport, there are two ways to represent my name in English; one would suggest that I am of Chinese descent, particularly from the province of Guangzhou in southern China; the other gives hints to a heritage passed down from a former British-colonized Southeast Asian country—Singapore. I also have an informal English name that my high school band teacher gave to me to "make it easier" for her to call on me. The Chinese characters (simplified Chinese) of my name are printed on my Singapore identification card. To add to the confusion, my father wrote the traditional form of Chinese characters on my birth certificate. When I was living in Singapore, my family name was always written before my given name. The practice is reversed in the United States, where my identity of "me" comes before my family name. Apparently, this soap opera of discombobulated identities is necessary to define my culture, heritage, acculturation, and assimilation histories.*

Although the first sounds I heard as an infant were Cantonese, English (British) became my first language shortly thereafter. When I was a teenager, the Ministry of Education (Singapore) upgraded Mandarin Chinese to my "second first language" status. Coming to the United States for my college education meant adjusting to the American English spelling of "behaviors" instead of "behaviours" and "colors" instead of "colours," and "practise" is no longer the verb form of "practice" in my English vocabulary. Through acculturation and assimilation, I now have splintered language skills in Cantonese and Mandarin Chinese. I probably have sufficient proficiency to understand a menu written in Chinese but not enough in the spoken form to place the order. And certainly not enough to conduct the multiplication and division tasks needed to figure out the amount for the tip as I only learned to count using the English language. Even though my English accent is linguistically sound, it is geographically unidentifiable. Others (collectively) commented that I speak with a Chinese–Korean– Hong Kong–British–German–American accent.

My ever-shifting geographical locations have landed me in places where I identified with the majority culture, places where I was the minority among many other large minority groups, places where I was the minority, and places where I became the minority of the minorities. It is in those places where I experienced a double or even triple whammy of minority status, where I became acutely and consciously aware of privilege, power, and my experiences of discrimination in the forms of racism, ageism, genderism, heterosexism, and homophobia. The outward façade of my intersecting identities as a female, immigrant, multicultured, gay person of color surfaces

differently and often unfolds in systematic layers according to how others view me through their own intersecting identity lens. As a third-generation Chinese born in Singapore and a first-generation Asian immigrant in the United States, the U.S. Department of Homeland Security labels me as a "legal alien" in my immigration documents. I was even assigned an alien identification number. I continue to wrestle with my answers to questions like "What are you?" and "Where are you from?" In the simplest form, I guess I am a Singaporean–Asian-American Queer Alien.

Feilin: *I am an Asian immigrant and became a U.S. citizen in 2008. After completing my college degree and five years of work experience in Taiwan, I began pursuing music therapy studies in New York City in 1991. Having grown up in a Westernized metropolitan city in Taiwan, I fit right in. There was little culture shock, except for minor daily customs I was not used to, for example, hugging and kissing, greeting exchanges such as "How are you?" and "I am fine," and making sure that I said "Bless you" when someone sneezed. I also learned that seeing a counselor or therapist was often part of daily conversation, which was still taboo in Taiwan in the '90s. On the other hand, growing up listening to the radio show American Top 40, hosted by Casey Kasem and aired by the Armed Forces Network Taiwan, I felt right at home with the music repertoire.*

My second stop was a college town in the Midwest, where I did have a bit of culture shock. I had to tone down my New Yorker attitude. I enjoyed the friendliness and simple lifestyle in a college town and started learning country and western music. However, my own experience as a patient was quite interesting. In the middle of my first year, I found myself having trouble reading fine print. After visiting the hospital, the doctor put me through many examinations and blood tests. He thought the symptoms might have been caused by an unknown disease that I had been infected with in Asia. However, these unnecessary procedures were based on unfamiliarity and lack of experience with patients from outside the United States, and the entire process put me in great distress. After a few weeks, another doctor finally diagnosed me with "convergence insufficiency," an eye muscle coordination problem, and prescribed for me weekly rehabilitation that was not covered by insurance. I later found out that I had developed symptoms of presbyopia, which is not uncommon for someone in his/her late 30s, and I simply needed another pair of glasses (with a reduced prescription) for reading.

I have been living in California for more than 10 years now, which is as diverse as NYC but has more of an Asian concentration. I learned about diversity within the Asian culture and the Chinese population, such as generational differences.

For example, although I speak fluent Mandarin Chinese, I have a hard time communicating with early Chinese immigrants who speak only Cantonese. In order to work with them and keep them interested, I began learning Cantonese operas. I also work with children of immigrants from Southeastern Asia, such as Hmong and Cambodians. Many of my students are Asian-Americans, while I also have a large extended family with a mix of first and second generations in southern California. In summary, these experiences have helped me to become a more culturally sensitive clinician and educator.

Introduction: Defining Asia

The United Nations termed the macrogeographical region of Asia as a confluence of Central Asia, Eastern Asia, Southern Asia, Southeastern Asia, and Western Asia (UN Statistics Division, 2013). The focus of this chapter centers on Eastern Asia, which includes China, Hong Kong, Macao, Taiwan, Japan, Mongolia, North and South Korea, and Southeastern Asia, which includes Vietnam, Thailand, Laos, Cambodia, Myanmar, Philippines, Malaysia, Singapore, Indonesia, Timor-Leste, and Brunei Darussalam. The history of Eastern Asia, and particularly Southeastern Asia, unfolds as a series of instances of colonization and Western imperialism. The major colonizing countries of the Asian territories include Great Britain (Singapore, Philippines, Malaysia, Brunei, Burma, Bangladesh, Bhutan, India, Maldives, Pakistan, Sri Lanka), United States (Philippines), Spain (Philippines), and France (Cambodia, Laos, Vietnam). Dutch and Spanish influences can be found littered and compounded upon each other in many areas in this part of the world, for example, in Indonesia. Thus, remnants of British, French, Portuguese, and U.S. colonization, trade, warfare, and migrational forces contribute to the richness and diversities of cultures found in the eastern and southeastern regions of Asia.

My (Feilin) grandparents and my father speak fluent Hokkien (a dialect originating from the southeastern part of China, considered the native language for Taiwanese) and Japanese because they were born and educated during the time when the Japanese ruled Taiwan (1895–1945). I speak both Mandarin Chinese and, less fluently, Hokkien. When I was going through school, the Nationalist government banned Hokkien in schools and the mass media, in order to assimilate Taiwanese. We were penalized (one dollar per sentence) if we spoke Hokkien in school. At that time, my father tried to enforce a counteraction at home, but he was eventually assimilated by we three kids and my mother, who is an elementary school teacher.

According to the U.S. Census Bureau (2010), there are currently 14.7 million people who identify as "Asian," and this group is proportionally the fastest-growing ethnic group in the United States. Within the past 10 years, the Asian population grew faster (43% increase) than any other ethnic group in the country (Hoeffel, Rastogi, Kim, & Shahid, 2012).

Although data on race had been collected since the first United States decennial census in 1790, it was not until 70 years later, in 1860, that the first Asian response category, "Chinese," was added to the question on race in the state of California (Hoeffel et al., 2012). Additional Asian response categories were added intermittently, and these categories eventually expanded across all states. In the most recent census (2010), the six Asian categories in rank order included Chinese, followed by Asian Indian, Filipino, Vietnamese, Korean, and Japanese (Hoeffel et al., 2012). With four million people, the Chinese population is the largest among the Asian group.

Diversity Within the Culture

The Asian-American identity is open to many interpretations within the culture itself. Some individuals might not consider adopting the term "Asian-American" but instead choose to identify themselves as Chinese Americans, Japanese Americans, or Vietnamese Americans. Asian-American immigrants are diverse within their cohort group based on cultural and societal differences among their countries of origin. Certain countries, Japan and Taiwan, for example, are far more homogeneous compared to multiracial countries such as Singapore and Malaysia. There are also vast differences in this identity based on immigration and generational factors. New immigrants from Asia will view themselves as distinctly different compared to a native-born third- or fourth-generation Asian-Americans.

Although Asian-American identity runs the gamut from immigrants to native-born individuals, from homogeneous to multiracial heritage cohorts, and from individuals from highly westernized Asian countries to those who kept their own traditions, there are still certain shared values and experiences among all (Mac, 2009). Researchers have identified more than 30 different cultural groups within the Asian-American population (Hall & Yee, 2012; Liu, Murakami, Eap, & Hall, 2009).

For many Asian-Americans, religion not only enriches their spiritual needs, but also solidifies the family structure, strengthens the support network and a sense of community, and ensures a smoother and faster assimilation into the dominant culture. According to the American Religious Identification Survey (2009), Asian-Americans follow Eastern religious faiths (21%) such as Buddhism, Hindu, and Taoism, as well as Christianity (21%) and Catholic (17%) faiths (Kosmin & Keysar, 2009).

Looking at countries of origin gives a different perspective on religious affiliations and serves to demonstrate the diversity within the Asian population. While more than half of Chinese Americans are not affiliated with any religion, 65% of the Filipinos are Catholics (Pew Research Center, 2012). This may be a result of Spain's occupation of the Philippines for almost 250 years (1565 to 1821). Most Korean Americans, meanwhile, practice the Christian faith, 43% of Vietnamese Americans are Buddhists, and Japanese Americans have similar percentages of Christians and people who are unaffiliated with any religion.

Worldviews

Individuals of Asian descent form the majority of the world population (Hall & Yee, 2012). Traditionally, the historical, cultural, religious, and Eastern philosophical influences drawn from the principles of Confucianism, Buddhism, and Taoism shroud the attitudes, beliefs, and behaviors of individuals from eastern and southeastern Asian countries, which emphasize collectivism, hierarchical relationships, emotional restraint, social harmony, and a sociological need to "save face" (Shea & Yeh, 2008).

Collectivism

The individualism versus collectivism idea refers to how people in society define themselves and their relationships with others (Jandt, 2009). Asian cultures, characterized by collectivism, emphasize relationships among people and interdependence within the group. People are likely to define themselves in relation to others within social context (Shea & Yeh, 2008). Collectivist cultures are tightly integrated, and the interest of the group precedes the interest of the individual person. Individual goals and aspirations are secondary compared to the common interest and welfare of the group.

Kim went back to graduate school to pursue a doctorate degree in order to find her place in society. She wants to acquire an academic identity through her title as "Dr. X." Kim has been married for many years but has not been able to have any children. In Korean society, married women are often referred to as "XX's mom," that is, society confers an identity to women through their children. Without children, Kim does not have an identity.

Fundamental Family Unit

The most fundamental level of collectivism can be found within the family unit. The family structure of Asian society is safeguarded through reciprocal obligations (Sheu & Fukuyama, 2007). Each member of the family has distinct responsibilities within the hierarchical construct. Adult children are responsible for taking care of their elderly parents, and the elderly take on the caregiving role for their grandchildren while the younger adults are at work. This is expressed in a Chinese word, " xiao." Therefore, it is not uncommon to find multiple generations of the same family living under the same roof.

As a third-generation Singaporean-Chinese, I (Xueli) *grew up in a three-generation household surrounded by nine adults: my parents, my father's siblings, and my grandparents. My grandmother's role in the family was to take care of the grandchildren while the rest of the adults were at work during the day. Being my primary caretaker for most hours of the day, she had a potpourri of health remedies for me that included herbal soups, prayers, Buddhist chants, traditional Chinese medicine, and having me walk around with a prayer inscription "stamped" onto the back of my t-shirt.*

In traditional Asian society, sending aging parents to a care facility is always associated with shame and guilt. However, this tradition has seen changes both here and in Asia. The growing aging population has forced some Asian countries to create more care facilities for their elderly population—something that barely existed in years gone by—and retirement communities for Asian-Americans are becoming increasingly accepted.

Hierarchy of Interpersonal Relationships

One of the key principles of Confucian teaching, *wu lun*, states that there are five basic types of relationships existing in society, namely, ruler/subjects, parent/child, older sibling/younger sibling, husband/wife, and older/younger friend. According to *wu lun,* these five relationships correlate with moral discipline and obligations (Gudykunst, 2001). The stability of society is based on mutual responsibilities between individuals in these relationships. This hierarchy means that respect and obedience toward the higher-ranking persons are expected from the junior members, and the seniors offer protection and consideration in reciprocity (Hofstede & Bond, 1988).

"Saving Face"

"Saving face," or *lien,* is a crucial yet abstract concept in Asian societies. To put it simply, to "save face" means to create a positive public image of oneself in front of other people. *Lien* is of central importance because of its pervasiveness in its influence on social discourse between the individual and his/her family and the outside world. *Lien* has been used interchangeably with sociological concepts such as status, authority, prestige, moral standards, standards of behavior, and social recognition (Ho, 1976). In contrast, to "lose face" implies a loss of dignity and self-esteem, often accompanied by feelings of shame and inadequacy.

In general, members of the Asian community tend to restrict discussion of personal problems, especially physical and mental illnesses (Sheu & Fukuyama, 2007). In order to "save face," individuals are encouraged to not express their problems outside the family. This mentality hinders the individual's willingness to seek professional help outside of their home environment and may act as an obstacle toward an open therapeutic relationship.

Display of Emotions

Researchers have found that Asians are more likely to exhibit dialectical thinking (tolerance of contradiction) and emotional complexity (co-occurrence of positive and negative emotions within onself) than Euro-Americans (Spencer-Rodgers, Peng, Wang, 2010; Wang, Leu, & Shoda, 2011). Asians, with the capacity to tolerate mixed emotions, are governed by the tendency to respect and accommodate others, thus making it more likely for them to choose to express positive emotions outwardly in front of others (Ni, 2010). Individuals in collectivistic societies may tend to avoid the intense experience of emotions. In particular, negative emotions may be withheld in order to preserve the harmony of social situations (Shea & Yeh, 2008).

Communication Styles

Asians are perceived to be less assertive and direct when they are engaged in verbal communication with others (Sheu & Fukuyama, 2007). Indirect communication, especially when discussing unpleasant topics or when conversing with authoritative figures, such as a supervisor or a teacher, allows both parties to "save face" by not offending the other person. This indirect way of expressing one's opinion is regarded as a sign of respect for others in Asian societies. Outside the culture, this form of communication may easily be misunderstood as passivity or lacking confidence.

Gender Roles and Expectations

The traditional Asian culture has well-defined social roles, while the self-identity of each individual is attached to these roles in the context of the family network. In general, family fame usually surpasses the individuals' needs and desires, while group orientation is emphasized over personal identity (Sheu & Fukuyama, 2007). If these expected behaviors are not observed, the individuals receive pressure from the community, often resulting in feelings of guilt and shame.

The male is usually the dominant member who occupies a higher status and controls resources and economic needs (Sue & Sue, 2007). Women, on the other hand, primarily considered as the child bearers, are expected to play subordinate roles. They are expected to take care of domestic needs while remaining compliant to the male members (Sheu & Fukuyama, 2007). Gender discrimination contributes to the common practice that only the eldest son is eligible to carry on the family heritage. As a result, from birth, females are considered of lesser value than males. This prevalent belief still exists today. Wives who are unable to produce male heirs often endure enormous pressure. The predominant stereotype often leads to oppression of Asian women, who are easily confined in their traditional gender roles.

In recent decades, the increased number of women in the workforce has expanded social roles of many Asian women. Their tasks have changed from devoting themselves solely to the family to finding a balance between work and family (Rogers & Amato, 2000). This has added complexity to their roles. While making equal efforts at the workplace, women are still expected to fully commit to their families and fulfill the household duties. They may choose work only to contribute to the family income instead of trying to achieve self-fulfillment. Thus, rather than empowering Asian women, strengthening their self-identity, and liberating them from traditional gender roles, the additional work load further constrains and burdens

Asian women in modern society.

Historical Realities Versus Popular Myths

Myth 1: Model Minority

Asian-Americans clinched the title of *model minority* in the 1980s (Liu, 1998). Specifically, the term was coined in 1983 when an investigation was initiated at Brown University, where allegations of possible quotas, or limitations, set on the admission and enrollment of Asian-Americans sparked debates across the nation (Nakanishi, 1989). Subsequently, other schools such as UC Berkeley, UCLA, Princeton, and Harvard became entangled in the controversy. Asian-Americans were not included in the data collection and analysis of minority groups in these universities because they were not considered to be "educationally disadvantaged." This exclusion meant that opportunities and resources initially set aside for minority groups, such as financial aid, were not awarded to Asian-Americans.

A Bloomberg article reported that Asian-Americans are held unfairly to higher standards for admission into private colleges because they are overrepresented at top universities relative to their population size (Golden, 2012). The report cited a quote in the book *No Longer Separate, Not Yet Equal* by sociologist Thomas Espenshade:

> If all other credentials are equal, Asian-Americans need to score 140 points more than Whites, 270 points higher than Hispanics, and 450 points above African-Americans out of a maximum 1600 on the math reading SAT to have the same chance of admission ... . (Golden, 2012, para 19)

This publicized image of Asian-Americans as high achievers projects the notion that all Asian-Americans achieve a higher level of success compared to the average population. This stereotype characterizes Asian-Americans as individuals who are more disciplined, intelligent, gifted in math and science, virtuous, orderly, polite, quiet, diligent, family-oriented, and law-abiding (Liu, 1998; Mac, 2009) than others. In addition, Asian-Americans are often considered to be a successful group that does not experience problems or difficulties, including health disparities, socioeconomic difficulties, and issues with acculturation. However, this perception of the Asian-American community as a whole is inaccurate because it fails to acknowledge the diversity within the culture (Walker-Moffat, 1995). A recent immigrant is likely to face vastly different challenges compared to a second- or third-generation Asian-American born in the United States.

The fallacy of the model minority stereotype is that when all Asian-Americans are viewed collectively as a homogeneous group of high achievers, then the group is portrayed as one with no needs (Lewin, 2008). This interpretation of a uniformly self-sufficient group gives the impression that there is no need for affirmative action or resource allocation for these individuals. Lee (1996) poignantly referred to the consequences of this stereotype as "silencing those who are not economically successful." Indeed, findings from a research study have proposed that using income averages to characterize the Asian-American population is misleading because the normal curve for income per capita for this group is wider, that is, has greater variance, than for other ethnic groups (Hu, 1989). Hu (1989) concluded that the term "double minority" would be a more accurate depiction of the group rather than the stereotypical "model minority." The assumption that all Asian-Americans are successful individuals who do not experience inequalities and discrimination is a form of denial and rejection of their reality. This form of denial is a type of microaggression (Sue, Bucceri, Lin, Nadal, & Torino, 2007).

Myth 2: Command of the English Language

"You speak such good English" might sound like a great compliment to someone of Asian descent. However, you might get curious looks if you make that comment to certain individuals, especially if they are born in the United States or are originally from the Philippines, Singapore, or India. English is the primary/official language in these three countries, and the majority of the people are conversant in both written and verbal English (www.britishcouncil.org).

Complimenting them on their English language abilities would be considered a form of microaggression known as microinvalidation. The message being conveyed is "You are not American," "You are a foreigner," "You are not American-born," or "You are the outsider"—all which is a form of denial of the reality and experiences of Asian-Americans. It is very likely that these individuals also speak at least one other language or dialect within their homes and community. For example, a Filipino might speak English and Tagalog; a Singaporean might speak English, Mandarin Chinese, and Malay; and an Indian might speak English and Hindi. Their multilingualism contributes to the distinct and varied English accents. Their accents might create the misapprehension that English is not their first/primary/official language. However, the different accents do not accurately reflect the individuals' ability to speak, write, or understand the English language.

Myth 3: Asian-Americans Constitute a Small Group in the United States

The total population of the United States grew by 9.7% from 281.4 million in 2000 to 308.7 million in 2010 (Hoeffel, Rastogi, Kim, & Shahid, 2012). Within that same period of time, the Asian population increased by 43% from 10.2 million to 14.7 million (Hoeffel et al., 2012). Regionally, the Asian population grew by at least 30% in all states (except Hawaii, with an 11% increase), with the greatest growth in the states of Nevada (116%), Arizona (95%), North Carolina (85%), North Dakota (85%), and Georgia (83%) (Hoeffel, Rastogi, Kim, & Shahid, 2012). Being the third largest ethnic minority group in the United States, Asian-Americans warrant greater attention due to their complex needs, the substantial diversity within their population, and, especially, with regard to decreasing health disparities (Hall & Yee, 2012).

Gender and Body Image

Body image is a central aspect to the formation of self-concept, especially for females. In general, Asian-American women report lower levels of appearance esteem and are dissatisfied with their appearance, especially because of features distinctive to their ethnic group, for example, the single eyelid (Mintz & Kashubeck, 1999). This is a reflection of the Asian-American woman's desire to endorse mainstream beauty standards of European-Americans (Evans & McConnell, 2003). On the other hand, Asian-American women who identify themselves strongly with traditional Asian values experience more pressure to maintain expected body shape and size to reflect well on their community. They are inclined to have a greater desire to be thin, while spending a great deal of effort in monitoring their diet and exercise regime (Lau, Lum, Chronister, & Forrest, 2006; Phan & Tylka, 2006).

After my (Feilin's) *first year of graduate study in the United States, my mom visited me in NYC. I was very anxious to see her, and the first thing she said to me was, "What have you done to yourself? You have put on a lot of weight!" Not wanting to show my emotion in front of her, I went outside of the apartment and sobbed, thinking "That's all you care about?" Now that she is a grandparent, my mom has relaxed her attitude. On the phone, she often says, "Are you still on a diet? You need to eat more to stay healthy." She also once admitted, "I'm worried about your niece's weight, but I couldn't even bring it up. Your brother said it might hurt her feelings." She has learned to hold back on her opinions. Growing up as the oldest child and only girl, my appearance was always being compared with my mom's. The recurring theme of family friends' comments was, "It's a shame that she does not have her mother's beauty. She looks exactly like her father." These insensitive comments were hurtful, and it took me a long time to learn to tune out the comments that I had internalized for years.*

The thin ideal and pursuit of perfect beauty is not unique to Asian cultures. Compared with their European-American counterparts, Asian-American women report similar or lower rates of body satisfaction (Smart & Tsong, 2014), particularly regarding facial features distinctive to their ethnic group, for example, single eyelids and flat noses (Nouri, Hill, & Orrell-Valentec, 2011). This trend reflects Asian-American women's desire to endorse the standards for beauty held by the dominant culture, which are sometimes impossible to meet without cosmetic surgery (Evans & McConnell, 2003).

Other factors associated with Asian-American women's dissatisfaction with their bodies include the stereotypical images of Asian women and the enforcement of a "thinness ethic" (Smart & Tsong, 2014, p. 6) in the family and culture via negative criticism and frequent appearance-related social comparisons. As a group, Asian-American women have lower body mass indexes (BMI) than European-American women (Yates, Edman, & Aruguete, 2004). Consequently, Asian women can feel pressured to live up to stereotypical images of petite femininity, which can be especially stressful for women whose body sizes fall outside of the stereotype. Asian-American women have also reported feeling unusually more self-conscious when around other Asian women (Kawamura, 2002). For most of their lives, many Asian women have repeatedly received blunt criticism from parents, extended family members, and friends regarding their body weight and appearance (Isono, Watkins, & Lian, 2009; Nouri et al., 2011), such as "You're fat" or "You're too ugly to be one of the *X* family." Asian women are also regularly compared with other women in their families and must endure the open humiliation.

Research has shown that Asian-American women who strongly identify with traditional Asian values experience more pressure to maintain an expected body shape and size to represent their family well (Lau, Lum, Chronister, & Forrest, 2006; Phan & Tylka, 2006). As such, they are inclined both to have a greater desire to be thin and to exert a great deal of effort in monitoring their diet and exercise regime. Desperate for approval, they consider achieving and maintaining an ideal body weight and shape as a means to be accepted by family members and the society in general. Since their self-worth ties into their self-control over their diet and body weight levels, significant guilt and shame associated with body weight gain can encourage them to adopt unhealthy weight control behaviors, as well as develop eating disorders (Masuda, Le, & Cohen, 2014).

Effective strategies for Asian-American women to overcome body dissatisfaction due to unique cultural influences include (1) strengthening internal validation through self-acceptance by creating personal standards for beauty, acknowledging other personal attributes such as education and personality, becoming desensitized to appearance-related criticism, and engaging in positive self-talk; (2) appreciating physical health and increasing activity levels; (3) understanding cultural influences; (4) setting healthy boundaries with family members; and (5) reaching out for social support (Smart & Tsong, 2014). What about Asian men? Are they affected by body image expectations?

Overlapping Identities: Dual and Triple Minority Statuses

Asian cultures strongly value heterosexuality. Being lesbian, gay, bisexual, or transgender (LGBT) is considered a threat to the family system and seen as being a rejection of typical gender roles. In addition, homosexuality challenges the tenets of collectivism by placing personal needs over family fame and honor. Parents of LGBT persons are believed to have failed to instill traditional family values and gender expectations in their children (Lee & Hahm, 2012). These cultural values affect how

sexual identities of Asian-Americans are formed, as well as how they emerge and are expressed. LGBT Asian-Americans who were more attached to Asian values had a higher level of internalized homophobia and were less likely to disclose their sexual orientation to others (Szymanski & Sung, 2013).

LGBT Asian-Americans typically encounter rejection in their family and cultural community and often experience confusion with identity and suffer social isolation (Lee & Hahm, 2012). In addition to heterosexism, it was reported that 82% of LGBT Asian-Americans face racism within the LGBT community (Szymanski & Sung, 2013). A combination of discrimination, internalized homophobia, social stigma, and conflicts between respecting cultural upbringing and establishing an LGBT identity often results in chronic stress and can exacerbate mental health complications (Lee & Hahm, 2012).

At one of the Lunar New Year family gatherings about 10 years ago, cousin Li pulled me aside and said, "I need to tell you something: I am gay. I told my parents last week." "I have known it for a long time," I responded. "For me, it makes no difference." I smiled. Cousin Li was quite relieved when he heard my reply. Li is considered the high achiever and model son in the Chen family; he graduated with the highest honors at every level of schooling, is a medical doctor with a promising career, and is always considerate, obedient, and compliant. He has never failed Auntie Mei's expectations. All he needed was a wife to make the picture perfect. Li's parents and the rest of the Chen family have chosen to stay in denial even to this day. This silence is more upsetting than any of the other family gossip. Family members continue to set up matchmaking dates for Li, claiming that all he needs is the "right" girl.

Cousin Chun has another story. He graduated with an advanced degree from an Ivy League college, and he is another high achiever in the family. However, being the first born of the eldest son, he carried a lot of guilt associated with being gay as he felt that he was unable produce descendants to carry on the family name ("xianghuo"). At that time, no one had even heard of the term "surrogacy." He fell into a deep depression and had several suicide attempts. No one in the family has ever talked about his sexual orientation or his mental illness; it is a taboo.

Models of Acculturation and Assimilation in Asian Culture

Asian immigrants worry that their American-born children might develop an accent if they converse in their native languages in the home. In order to help their children assimilate into society and make them "more acceptable as Americans" (Zia, 2000, p. 110), these parents choose to communicate with their children exclusively in English (Liu, 1998; Zia, 2000). The majority of literature written by Asian-Americans is focused on the themes of claiming an American, as opposed to an Asian, identity (Kim, 1990). Researchers explored this phenomenon and postulated that it constitutes accommodation, acculturation, assimilation, a colonized spirit, or a fervent attempt to "hide our ancestry" (Kim, 1990, p. 147).

Sue and Sue (2003) defined assimilated individuals as those who had completely adopted the norms of the dominant culture while excluding their membership in their own cultural group. Acculturation, also referred to as integration or biculturalism, referred to the preservation of Asian values while the individuals adapt to the dominant culture by acquiring necessary skills and values. The process of acculturating or assimilating the Asian-American identity is best explained by an ecological model that factors in the influences of acculturation, exposure to cultural differences, environmental negativism toward differences, personal styles of conflict resolution, and effects of group/social movements (Kim, 1981). This ecological model presents progressive and sequential stages of native Asian-American identity development: (1) ethnic awareness, (2) White identification, (3) awakening to sociopolitical consciousness, (4) redirection to Asian-American consciousness, and (5) incorporation (Kim, 1981).

In this first stage, ethnic awareness occurs when the child becomes aware of his/her Asian descent through interactions with the immediate family and relatives. The family is the primary reference group at this point in the child's developmental stage. Kim (1981) found a direct relationship between exposure and participation in Asian ethnic activities and the child's self-concept as Asian-American.

The second stage, White identification, occurs as the child's sphere of influence expands upon entering the school system. This stage is marked by a sudden onset of a strong sense of being different from others. The participants in her study associated this stage with feelings of isolation, guilt, inferiority, and alienation from self as the sense of being different carried a negative evaluation for them (Kim, 1981). Their coping mechanism was to separate themselves entirely from identifying with their Asian identity and assimilate themselves with the dominant White culture.

Next, awakening to sociopolitical consciousness is the most important stage in this model (Kim, 1981). At this stage, individuals acquire a renewed perspective on their identity in the society. It is marked by an awareness of their membership in a minority group and a gradual refamiliarization with the Asian culture. Awakening to sociopolitical consciousness is followed by redirection, a stage where individuals make the conscious decision to refocus themselves toward an Asian-American identity. This experience brings a sense of security, self-confidence, and self-esteem as individuals immerse themselves into the Asian-American experience.

Incorporation, the last stage in this process, exemplifies the final stage of identity evolution. At this stage, individuals are able to relate to people from other minority groups as well as from the dominant culture without losing their own Asian-American identity. Perhaps the idea of "incorporation" (Kim, 1981) is similar to the concept of "acculturation" or "biculturalism" (Sue & Sue, 2003), where preservation of Asian values blends with adopting the ways of the dominant culture.

Kim (1981) explained that these five stages are progressive and temporal. The amount of time spent in a given stage and the meanings attributed to the experience vary for each individual as they negotiate their paths along this continuum. Furthermore, some stages may be totally eliminated for Asian-Americans who emigrated from an Asian country to the United States, that is, non–native-born Asian-American. They are likely to skip the stage of ethnic awareness and plunge directly into the second stage of White identification. Depending on their time of entry into the country, this stage may take place when these immigrants are well into their adulthood years. Some immigrants might never reach the incorporation stage, due either to their strong affiliation with their Asian roots or to language, economic, or social limitations that inhibit their ability to balance and fuse together their dual identities as both Asians and Americans.

Meaning of Medicine and Well-Being

The most distinct difference in Asian health systems, compared to Western biomedicine, is the emphasis on maintaining balance among the elements of the physical body, the mind, the spirit, and the natural environment (Mulatu & Berry, 2001). In contrast to the biomedical view of health, which emphasizes the absence of pathophysiology (e.g., infections, wounds, high blood pressure) as chief markers of health, Asians/Asian-Americans may tend to consider the human physiology, mythology, superstition, and religious beliefs as factoring into the meaning of health and well-being. Thus, Asian healing practices aim to promote harmony and balance between physical, mental, social, and spiritual dimensions of the human experience.

Growing up in a household with multiple asthma sufferers meant that our diet was geared toward "warm" foods. It was rare to find "cold" foods such as watermelons, pears, daikon radishes, mung beans, or winter melons in our everyday meals. Instead, my grandmother would cook nourishing herbal soups to "warm" up the body in order to combat asthma attacks. Whenever I encountered severe bouts of asthma, a "Western doctor" would prescribe steroids for me, my grandmother would boil herbal soups all day long, and she and her sister would perform a religious ritual to ward off any ill spirits that might be impeding my health. The result? I combatted my poor health with doses of steroids, herbal soups, prayer sessions led by my grandmother and her sister, and shots of ash water concocted from mixing ashes of burnt talisman paper with water.

The conglomeration of health practices adopted by Asian families afforded an insight into Asian families' holistic worldview about health maintenance and restoration. Since these dimensions are interconnected and interdependent, it is not surprising to find multiple approaches working in tandem in an Asian household. Medicine and health treatments may include acupuncture, cupping, acupressure, and herbal treatments provided by a doctor of Chinese medicine, chiropractor, or acupuncturist. On the other hand, a religious or spiritual healer or spiritualist may offer prayers or cite mantras either to drive away unhealthy spirits that are impeding the patient's well-being or to accrue karma. The religion of Buddhism, practiced by many Asian-Americans, promotes beliefs about reincarnation and spiritual karma. More traditional Asians may attribute the reasons for their illnesses and sufferings to having not accumulated enough karma in their present or past lives.

When my mom found out that she had colon cancer five years ago, it was very difficult for her to accept it. "Why me? I have been eating healthy all my life," she said, but deep down, I knew what really crushed her was the belief that people who acquire a major illness like cancer must have done something wrong in the past, and it is a form of punishment. It took her a long time to make peace with herself. This fear was no less than the physical discomfort caused by her chemotherapy or the anxiety associated with the possible relapse.

Thus, Asians adopt both an internal locus of control over their health by their daily choices of diet and physical activities and an external locus of control by attributing illnesses and well-being to past lives and godly spirits.

In a collectivist, hierarchical, and patriarchal society, the caregiver role is usually awarded to the female members of the family, although the male family members make major decisions about health care. In traditional Asian-American families, the father is usually the first to be consulted in regard to health care decisions. The next in line is the oldest son, based on the assumption that the first male offspring has greater responsibility in the care of the immediate and extended family (Kramer, Kwong, Lee, & Chung, 2002).

Understanding family dynamics and worldviews of Asian-Americans in regard to health, medicine, and well-being will help to furnish health practitioners with a more culturally sensitive approach to health management. Recommendations that are worthwhile considerations to keep in mind while enabling the health and well-being of Asian-Americans (Constantine, Myers, Kindaichi, & Moore, 2004; Sue & Sue, 2003) include examining therapists' own worldviews and cultural biases to recognize ways that they may consciously or unconsciously interfere with their effectiveness; being aware of cultural differences between the therapist and the client, especially considering the collectivistic, hierarchical, and patriarchal orientation of Asian-Americans; building rapport by reassuring confidentiality; encouraging and supporting clients in sharing their beliefs about the etiology of their distress; listening attentively to clients' reports of their physical ailments and concerns, as Asians are more likely to describe physical symptoms rather than emotional/psychological distress; being open to clients' multifaceted approaches to restoring health and balance; assessing the client from multiple perspectives, including the individual, family, community, and societal influences on the problems/issues; investigating the strengths of the individual and the family; determining the hierarchical structure and communication patterns of the family; determining the way that caring, support, or affection is shown

within the family (e.g., among traditional Asians, providing for the needs of others is more important than verbalizing or showing affection); and assessing for possible acculturation/assimilation conflicts among different generations within the family.

Health-Seeking Behaviors and the Use of Mental Health Services

Mental health issues are highly stigmatized in the Asian-American culture (Li & Seidman, 2010). In a study with Asian-American students, researchers found that those who needed professional psychology help tend to avoid seeking assistance to avoid embarrassment, shame, and a "loss of face" (Shea & Yeh, 2008). According to an analysis of a national sample, Asian-Americans generally use mental health–related services 50% less than the general population (Abe-Kim et al., 2007). A similar trend prevails even among Asian-Americans diagnosed with mental illness (Lee, Martins, Keyes, & Lee, 2011), and especially women with mood disorders (Xu et al., 2011). Compared with other ethnic groups, Asian-Americans exhibit more negative attitudes regarding seeking help with mental health issues (Leong & Lau, 2001; Masuda & Bonne, 2011; Shea & Yeh, 2008; Snowden & Yamada, 2005), which can delay necessary treatments, prematurely terminate service, and prompt their seeking informal help from friends, family, and/or spiritual advisors (Spencer, Chen, Gee, Fabian, & Takeuchi, 2010). Cultural-specific factors associated with inconsistent and infrequent use of mental health services include acculturation level (Miller, Yang, Hui, Choi, & Lim, 2011), stigma associated with help-seeking outside of the family (Hall & Yee, 2012), resistance to self-disclosure and emotional expression during treatment, low English-language proficiency and mental health literacy (Spencer et al., 2010), and a lack of culturally and linguistically accommodating mental health services (Spencer et al., 2010; Xu et al., 2011). United States–born Asian-Americans were more likely to use alternative medicine compared to Asian-American immigrants in the realm of psychiatric health (Meyer, Zane, Cho, & Takeuchi, 2009).

Asian-Americans who immigrated to the United States later in life and who are therefore less acculturated to the United States use mental health services at lower rates than United States–born counterparts (Miller et al., 2011; Xi, 2014). At the same time, Asian-Americans born and raised in the United States are comparable to the general U.S. population in terms of their use of these services (Miller, 2011); they also exhibit more positive attitudes toward discussing personal problems with mental health professionals (Li, Friedman-Yakoobian, Min, Granato, & Seidman, 2013).

To avoid disgracing their families, Asian-Americans are often reluctant to admit or acknowledge psychological problems (Hall & Yee, 2012). In fact, seeking mental health services has been considered to indicate family inadequacy and dysfunction, as well as failed parenting. Instead, Asian-Americans tend to prefer to resolve these problems within the family or by seeking informal treatment within community networks (Kim & Omizo, 2003). Decisions regarding help-seeking, treatment, and follow-up care typically involve not only the person seeking treatment, but also his or her entire family (Park, 2012; Yang, Wonpat-Borja, Opler, & Corcoran, 2010).

Traditional mental health treatment methods rely heavily on open, direct verbal communication. By contrast, Asian ways of communication tend to be indirect, implicative, and somewhat ambiguous, especially when expressing disagreement; they also value emotional restraint in order to prevent conflicts and preserve in-group harmony (Hall, Hong, Zane, & Meyer, 2011). For Asian-Americans with poor English proficiency and mental health literacy, a lack of bilingual professionals in the United States prevents their seeking timely, consistent treatment and turns them to informal services (Gilmer et al., 2009; Spencer, 2010). Instead of using active coping strategies and seeking help, Asian cultures promote avoidance and endurance when one faces difficulty, which can be achieved by concealing the problem, suppressing individual needs, and focusing on the greater good of the group (Hall et al., 2011).

To increase Asian-Americans' use of mental health services, especially among those less acculturated to the United States, more efforts should focus on community outreach and on providing culturally and linguistically prepared services via modalities that allow for nonverbal expression (Lee et al., 2011). Mental health professionals are encouraged to be culturally sensitive when facing a patient's and/or a family's resistance to treatment; instead of antagonizing these patients and their families, mental health care professionals should meet such resistance with empathy and cultural sensitivity (Li et al., 2014).

Meaning and Function of Music

Sacred Music

Music has always been essential and inseparable from Asian religious practice. For example, in Buddhism, "mantras" or *"nianfo"* are chants commonly used by Buddhists in daily practice for the purpose of protecting themselves from evil spirits, purifying negative karma, and accumulating positive energy (Yun, 2006). The mantra is often chanted in stepwise melodic lines, accompanied by simple instrumentation such as temple blocks, finger cymbal/*tingsha,* bells, and singing/bell bowls. *Nianfo,* on the other hand, is the repetitive recitation of the Amitabha Buddha's name *(Na-mo-e-mi-tio-fo).* The recitations are usually chanted in Sanskrit, which is the liturgical language of Buddhism originating from India. Older generations who are not ready to immerse themselves in mainstream American music often find connections with this new world via the shared musical experience in routine religious practice through hymns or chants.

Secular Music

Like those of most Americans, the musical tastes of younger-generation Asian-Americans are heavily influenced by their parents. These youngsters grew up listening to music from their parents' generation and countries of origin. In addition to mainstream American music, they also follow the trends of Asian popular music fervently.

Due to the globalization of the music industries, Asian popular music has been dominated by Westernized music styles as evidenced by the use of hip-hop, R&B, electro, and rap styles with Asian lyrics. The coexistence of multiple languages in one song, for example, English and Japanese, is commonly found in song lyrics. In recent years, many artists/composers have incorporated traditional elements into their creations to enhance the Asian cultural character. For example, incorporating traditional Chinese instruments or setting Western pop music styles to traditional poems adds new flavors by imbuing Western musical tonality with Asian elements.

The popularity of K-pop, or Korean popular music, has noticeably increased lately. Due to media technology and internet services, K-pop has managed to reach the global audience almost overnight. For example, South Korean rapper Psy's "Gangnam Style" music video received more than 300 million hits on YouTube and was named the most liked video in the history of YouTube. The song was ranked number one in the iTunes Music Store in 31 countries (Sonicscape, 2012). Although the success of "Gangnam Style" enhances the visibility of Asian artists and demonstrates the readiness of Asian music productions for the global stage, its impact on enforcing the image of Asians is yet to be determined. The distorted portrait of the peculiar upper-class lifestyle and the comic acts and dance moves may lead to another stereotypical view of Asian-Americans. I would like to see more information about music and genres.

Conclusion

The Asian-American community not only has been the fastest-growing minority group in the United States during the past 10 years, but also is one of the most diverse in the country. Collectivist, hierarchical, and patriarchal systems are the characteristics of the Asian society, with great emphasis placed on group interest, harmony, and respect. Indirect and nonassertive forms of communication are viewed to be proper for Asian-Americans as a way to show respect, "save face," and not offend others. The stereotype of being the model minority brings forth many discriminatory discourses for many years. The holistic approach to health and well-being implies that Asian-Americans are more likely to embrace mainstream and alternative/complementary medicine with equal valor. Continual emigration trends from across the Pacific Ocean will continue to shape and transform the geographical landscape and musical soundscape of the Asian-American community.

References

Abe-Kim, J., Takeuchi, D., Hong, S., Zane, N., Sue, S., Spencer, M., ... & Alegría, M. (2007). Use of mental health–related services among immigrants and United States–born Asian-Americans: Results from the national Latino and Asian-American study. *American Journal of Public Health, 97*(1), 91–98. doi:10.2105/AJPH.2006.098541

Asian-American Health Initiative. (2005). *Who are Asian-Americans?* Retrieved from http://www.aahiinfo.org/english/asianAmericans.php#myth

Central Intelligence Agency. (2012). *The world factbook.* Central Intelligence Agency. Retrieved from https://www.cia.gov/library/publications/the-world-factbook/fields/2028.html

Chang, T., & Subramaniam, P. R. (2008). Asian and Pacific Islander American men's help-seeking: Cultural values and beliefs, gender roles, and racial stereotypes. *International Journal of Men's Health, 7*(2), 121–136. doi:10.3149/jmh.0702.121

Chiang, J., Chow, A., Chan, R., Law, C., & Chen, E. (2005). Pathway to care for patients with first-episode psychosis in Hong Kong. *Hong Kong Journal of Psychiatry, 15,* 18–22. Retrieved from http://easap.asia/journal_file/0501_V15N1_p18.pdf

Chiroro, P., & Valentine, T. (1995). An investigation of the contact hypothesis of the own-race bias in face recognition. *The Quarterly Journal of Experimental Psychology, 48A,* 879–894. doi:10.1080/14640749508401421

Constantine, M. G., Myers, L. J., Kindaichi, M., & Moore, J. L. (2004). Exploring indigenous mental health practices: The roles of healers and helpers in promoting well-being in people of color. *Counseling and Values, 48,* 110–125. doi:10.1002/j.2161-007X.2004.tb00238.x

Evans, P. E., & McConnell, A. R. (2003). Do racial minorities respond in the same way to mainstream beauty standards? Social comparison processes in Asian, Black, and White women. *Self and Identity, 2,* 153–167. doi:10.1080/15298860309030

Ferguson, D. P., Rhodes, G., Lee, K., & Sriram, N. (2001). "They all look alike to me": Prejudice and cross-race face recognition. *British Journal of Psychology, 92*(4), 567–577. doi:10.1348/000712601162347

Gilmer, T. P., Ojeda, V. D., Barrio, C., Fuentes, D., Garcia, P., Lanouette, N. M., & Lee, K. C. (2009). Adherence to antipsychotics among Latinos and Asians with schizophrenia and limited English proficiency. *Psychiatric Services, 60*(2), 175–182. doi:10.1176/appi.ps.60.2.175

Golden, D. (2012, February). Harvard targeted in U.S. Asian-American discrimination probe. *Bloomberg News.* Retrieved from http://www.bloomberg.com/news/2012-02-02/harvard-targeted-in-u-s-asian-american-discrimination-probe.html

Gudykunst, W. B. (2001). *Asian-American ethnicity and communication.* Thousand Oaks, CA: SAGE.

Hall, G. C., Hong, J. J., Zane, N. W. S., & Meyer, O. L. (2011). Culturally-competent treatments for Asian-Americans: The relevance of mindfulness and acceptance-based psychotherapies. *Clinical Psychology: Science and Practice, 18,* 215–231. doi:10.1111/j.1468-2850.2011.01253.x

Hall, G. C. N., & Yee, A. (2012). U.S. mental health policy: Addressing the neglect of Asian-Americans. *Asian-American Journal of Psychology, 3*(3), 181–193. doi:10.1037/a0029950

Ho, D. Y-F. (1976). On the concept of face. *American Journal of Sociology, 81*(4), 867–884.

Hoeffel, E. M., Rastogi, S., Kim, M. O., & Shahid, H. (2012). *The Asian Population: 2010.* United States Census Bureau. Retrieved from http://2010.census.gov/news/press-kits/summary-file-1.html

Hofstede, G. (1991). *Cultures and organizations.* London, UK: McGraw-Hill.

Hofstede, G., & Bond, M. H. (1988). The Confucius connection: From cultural roots to economic growth. *Organizational Dynamics, 16*(4), 5–21. doi:10.1016/0090-2616(88)90009-5

Hu, A. (1989). Asian-Americans: Model minority or double minority? *Amerasia Journal, 15*(1), 243–257. Retrieved from http://aascpress.metapress.com.proxy.lib.uiowa.edu/content/e032240687706472/fulltext.pdf

Isono, M., Watkins, P. L., & Lian, E. L. (2009). Bon bon fatty girl: A qualitative exploration of weight bias in Singapore. In E. Rothblum & S. Solovay (Eds.), *The fat studies reader* (pp. 127–138). New York, NY: New York University Press.

Jandt, F. E. (2009). *An introduction to intercultural communication: Identities in a global community* (6th ed.). Thousand Oaks, CA: SAGE.

Kawamura, K. (2002). Asian-American body images. In T. F. Cash & T. Pruzinsky (Eds.), *Body image: A handbook of theory, research, and clinical practice* (pp. 243–249). New York, NY: Guilford Press.

Kim, B. S. K., & Omizo, M. M. (2003). Asian cultural values, attitudes toward seeking professional psychological help, and willingness to see a counselor. *The Counseling Psychologist, 31,* 343–361. doi:10.1177/0011000003031003008

Kim, E. H. (1990). Defining Asian-American realities through literature. In A. R. JanMohamed & D. Lloyd (Eds.), *The nature and context of minority discourse.* New York, NY: Oxford University Press.

Kim, J. (1981). *Processes of Asian-American identity development: A study of Japanese American women's perceptions of their struggle to achieve positive identities as Americans of Asian ancestry.* Unpublished doctoral dissertation. University of Massachusetts, Boston, MA.

Kosmin, B. A., & Keysar, A. (2009). *American religious identification survey: Summary report.* Hartford, CT: Trinity College.

Kramer, E. J., Kwong, K., Lee, E., & Chung, H. (2002). Cultural factors influencing the mental health of Asian-Americans. *The Western Journal of Medicine, 176*(4), 227–231. Retrieved from http://www.ncbi.nlm.nih.gov/pmc/articles/PMC1071736/pdf/wjm17600227.pdf

Lau, A. S. M., Lum, S. K., Chronister, K. M., & Forrest, L. (2006). Asian-American college women's body image: A pilot study. *Cultural Diversity and Ethnic Minority Psychology, 12,* 259–274. doi:10.1037/1099-9809.12.2.259

Lee, J., & Hahm, H. C. (2012). HIV risk, substance use, and suicidal behaviors among Asian-American lesbian and bisexual women. *AIDS Education and Prevention, 26*(6), 549–563.

Lee, S. J. (1996). *Unraveling the "Model Minority" stereotype: Listening to Asian American youth.* New York, NY: Teachers College Press.

Lee, S. Y., Martins, S. S., Keyes, K. M., & Lee, H. B. (2011). Mental health service use by persons of Asian ancestry with DSM-IV mental disorders in the United States. *Psychiatric Services, 62,* 1180–1186. doi:10.1176/appi.ps.62.10.1180

Leong, F. T. L., & Lau, A. S. L. (2001). Barriers to providing effective mental health services to Asian-Americans. *Mental Health Services Research, 3,* 201–214. doi:10.1023/A:1013177014788

Lewin, T. (2008, June 10). Report takes aim at "model minority" stereotype of Asian-American students. *The New York Times.* Retrieved from http://www.nytimes.com/2008/06/10/education/10asians.html?_r=0

Li, H., Friedman-Yakoobian, M., Min, G., Granato, A. G., & Seidman, L. J. (2013). Working with Asian-American youth at clinical high risk for psychosis: A case illustration. *Journal of Nervous and Mental Disease, 201*(6), 484–489. doi:10.1097/NMD.0b013e3182948084

Li, H., & Seidman, L. (2010). Engaging Asian-American youth and their families in quality mental health services. *Asian Journal of Psychiatry, 3*(4), 169–172. doi:10.1016/j.ajp.2010.08.008

Liu, C. H., Murakami, J., Eap, S., & Hall, G. C. N. (2009). Who are Asian-Americans? An overview of history, immigration, and communities. In N. Tewari & A. Alvarez (Eds.), *Asian-American psychology: Current perspectives* (pp. 1 – 30). New York, NY: Erlbaum.

Liu, E. (1998). *The accidental Asian: Notes of a native speaker.* New York, NY: Random House, Inc.

Mac, J. (2009). *Myths and mirrors: Real challenges facing Asian-American students. Japanese American Citizens League.* Retrieved from http://www.jacl.org/leadership/documents/MythsandMirrorsFinal.pdf

Masuda, A., & Boone, M. S. (2011). Mental health stigma, self-concealment, and help-seeking attitudes among Asian-American and European-American college students with no help-seeking experience. *International Journal of Advanced Counseling, 33*(4), 266–279. doi:10.1007/s10447-011-9129-1

Masuda, A., Le, J., & Cohen, L. L. (2014). The Role of Disordered-Eating Cognitions and Psychological Flexibility on Distress in Asian-American and European-American College Females in the United States. *International Journal of Advanced Counselling, 36,* 30–42. doi:10.1007/s10447-013-9188-6

Meyer, O. L., Zane, N. W., Cho, Y. I., & Takeuchi, D. T. (2009). Use of specialty mental health services by Asian-Americans with psychiatric disorders. *Journal of Consulting and Clinical Psychology, 77*(5), 1000–1005. doi:10.1037/a0017065

Miller, M. J., Yang, M., Hui, K., Choi, N-Y., & Lim, R. H. (2011). Acculturation, enculturation, and Asian-American college students' mental health and attitudes toward seeking professional psychological help. *Journal of Counseling Psychology, 58,* 346–357. doi:10.1037/a0023636

Mintz, L. B., & Kashubeck, S. (1999). Body image and disordered eating among Asian American and Caucasian college students. *Psychology of Women Quarterly, 23*(4), 781–796. doi:10.1111/j.1471-6402.1999.tb00397.x

Mojaverian, T., Hashimoto, T., & Kim, H. S. (2013). Cultural differences in professional Help-seeking: A comparison of Japan and the U.S. *Frontiers in Psychology, 3,* 1–8. doi:10.3389/fpsyg.2012.00615

Mulatu, M. S., & Berry, J. W. (2001). Health care practice in a multicultural context: Western and non-Western assumptions. In S. S. Kazarian & D. R. Evans (Eds.), *Handbook of cultural health psychology* (pp. 45–61). Waltham, MA: Academic Press.

Nakanishi, D. T. (1989). A quota on excellence? The Asian-American admissions debate. *Change: The Magazine of Higher Learning, 21*(6), 39–47. doi:10.1080/00091383.1989.9937604

Ni, P. (2010). Asian-Americans and emotional intelligence. *Asian Week: The Voice of Asian-America.* Retrieved from http://andersonservices.com/2011/05/asian-american-and-emotional-intelligence/

Nouri, M., Hill, L. G., & Orrell-Valentec, J. K. (2011). Media exposure, internalization of the thin ideal, and body dissatisfaction: Comparing Asian-American and European-American college females. *Body Image 8*(4), 366–372. doi:10.1016/j.bodyim.2011.05.008

Ohnishi, H., Ibrahim, F. A., & Grzegorek, J. (2006). Intersection of identities: Counseling lesbian, gay, bisexual, and transgender Asian-Americans. *Journal of LGBT Issues in Counseling, 1,* 77–94. doi:10.1300/J462v01n03_06

Park, M. (2012). Filial piety and parental responsibility: An interpretive phenomenological study of family caregiving for a person with mental illness among Korean immigrants. *BMC Nursing, 11.* Retrieved from http://www.biomedcentral.com/1472-6955/11/28

Pew Research Center. (2012). Asian-Americans: A mosaic of faiths. Retrieved from http://www.pewforum.org/2012/07/19/asian-americans-a-mosaic-of-faiths-overview/

Phan, T., & Tylka, T. L. (2006). Exploring a model and moderators of disordered eating with Asian-American college women. *Journal of Counseling Psychology, 53*(1), 36–47. doi:10.1037/0022-0167.53.1.36

Rogers, S. J., & Amato, P. R. (2000). Have changes in gender relations affected marital quality? *Social Forces, 79*(2), 731–753. doi:10.1093/sf/79.2.731

Ryder, A. G., Bean, G., & Dion, K. L. (2000). Caregiver responses to symptoms of first-onset psychosis: A comparative study of Chinese- and Euro-Canadian families. *Transcultural Psychiatry, 37*(2), 225–236. doi:10.1177/136346150003700207

Sabik, N. J., Cole, E. R., & Ward, L. M. (2010). Are all minority women equally buffered from negative body image? Intra-ethnic moderators of the buffering hypothesis. *Psychology of Women Quarterly, 34*(2), 139–151. doi:10.1111/j.1471-6402.2010.01557.x

Schoenborn, C. A., & Heyman, K. M. (2009, July). Health characteristics of adults aged 55 years and over: United States, 2004–2007. *National Health Statistics Reports, 16*, 1–32. Retrieved from http://198.246.124.22/nchs/data/nhsr/nhsr016.pdf

Shah, H. (2003). "Asian culture" and Asian-American identities in the television and film industries of the United States. *Studies in Media & Information Literacy Education, 3*(3), 1–10. doi:10.3138/sim.3.3.002

Shea, M., & Yeh, C. J. (2008). Asian-American students' cultural values, stigma, and relational self-construal: Correlates of attitudes toward professional help-seeking. *Journal of Mental Health Counseling, 30*(2), 157–172.

Sheu, H. B., & Fukuyama, M. A. (2007). Counseling international students from East Asia. In H. D. Singaravelu & M. Pope (Eds.). *A handbook for counseling international students in the United States* (pp. 173–194). Alexandria, VA: American Counseling Association.

Skeate, A., Jackson, C., Birchwood, M., & Jones, C. (2002). Duration of untreated psychosis and pathways to care in first-episode psychosis: Investigation of help-seeking behavior in primary care. *The British Journal of Psychiatry, 181*, 73–77. doi:10.1192/bjp.181.43.s73

Smart, R., & Tsong, Y. (2014, April 7). Weight, body dissatisfaction, and disordered eating: Asian-American women's perspectives. *Asian-American Journal of Psychology.* Advance online publication. Retrieved from doi:10.1037/a0035599

Snowden, L. R., & Yamada, A-M. (2005). Cultural differences in access to care. *Annual Review of Clinical Psychology, 1*, 143–66. doi:10.1146/annurev.clinpsy.1.102803.143846

Sonicscape. (2012, September 6). *CFP: K-pop politics: digital mediation and global fandom.* Retrieved from http://interasiapop.org/

Spencer, M. S., Chen, J., Gee, G. C., Fabian, C. G., & Takeuchi, D. T. (2010). Discrimination and mental health–related service use in a national study of Asian-Americans. *American Journal of Public Health, 100*(12), 2410–2417. doi:10.2105/AJPH.2009.176321

Spencer-Rodgers, J., Peng, K., & Wang, L. (2010). Dialecticism and the cooccurrence of positive and negative emotions across cultures. *Journal of Cross-Cultural Psychology, 41*(1), 109–115. doi:10.1177/0022022109349508

Sue, D. W., Bucceri, J., Lin, A. I., Nadal, K. L., & Torino, G. C. (2009). Racial microaggressions and the Asian-American experience. *Asian-American Journal of Psychology, S*(1), 88–101. doi:10.1037/1948-1985.S.1.88

Sue, D. W., & Sue, D. (2003). *Counseling the culturally diverse: Theory and practice* (4th ed.). Hoboken, NJ: John Wiley & Sons.

Szymanski, D. M., & Sung, M. R. (2013). Asian cultural values, internalized Heterosexism, and sexual orientation disclosure among Asian-American sexual minority persons. *Journal of LGBT Issues in Counseling, 7,* 257–273. doi:10.1080/15538605.2013.812930

Takeuchi, D., Zane, N., Hong, S., Chae, D., Gong, F., Gee, G., ... & Alegría, M. (2007). Immigration-related factors and mental disorders among Asian-Americans. *American Journal of Public Health, 97*(1), 84–90. doi:10.2105/AJPH.2006.088401

Ting, J. Y., & Hwang, W. C. (2009). Cultural influences on help-seeking attitudes in Asian-American students. *American Journal of Orthopsychiatry, 79*(1), 125–132. doi:10.1037/a0015394

U.S. Department of Commerce. (2012, March). *Profile America facts for features: Asian/Pacific American Heritage Month: May 2012.* Retrieved from http://www.census.gov/newsroom/releases/pdf/cb12ff09_asian.pdf

Walker-Moffat, W. (1995). *The other side of the Asian-American success story.* San Francisco, CA: Jossey-Bass Inc.

Wang, J., Leu, J., & Shoda, Y. (2011). When the seemingly innocuous "stings": Racial microaggressions and their emotional consequences. *Personality and Social Psychology Bulletin, 37*(2), 1666–1678. doi:10.1177/0146167211416130

Xu, Y., Okuda, M., Hser, Y-I., Hasin, D., Liu, S-M., Grant, B. F., & Blanco, C. (2011). Twelve-month prevalence of psychiatric disorders and treatment-seeking among Asian-Americans/Pacific Islanders in the United States: Results from the National Epidemiological Survey on Alcohol and Related Conditions. *Journal of Psychiatric Research, 45*, 910–918. doi:10.1016/j.jpsychires.2010.12.009

Yang, L. H., Wonpat-Borja, A. J, Opler, M. G., & Corcoran, C. M. (2010). Potential stigma associated with inclusion of the psychosis risk syndrome in the DSM-V: An empirical question. *Schizophrenia Research. 120*, 42–48. doi:10.1016/j.schres.2010.03.012

Yates, A., Edman, J., & Aruguete, M. (2004). Ethnic differences in BMI and body/self-dissatisfaction among Whites, Asian subgroups, Pacific Islanders, and African-Americans. *Journal of Adolescent Health, 34*(4), 300–307. doi:10.1016/j.jadohealth.2003.07.014

Yoo, H. C., & Castro, K. S. (2011). Does nativity status matter in the relationship between perceived racism and academic performance of Asian-American college students? *Journal of College Student Development, 52*(2), 234–245. doi:10.1353/csd.2011.0031

Yun, H. (2006). *Sounds of the Dharma: Buddhism and music.* Taipei, Taiwan: Buddha's Light.

Zia, H. (2000). *Asian-American dreams: The emergence of an American people.* New York, NY: Farrar, Straus, and Giroux.

Chapter 6

MUSIC THERAPY IN THE
SOUTH ASIAN–AMERICAN DIASPORA

Sangeeta Swamy

"Where are you from?" It was a phrase I must have heard thousands of times as a young girl growing up in southern Illinois. I scrunched my toes inside my tennis shoes, drawing circles in the dirt with my feet. "India," I said, anticipating the next string of questions, the quizzical looks and hesitations that inevitably followed. "What tribe are you from?" "Were you born here?" "Have you ever gone back?" "Don't you read the Bible?"

Born in South India and immigrating with my family to the United States at six months of age, I grew up as a second-generation Indian-American in a middle-class, Hindu family. Because I was raised in a small, conservative, Midwestern, university town, it took me a long time, however, to fully embrace my Indian heritage, facing microaggressions on a regular basis, feeling excluded, and being one of only a few children of color in my school. I played European classical music and American folk songs on the violin, wore jeans and t-shirts, and spoke with an American accent. I refused to speak Tamil, my family's native language, or learn Karnatic music, an elaborate, South Indian classical genre. Raised as a Brahmin, a member of the most privileged caste in India, I was imprinted with values of art, music, education, and spirituality. However, while I drove with my family to Hindu temples hours away for religious rituals, I understood little about the social and cultural complexities of my native country.

As I began my studies in music therapy and transpersonal psychology in graduate school, I found myself a victim of overt racism and started to question my allegiance to American and European values. In fact, at the time, I could not tolerate the European classical music that I had spent my life mastering. While I was initially skeptical of psychology, I began to embrace it through my program, delving into self-reflection and self-inquiry and experiencing psychotherapy and music therapy for the first time. However, as a music therapist, I soon faced a dilemma. I realized that the music therapy in which I was trained was not able to address the internal ethnic conflict I was experiencing and would not necessarily be appropriate for South Asian populations.

On multiple trips to India to reclaim my heritage, I finally embraced yoga, Vipassana meditation, and Indian classical music and began to address the internalized racism buried deep in my psyche. I learned to speak my mother tongue and opened my heart to the profound spirituality and beauty of the land of my ancestors. However, as I came out as bisexual and connected with queer South Asian communities around the United States, I felt disheartened at the homophobia within my native land. I met South Asians from Muslim, Caribbean, and many other backgrounds and, for the first time, realized how

narrow my view of India was. Once, as I was practicing Tamil phrases that I had learned from my family, a group of Indian friends began poking fun at me. "Ohhhh!" they laughed. "You're speaking Brahmin Tamil!" While I thought I was speaking a universal form of Tamil, my friend explained that I was using a Brahmin dialect, often interpreted as elite. I was also shocked to discover that many Brahmins had historically oppressed and discriminated against lower caste groups. As a result, I committed myself to acknowledging the caste, educational, middle-class and Hindu privileges I had inherited, while simultaneously standing up to the sexism, homophobia, and hetero-normative expectations within my ethnic community. Over time, I learned to feel pride in my caste and honor the multiple voices and identities within myself. I realized that my ethnic identity is a creative, dialectical, and fluid process, ever changing and evolving based on various contexts.

While South Asians do not typically seek out therapy, my music therapy colleagues working with South Asian clients in early intervention, special education, and medical settings began to approach me for advice. I knew from personal experience that many South Asian community members were in need of culturally competent services, with struggles around sexual abuse, depression, anxiety, posttraumatic stress, alcoholism, domestic violence, and coming out as lesbian, gay, bisexual, or transgender, among others. Unable to find any music therapy literature on this population, I began to search for ways to contextualize music therapy for South Asians in the United States.

In my doctoral study with Indian adults (2011), I researched Culturally Centered Music and Imagery (CCMI), an approach I developed that integrates context, identity, musical structure, and musical meaning with supportive and re-educative music and imagery. Using qualitative methodology, I inquired into how Hindu adults living in the United States experienced their ethnic identity, interviewing and facilitating several Culturally Centered Music and Imagery sessions for five cisgender men and women. I then created supportive and re-educative listening programs by analyzing the purpose, role, and musical structure of several different Indian genres of music, taking into consideration each participant's religion, caste, class, regional identity, and personal musical preferences. While Indian music was not necessarily the preferred listening choice of participants, I found that it served an important purpose in stimulating identity-based images and narratives. As participants discussed and reflected on the meaning of their images and responses to the music, I found that they were better able to understand and reconcile internal conflicts

65

related to their ethnic identity. CCMI also served as a prototype for an ethnic identity assessment that could capture fluidly nonlinear, creative, and aesthetic experiences that traditional identity models could not. As a result of my research and personal experiences, I began to offer support, wellness, and psycho-education to lesbian, gay, bisexual, and transgender South Asians around the country, use Culturally Centered Music and Imagery with young immigrants struggling with culture shock, and provide community music therapy to young South Asian children. It is through these professional and personal experiences, self-reflection, and the support of literature, theories, and research that I present this chapter.

Introduction

South Asians are one of the most diverse and fastest-growing immigrant groups in the United States, reaching a population of close to four million people (United States Census, 2012). South Asian immigrants in the United States originate from India, Pakistan, Bangladesh, Sri Lanka, Bhutan, Nepal, and the Maldives (South Asian Association for Regional Cooperation, 1985). In addition, some South Asians immigrate to the United States as residents of England, as well as from South Africa, Malawi, Jamaica, Fiji, Guyana, Dubai, Uganda, Ghana, and Trinidad, where they settled as indentured servants generations ago (Baptiste, 2005, p. 347). Today, South Asians emigrate to the United States voluntarily for economic opportunities or to join family members (Giri, 2005; Inman & Tummala-Narra, 2010). (Please refer to the section on acculturation for more details on immigration.)

However, because it is not possible to give justice to immigrants from all of these countries within the scope of this paper, this chapter will focus primarily on those with origins on the Indian subcontinent. This includes India, Pakistan, and Bangladesh, whose natives comprise the majority of South Asians in the United States. Although they share a similar ethnicity, each country is composed of different religions, customs, and histories. Because of its prime location for trade and rich resources, the Indian subcontinent also shares a colonial history, having been invaded, taken over, and colonized by other countries many times over the past 400 years (Almeida, 2005).

The role of colonization is a crucial piece in understanding and successfully working with South Asians. Because its impact on the current economy, well-being, and South Asian consciousness cannot be underestimated, I will briefly describe the history of British colonization and independence on the Indian subcontinent. From the mid–18th through mid–20th centuries, the British Empire colonized the Indian subcontinent, levying heavy taxes upon Indian farmers; depleting the country of resources such as spices, teas, and textiles; and contributing to famines and mass starvation (Mukherjee, 2011). Christian missionaries also unsuccessfully attempted a mass conversion of Indians to Christianity and created schools taught only in English (Allender, 2003). The

British called Indians derogatory terms, such as "coolies" (Dubois, 2012), and bred animosity and violence between Hindus and Muslims (Larson, 2014; Wilkinson, 2015). Finally, after many years of civil disobedience and nonviolent resistance by Mahatma Gandhi and his followers, India was finally granted independence in 1947. However, during this period of time known as "partition," religious conflict led to the division of India into what is now known as India, Pakistan, and Bangladesh (the latter two formerly being West and East Pakistan, respectively). Forced migration across the new borders led to the loss of land and property and contributed to tension and mass bloodshed between Muslims and Hindus. While independence occurred over 60 years ago, every South Asian with family from the Indian subcontinent will be familiar with a colonial narrative and have experienced its effects within their extended family.

Since there is such diversity within the South Asian population, I will be using a few different terms in addition to naming individual countries to describe the various South Asian populations and communities in this chapter. These include the Indian subcontinent, consisting of India, Pakistan, and Bangladesh; South Asia, which refers the larger geographical region; the South Asian diaspora, which refers to pockets of self-identified South Asians living elsewhere who maintain some form of connection to their original homeland; and the South Asian–American diaspora, referring to South Asians living in the United States. It should be noted that while originally the term "diaspora" referred only to displaced ethnic groups, such as Jews leaving in exile and settling in disperse locations around the word, the word "diaspora" has taken on new meaning in the postcolonial age. "Diaspora" also refers to a wide range of groups, such as "political refugees, alien residents, guest workers, immigrants, expellees, racial and ethnic minorities, overseas communities" and other identities (Lal, Saffron, & Sahoo, 2013; Shuval, 2000, pp. 40–41).

Worldview

When speaking about gender roles, worldviews, and other general topics within the South Asian diaspora, it is important to avoid cultural stereotypes. Cultural stereotypes, even with the intent of understanding, can be misleading and cause misdiagnoses or inaccurate assessments. I am reminded of a music and movement class for adults with cancer that I co-led when I was a graduate intern. One client I will call "Mr. Xiao" was a married, heterosexual, Chinese man in his 30s who did not speak much English. Literature from my multicultural psychology course at the time (Garcia-Preto, Giordano, & McGoldrick, 2005; Sue & Sue, 2013) suggested that Asians were indirect and restrained in expressing their emotions to outsiders, responding better to structured and solution-focused therapy. Based on this information, I anticipated that Mr. Xiao might be uncomfortable with some of the open-ended expressive arts techniques of free movement and sound improvisation that my coleader had prepared. To my surprise, however, he embraced it wholeheartedly, making silly animal sounds and crawling around on the floor in various configurations. Whether it was his individual personality, the effect of a life-threatening diagnosis, or other unknown factors that allowed him try something new, it became obvious that generalizing values for an entire culture of people, even with the intent of multicultural understanding, was dangerous territory.

Instead of thinking of culture as fixed or concrete, theorists recommend considering culture as a fluid, changing, and cocreated phenomenon (Stige, 2002). Psychologist Jose Stevens (1989) goes further to suggest that we are influenced or conditioned by various social and cultural narratives, comparing this process to children who are imprinted with values from their parents. This includes norms, values, and expectations around behavior and social interactions that we learn implicitly and explicitly from the culture, society, and environment in which we were raised. Over time, however, each individual has the choice to embrace, reject, or shed these cultural norms to varying degrees. Therefore, the following description of worldviews in the South Asian diaspora is meant as an overview, not a generalization, of common influences and norms with which members of this group contend.

Collectivism

South Asians are heavily influenced by a collective mindset and are encouraged to rely on extended family and neighbors for support and community. This can manifest as a sense of connection to others that overrides the development of an autonomous self (Almeida, 2005; Baptiste, 2005; Nath, 2005). For instance, South Asian teenagers may be expected to consider the needs of their whole family rather than their individual interests in choosing a career. It is also common for South Asian immigrants to make spontaneous visits to each other's homes and spend free time together rather than alone.

In my research with Indian adults, I found that participants experienced this collective norm in varying ways, despite similar levels of education and years spent living in the United States (Swamy, 2011). In one example, "Sarav," a 36-year-old, gay male, was reminded about how difficult it was to move from a collectivist to an individualistic society during an imagery session. While he described the music of Bach as beautiful and touching, it reminded him of his first Christmas after immigrating to the United States 11 years before. "It was a *very* difficult time because I thought it would be—we are friends and caring and stuff. Christmas comes and Thanksgiving comes and people don't invite me to anything and you're alone. And it's not what I grew up with. [...] If we know of a friend who is alone, we'll invite him, we'll never let him go hungry or be alone, that's our culture" (2011, p. 201).

In contrast, "Siddarth," a 37-year-old heterosexual immigrant from South India, completely rejected the collective norm in which he was raised. He preferred being alone, having felt at home in the Northeast from the moment he arrived 13 years previously. For him, listening to European classical music

stimulated positive images of freedom, openness, space, and being alone with nature and the universe. In fact, he complained about the collective norm in India and preferred living in the United States, where he was assured of not getting any unannounced visitors. "[In America], if I feel down or depressed, I can go and just sit and stare into outer space for three hours on end. I can't do that back in India without my family constantly pestering me" (Swamy, 2011, p. 181). "That's another good thing about the U.S.—very rarely do people drop by unannounced!" (p. 167).

Nonviolence

Nonviolence, karma, and dharma are also prominent cultural and spiritual influences in many South Asian communities (Almeida, 2005). Nonviolence refers to the Hindu, Jain, and Buddhist principle of *ahisma,* or the sacredness of all living things. Mahatma Gandhi, for instance, was famous for using nonviolence, along with civil disobedience, in the struggle for Indian independence. In 1930, for instance, Indians were forced to pay the British a hefty tax for using natural resources on their own land, including salt-making from Indian water sources. In a heroic act of civil disobedience, Gandhi and tens of thousands of Indians marched to the sea to break British law and produce their own salt. In response, British guards violently beat protesters with clubs and threw them in jail (Gandhi, 2001; Weber, 2002). Although they were defenseless, Gandhi and his followers refused to fight back out of *ahisma* and set up medical stations to care for the wounded. It was a powerful historical event that would go down in history and influence South Asian attitudes for decades to come, as well as inspire Martin Luther King's strategy in the battle for civil rights in the United States. Today, nonviolence is often practiced as an attitude, with many South Asians choosing vegetarianism and peaceful resolution of conflict as an expression of nonviolence.

Karma

Karma is the concept of destiny, a belief that everything, every action, will have a consequence, either in this life or in the next reincarnation of the soul. In fact, some South Asians believe that mental illness or disabilities are due to wrongdoing from a previous life (Gabel, 2004). In one ethnographic study of Hindu families living in the midwestern United States, a mother used the concepts of karma and past lives to explain why she had a child with disabilities. "I think she was my mother in a previous life, and now she comes back to give to me the problems I gave to her. [...] She is teaching me the lessons I did not learn in my previous body" (Gabel, 2004, p. 19). In another ethnographic study in the state of Orissa, a blind widower who had lost her daughter and husband believed that her suffering was caused by sins from a previous life. "I cannot say which sin I have committed in life, but I am suffering now because I have done something wrong in one of my births" (Schweder, 1991, p. 159). More acculturated or secular South Asians in the United States, however, may reject the idea of karma altogether or interpret and make meaning out of karma in their own way.

Dharma

While there are various definitions of dharma based on context and religion, dharma basically means a spiritual or moral code of living, "encompassing duty, responsibility, morality, law, and religion" (Babbili, 1997; Rinehart, 2004, p. 22). It is sometimes used synonymously with one's calling, spiritual duty, or responsibility to an entity greater than oneself. It is historically a Hindu concept but has broad implications to Jainism and Buddhism as well. Dharma can also refer to teachings, such as Buddhists who follow or receive *dhamma*, and may influence decisions around all aspects of South Asians' lives, including career choices, marriage, or relocation (Bhangaokar & Kapadia, 2009; Gupta & Tracey, 2005).

For instance, in one study, Hindu women who were street sweepers at a popular pilgrimage site in Pune described a sense of dharma, believing that they were doing God's duty. By focusing on purification and cleanliness when others looked down on them or refused to clean, they felt convinced that it was part of their dharma. "They sit anywhere, eat anywhere, and throw things around. We clean it all up. We just assume we found Pandurang [native word for a Hindu God] in cleaning up after them. We just assume we actually see Him," said one woman (Buzzenell & Shenoy-Packer, 2013, p. 156). In another quantitative study of Indian-American college students, Indian men, in particular, reported more of a sense of duty, or dharma, to their parents in choosing a career (Gupta & Tracey, 2005). In working with South Asians in the United States, it is important to note that many South Asians may simply follow general principles of dharma as a cultural heritage, without naming it as such. Even second-generation and highly acculturated South Asians who do not identify as religious may feel a responsibility and moral duty to provide for their elderly parents or produce offspring.

Privacy

Many South Asians are conditioned to have a strict sense of privacy, keep family business within the family, and share information with health care professionals only when absolutely necessary (Baptiste, 2005). Often this is due to a fear that problems such as mental illness, a disability, or sexual abuse will bring shame on families and affect their children's prospects for marriage. Therefore, instead of seeking outside help from community members or professionals, families tend to turn to extended family members for help. In a study of South Asian immigrant women with depression in the United Kingdom, a Pakistani woman described her reluctance to talk about personal problems with the local South Asian community. "I didn't tell anyone (about the problems with my husband) because at the end of the day it's private, and if I tell someone, they'll tell someone else and they'll tell someone

else. They do that. I mean, they sympathize and say "Isn't it awful?," but then they join in and add their own bit ... so that's no solution. No matter who we talk to, there's no way forward" (Cochrane & Hussain, 2002, p. 296). Instead, she sought help from her sister-in-law and mother-in-law, who took over household duties for her when she was too depressed to get out of bed. "My mother-in-law, too ... she was so good, and when I was ill and couldn't get out of bed, she would get me out of bed and help me wash and get dressed and she would feed my children and my husband ... you know, doing all the things I was supposed to do but just couldn't" (2002, p. 296).

In summary, values of collectivism, nonviolence, dharma, karma, and privacy are commonly passed down through extended family members and South Asian pockets in the United States. When families immigrate, begin to acculturate, and develop new identities, however, the manifestation of these cultural norms within each person and community varies.

Diversity Within the Indian Subcontinent

While people originating from the Indian subcontinent share many common characteristics, within each country there are distinct religions, castes, regions, customs, cuisines, and languages, along with separate political histories within and between countries. South Asian immigrants in the United States also span a wide range in terms of class, socio-economic status, generation, education, ability, sexual orientation, and gender identity.

Language

Once, when I was a student, my internship site supervisor, a White, middle-aged, heterosexual social worker, raved about *Monsoon Wedding,* a Hollywood film by Mira Nair (Dhawan & Nair, 2001). I had not seen it yet but was eager to watch it after hearing positive reviews. Out of curiosity, I asked him, "What language is it in?" He stuttered, "Uh ... I think it's just in Indian." I did not have the heart to tell him that India has over 20 official languages and that "Indian" was not one of them. In India, languages include Hindi, Tamil, Kannada, Gujarati, Malayalam, Punjabi, Bengali, Urdu, Oriya, Marathi, Telegu, and others, while Urdu, Pashto, Punjabi, Sindhi, and Balochi are more common languages spoken in Pakistan. In Bangladesh, the majority of the population speaks Bengali. However, languages vary according to region and state and include hundreds of local dialects and subprovincial languages (Subbarao, 2012). Most middle-class and urban populations are also fluent in English, due to the influence of British colonization, and often speak English along with their local language. Others who conduct business with international clients may speak primarily English in the workplace and converse in their native language at home. However, language is an important regional identity, and local languages are still spoken in everyday interactions in many South Asian families and communities, even in the United States. In addition, some recent immigrants may not be fluent in English, depending on their age, education level, class, socioeconomic status, and region. With so much linguistic diversity on the Indian subcontinent, when working with South Asian clients in the United States, it is important for music therapists to inquire about the languages that clients speak and seek out translations of song lyrics from South Asian songs.

Caste

The concept of caste, or *varna,* is a socially constructed system of rank and status based on ancient Hindu texts that plays a significant role in South Asian communities in the United States. Although caste is a Hindu concept, elements of caste are found across the Indian subcontinent in other religions as well (Ali, 2002). In addition, caste is complicated by thousands of *jati* or sub-castes, which are defined based on location, linguistic, local area, occupation, and genetic factors (Bob, 2007; Kumar, 2012). Caste is generally a taboo subject across South Asian societies today, so it is unlikely that South Asian clients in the United States will mention it. However, more privileged and upper castes often experience caste as a source of pride and may openly discuss their own caste associations. In addition, caste impacts relationships between South Asians, individual and community identities, attitudes about religion and the arts, careers, diets, matrimonial choices, access to education, and resources and opportunities, and can contribute to oppression and violence within South Asian communities.

In particular, lower castes, also known as scheduled castes and tribes, are particularly vulnerable and have been subject to increasing oppression and violence in India (National Crime Records Bureau Ministry of Home Affairs, 2014). Dalits, for instance, are believed by some Hindus to be so impure that touching them will make one impure. Historically, right-wing Hindus as well as the British government forced Dalits into menial sanitation work and refused to offer them any other possibilities for livelihood (Prashad, 2001; Rajan, 2011; Rinehart, 2004). As a result, Dalits became outcasts of society and were considered to be equivalent to "Black Indians," following and identifying with the civil rights struggle in the United States. However, led by visionaries Jyotirao, Phule, Ambedkar, and others, Dalits fought for social justice and legal and protective rights. As a result, caste discrimination became illegal, and Dalits are recipients of affirmative action in education, work, and political settings (Omvedt, 2003). However, caste discrimination is still alive in the Indian subcontinent in some areas. In a recent study, over 30% of Indians admitted that they still prohibit lower castes from entering temples, socializing, or sharing food with higher castes (Chisthi, 2014; Desai & Vanneman, 2012).

In the United States, this prejudice manifests in many overt but subtle ways. Unlike other groups and institutions that have formed in the South Asian diaspora and provide community support, there are no formal social structures for Dalits. They are forced to connect through underground networks of unofficial communities and social media and continually fight for their right to be seen and heard (Medina, 2016). "It's dangerous, this culture of caste-based intolerance in the diaspora, for it extends beyond individual relationships. Individuals build institutions, and institutions are steeped in caste. From Hindu temples to Gurudwaras, there is a separate yet unspoken policy of worship for those that are Dalit" (Soundararajan, 2012, para. 5). Overall, lower-caste South Asian families in the United States are more vulnerable to stressors, lack the support of community, experience caste-based discrimination within South Asian communities, face racism within the White community, and may struggle to adjust to living in the United States. As a result, many feel that they have to hide their Dalit identities and histories.

When facilitating music therapy groups with multiple South Asian families or recommending community resources, it is important for music therapists to be aware of microaggressions within the South Asian community that can lead lower-caste families to feel marginalized. For instance, questions and comments from other South Asians that may seem innocuous, such as "Where is your family from?" or queries about religion and diet can be designed to identify and exclude lower-caste families. In addition, higher-caste families may discuss wanting a "good match" or finding a "good family" for their children to marry into as a code for marrying within their caste. Even questions about diet can reveal caste associations. For example, cows are considered sacred according to Brahmin caste culture and, as a result, many Brahmins are vegetarian or will not eat beef. Slaughtering and consuming beef is also illegal in many states in India, carrying a hefty fine and up to 10 years' imprisonment; in some extreme cases, it can lead to violence (McCarthy, 2015). For Dalits, however, since beef is easily obtainable and affordable in India, it has become a common staple food. As a result, even in the United States, many Dalits view the consumption of beef as a form of pride and caste resistance ("Osmania beef fest," 2015). Rather than asking families directly about caste, music therapists are advised to inquire about clients' local communities and relationships between community members and listen for code language or hidden meanings.

The first time I encountered the influence of caste as a professional, I was working with two girls in a second-generation Telegu family. I had eaten lunch earlier in my office, and the aroma of meat was still lingering. The youngest sibling smelled something in the air and asked me what I had been eating. After I reported pasta and meatballs, she appeared stunned. "You eat meat!?," she asked, with a look of disbelief on her face. When she inquired further, she seemed relieved to discover that the meatballs I had been eating were made of turkey and not beef. "Ooohhhh, I thought ... we eat turkey too, just not like, you know, *meat.*" After several other similar incidents, I quickly realized that this family identified as Brahmin. Rather than risk offending me, their subtle comments and questions gave them a chance to figure out where I fit into their social strata.

Religion

The major religions on the Indian subcontinent are Buddhism, Islam, Hinduism, Jainism, Christianity, Sikhism and Zoroastrianism (Baptiste, 2005). While some sects of Buddhism and Islam do not use music in sacred rituals, music and chanting are at the core of most South Asian religions. This includes chanting and melodic recitations of the Qur'an, Buddhist sutras, Christian hymns sung in South Asian languages, Hindu sacred verses and mantras, and Sikh prayers as well as songs and devotional music which "still constitute the most common form of access to the sacred for the pious multitude of Hindus" (Beck, 2012, p. 5).

Hinduism. Hinduism is the religion of the majority population in India and is most known for its worship of multiple gods and goddesses and elaborate mythology. It is unique in that it does not have one founder, utilizes multiple sacred scriptures, has no overarching structure of authority, and consists of many forms of worship and belief systems, such as reincarnation (Narayan, 2006). Most communities and temples follow one particular deity, such as Shiva or Kali, but honor other gods and goddesses on certain occasions. For instance, Lord Ganesh, depicted with an elephant head, is the remover of obstacles and is often prayed to before any major events, such as a marriage or new job or to assist with particular challenges. Saraswati, the goddess of knowledge, music, and the arts, is also worshiped every year as part of Navratri, a popular Hindu festival lasting nine nights.

Hinduism is considered a way of life, with guidelines around daily life, worship, and prayer taking place in temples as well as in home altars (Sharma & Tummala-Narra, 2014). Daily rituals and rites around important life events, such as birth, marriage, and puberty, are an important part of cultural and religious practice (Tarakeshwar, 2013). However, since there are slight variations between different sects of Hinduism, music therapists would do well to inquire into how clients practice and make meaning out of their religion. While Hinduism is founded upon principles of nonviolence, its association with an unjust and oppressive caste system has led many South Asians to become secular.

Buddhism. In response to caste oppression, Buddhism developed as a caste-free religion from the teachings of Siddartha Gautama. Still embodying the principles of karma and cycles of rebirth, the goal of Buddhism is to attain spiritual liberation through *sila* (morality), *samadhi* (concentration) and *panna* (wisdom) (Hart, 2009). Buddhism is also nontheistic and based on knowledge through direct experience rather than deferring to a God or divinity. The Buddha taught and traveled throughout northern India, whence his disciples spread his teachings farther east to China, Korea, Japan, Burma, Tibet, and other countries. He also tried many different types of meditation and spiritual practices in his search for enlightenment, leading to many different branches of Buddhism, such as Theravada, Mahayana, and Vajrayana. Buddhism is practiced by only a small percentage of South Asians, such as Dalits, many of whom have embraced Buddhism as a caste-free dharma, as well as those living near the Himalayas, Tibetans in exile, and Vipassana meditators (Warder, 2004).

Sikhism. Sikhism is a monotheistic religion that developed in the state of Punjab in the 15th century. With a focus on selfless service for the well-being of the family and community, Sikhism also holds the belief that all humans are equal in the eyes of God, rejecting caste and gender discrimination (Emblen & Labun, 2007). In Sikhism, God is genderless, and worldly attractions and distractions are considered an illusion. Sikhs worship at a Gurdwara or temple and engage in meditation and prayer, singing Kirtan and devotional songs (Ahluwalia et al., 2014). Because men traditionally wear turbans, many Sikhs are mistaken for Muslims in the United States and have been subject to harassment and hate crimes (Santora, Schwirtz, & Yaccino, 2012; Wang, 2016). (See Historical Realities Versus Popular Myths for more details.) Thousands of Sikhs were also profiled and killed by other Indians after two Sikh bodyguards assassinated Prime Minister Indira Gandhi in 1984 (Mohanka, 2005). Music therapists working with this population will need to be sensitive to the hate crimes and racial and religious profiling that this population experiences.

Jainism. Like Buddhism and Hinduism, Jainism shares a focus on spiritual salvation and a belief in karma, rebirth, and nonviolence. However, Jainism goes further, with followers focusing on protecting the environment and seeking to do no harm to insects and microorganisms. Jains focus on a "mutual sensitivity toward living things, a recognition of the interconnectedness of life forms, and support programs that educate others to respect and protect living systems" (Chapple, 2006, p. xiii).

Islam. South Asia is home to the largest concentration of Muslims in the world. A majority in both Pakistan and Bangladesh, Muslims constitute approximately 10% of the population in India. Islamic values include the belief that all people are equal, benevolence and care for others, cooperation, empathy, equality, and justice. In addition, Islam emphasizes community development and group success. In traditional Islamic faith, the five main pillars include full devotion to Allah *(shahadah),* performing ritual prayers daily *(salat),* giving alms *(zakat),* yearly fasting *(sawm),* and embarking on a pilgrimage *(hajj)* (Hodge, 2005). These values are interpreted in two ways, based on a personal relationship with God (Sunni Muslims) or based on the teachings of religious leaders (Shiite Muslims).

Music therapists should be aware that in the South Asian–American diaspora, religious groups often congregate in separate communities based on language, region, and religion. Historical tension, bloodshed, invasions, and political events, as well as discrimination between religious groups, may play a role in current relations between South Asian immigrants in the United States. For example, some may have lost family members during partition, become refugees due to displacement, or harbor long-seated animosity toward other groups (Paul, 2005).

Despite differences and divisions between religions, music therapists should understand that religious and spiritual identity, like other identities, is self-constructed (Dwyer, 2000; Jain & Forest, 2004). For example, in my research on Indian adults, I found that participants spoke about religion and spirituality in very personal ways. Some completely rejected their religion of origin. "I had all sorts of issues with the caste system, and, you know, like the history of oppression that the Brahmins perpetrated," said "Siddarth," a 36-year-old immigrant from India. "I never found that an admirable quality, so I just rejected it … *outright*" (Swamy, 2011, p. 163). Instead, he adopted a philosophical, Buddhist perspective. "[The] Buddhism that I practice is very secular and skeptical in nature, sort of questioning" (p. 164). Other participants were selective about which aspects of Hinduism they subscribed to and practiced, embracing some of the cultural and traditional beliefs of Hinduism but not all of its customs or practices. "Maya," a second-generation, 41-year-old, Indian-American lesbian, identified as "spiritual, more than religious, if there's a difference. It's more of a spiritual kind of feeling, than [to] have to follow all the rites and rituals, and orthodox and all that. It's more of a cultural feeling or a traditional feeling. Sometimes I go to the temple in Ashland, but not like, you know— *religiously*. […] Like some of the beliefs, but not a lot of the customs" (p. 153).

In an ethnographic study at a high school in Cambridge, Massachusetts, Maira (2004) also found that South Asian Muslims expressed their identities in creative ways. Interviewing working-class, urban, South Asian, Sunni Muslim youth, she found that their Muslim identities differed significantly from those of upper middle-class South Asian Muslims, manifesting particular political, social, and philanthropic values. For example, participants expressed their values through forming friendships with other ethnicities, including Latinx and African-Americans, even though their upper-class South Asian friends questioned these choices. Other participants expressed their Muslim identities by standing up against discrimination in the United States or by professing a strong allegiance to their host country despite the discrimination they faced. "Islam teaches [us that] whatever country you live in, you should support them. … See, if I live in America, I have to support America; I cannot go to India" (p. 224).

Christianity. South Asian Christians are a minority within the South Asian community, both abroad and in the United States. Many trace their Christian lineage back centuries ago, believing that St. Thomas traveled to India in the first century to establish churches there (Thangaraj, 2006). Others are newly converted, such as Dalits who may have embraced Christianity as a rejection of Hinduism (see the section on Folk Music). In the United States, Christianity was initially maintained by South Asian immigrants in the United States through small prayer groups, and flying in South Asian student priests from abroad for clerical support. As the community grew, however, South Asian congregations, parishes, and dioceses were established in the United States under the auspices of St. Thomas,

Orthodox, Syrian and other Catholic rites, and Protestant parishes in major cities in the United States.

Because of the regional, caste, and linguistic diversity within South Asian populations, South Asian Christian identity is complex. In addition to variations in Christian denominations, South Asians identify regionally and linguistically, calling themselves "Goan Christians, Tamil Christians, Malayalee Christians, Dalit Christians, Mangalorean Christians, and adivasi (tribal) Christians" (Jacobsen & Raj, 2008, p. 3). However, the majority of Christians in India are from the southern states of Kerala, Tamilnadu and Andra Pradesh. This regional and linguistic diversity affects worship, liturgical practices, rituals, rites, and ceremonies such as weddings and funerals, with communities combining particular aspects of the dominant religions around them. For instance, some have transferred the Diwali tradition of wearing new clothes to Christmas, while others may have grown up witnessing the Catholic community pulling a chariot through the street, bearing similarity to Hindu festivals (Thangaraj, 2006).

Because of the diversity of how Christianity is practiced among the South Asian community, the process of acculturation and formation of ethnic identity is challenging for this subgroup. While they are finally living in a country where their religion is in the majority, finding appropriate resources, community and support that reflects their language, values, dress, cuisine, caste, music, child rearing philosophy, and cultural norms, in particular, is often difficult. As a result, many immigrants in the United States will assimilate to larger churches within their denomination but meet informally with other South Asian Christians on a monthly or seasonal basis. Music therapists can direct clients to South Asian Christian associations in the United States, such as "the India Christian Fellowship or the National Association of Indian Christians" (Coward, Hinnells, & Williams, 2000, p. 18), or to the North American or national conferences that take place annually, such as the Malayalee Pentecostal Conference of North America.

Zoroastrianism. Zoroastrians are also a minority within South Asia and in the Diaspora. There are approximately several thousand Zoroastrians in the United States, primarily lawyers, engineers, doctors, and scientists settled in California and Houston (Coward et al., 2000). An ancient religion based on the teachings of the prophet Zarathustra, Zoroastrianism originated in Persia, or modern day Iran. Known as Parsis, these Indo-Iranians fled to the state of Gujarat in the tenth century to escape religious persecution, migrating to Bombay and eventually travelling around the world. Famous Zoroastrians include Zubin Mehta and Freddy Mercury.

While modern Parsis are both secular and orthodox, Zoroastrianism is a monotheistic religion where human beings are seen as essentially good, characterized by the concepts of heaven and hell, free will, and taking responsibility for one's actions. The Creator is considered the father of *asha* (truth, purity, righteousness, or eternal truth), fighting against *druj,* (evil, deceptive or harmful actions) (Boyce, 2001; Luhrmann, 2006). However, because no written texts existed before the sixth century, some details of the current cosmology are unclear. For example, some texts refer to evil as the material, external world while others define evil as within, in deviation from righteousness and an individual's immoral thoughts (Luhrmann, 2006).

For Zoroastrians, prayer is considered a solitary act, except for major life cycle rituals such as the *navjote* ceremony where children receive their sacred clothing. Zoroastrians are expected to wear the sacred shirt and thread, *sudreh and kusti*, recite kusti prayers, and shake off impurity by untying and retying the sacred thread. Because the element of fire represents the creator and is the focus of religious prayer, fire temples are a central place of worship in Bombay and other Indian locations. However, these are usually not accessible in the Diaspora.

> For Parsis the most important rites are the sudreh and kusti prayers, traditionally said five times each day. Even if not said so often, they are said regularly by many, as the Survey figures quoted above show. They take about five minutes and remind Zoroastrians of their duty to commit themselves to good and to fight evil. A number of devout Zoroastrians also keep a divo, a small oil lamp, to remind them of the divine, for all fire is sacred, not just the temple fire" (Coward, Hinnells, & Williams, 2000, p. 45).

Parsis in larger cities can often find support from local associations who host gatherings and community dinners. However, for those without local support, music therapists can refer clients to national organizations, such as the Federation of Zoroastrian Associations of North America (FEZANA), which organizes congresses, youth activities, religious education, and publishes a journal. In addition, clients can look for support and community at the North American Zoroastrian Conference.

In summary, it is important for music therapists to assess the degree of religiosity of each client or family they work with, pay attention to historical influences and political undercurrents in individuals, and consider the dynamics between group members and families with mixed religions. The role and purpose of music in each religion is also important when choosing appropriate music for client sessions and will be discussed further in the section on the Meaning and Function of Music.

Class

Music therapists will find that South Asians in the United States come from a variety of educational and class backgrounds, with the first wave of immigrants from the Indian subcontinent consisting of farmers (Baptiste, 2005). Due to the Immigration Act of 1965, more highly educated and skilled immigrants from South Asia began arriving in the United States. Commonly known as causing the "brain drain," this act lifted discriminatory policies against Asians and allowed the United States to

compete more competitively in the world market. These English-speaking South Asian professionals were given preferential treatment for visas, with tens of thousands arriving in the late '60s and early '70s, quickly establishing middle-class status (Agarwal, 1991). However, more recent waves of South Asian immigrants in the United States include family members of previous immigrants and working-class populations.

Sexual Orientation and Gender Identity

On the Indian subcontinent, the terms "lesbian," "gay," "bisexual," "queer," and "transgender" are sometimes viewed as Westernized terminology. Instead, various regional phrases in local languages are often used, such as *hijra* and *kothi*. Kothi is a term used to describe someone who plays a feminine role in sexual relationships but identifies as male (Arafat et al., 2009; Nanda & Reddy, 2005; Regi & Rani, 2012). Hijras, on the other hand, are seen as a third gender, identifying as neither male nor female, and may be intersex, transgender, or genderqueer. This is often translated roughly as "eunuch" or hermaphrodite in English. Hijiras have attained legal status as a third gender in Bangladesh and India and live in separate communities, performing rituals for weddings and birth ceremonies. While they are considered auspicious, however, many are sex workers and experience abuse and discrimination.

Homosexuality is currently criminalized on the Indian subcontinent, although the legality of same-sex relationships is being challenged in Indian Supreme Court battles. While queer communities are growing stronger in Pakistan and India, holding pride parades and fighting for legal rights (Dave, 2012; Gopinath, 2005), the fear of violence, arrest, discrimination, and job loss leads many queer South Asians to emigrate to the United States, Europe, or other regions.

South Asians who identify as lesbian, gay, bisexual, transgender, intersex, hijira, kothi, gender queer, gender nonconforming, or other queer identities or are questioning their identity are at a much higher risk for social isolation, substance abuse, mental health issues, hate crimes, and violence, even in the United States. Queer South Asians in the United States risk rejection by their family and culture, discrimination by the White queer community (Islam, 1998; Kawale, 2003; Swamy, 2011), and homophobia and racism by the White, heterosexual community. Because South Asian society is so collective and family-centered, social rejection on so many levels can be devastating (Ahmed & Lemkau, 2000; Inman & Tewari, 2003; Pettys & Balgopal, 1998).

In my research with Indian adults, "Maya" described the difficulties she faced in getting culturally sensitive support as an Indian lesbian in college. "The groups that were there were very homogenous at the university...White. It was very difficult, yeah." Not knowing any other gay Indians at the time, she found herself avoiding Indian campus associations and events. "It was hard," she says softly, "and especially when I thought I was alone. Then it was *extremely* hard. I mean, I had friends, and other friends who were straight but supportive, I just didn't know Indians. The bigger community, was there one out there?" (Swamy, 2011, pp. 144–145). "Sarav" also struggled with issues of feeling exiled from his mother country as a gay South Indian. "They are mutually exclusive distinct identities. I cannot accept myself as gay because I'm Indian. For the LGBT community, the core family doesn't happen that easily," he said. "Especially for immigrants, it's very rare that it happens" (pp. 222–223).

Because the topic of sexuality and sexual orientation is so taboo within South Asian communities, many South Asian clients may not feel comfortable talking openly about their sexual orientation or gender identity with friends, family, health care professionals, or therapists. Immigrants, as well as second- or third-generation South Asians, may not have come out to anyone, or they may be grappling with internalized oppression. Others may have been pressured or blackmailed by their family to marry an opposite sex partner, struggling with their decision and living a dual life. Because of these challenges, music therapists will need to educate themselves about South Asian LGBTQ client needs and follow best practices to gain the trust of South Asian queer clients.

Established music therapists have recommended a series of best practices for LGBTQ clients, such as allowing options for self-identification on all written forms, using inclusive, gender-neutral language and client-preferred language and terminology (Whitehead-Pleaux et al., 2012). Posting signs and posters in offices will also indirectly indicate safety for queer clients, such as an equal sign, rainbow flag, or pink triangle, as well as offering queer magazines in the waiting room.

In addition to these guidelines, however, music therapists should have a list of South Asian queer resources and contact information available for clients. A few important resources include the Desi Queer Helpline (1-908-FOR-DEQH), an anonymous helpline for queer South Asians and their family and friends; MASGD, the Muslim Alliance for Sexual and Gender Diversity; and South Asian queer organizations around the country, which provide local support groups, outings, community events, and advocacy. Today, South Asian queer organizations exist in almost every major city in the United States and include TRIKONE in Chicago, Atlanta, Seattle, and San Francisco; the South Asian Lesbian and Gay Association (SALGA) in New York; Satrang in Los Angeles; the Massachusetts Lambda Association (MASALA) in Boston; and many others. The National Queer Asian Pacific Islander Association (NQAPIA) also hosts conferences and provides leadership and training for LGBTQ Asians, Pacific Islanders, and South Asians around the United States. Along with the Asian Pride Project, NQAPIA has also launched major educational and media advocacy campaigns which may be especially useful in educating South Asian family members. These ads were designed to combat cultural misinformation and stigmas about queer identities and include photo diaries, leaflets translated into 19 languages, and public service announcements in local languages on Asian and South Asian television stations.

In review, music therapists should examine their assumptions around what they consider to be South Asian and include all aspects of language, caste, religion, class, sexual orientation, and gender identity in their assessment process. In addition, music therapists should reassure South Asian clients about their intent to be nonjudgmental, as well as their openness to learning about their clients' values, religions, communities, and experiences.

Gender Differences

With a few exceptions, the Indian subcontinent is fundamentally a patriarchal society, influencing values in the South Asian diaspora. Family structure in South Asian families tends to be vertical and hierarchical according to age and gender, with the eldest males in the family having the most privileges (Baptiste, 2005). Women, in particular, are often expected to fulfill family obligations before their own individual needs. In many families, gender roles are more defined than those in the United States, with women responsible for feeding the family and raising children and men working outside the home. With the surge of the middle class in India, however, both parents are often working outside the home, and many acculturated and second-generation South Asians may adopt more egalitarian gender roles.

The Role of Women

The role of women on the Indian subcontinent is complex. On the one hand, India elected a female Prime Minister as early as 1966 and has historically worshiped female Hindu goddesses, honored through rituals and holidays. India also has a constitution that explicitly prohibits gender discrimination, and in the state of Kerala, family structure was legally matrilineal for many years, with female lineage determining inheritance and bloodlines (Jeffrey, 2004). However, these progressive practices are juxtaposed with discrimination and increased violence against women (Almeida, 2005).

The status of women on the Indian subcontinent varies based on country, caste, education level, income, religion, state, and region. Laws vary by country and state, some enforced more than others. For instance, in the Indian state of Bihar, tribal women are prevented from inheriting their husband's property, and Muslim law states that daughters inherit only half the amount that sons do. In rural and poor areas, women are prohibited from having equal custody of their children, getting a divorce, or attending certain events in public (Singh, 2013). Ancient South Asian scriptures also state that women belong to their husband's family and are expected to put their family before their own needs and that a woman's status is linked to her ability to marry a man and have children (Mahalingam, 2007). In addition, in some areas of South Asia, hundreds of thousands of women have been subject to illegal kidnapping, rape, abduction, domestic violence, child marriages, assault, and denial of civil rights due to police and judicial corruption (Aleksandrowicz et al., 2011; Goswami, 2013; Singh, 2013).

While I was unable to find statistics on the treatment of South Asian women in the United States, the experience of girls and women varies widely in the diaspora. This manifests differently depending on the maturity, education, class, religion, regional history, and acculturation level of the family (see the section on Acculturation for more details). In addition, for immigrant families in the United States, the process of acculturation may cause turbulence in family roles. Women who have focused solely on child-rearing may suddenly need to find a job and take on a more independent identity outside of the family. While some families may attempt to maintain oppressive attitudes toward women, in other families in the diaspora, girls are treated respectfully and given equal access to educational opportunities. Instead, differential treatment of unmarried women and girls may take other forms.

For example, researchers and therapists have found that Indian-American women felt pressured to conform to Indian standards of purity and authenticity and experienced restricted personal freedom and autonomy around curfews, dating, marriage, and other social behaviors (Baptiste, 2005; Maira, 1998/2002; Haritatos & Mahalingam, 2006). Interviewing 24 Indian-American college students in New York City, Maira (1998) found that the women's identities revolved around themes of beauty and chastity, with overprotective parents restricting their sexual activity, dating, and socializing in comparison to that of their male counterparts. "Most male informants were aware that the rules they were expected to follow about dating and socializing were more permissive for them than for their sisters or female friends" (Maira, 1998, p. 210). In his clinical psychotherapy practice with South Asians, Baptiste also found that sexism often manifested as microaggressions, such as women and girls being asked to pick up after male siblings or cousins or being told that behaving too independently would damage their chances for marriage.

Researchers and theorists also report that Indian women are more expected to maintain and pass on cultural values (Bhatia & Ram, 2004; Dasgupta, 1998; Gopinath, 2003/2005), as well as be given the task of "perpetuating anachronistic customs and traditions" (Dasgupta, 1998, p. 5). In addition, researchers found that Indian-American women's identities revolve around issues of sexuality, gender roles, and a dichotomy of sexual purity and immodesty (Maira, 1998). For example, Das Gupta and Dasgupta (1998) suggested that White America often views Indian women as hypersexualized or hyperintellectual:

> Indeed, in White America's categorization of racial others as sexually deviant, the Asian-Indian immigrant community is caught in a dual metaphor of both asexual and hypersexual. [...] In this context, the "exotic" Indian-American woman is associated with the *Kama Sutra*, primal sexual energy, and other images of hypersexuality. Simultaneously, the alien, "ugly" Indian-American woman is associated with chastity, sexual repression, and hyperintellectualism. (p. 122)

The Role of Men

Because gender is polarized and segregated in many parts of the Indian subcontinent, men and women do not generally touch or show physical affection in public. As a result, homosocial behavior is encouraged, with men and boys creating close bonds with each other (Aggleton, Hasan, & Persson, 2015; Ross & Wells, 2000). In fact, in the Indian subcontinent, it is common to see male friends holding hands or in close physical proximity. In addition, men in the diaspora are often pressured to choose from limited financially stable and successful career options and take care of their parents in their old age (Gupta & Tracey, 2005). Beyond this, there seems to be a scarcity of literature on South Asian men's health and therapeutic needs. Aggleton, Hasan, and Persson (2015) reviewed over 100 articles on gender in South Asian populations and found that gender was primarily framed as a women's issue, with men absent from research studies or positioned as barriers to women's health.

In working with South Asians, music therapists should remember that it is not always possible to alter a family or individual's core belief system in therapy unless clients are open to change, especially around unconscious attitudes related to gender. To successfully ally with South Asian clients, music therapists will need to evaluate their own assumptions and biases around gender roles, attend to women's needs and safety issues, and find ways to work with a family's existing structure before making any desired changes.

Acculturation

The acculturation level, or the degree that immigrants and immigrant families adapt to United States customs and maintain South Asian values, varies according to "education, class, caste, family size, economic support, connection to their traditional culture, degree of religiosity, past migration history, and how they have dealt with the loss of their country of origin" (Almeida, 2005, p. 400). In addition, South Asian acculturation is also influenced by current immigration status, level of English proficiency, age, and generation (Inman & Tummala-Narra, 2010). Families with young children, young couples, and single adults, for instance, tend to move more quickly through the acculturation process. In fact, with more exposure to mainstream United States society through school and work environments, at times families may internalize the values of their host country more than those of their native country.

For instance, "Siddarth" welcomed the emotional challenges associated with acculturation. During his first Culturally Centered Music and Imagery session to the music of Dvorak, he described floating on the ocean in a "wide open space, pure space in all directions, as wide as the universe!" (Swamy, 2011, p. 168). For him, the images were a metaphor for the mental, emotional, physical, and psychological freedom he felt upon moving to the United States from an oppressive upbringing in India. "I think for me, coming to the United States was more than just a move, it was like a *rebirth*, I was starting fresh. Making new friends. ... I mean, being here by myself was liberating. Starting off life on my own, and doing things the way I want to. Just having that space. In a figurative sense, that's sort of the same idea of space and expanse" (Swamy, 2011, p. 170).

In addition, political and social tensions in the United States, such as 9/11 and the war on terror, affect the climate toward South Asians and the amount of racism and discrimination they experience (see Historical Realities Versus Popular Myths for more details). This in turn impacts their experience of acculturation and can contribute to fears and foster a lack of trust in their host country. For instance, "Anjali," a 29-year-old heterosexual, Hindu woman, struggled with her acculturation process. "It was so hard—leaving home, and then finances, and worrying about that all the time, and trying to get a job, and trying to fit in, trying to make sense of all this information that I was being bombarded with. [...] When you're kind of ... confronted with racism, or like this dominant culture which I brushed up against, which sort of viewed me as ... lesser ... or not as good? It actually really hurt that pride" (Swamy, 2011, pp. 120–121).

Overall, music therapists can show solidarity with South Asian clients by expressing empathy with their losses, considering the impact of current events on their lives, and inquiring how clients may feel about recent hate crimes. (See Enabling Health and Well-Being for more information on treatment strategies.)

Generational Differences and Ethnic Identity

On the surface level, identity manifests in the terms that South Asians use to define themselves. Understanding these terms can provide starting clues to music therapists about how clients relate to their ethnicity and how best to serve them. While in their homeland or within a related community, for instance, it is common for South Asians to identify with their region or state, calling themselves Bengali, Kashmiri, or other regional names. However, in the United States, because South Asian immigrants are a minority population, they tend to identify themselves with their nationality, such as Pakistani, Indian, or Bangladeshi. For instance, "Anjali," an immigrant from Calcutta, described this by saying, "When you're in India, you just are. When you come here, you become Indian" (Swamy, 2011, p. 114). On the other hand, census records often use the terms "East Indian" or "Asian Indian" to distinguish between American Indian and Native American populations (United States Census, 2012), while academic and activist communities often use the term "South Asian." However, many South Asians choose to use the term "Desi" (pronounced DHEY-see), meaning "native" in Hindi, to define themselves and others in relation to a shared ethnicity. Second- or third-generation

South Asians may also identify with a hyphenated identity such as Pakistani-American or Indian-American, or simply American.

How individuals make meaning out of these terms and experience their ethnic identity, however, is a more complex process. Through narrative portraits combining phenomenology, case study, biography, and ethnography (Davis & Lawrence-Lightfoot, 1997), I investigated the complexity and fluid nature of ethnic identity. Using Culturally Centered Music and Imagery as an arts-based assessment tool, I focused on capturing the authentic, ambiguous, contradictory, and multiple aspects of identity, letting participants construct their own meaning out of the images they experienced. I found that some participants did identify strongly with the label of being Indian, experiencing their ethnic identity as central to who they are. "Sarav," for example, described himself as literally Indian at the core, explaining that his ethnic identity supersedes all of his other identities. "I have a very *strong* identity as an Indian. That doesn't go away, [...] no matter gay or straight, or my past experiences, or ... my family and all that stuff. Identity is very different, it's cultural identity" (Swamy, 2011, p. 195). This is consistent with a modernist approach to ethnic identity, in which individuals define themselves in relationship to a dominant culture and follow stages of development from unawareness to acceptance (Erickson, 1994; Phinney, 1990, 2001, 2004).

Other participants in my study identified themselves within individual, spiritual, gendered, or globalized contexts. Some of the images and terms they used to describe their identity included "world citizen," "global nomad," or even "not Indian" (Swamy, 2011, p. 214). Still other participants particularly resonated with globalization theories highlighting newer postmodern approaches to identity, such as the dialogical voice, in which each person's identity consists of varying and sometimes opposing voices, existing in varying contexts and negotiating local, global, political, and historical lenses (Bhatia, 2002; Hermans, 2003). "Siddarth," for instance, described his Indian identity in polar opposites, experiencing both a sense of "Indian-ness" and feeling "not Indian." "Sarav" described living in the United States as "opening gates" and providing an invaluable sense of freedom, but yet said, "*You don't feel that you belong here.*" I also found that some participants viewed their ethnic identity not as singular, but multiple. For example, "Maya" saw herself as not just Indian, but embodying a kaleidoscopic identity. "Sometimes I'm Indian, sometimes I'm American. Sometimes I'm a sci-fi geek. Or gay or straight. Um ... there's a whole mixture of stuff that's me" (p. 217).

For music therapists, ethnic identity particularly impacts the choice of music used in sessions. When clients are questioning, reconstructing, or experiencing dialogue or conflict between identities, they may be confused about their musical preferences. In addition, their musical preferences may change between sessions, depending on the context of their experience and which dialogical voice is most prominent. The music from a client's ethnicity, for instance, may not necessarily be appropriate for clinical work. For example, I once worked with a young South Indian woman who had come to the United States several years ago to attend university, married an American man, and decided to proceed with the immigration process. However, after her husband suddenly left her, she found herself depressed and confused about her ethnic identity. She approached me to help her stabilize during her divorce and figure out whether to move back to India or stay in the United States. In the initial assessment, her dialogical voices expressed conflict. She told me that she hated living in the United States but did not want to go back to India. She said that she hated Indian classical music but was also hesitant to listen to "rock music" and other American pop genres, which she was forbidden to listen to as a child. One day, however, she requested to use a piece of Karnatic fusion music in our session, which she claimed that she found soothing. However, as we listened to it together, she seemed to dissociate. I became concerned and stopped the music. She finally revealed, after some probing on my part, that this piece was played in her boarding school in India, which she associated with emotional and psychological abuse that she experienced there. She also shared a background of physical abuse by her mother, who used to teach her Karnatic South Indian classical music. It became clear to me that due to her trauma history, recent divorce, and ethnic identity confusion, she was not yet able to determine which pieces and genres of music would best support her. Karnatic music was clearly not appropriate, as it could easily retraumatize her. However, she also had a conflicted relationship with many other forms of Western music. As a result, a major goal of therapy became finding safe, supportive music to help her heal and recover from her divorce.

Because of the complex nature of identity as well as the breadth of diversity within the South Asian–American diaspora, an ethnomusical assessment is important when engaging in clinical work with this population. This can begin with a brief interview about immigration history, class, caste, religious, and regional and other backgrounds, as well as asking clients or families how they identify or what they prefer to be called. However, an assessment should also involve discussing and listening to music from various South Asian and American genres and eliciting reactions, images, or feelings about the music. This will help music therapists understand more about what is out of the client's awareness, or in the cultural unconscious (Henderson, 1990; Kimbles & Singer, 2004).

Minority Stress

Although South Asians in the United States come from a variety of class, socioeconomic, and educational backgrounds, high levels of professional and academic success contribute to a perception of South Asians as a "model minority" (Algeria, Chen, & Tummala-Narra, 2012). While many consider this to be a positive stereotype, such a label can lead music therapists to overlook the acculturative stress that South Asian immigrants may experience, including feelings of loss, separation, alienation, and anxiety; disruption in their nuclear and extended

family; concerns about immigration or legal status; pressure to appear as a model minority; and feelings of guilt for leaving one's country of origin (Ahmed & Lemkau, 2000; Bhattacharya & Schoppelrey, 2004; Frey & Roysircar, 2006; Gee et al., 2007; Masood et al., 2009; Tummala-Narra, 2009).

South Asian families also may experience intergenerational conflicts and stress as a result of raising second-generation children in a new country. This can include conflicts around whether children are allowed to date, party, wear revealing clothing, eat meat (including pork), and/or drink alcohol, and, to some extent still, whether marriage partners will be chosen by children or completely or partially arranged by parents and elders (Baptiste, 2005, p. 357).

In addition, South Asians in the United States have been targets of violence, hate crimes, and discrimination since their arrival in the 1800s (Inman, Yeh, Madan-Bahel, & Nath, 2007; Lal, 1999; Mio, Nagata, Tsai, & Tewari, 2007). Since the terrorist attacks on 9/11, hate crimes against South Asian–Americans have increased exponentially (see Historical Realities Versus Popular Myths for more specifics). South Asians also face microaggressions, racial profiling, and high levels of self-reported discrimination, with several studies showing that perceived prejudice contributes to depression (Algeria, Chen, & Tummala-Narra, 2012; Rahman & Rollock, 2004). In response to these stressors, South Asians tend to somaticize emotional and psychological struggles and may approach doctors rather than therapists with signs of headaches, fatigue, digestive problems, or other physical symptoms.

Meaning of Medicine and Well-Being

Medicine and Healing

South Asians often make decisions about their health care and illness by consulting with their families, with many acculturated families in the United States relying solely on Western medicine (Porter, 1997). Others, however, tend to use alternative medicines and lifestyles as a complement to their health care, such as vegetarianism, special diets, herbal medicines, alternative practitioners, or traditional South Asian medicine (Balagopal et al., 2010; Becerra et al., 2006).

Some of the more common South Asian traditional systems of medicine include Ayurveda, yoga and naturopathy, Unani and Siddha, and homeopathy (Bahadur, Chaudhary, Debnath, & Mukherjee, 2015). In addition, traditional healing in Muslim traditions involves spiritual healing and prayers from the Qur'an, the use of amulets and fortune-telling, mind–body therapies, medicinal herbs, and folk therapies (Ahmed, Bhugra, Desai, & Rabbani, 2015; AlRawi, Fetters, Killawi, Hammad, & Padela, 2011).

An increasingly popular form of healing in the United States, Ayurveda, meaning the science of life, is an ancient method of healing tracing back to 500 B.C. (Lad, 2006). Originating from India, it is practiced in Sri Lanka, Nepal, and parts of the South Asian diaspora. While it is not specifically religious, Ayurveda has its roots in Hinduism. A comprehensive and holistic medical system, Ayurveda focuses on both alleviating symptoms and correcting imbalances in the body that contribute to disease through diet, herbs, cleansing techniques, and lifestyle recommendations. Healing comes about through balancing the doshas or elements that make up the body, known as vata (air), pitta (fire), and kapha (water and earth). However, because it has become integrated into everyday life, some South Asians utilize principles of Ayurveda without naming it as such. For instance, Ayurvedic influences may manifest in fasting or the use of certain spices or herbs in cooking, such as home remedies from "old family recipes passed down through generations" (Burke et al., 2008, p. 1251).

Music Therapy

Sound and music have been used as forms of healing and spiritual well-being for thousands of years in South Asia. In Hindu traditions, Ancient Vedic scriptures refer to the use of mantras, spells, hymns, and prayers to mythological Gods for healing illness, affairs of love, and influencing important life rituals (Sundar, 2007). Ayurvedic texts describe how music can be used to modulate the doshas for balance and symptom relief, while certain ragas "are believed to act on specific chakras or energy centers, to bring about harmony in the body and consequent healing" (Chaturvedi, Desai, & Moirangthem, 2015, p. 75). Indian music therapists Sundar and Sairam also describe several ancient healing traditions that they have modernized, such as Nada yoga, or tuning into the subtle vibrations of the flow of consciousness, and Raga Chikitsa, based on a Sanskrit treatise outlining the therapeutic and mood-enhancing powers of ragas (Hersey, 2014; Sundar, 2005; Sundar, 2007). (Please see Meaning and Function of Music for more information about ragas and South Asian music.)

In Islamic traditions, since illness is thought to arise due to a separation from God, singing or listening to sacred verses provides a spiritual form of healing, promoting peace and tranquility over sadness and grief. In addition, some Indigenous doctors and Islamic spiritual leaders have recommended Qawwali performances for those suffering from mental illness (Joomal, 2003; Newer, 2007).

However, music therapy as a professional, clinical discipline is a relatively new field on the Indian subcontinent. In its early developmental stages in India, music therapy is being championed by a handful of practitioners who are consulting with ancient texts, developing music therapy theories indigenous to their region, working to establish national credentials, collaborating with other music therapists internationally, and conducting research on various clinical populations (Antony et al., 2006; Deshmukh, Nayak, Sarvaiya, & Seethalakshmi, 2009; Gupta & Gupta, 2005; Jagdev & Sharma, 2012; Rumball, 2010; Sairam, 2006a; Sundar, 2007). Given music therapy's relatively young status in South Asia, members of the South Asian–American diaspora may be more familiar with the concept of music as

a healing tool or spiritual path rather than with music therapy as a professional discipline.

Common Stressors

Although South Asians tend to underutilize Western medicine, counseling, and music therapy, South Asians, like other populations, are vulnerable to a wide range of psychological disorders, disabilities, and health problems. Besides minority stressors, some problems that lead South Asians to seek therapy when all else fails include domestic violence, alcoholism, sexual abuse, behavior problems with children, mental illness, mood disorders, learning or developmental disorders, and medical conditions such as diabetes or heart disease (Kanukollu & Mahalingam, 2011; Tummala-Narra, 2007). Many middle- and upper-class South Asian children and teenagers also suffer from academic stress and ethnic identity conflict due to being raised in a society completely different from their parents (Baptiste, 2005).

Barriers to Help-Seeking Behaviors

Kanukollu and Mahalingam (2011) suggested that the myth of the model minority, along with social marginalization, affects help-seeking behaviors in the South Asian–American diaspora. Many feel pressured by society and family members to be seen as model minority members in the larger community, discouraging those who need help from speaking out and seeking support around taboo subjects such as mental illness, disabilities, or sexual abuse. In addition, there are cultural stigmas around seeing a therapist or psychologist for mental or emotional issues (Gabel, 2004; Kanukollu & Mahalingam, 2011), as well as a shortage of culturally competent therapists in the United States.

In a study of the South Asian diaspora in Great Britain, cultural insensitivity by providers, fear of public exposure, and a lack of knowledge of existing resources prevented families from seeking help (Aktar & Gilligan, 2006). In addition, shame and embarrassment, fear of rejection by the South Asian community, lack of social support, and the expectation of women to preserve their marriage and fulfill their gender roles often prevent South Asian women from seeking help for domestic violence and other problems (Ahmed et al., 2007; Ayyub, 2000; Dasgupta & Warrier, 1996; Kallivayalil, 2010). Immigrants from the Indian subcontinent may also be less inclined to report violence or illegal activity against them because of their experience on the Indian subcontinent with a corrupt and biased police force and judicial system (Singh, 2013).

Many South Asians also have a more fatalistic view about disease and psychosocial issues, believing that they are the result of karma and past life wrongdoings, the will of God, or simply their fate. This often prevents South Asians from reaching out to seek help. For instance, in one qualitative research study, South Asian immigrant mothers said, "What is going to happen is going to happen" and "I do not believe that my health can be good or bad, whether I take care of it or not. It all depends on Allah" (Wardle & Wrightson, 1997, para. 26). In another study of Sikh immigrant men in Canada who suffered from myocardial infarctions, only a few men followed their doctor's recommendations. Some reported using prayer instead of medicine and emphasized the importance of accepting one's diagnoses, saying, "You shouldn't panic about these things, you shouldn't be afraid of death" (Galdas et al., 2012, p. 261). Even some acculturated South Asians may believe that accepting and facing these difficult lessons will benefit them or help them achieve spiritual salvation, but talking about it will increase their suffering (Gabel, 2004). As a result, many South Asians do not see the value in talk therapy.

Another barrier to treatment is that South Asians do not necessarily have words in their own languages that parallel Western diagnoses. For instance, there are no terms that are equivalent to developmental disability in local and regional South Asian languages. In Hindi, *mundh buddhi* is commonly used, a term correlating to mental retardation that translates as a "slow brain." However, in an ethnographic study with South Asian families in the midwestern United States, Gabel (2004) found that families defined, interpreted, and made meaning out of these terms in many different ways. Only a few South Asians who were educated in the social sciences described a definition similar to those of their Western providers. Some interpreted the term *mundh buddhi* literally, meaning that those with disabilities were sinful, or had "bad desires of the heart" (p. 19). Still others thought that those with a disability could still learn as much as everyone else, but just more slowly. If they did not, they were sometimes perceived as lazy or stubborn. Some participants also translated the term learning disability as *apung,* meaning without a limb. In this context, learning disability meant "without learning" and was considered more severe than an intellectual disability. However, despite the exact terminology used as well as the translation, music therapists should assume that most South Asian families are genuinely interested in the well-being of their children and are acting in ways that they feel are best. (Please see the next section on Enabling Health and Well-being for further treatment suggestions.)

Overall, South Asian–Americans face substantial obstacles to receiving the therapeutic care they need. These include external barriers such as a shortage of culturally competent providers, discrimination, immigration status, a lack of resources or social support, and internal barriers such as cultural stigmas, language barriers, gender expectations, and fatalistic worldviews.

Enabling Health and Well-Being

Because of the stigmas around receiving therapy and cultural values related to privacy, South Asians need basic psycho-education about the issues they are facing and reassurances of confidentiality. Baptiste (2005) recommends focusing on limited, direct, behavioral interventions and not attempting to change

families' core values too quickly. Inman and Tewari (2003) suggest considering the needs of the whole family when treating individuals of South Asian origin. For instance, in South Asia and parts of the diaspora, many families live in intergenerational households, with as many as three generations under one roof. Problems that appear to be isolated may in fact be related to conflicts with in-laws or other family members. In addition, Inman and Tummala-Narra (2010) recommend asking families and individuals how they understand and interpret their own symptoms or problems; how these would be treated or addressed in their native country, community, or religion; how the client has dealt with challenges in the past; and how they are managing in the present. Music therapists should also consider which therapeutic roles would be most beneficial for clients (Stige, 2002). For instance, Inman and Tummala-Narra recommend considering the role of helper, advocate, consultant, educator, caregiver, caseworker, crisis worker, mobilizer, and community planner in working with South Asians (2010, p. 128). For many immigrants, a connection to a larger cultural community can reduce symptoms of emotional and psychological stress, providing a safe place to adjust to a new country and advocate as a community (Kurien, 2003). Based on this, therapists are also advised to assess all levels of the ecosystem, including the individual, family, community, and political, social, school, and workplace arenas.

In working with South Asian adolescents in the diaspora around family conflict, music therapists are advised to be cautious of encouraging teenagers to move toward independence from the family according to Western psychological standards. Expecting adolescents to rebel against parental norms, explore their own career interests, experiment with dating, or spend time socializing with peers instead of their family can often conflict with cultural norms around the role of education, preparing for marriage, childbearing, and economic responsibility for the extended family (Almeida, 2005). Almeida describes her psychotherapy work with an immigrant family experiencing intergenerational conflict with their teenage daughter and difficulties navigating cultural differences in educational and social contexts. Their 14-year-old daughter had recently attempted suicide, leading the family to seek family therapy. In one session, the daughter reported feeling depressed about the prospect of having an arranged marriage and not being allowed to speak to boys, Hindu traditions that are still practiced in many South Asian communities today. The therapist suggested a compromise between following these strict religious and cultural guidelines and permitting her to participate in American coeducation. The parents agreed, allowing their daughter to go on social outings with the other males as long as she was chaperoned by a parent or one of her siblings. However, due to differences in values around dating and sexuality, they were not comfortable with her engaging with non-Indian males. Although marriage in South Asian communities is often considered an important developmental milestone and age-specific rite of passage, they also clarified that she would not be expected to marry anyone she did not like or marry before she finished her education. Therapy helped the family understand the importance of communicating about problems before they escalated and helped the parents to reassure their daughter of how much she meant to them. The daughter was also able to express her fears for the first time and improve her relationship with her parents (Almeida, 2005).

Families are also expected to care for children with disabilities for their entire lives rather than encouraging independent or group living (Gabel, 2004). Paying attention to the nature of family connection in a South Asian context is also important, as a feeling of closeness and support from nuclear and extended family can serve as a coping strategy and contribute to positive mental health for South Asians (Inman, Yeh, Madan-Bahel, & Nath, 2007; Yeh, Inman, Kim, & Okubu, 2006). In working with children, a helpful course of action is validating parents' concerns while educating them about identity formation and differences in cultural norms between each country (Inman & Tummala-Narra, 2010).

When considering diagnoses and symptoms in the treatment process, music therapists are advised to employ a narrative approach. Gabel suggests utilizing the family's terminology and their socially and culturally constructed understanding of the client's condition, even if it may sound offensive (2004). Allowing the coexistence of various perspectives can help to create a therapeutic alignment. In addition, treatment and support can then begin without engaging in power struggles or trying to change the family's fundamental understanding or meaning-making of diagnoses. In her study, Gabel (2005) provides several additional suggestions for providers in working with children. These include asking families open-ended questions about the educational needs of their children, why they think their children struggle with particular issues, and how they learn best; creating partnerships among schools, institutions, and South Asian communities; focusing on the basic safety, dignity, respect, and resources of individuals with disabilities and mental health diagnoses; and utilizing not only language interpreters but also a "culture interpreter" to intervene in challenging situations (p. 23).

Overall, music therapists can best support South Asian–Americans by offering direct interventions, emphasizing confidentiality, understanding cultural needs, noting differences in developmental stages and diverse identities, paying attention to language differences and variations in meaning-making, providing relevant community and social resources, and considering various roles such as advocate, caregiver, consultant, or community planner.

Historical Realities Versus Popular Myths

A wave of spoofs on ethnic stereotypes has recently exploded on the Internet, with videos showing White women and men saying, "I just want a big Bollywood wedding," "Why don't you wear a turban?," and "Do you, like, have to be a doctor?" (Kohlhatkar, 2014). Despite the popularization of yoga, Netipots, and Bollywood beats, South Asian culture is often misunderstood. Below are a few stereotypes and myths that are important for music therapists to deconstruct.

Myth 1: South Asians in the United States Do Not Experience Oppression

While many South Asians experience discrimination in the form of minor incidents or microaggressions, violence against South Asians in the United States has increased dramatically in recent years. High-profile crimes in the last few decades began with the "dot busters," a group of neo-Nazis who murdered and harassed Indian Hindus in New Jersey, vandalizing their property in the late '90s (Anand, 2006). Discrimination against South Asians then began to escalate in the three weeks following the September 11, 2001, terrorist attacks, when over 700 hate crimes were reported against South Asians who appeared to be Arab or Muslim (Maira, 2004). More recently, illegal racial profiling of South Asians in airports and on public transportation has increased, including intrusive searches, detentions, and prohibition of passengers from boarding due to "security risks" because aircraft personnel and passengers felt "uncomfortable" in their presence or because they were overheard speaking another language and falsely accused (Chandrasekar, 2003; *Dasrath vs. Continental Airlines*, 2002; Wang, 2016). Daljeet Singh, a Sikh man who was restrained and refused passage on a Greyhound bus, demanded that Texas authorities file criminal charges against his accuser. "The only crime I committed was wearing a turban, having a beard, and speaking in a different language to another brown man on a bus," said Singh. "I still cannot believe that this happened to me in America" (Wang, 2016, para. 2).

Police brutality against South Asians in the United States also has increased. In 2014, Chaumtoli Huq, a Muslim human rights lawyer from Bangladesh, was illegally arrested for blocking the sidewalk in New York while she waited for her husband and children to use the restroom at a local restaurant (Wang, 2014). In 2015, Sureshbhai Patel, an elderly man visiting his family from India, was violently thrown to the ground by police while taking a walk in Alabama. Authorities responded to a call from a neighbor that he looked suspicious and claimed that he was dangerous because he did not respond to their questions (because he could not speak English). Patel was left partially paralyzed with spinal injuries (Candea, 2015), and the police officer was acquitted of all crimes. Because of these experiences as well as the influence of colonization, South Asians may be wary of working with non–South Asian therapists. Music therapists will need to take extra time to build trust in the therapeutic relationship, be supportive of the potential discrimination that South Asians face, and be transparent about ethnic differences between therapist and client.

Myth 2: Yoga, Meditation, and Chanting Are Universal

Due to globalization, "the explosion of exchange, technology, and communication around the world" (Swamy, 2014, p. 37), yoga, meditation, and other spiritual practices have become cultural icons of what the Indian subcontinent, in particular, is most famous for. Talk shows, movies, and sitcoms show main characters going to yoga classes and chanting mantras. Yoga centers populate the corners of many major and minor cities in the United States. Due to their global proliferation, these practices may seem universal. However, they originate from specific South Asian traditions and require deconstruction. From an ethical perspective, it is important to understand the context of these practices and the influence of globalization and to distinguish ancestral practices from the various hybrid or Americanized forms that have emerged.

The word "yoga" is a Sanskrit word meaning "union" or "yoke" and is defined as a way of life that unites body and spirit. *Asanas,* or physical poses, are only one branch of eight limbs that make up a complete yoga practice, which include the development of morality, self-purification, selflessness, renunciation, concentration, meditation, and other qualities (Iyengar, 2006). South Asian Hindus who ascribe to the religious roots of yoga practice often feel that true yoga cannot be separated from its ancestral origins. However, many studios and centers in the United States have removed cultural or spiritual references to yoga and meditation in order to market yoga to American consumers, divorcing these ancient practices from their roots and focusing heavily on the physical benefits (Coskunar-Balli & Ertimur, 2015).

In addition, chanting Kirtan and Bhajans is a devotional and religious practice from South Asia, a humble communal offering to God practiced in homes and temples free of charge (see Meaning of Music for more details). The American Kirtan movement, however, has commercialized Kirtan through recordings and event fees, borrowing and adapting these South Asian chanting forms for the benefit of American audiences. Led by White Americans who have taken on South Asian names, such as Krishna Das, Bhagwan Das, and Deva Premal, American Kirtan merges folk, rock, bluegrass, and other American styles of music with original Sanskrit and Kirtan texts. American Kirtan has been called "the Universal language of Spirit," "a sing-along," and a "hootenanny with meditation" (Stern, 2016).

In the global age, navigating realms of who owns cultural and spiritual property is complicated. It is important to remember that those who have access to music, information, practices, and exposure to people from around the world are able to do so only because of their privilege and economic means. While mutual cultural exchange can be fruitful when it is beneficial to both cultures, removing South Asian practices from their cultural roots increases the risk of cultural appropriation, or taking or using artifacts, arts, and spiritual practices from another culture in a manner that causes harm (Young, 2010).

Doing so can often remind South Asians of oppressive colonial practices, where the British, for instance, exploited South Asian resources and labor without providing due compensation. Anthony (2014) suggests that dominant cultures borrowing and adapting practices from a previously colonized culture is problematic, does not allow for true intercultural understanding, and never constitutes an equal exchange.

> Historically, the borrowing culture stands to gain considerably more than the original culture from this process—a dynamic that prompts particularly contentious and antagonistic responses among postcolonial and previously colonized nations that are endeavoring to articulate a distinctive global cultural identity. In these instances, cultural appropriation can entail significant sociopolitical ramifications, prompting concerns about the appropriation of ethnic artifacts from previously oppressed cultural groups. (Anthony, 2014, p. 65)

Before using South Asian practices, chanting, or symbols in their work with others, music therapists should consider the cultural context of their engagement and assumptions around yoga, meditation, chanting, and other spiritual and artistic practices. Where were these traditions learned? Were they taught from South Asian sources or from non–South Asian teachers? Are these practices authentic, or hybrid or Americanized forms? If they are not authentic renditions, is the original name still being used? If so, why? Who is benefiting from these practices economically? The culture that created these practices or the host group that is selling them? In addition to this type of honest self-reflection, music therapists who engage in these practices can also avoid cultural appropriation by finding a way to honor and give back to South Asian people their sources, lineages, and communities and by focusing on borrowing the qualities of spiritual practices rather than the culturally specific forms.

Myth 3: All South Asians Practice Yoga and Meditation

In working with South Asians, it is important to understand the role that colonization and caste plays in South Asian practices in the diaspora. For instance, since yoga has its roots in Hinduism, many lower-caste South Asians have rejected yoga and other Hindu practices due to oppression by upper-caste Hindus (Ambedkar, 1987). Therefore, even though yoga in the United States has often become a secular practice, it is not safe to assume that all South Asians will be interested in practicing or including yoga as part of their treatment.

In addition, it is important to remember that during colonization, the British suppressed yoga, Ayurveda, and other indigenous practices in favor of Western medicine and approaches (Porter, 1997). As a result, Western medicine overshadowed indigenous forms of healing in South Asian countries and has influenced South Asian contemporary values. Today, South Asian immigrants—particularly those working in the fields of science, engineering, and information technology—are sometimes wary of any practices with religious overtones or superstitions and may use yoga and meditation only as a last resort to Western medical treatment. Other South Asians may be reluctant to attend yoga or meditation classes taught by non–South Asians due to the cultural appropriation and commercialization of these practices in the United States. A nuanced ethnic identity assessment will help music therapists to understand the preferences and needs of each South Asian client or family.

Meaning and Function of Music

The popularization of music from the Indian subcontinent began in the '70s with Beatles guitarist George Harrison learning sitar from Ravi Shankar and incorporating it in the songs *Help!* and *Norwegian Wood* (Lennon, 1965). With the hit song *Jai Ho* winning an Oscar, a Grammy, and an Academy award (Rahman, 2008), Bollywood has become one of the most popular and well-known South Asian musical styles on the planet. Other major genres include classical, light classical, film music, bhangra, folk, religious and devotional, and fusion or club music.

Classical Music

Although some European classical music is played and taught in South Asian countries, classical music on the Indian subcontinent primarily consists of Hindustani and Karnatic styles. Classical music is based on oral traditions, rooted in ancient scriptures, and considered serious art music. The purpose of music in this context is aesthetic appreciation, scholarship, spiritual growth, healing, and maintaining and preserving cultural values. Much like European classical music, classical music from the Indian subcontinent is considered refined and generally requires knowledge or experience to enjoy. In the South Asian–American diaspora, families often enroll their children in Hindustani or Karnatic music lessons to help maintain and pass on cultural values. Because of this, South Asian communities have built music centers, temples, and regional associations around the country to carry on these traditions.

However, because the Indian subcontinent is so regional and diverse, it is important for music therapists to understand which music is associated with which region and caste. Members of the Brahmin caste, for instance, have been accused of excluding lower-caste musicians from the classical music community (Tilak, 2015). Because of this, classical music is sometimes considered an elitist art form. In addition, Hindustani music is found in North India, with distinct subgenres in Pakistan and Bangladesh, while Karnatic music is associated with and practiced primarily in South India.

Hindustani styles of music commonly utilize the voice as the solo instrument, along with violin, flute, sitar, and sarod (a plucked string instruments with sympathetic strings). The tabla, a set of upright drums with the capability of bending pitches, provides the rhythm, along with a tanpura or harmonium, which serves as both drone and accompaniment. Karnatic music shares similar characteristics, utilizing voice, violin, flute, or veena as solo instruments. The mrigdangam, a long, two-headed drum, commonly provides the rhythmic accompaniment, and a tambura, a string instrument with sympathetic strings, creates a drone. More recently, digital tamburas and smartphone apps are being used, which eliminate the need for repeated tunings during performances. Both Hindustani and Karnatic traditions are primarily vocal, with instrumentalists either accompanying a singer or playing solo as an "imitation/extension of the voice." Both forms involve lengthy and complex improvisations (Rao & Rao, 2014). Musicians from each of these traditions generally stay within the boundaries of each genre, unless a mixed group decides to perform together in what is known as a *jugalbandi*.

Hindustani and Karnatic music are both based on an ancient system of raga, rasa, and tala, focusing on text, melody, rhythm, and improvisation. Raga describes a unique melodic motif with a specific ascending and descending scale pattern. It contains characteristic idioms that are recognizable to a *rasika*, a connoisseur of classical music, in an instant. In addition, ragas are generally associated with a time of day and season, with certain scale degrees considered more important than others. Each raga is expressed through microtones, melismas, and ornamental slides and associated with particular *rasas*, or emotional states capable of evoking transcendence (Clayton, 2003). The concept of *rasa* is a beautiful one and actually means "flavor" or "taste." In other words, each raga has its own flavor and is designed to satisfy and touch the emotional and musical palate of each listener. The performer's job is to bring out the flavor of the raga by paying attention to the rasa. Finally, tala refers to the rhythmic cycle used in a song. In other words, instead of a fixed meter with three or four beats in each measure, a tala may contain 12 or 24 beats, with a characteristic rhythmic pattern leading back to the first beat. The concept of European harmonies, such as major or minor chords played vertically, is not a part of traditional Indian classical music (Rao & Rao, 2014).

While including Hindustani or Karnatic improvisation in music therapy would take years of intensive study, basic elements and characteristics can help to shape sessions with this population. For instance, *sargam,* the Indian equivalent of Solfege using the syllables "Sa, Re, Ga, Ma, Pa, Dha, Ni, Sa" (Rao & Rao, 2014, p. 25), can be used in simple improvisations above the sounds of a digital tanpura easily downloaded on a smartphone or iPad.

Film Music

Indian cinema and film music is very prolific and has been popular for many decades in India, South Asia, and the South

Asian diaspora, with the industry producing close to 1,000 films and grossing almost four billion dollars each year. Cinema music serves as entertainment and enjoyment, with the soundtracks often more popular than the films. It also functions as a global cultural icon for many South Asians at home or in the diaspora and crosses caste, class, age, religious, and regional and national boundaries.

While Bollywood music is most well-known globally, it refers to the Hindi cinema industry in Mumbai. Bollywood is only one of many producers creating films in various languages across the Indian subcontinent. These films are primarily musicals, characterized by "song-dance, melodrama, lavish production values, emphasis on stars, and spectacle" (Ganti, 2013, p. 3). Influenced by regional myths, Sanskrit dance-dramas, folk and Parsi theatre, Hollywood and MTV (Dissanayake & Gokulsing, 2004), there is potential in music therapy for the use of recorded film music, dance, and drama with this population. While the songs and melodies in cinema music contain elements of South Asian classical music, the orchestration and accompaniment often include European harmonies and instruments.

Club Music

South Asian club music integrates hip-hop, jazz, rock, pop, reggae, techno, jungle, heavy metal, or other global styles with elements of Indian classical music. For instance, melodic elements of ragas are often incorporated into club remix music, which middle-class, second-generation straight and queer Desis have embraced as a way to "define their ethnic identity and gender relationships" (Badruddoja, 2008; Maira, 2002). Qawwali music has also found its way into popular South Asian culture and is featured in Hindi films. Known as *filmi qawwali*, this subgenre is considered entertainment, although it may follow traditional qawwali forms (Alam & Bhattachatarjee, 2012).

Religious Music

A Bhajan or Kirtan is a genre of devotional music from Hindu roots that "praises or glorifies a God or deity" or "results in a personal communion or emotional exchange with the divine" (Beck, 2012, p. 133). Widely used in South Asia and in the South Asian diaspora, both song forms function in ways similar to those of biblical hymns or psalms and are typically sung in temple or religious settings. They are generally part of a larger system of puja, or worship, with the worshiper offering songs in addition to sweets, flowers, clothing, incense, and other material goods to their chosen deities. According to ancient scripture, these songs were translated directly from God into the sacred language of Sanskrit. However, over time, thousands of poets and singer-saints have composed hymns to various other divinities in many different vernacular languages (Beck, 2012). Bhajans and Kirtans consist of call-and-response–style chanting by a lead singer, accompanied by

percussion, drones, or a harmonium, free of charge. They are often performed in small groups, with performers seated on the floor close to the lead singer. Typically, group members or audiences repeat in unison after the leader. However, some semiclassical performances may involve less audience participation (Beck, 2012).

Qawwali, the most well-known form of Sufi devotional music in North India and parts of Pakistan and Bangladesh, is a mixture of Persian and Indian music, utilizing ragas, harmonium, percussion, lead singers, and an accompanying chorus, with the rhythmic clapping of hands. A mystical, Islamic tradition, Qawwali comes from an oral tradition that is more than a thousand years old. Drawn from ancient Persian Sufi poetry, the music is considered secondary to the texts. Containing melody, sung verses of poetry, repetition, call-and-response, melismas, and improvisation, Qawwali songs often describe the pain of separation and longing for the divine. Although the performance of Qawwali is mostly male-dominated, a few female Qawwali artists have recently come to the forefront (Alam & Bhattacharjee, 2012; Bambarger & Soffer, 1996; Newer, 2007).

Folk Music

Folk music in South Asia consists of rural or regional songs in local languages, containing simple structures and instrumental accompaniment. In addition to entertainment, South Asian folk songs have served several functions, including as "celebrations of the rural landscape and village life" (Chacko & Menon, 2013, p. 103), to preserve cultural and behavioral codes of conduct, as a historical record, as an emotional expression, as a forum for instruction for adulthood, and as social critique (Jassal, 2012).

While folk music in the Indian subcontinent has generally been centered in villages and rural areas, in recent years, there has been a resurgence of interest in folk music in urban India and the diaspora, with international folk festivals sprouting around the subcontinent and popular shows such as *Indian Idol* requiring contestants to sing folk songs from their regional backgrounds (Fiol, 2015). More commonly, folk elements and instruments are combined with cosmopolitan musical genres and sometimes appropriated to create a rustic and indigenous feel, such as the integration of hip-hop and reggae with Bhangra, a Punjabi folk dance. In addition, folk music is showing up in the United States in intercollegiate dance competitions such as Bhangra Beat and Rass Chaos, featuring Bhangra and Rass-Garba, a Gujarati communal circle dance with sticks, spinning, and clapping to the beat (Chacko & Menon, 2013).

For Dalits and other lower caste groups, however, folk music has also served as an everyday form of resistance against religious and caste oppression (Appavoo, 1986; Scott, 1985). For example, Sharinian (2014) found that Tamil Christian music plays a sociopolitical role similar to what African-American spirituals did in combating slavery in the United States. One reason for the inclination toward folk music is that classical and religious music often uses the Sanskrit language, which is often seen as elite and inaccessible for lower caste groups. "Sarav," a lower-caste South Indian who preferred Tamil songs, described this very phenomenon. "The Indian temples predominately they use Sanskrit mantras and stuff. Which not many people understand. They chant all these mantras and you have no idea what they're saying. And you don't feel connected. [...] They don't let you into the temple, up to this level. Nobody else can go except these Brahmin priests, and you have to pay them for blessings. That really doesn't sit well with me" (Swamy, 2011, pp. 202–203).

In review, Hindustani, Karnatic, and Qawwali classical music are more serious and complex art forms, while Bhajans and Kirtans serve as spiritual and religious expressions. Bollywood, film, club, and fusion music represent and appeal to global audiences, while folk songs often represent regional, class, or caste identities. While South Asian individuals may listen to all forms of music, such as rock, pop, European classical, hip-hop, reggae, trance, folk, country, African, world, or other genres, South Asian music encompasses unique elements and forms that will likely require study for the untrained ear. In particular, music therapists will need to learn about microtones, ornamentation, melismas, and raga improvisation in order to successfully use indigenous music in interventions with South Asian–Americans.

Conclusion

The South Asian–American diaspora is a diverse, multilingual population of multiple identities and faiths, characterized by close-knit communities, complex social structures, powerful ancient spiritual and healing practices, and elaborate music and artistic genres and is claiming its place as a leader in the technological, science, and mathematics industries. Despite racial discrimination, a colonial history, and immigration struggles, South Asians in the United States are remarkably resilient. However, while they have not traditionally sought music therapy or counseling in the United States, they are a population in need of more culturally appropriate services and support. Because talk therapy still carries a stigma, music therapy has the potential to significantly benefit this group. However, this will require culturally centered education of music therapists and outreach to South Asian communities about the scientific, personal, and spiritual benefits of music therapy. In particular, community music therapy contexts and approaches that are music-centered and incorporate South Asian spiritual, alternative practices or cultural norms are likely to be most effective. Armed with knowledge, cultural sensitivity, self-awareness, and outreach, music therapists can make a difference in the lives of South Asians in the United States.

References

Agarwal, P. (1991). *Passage from India: Post-1965 Indian immigrants and their children: Conflicts, concerns, and solutions.* Palos Verdes, CA: Yuvati.

Aggleton, P., Hasan, M. K., & Persson, A. (2015). Rethinking gender, men and masculinity: Representations of men in the South Asian reproductive and sexual health literatures. *International Journal of Men's Health, 14*(2), 146-162.

Ahluwalia, M. K., Locke, A. F., & Hylton, S. (2014). Sikhism and positive psychology. In C. Kim-Prieto (Ed.), *Religion and spirituality across cultures* (pp. 125–136). Netherlands: Springer.

Ahmed, H. U., Bhugra, D., Desai, G., & Rabbani, G. (2016). The Bangladesh Perspective. In D. Bhugra, R. Ng, N. Takei, & S. Tse (Eds.), *The Routledge handbook of psychiatry in Asia* (pp. 39–48). London, UK: Routledge.

Ahmed, K., Mohan, R. A., & Bhugra, D. (2007). Self-harm in South Asian women: A literature review informed approach to assessment and formulation. *American Journal of Psychotherapy, 61*(1), 71–81.

Ahmed, S. M., & Lemkau, J. P. (2000). Cultural issues in the primary care of South Asians. *Journal of Immigrant Health, 2,* 89–96.

Akhtar, S., & Gilligan, P. (2006). Cultural barriers to the disclosure of child sexual abuse in Asian communities: Listening to what women say. *British Journal of Social Work, 36*(8), 1361-1377.

Alam, S., & Bhattacharjee, A. (2012). The origin and journey of Qawwali: From sacred ritual to entertainment? *Journal of Creative Communications, 7*(3), 209–225.

Aleksandrowicz, L., Banthia, J., Bassani, D., Chandra, S., Jha, P., Kesler, M., & Ram, U. (2011). Trends in selective abortions of girls in India: Analysis of nationally representative birth histories from 1990 to 2005 and census data from 1991 to 2011. *The Lancet, 377*(9781), 1921–1928.

Ali, S. (2002). Collective and elective ethnicity: Caste among urban Muslims in India. *Sociological Forum, 17*(4), 593–620.

Allender, T. (2003). Anglican evangelism in north India and the Punjabi missionary classroom: The failure to educate "the masses." 1860–77. *History of Education, 32*(3), 273–288.

Almeida, R. (2005). Asian Indian families: An overview. In M. McGoldrick, J. Giordan & N. Garcia-Preto (Eds.), *Ethnicity and family therapy* (pp. 377–394). New York, NY: Guilford Press.

Alrawi, S., Fetters, M., Killawi, A., Hammad, A., & Padela, A. (2011). Traditional healing practices among Muslim Americans: Perceptions of community leaders in Southeast Michigan. *Immigrant Minority Health, 14*(3), 489–496.

Ambedkar, B. R. (1987). Philosophy of Hinduism. In V. Moon (Ed.), *Dr Babasaheb Ambedkar: Writings and Speeches*

(Vol. 3, pp. 1–94). Bombay, India: Government of Maharashtra. (Original work published 1936).

Anand, V. (2006). The dotbuster effect on Indo-American immigrants. *Journal of Immigrant and Refugee Studies, 4*(1), 111–113.

Antony, M. G. (2014). "It's not religious, but it's spiritual": Appropriation and the universal spirituality of yoga. *Journal of Communication & Religion, 37*(4), 63–81.

Appavoo, J. T. (1986). *Folklore for change.* Madurai, India: T.T.S. Publications.

Arafat, S., Khan, S. I., Hussain, M. I., Parveen, S., Bhuiyan, M. I., Gourab, G., ... Sikder, J. (2009). Living on the extreme margin: Social exclusion of the transgender population (Hijra) in Bangladesh. *Journal of Health, Population, and Nutrition, 27*(4), 441-451.

Ayyub, R. (2000). Domestic violence in the South Asian Muslim immigrant population in the United States. *Journal of Social Distress and the Homeless, 9*(3), 237–248.

Babbili, A. S. (1997). Ethics and the discourse on ethics in post-colonial India. In C. Christians, & M. Traber (Eds.), *Communication ethics and universal values,* (pp. 128-158). London, UK: Sage.

Badruddoja, R. (2008). Queer spaces, places, and gender: The tropologies of Rupa and Ronica. *National Women's Studies Association Journal, 20*(2), 156-188.

Bahadur, S., Chaudhary, S. K., Debnath, P. K., & Mukherjee, P. K. (2015). Ethnopharmacology and integrative medicine: An Indian perspective. In M. Heinrich & A. K. Jager (Eds.), *Ethnopharmacology* (pp. 279–292). West Sussex, UK: John Wiley & Sons.

Bambarger, B., & Soffer, I. (1996). Sufi Music's rich past. *Billboard, 108*(5), 1.

Baptiste, D. A. (2005). Family therapy with East Indian immigrant parents rearing children in the United States: Parental concerns, therapeutic issues, and recommendations. *Contemporary Family Therapy, 27*(3), 345–366.

Beck, G. L. (2012). *Studies in comparative religion: Sonic liturgy: Ritual and music in Hindu tradition.* Columbia, SC: University of South Carolina Press.

Bhangaokar, R., & Kapadia, S. (2009). At the interface of 'Dharma'and 'Karma': Interpreting moral discourse in India. *Psychological Studies, 54*(2), 96-108.

Bhatia, S. (2002). Acculturation, dialogical voices and the construction of the diasporic self. *Theory & Psychology, 12*(1), 55–77.

Bhatia, S., & Ram, A. (2004). Culture, hybridity, and the dialogical self: Cases from the South Asian Diaspora. *Mind, Culture, and Activity, 11*(3), 224–240.

Bhattacharya, G. (2008). The Indian Diaspora in transnational context: Social relations and cultural identities of immigrants to New York City. *Journal of Intercultural Studies, 29*(1), 65–80.

Bhattacharya, G., & Schoppelrey, S. L. (2004). Pre-immigration beliefs of life success, postimmigration experiences, and

acculturative stress: South Asian immigrants in the United States. *Journal of Immigrant Health, 6*(2), 83–92.

Bhattacharya, G., & Shibusawa, T. (2009). Experiences of aging among immigrants from India to the United States: Social work practice in a global context. *Journal of Gerontological Social Work, 52*(5), 445–462.

Bob, C. (2007). "Dalit rights are human rights": Caste discrimination, international activism, and the construction of a new human rights issue. *Human Rights Quarterly, 29*(1), 167-193.

Bose, S. (1990). Starvation amidst plenty: The making of famine in Bengal, Honan and Tonkin, 1942–45. *Modern Asian Studies, 24*(4), 699–727.

Boyce, M. (2001). *Zoroastrians: Their religious beliefs and practices.* London, UK: Routledge.

Brah, A. (2005). *Cartographies of Diaspora: Contesting identities.* London, UK: Routledge.

Burke, A., Satow, Y. E., Kumar, P. D., & Inciardi, J. F. (2008). Exploring the prevalence of Ayurveda use among Asian Indians. *The Journal of Alternative and Complementary Medicine, 14*(10), 1249-1253.

Buzzanell, P. M., & Shenoy-Packer, S. (2013). Meanings of work among Hindu Indian women: Contextualizing meaningfulness and materialities of work through Dharma and Karma. *Journal of Communication & Religion, 36*(1), 149-172.

Candea, B. (2015). Alabama police officer arrested, accused of injuring Indian man in dashcam video. Retrieved from http://abcnews.go.com/US/alabama-police-officer-arrested-accused-injuring-indian-man/story?id=28936001

Chacko, E., & Menon, R. (2013). Longings and belongings: Indian-American youth identity, folk dance competitions, and the construction of "tradition." *Ethnic & Racial Studies, 36*(1), 97–116.

Chandrasekhar, C. A. (2003). Flying while brown: Federal civil rights remedies to post-9/11 airline racial profiling of South Asians. *Asian Law Journal, 10,* 215.

Chapple, C. K. (2006). *Jainism and ecology: Nonviolence in the web of life.* Delhi, India: Motilal Banarsidass Publishers.

Chaturvedi, S. K., Desai, G., & Moirangthem, S. (2015). Mental health in India II. In D. Bhugra, R. Ng, N. Takei, & S. Tse (Eds.), *The Routledge handbook of psychiatry in Asia,* (pp. 67–79). London, UK: Routledge.

Cheshire, T. C. (2001). Cultural transmission in urban American Indian families. *American Behavioral Scientist, 44*(9), 1528–1535.

Chisti, S. (2014). Biggest caste survey: One in four Indians admit to practicing untouchability. Retrieved from http://indianexpress.com/article/india/india-others/one-in-four-indians-admit-to-practising-untouchability-biggest-caste-survey/

Chiu, L., Ganesan, S., Clark, N., & Morrow, M. (2005). Spirituality and treatment choices by South and East Asian women with serious mental illness. *Transcultural Psychiatry, 42*(4), 630–656.

Clayton, M. (2003). Comparing music, comparing musicology. In M. Clayton, T. Herbert, & R. Middleton, (Eds.), *The cultural study of music: A critical introduction* (pp. 57-68). New York, NY: Routledge.

Cochrane, R., & Hussain, F. A. (2002). Depression in South Asian women: Asian women's beliefs on causes and cures. *Mental Health, Religion & Culture, 5*(3), 285-311.

Coskuner-Balli, G., & Ertimur, B. (2015). Creating hybridity: The case of American yoga. *NA - Advances in Consumer Research, 43,* 494–497.

Coward, H. G., Hinnells, J. R., & Williams, R. B. (2000). *The South Asian Religious Diaspora in Britain, Canada, and the United States.* Albany, NY: State University of New York Press.

Dasgupta, S. D. (1998). *A patchwork shawl: Chronicles of South Asian women in America.* New Brunswick, NJ: Rutgers University Press.

Dasgupta, S. D., & Warrier, S. (1996). In the footsteps of "Arundhati": Asian Indian women's experience of domestic violence in the United States. *Violence against Women, 2*(3), 238-259.

Dasrath vs. Continental Airlines, 02 2683-2684 (New Jersey 2002). Retrieved from http://law.justia.com/cases/federal/district-courts/FSupp2/228/531/2413449/

Dave, N. N. (2012). *Queer activism in India: A story in the anthropology of ethics.* Durham, NC: Duke University Press.

Davis, J., & Lawrence-Lightfoot, S. (1997). *The art and science of portraiture.* San Francisco, CA: Jossey-Bass.

Desai, J. (2003). *Beyond Bollywood: The cultural politics of South Asian Diasporic film.* London, UK: Routledge.

Desai, S., & Vanneman, R. (2012). India Human Development Survey-II (IHDS-II). doi:10.3886/ICPSR36151.v4

Deshmukh, A. D., Sarvaiya, A. A., Seethalakshmi, R., & Nayak, A. S. (2009). Effect of Indian classical music on quality of sleep in depressed patients: A randomized controlled trial. *Nordic Journal of Music Therapy, 18*(1), 70–78.

Dhawan, S. (Writer), Nair, M. (Producer & Director). (2001). *Monsoon wedding* [Motion picture]. India: Myndform.

Dissanayake, W., & Gokulsing, K. M. (2004). *Indian popular cinema: A narrative of cultural change.* Hyderabad, India: Orient Longman.

Du Bois, D. (2012). The "coolie curse": The evolution of white colonial attitudes towards the Indian question, 1860–1900. *Historia, 57*(2), 37–67.

Dwyer, C. (2000). Negotiating Diasporic identities: Young British South Asian Muslim women. *Women's Studies International Forum, 23*(4), 475–486.

Emblen, J., & Labun, E. (2007). Spirituality and health in Punjabi Sikhs. *Journal of Holistic Nursing, 25,* 141–148.

Erikson, E. (1994). *Identity: Youth and crisis.* New York, NY: W.W. Norton & Co.

Fiol, S. (2015). One hundred years of Indian folk music: The evolution of a concept. In V. L. Levine & P. V. Bohlman (Eds.), *This thing called music: Essays in honor of Bruno Nettl* (pp. 317–329). Maryland, MD: Rowman & Littlefield.

Frey, L. L., & Roysircar, G. (2006). South Asian and East Asian international students' perceived prejudice, acculturation, and frequency of help resource utilization. *Journal of Multicultural Counseling and Development, 34*(4), 208–222.

Gabel, S. (2004). South Asian Indian cultural orientations toward mental retardation. *Mental Retardation, 42*(1), 12–25.

Galdas, P., Cheater, F., & Marshall, P. (2007). What is the role of masculinity in white and South Asian men's decisions to seek medical help for cardiac chest pain? *Journal of Health Services Research & Policy, 12*(4), 223–229.

Galdas, P. M., Oliffe, J. L., Wong, S. T., Ratner, P. A., Johnson, J. L., & Kelly, M. T. (2012). Canadian Punjabi Sikh men's experiences of lifestyle changes following myocardial infarction: Cultural connections. *Ethnicity & Health, 17*(3), 253–266.

Gandhi, M. K. (1990). *An autobiography, or the story of my experiments with Truth.* Ahmedabad, India: The Navjivan Trust.

Gandhi, M. K. (2001). *Nonviolent resistance.* Mineola, NY: Dover Publications.

Ganesh, K. (2008). Intra-community dissent and dialogue: The Bombay Parsis and the Zoroastrian Diaspora. *Sociological Bulletin, 57*(3), 315-336.

Ganti, T. (2013). *Bollywood: A guidebook to popular Hindi cinema.* New York, NY: Routledge.

Gee, G. C., Spencer, M., Chen, J., Yip, T., & Takeuchi, D. T. (2007). The association between self-reported racial discrimination and 12-month DSM-IV mental disorders among Asian-Americans nationwide. *Social Science & Medicine, 64*(10), 1984–1996.

Giri, B. P. (2005). Diasporic postcolonialism and its antinomies. *Diaspora: A Journal of Transnational Studies, 14*(2), 215–235.

Gopinath, G. (2003). Nostalgia, desire, diaspora: South Asian sexualities in motion. *Positions: East Asia Cultures Critique, 5*(2), 468–489.

Gopinath, G. (2005). *Impossible desires: Queer Diasporas and South Asian public cultures.* Durham, NC: Duke University Press.

Goswami, A. (2013). *Crime in India.* Delhi, India: Ministry of Home Affairs.

Gupta, S., & Tracey, T. J. (2005). Dharma and interest-occupation congruence in Asian Indian college students. *Journal of Career Assessment, 13*(3), 320–336.

Gupta, U., & Gupta, B. S. (2005). Psychophysiological responsivity to Indian instrumental music. *Psychology of Music, 33*(4), 363–372.

Harikumar, R., Mehroof, R., Antony, P., Harish, K., Sunil, K. K., Sandesh, K., Syed, A., & Varghese, T. (2006). Listening to music decreases need for sedative medication during colonoscopy: A randomized, controlled trial. *Indian Journal of Gastroenterology, 25,* 3–5.

Hart, W. (2009). *The art of living: Vipassana meditation as taught by S. N. Goenka.* Onalaska, WA: Pariyatti Publishing.

Henderson, J. (1990). The cultural unconscious. In J. Henderson (Ed.), *Shadow and self: Selected papers in analytical psychology* (pp. 103-113*)*. Wilmette, Illinois: Chiron Publications.

Hermans, H. (2003). The construction and reconstruction of a dialogical self. *Journal of Constructivist Psychology, 16*(2), 89–130.

Hersey, B. (2013). *The practice of Nada Yoga: Meditation on the inner sacred sound.* Rochester, VT: Inner Traditions.

Hodge, D. R. (2005). Social work and the house of Islam: Orienting practitioners to the beliefs and values of Muslims in the United States. *Social Work, 50*(2), 162–173.

Hsiao, A-F., Wong, M. D., Goldstein, M. S., Becerra, L. S., Cheng, E. M., & Wenger, N. S. (2006). Complementary and alternative medicine use among Asian-American subgroups: Prevalence, predictors, and lack of relationship to acculturation and access to conventional health care. *Journal of Alternative & Complementary Medicine, 12*(10), 1003–1010.

Hussain, F. A., & Cochrane, R. (2002). Depression in South Asian women: Asian women's beliefs on causes and cures. *Mental Health, Religion & Culture, 5*(3), 285–311.

Inman, A. G., Howard, E. E., Beaumont, R. L., & Walker, J. A. (2007). Cultural transmission: Influence of contextual factors in Asian Indian immigrant parents' experiences. *Journal of Counseling Psychology, 54*(1), 93.

Inman, A. G., & Tewari, N. (2003). The power of context: Counseling South Asians within a family context. In G. Roysircar, D. S. Sandhu, & V. B. Bibbins (Eds.), *A guidebook: Practices of multicultural competencies* (pp. 97–107). Alexandria, VA: ACA Publishers.

Inman, A., & Tummala-Narra, P. (2010). Clinical competencies in working with immigrant communities. In J. A. E. Cornish, B. A. Schreier, L. I. Nadkarni, L. H. Metzger, & E. R. Rodolfa (Eds.), *Handbook of multicultural counseling competencies* (pp. 117–152). New York, NY: John Wiley & Sons.

Inman, A. G., Yeh, C. J., Kim, A. B., & Okubo, Y. (2006). Asian American families' collectivistic coping strategies in response to 9/11. *Cultural Diversity and Ethnic Minority Psychology, 12*(1), 134-148.

Inman, A. G., Yeh, C. J., Madan-Bahel, A., & Nath, S. (2007). Bereavement and coping of South Asian families post 9/11. *Journal of Multicultural Counseling and Development, 35*(2), 101-115.

Islam, N. (1998). Naming desire, shaping identity: Tracing the experiences of Indian lesbians in the United States. In S. D. Dasgupta (Ed.), *A patchwork shawl: Chronicles of South Asian women in America* (pp. 72–96). New Brunswick, NJ: Rutgers University Press.

Iyengar, B. K. S. (2006). *Light on Yoga.* Pradesh, India: Harper Collins Publishers.

Jagdev, T., & Sharma, M. (2012). The use of music therapy for enhancing self-esteem among academically stressed adolescents. *Pakistan Journal of Psychological Research, 27*(1), 53–64.

Jacobsen, K., & Raj, S. (2008). *South Asian Christian Diaspora: Invisible Diaspora in Europe and North America.* Abingdon, GB: Routledge.

Jain, N., & Forest, B. (2004). From religion to ethnicity: The identity of immigrant and second generation Indian Jains in the United States. *National Identities, 6*(3), 277-297.

Jassal, S. (2012). *Unearthing gender: Folksongs of North India.* Durham, NC: Duke University Press.

Jeffrey, R. (2004). Legacies of matriliny: The place of women and the "Kerala model." *Pacific Affairs, 77*(4), 647–664.

Joomal, A. (2003). Music and Islam. *Al-Balagh, 28,* 52-58.

Kanukollu, S. N., & Mahalingam, R. (2011). The idealized cultural identities model on help-seeking and child sexual abuse: A conceptual model for contextualizing perceptions and experiences of South Asian–Americans. *Journal of Child Sexual Abuse, 20*(2), 218–243.

Kawale, R. (2003). A kiss is just a kiss … or is it? South Asian lesbian and bisexual women and the construction of space. In N. Puwar & P. Raghuram (Eds.), *South Asian women in the Diaspora* (pp. 179–198). New York, NY: Bloomsbury Academic.

Khan, S. I., Hussain, M. I., Parveen, S., Bhuiyan, M. I., Gourab, G., Sarker, G. F., & Sikder, J. (2009). Living on the extreme margin: Social exclusion of the transgender population (Hijra) in Bangladesh. *Journal of Health, Population, and Nutrition, 27*(4), 441–451.

Kohlhatkar, N. (2014, September 14). *What white people say to brown people reversed.* Retrieved from: https://www.youtube.com/watch?v=glfVFc7PlxQ

Kumar, P. P. (2012). Place of subcaste (jati) identity in the discourse on caste: Examination of caste in the diaspora. *South Asian Diaspora, 4*(2), 215-228.

Kurien, P. (2003). To be or not to be South Asian: Contemporary Indian American politics. *Journal of Asian American Studies, 6*(3), 261-288.

Lad, V. (2006). *Textbook of Ayurveda: A complete guide to clinical assessment* (Vol. 2). Albuquerque, NM: Ayurvedic Press.

Lal, B. V., Safran, W., & Sahoo, A. (2013). *Transnational migrations: The Indian Diaspora.* New Delhi, India: Routledge.

Lal, V. (1999). Establishing roots, engendering awareness: A political history of Asian Indians in the United States. In L. Prasad (Ed.), *Live Like the Banyan tree: Images of the Indian-American experience* (pp. 42–48). Philadelphia, PA: Balch Institute for Ethnic Studies.

Larson, G. J. (2014). Partition: The "Pulsing heart that grieved." *The Journal of Asian Studies, 73*(1), 5–8.

Lennon, J. (1965). *Help!* London, UK: Parlaphone/EMI Studios.

Luhrmann, T. M. (2006). Indian Zoroastrian tradition. In S. Mittal, & G. Thursby (Eds.), *Religions of South Asia: An introduction* (pp. 151-168). Abingdon, GB: Routledge.

Mahalingam, R. (2007). Beliefs about chastity, machismo, and caste identity: A cultural psychology of gender. *Sex Roles, 56*(3–4), 239–249.

Mahalingam, R., & Haritatos, J. (2006). Cultural psychology of gender and immigration. In R. Mahalingam (Ed.), *Cultural psychology of immigrants* (pp. 259–278). London, UK: Psychology Press.

Maira, S. (1998). Chaste identities, ethnic yearnings: Second-generation Indian Americans in New York City. *Dissertation Abstracts International: Section A* 59(04), 1238. (AAT No. 9830064)

Maira, S. (2002). *Desis in the house: Indian-American youth culture in NYC.* Philadelphia, PA: Temple University Press.

Maira, S. (2004). Youth culture, citizenship and globalization: South Asian Muslim youth in the United States after September 11th. *Comparative Studies of South Asia, Africa, and the Middle East, 24*(1), 219–231.

Masood, N., Okazaki, S., & Takeuchi, D. T. (2009). Gender, family, and community correlates of mental health in South Asian–Americans. *Cultural Diversity & Ethnic Minority Psychology, 15*(3), 265–274.

McCarthy, J. (2015). India's ban of beef leads to murder and Hindu-Muslim friction. Retrieved from http://www.npr.org/sections/parallels/2015/10/13/448182574/indias-ban-on-beef-leads-to-murder-and-hindu-muslim-friction

McGoldrick, M., Giordano, J., & Garcia-Preto, N. (Eds.). (2005). *Ethnicity and family therapy.* New York, NY: Guilford Press.

Medina, J. (2016). California to revise how India is portrayed in textbooks. *The New York Times.* Retrieved from http://www.nytimes.com/2016/05/20/us/california-to-revise-how-india-is-portrayed-in-textbooks.html

Mio, J., Nagata, D., Tsai, A., & Tewari, N. (2007). Racism against Asian/Pacific island Americans. *Handbook of Asian-American Psychology, 2,* 341–361.

Mohanka, P. S. (2005). Religion and conflict in India: A Sikh perspective. *Round Table, 94*(382), 589–598.

Mukherjee, M. (2011). *Churchill's secret war: The British Empire and the ravaging of India during World War II.* New York, NY: Basic Books.

Narayan, B. (2006). *Women heroes and Dalit assertion in north India: Culture, identity and politics.* New Delhi, India: Sage Publications India.

Nath, S. (2005). Pakistani families. In M. McGoldrick, J. Giordan, & N. Garcia-Preto (Eds.), *Ethnicity and family therapy* (pp. 407–420). New York, NY: Guilford Press. National Crime Records Bureau Ministry of Home Affairs. (2014). Crime in India, 2014. Retrieved from http://ncrb.nic.in

Newer, J. R. (2007). Unseen power: Aesthetic dimensions of symbolic healing in Qawwālī. *Muslim World, 97*(4), 640–656.

Omvedt, G. (2003). *Buddhism in India: Challenging Brahmanism and caste.* New Delhi, India: SAGE Publications India.

Osmania beef fest puts Hyderabad on the boil (2015, December 2). *The Times of India.* Retrieved from http://timesofindia.indiatimes.com/india/Osmania-beef-fest-puts-Hyderabad-on-the-boil/articleshow/50004402.cms

Paul, B. K. (2005). Islam in South Asia. *Education about Asia, 10*(1), 24–27.

Pettys, G., & Balgopal, P. (1998). Multigenerational conflicts and new immigrants: An Indo-American experience. *Families in Society: The Journal of Contemporary Social Services, 79*(4), 410-423.

Phinney, J. (1990). Ethnic identity in adolescents and adults: A review of research. *Psychological Bulletin, 108*(3), 499–514.

Phinney, J. (2001). Ethnic identity, immigration, and well-being: An interactional perspective. *Journal of Social Issues, 57*(3), 493–510.

Phinney, J. (2005). Ethnic identity in late Modern Times: A response to Rattansi and Phoenix. *Identity: An International Journal of Theory and Research, 5*(2), 187–194.

Porter, A. (1997). 'Cultural imperialism' and protestant missionary enterprise, 1780–1914. *The Journal of Imperial and Commonwealth History, 25*(3), 367-391.

Prasad, A. N. (2001). *Critical response to Indian fiction in English.* New Delhi, India: Atlantic Publishers & Distribution.

Qureshi, R. (1972). Indo-Muslim religious music, an overview. *Asian Music, 3*(2), 15–22.

Qureshi, R. (1992). "Muslim devotional": Popular religious music and Muslim identity under British, Indian, and Pakistani hegemony. *Asian Music, 24*(1), 111–121.

Rahman, A. R. (2008). Jai Ho! On *Slumdog Millionaire.* Chennai, India: N.E.E.T.

Rahman, O., & Rollock, D. (2004). Acculturation, competence, and mental health among South Asian students in the United States. *Journal of Multicultural Counseling & Development, 32*(3), 130–142.

Rajan, R. S. (2011). The politics of Hindu "tolerance." *Boundary 2, 38*(3), 67–86.

Rao, S., & Rao, P. (2014). An overview of Hindustani music in the context of computational musicology. *Journal of New Music Research, 43*(1), 24–33.

Reddy, G., & Nanda, S. (2005). Hijras: An "Alternative" Sex/Gender. In C. Brettell (Ed.), *Gender in cross-cultural perspective* (pp. 275–282). Upper Saddle River, NJ: Pearson-Prentice Hall.

Regi, A. A., & Rani, E. S. (2012). Social isolation of eunuchs and illegal practices. *Indian Social Science Journal, 1*(1), 11.

Rinehart, R. (2004). *Contemporary Hinduism: Ritual, culture, and practice*. Santa Barbara, CA: ABC-CLIO.

Rumball, K. (2010). The effects of group musical activity on psychiatric patients in India. *Voices: A World Forum for Music Therapy, 10*(2). doi:10.15845/voices.v10i2.164

Sairam, T. V. (2006). Melody and rhythm—"Indianness" in Indian music and music therapy. *Music Therapy Today* (Online), *7*(4), 876–891. Retrieved from http://www.musictherapyworld.de

Santora, M., Schwirtz, M., & Yaccino, S. (2012). Gunman kills 6 at a Sikh temple near Milwaukee. *The New York Times.* Retrieved from http://www.nytimes.com/2012/08/06/us/shooting-reported-at-temple-in-wisconsin.html

Scott, J. C. (1985). *Weapons of the weak: Everyday forms of peasant resistance*. New Haven, CT: Yale University Press.

Sharma, A. R. (2000). Psychotherapy with Hindus. In P. S. Richards & A. E. Bergin (Eds.), *Handbook of psychotherapy and religious diversity* (pp. 341–365). Washington, DC: American Psychological Association.

Shenoy-Packer, S., & Buzzanell, P. M. (2013). Meanings of work among Hindu Indian women: Contextualizing meaningfulness and materialities of work through dharma and karma. *Journal of Communication & Religion, 36*(1), 149–172.

Sherinian, Z. (2015). *Tamil folk music as Dalit liberation theology*. Bloomington, IN: Indiana University Press.

Shukla, S. (2001). Locations for South Asian Diasporas. *Annual Review of Anthropology, 30*(1), 551.

Shuval, J. T. (2000). Diaspora migration: Definitional ambiguities and a theoretical paradigm. *International migration, 38,* 41–57.

Shweder, R. A. (1991). *Thinking through cultures: Expeditions in cultural psychology*. Cambridge, MA: Harvard University Press.

Singh, K. (2013). *Laws and son preference in India: A reality check*. New Delhi, India: United Nations Population Fund.

Soundarajan, T. (2012, August). The Black Indians: Growing up Dalit in the US, finding your roots, fighting for your identity. *Outlook: The magazine.* Retrieved from http://www.outlookindia.com/magazine/story/the-black-indians/281938

South Asian Association for Regional Cooperation (1985). SAARC Charter. Retrieved from http://www.saarc-sec.org/SAARC-Charter/5/

Stern, K. (2016, June). *What is Kirtan?* Retrieved from http://newworldkirtan.com/what-is-kirtan

Stevens, J. (1989). *Tao to earth*. Sante Fe, NM: Bear & Company Publishing.

Stige, B. (2002). *Culture-centered music therapy*. Gilsum, NH: Barcelona Publishers.

Subbārāo, K. V. (2012). *South Asian languages: A syntactic typology*. New York, NY: Cambridge University Press.

Sue, D. W., & Sue, D. (2013). *Counseling the culturally diverse: Theory and practice*. Hoboken, NJ: John Wiley & Sons.

Sundar, S. (2005). Can traditional healing systems integrate with music therapy – Sumathy Sundar interviews T. V. Sairam. *Voices: A World Forum for Music Therapy, 5*(2). doi:10.15845/voices.v5i2.226

Sundar, S. (2007). Traditional healing systems and modern music therapy in India. *Music Therapy Today, 8*(3), 397–407.

Sundaresh, J. (2013). *Beyond bindis: Why cultural appropriation matters.* Retrieved from http://theaerogram.com/beyond-bindis-why-cultural-appropriation-matters/

Swamy, S. (2011). *Temple of ancient knowing: Music therapy portraits of globalized Indian identity* (Doctoral dissertation). Available from ProQuest Dissertations & Theses Full Text. (1368992873).

Swamy, S. (2014). Music therapy in the global age: Three keys to successful culturally centred practice. *New Zealand Journal of Music Therapy, 12,* 34-57.

Tarakeshwar, N. (2013). What does it mean to be a Hindu? A review of common Hindu beliefs and practices and their implications for health. In K. I. Pargament, J. J. Exline, & J. W. Jones (Eds.), *APA handbook of psychology, religion, and spirituality (Vol. 1): Context, theory, and research* (pp. 653–664). Washington, DC: American Psychological Association.

Thangaraj, T. (2006). Indian Christian tradition. In S. Mittal, & G. Thursby (Eds.), *Religions of South Asia: An introduction* (pp. 185-200). Abingdon, GB: Routledge.

Tilak, S. (2014, June 13). How do you solve a problem like TM Krishna? *Outlook.* Retrieved from http://www.outlookindia.com/website/story/how-do-you-solve-a-problem-like-tm-krishna/294587

Tummala-Narra, P. (2001). Asian trauma survivors: Immigration, identity, loss, and recovery. *Journal of Applied Psychoanalytic Studies, 3*(3), 243–258.

Tummala-Narra, P. (2007). Conceptualizing trauma and resilience across diverse contexts: A multicultural perspective. *Journal of Aggression, Maltreatment, & Trauma, 14*(1–2), 33–53.

Tummala-Narra, P. (2009). The immigrant's real and imagined return home. *Psychoanalysis, Culture & Society, 14*(3), 237–252.

Tummala-Narra, P., Alegría, M., & Chen, C. (2012). Perceived discrimination, acculturative stress, and depression among South Asians: Mixed findings. *Asian-American Journal of Psychology, 3*(1), 3.

Tummala-Narra, P., Inman, A. G., & Ettigi, S. P. (2011). Asian Indians' responses to discrimination: A mixed-method examination of identity, coping, and self-esteem. *Asian-American Journal of Psychology, 2*(3), 205.

United States Census Bureau. (2012). *The Asian population 2010: 2010 census briefs.* Retrieved from http://www.census.gov/prod/cen2010/briefs/c2010br-11.pdf

Wang, F. (2014). Human rights lawyer sues NYPD after arrest for blocking sidewalk. Retrieved from http://www.nbcnews.com/news/asian-america/human-rights-lawyer-sues-nypd-after-arrest-blocking-sidewalk-n198211

Wang, F. (2016). Sikh man falsely accused of terrorism demands accountability for accuser. Retrieved from http://www.nbcnews.com/news/asian-america/sikh-man-falsely-accused-terrorism-demands-accountability-accusers-n564311

Warder, A. K. (2004). *Indian Buddhism*. Delhi, India: Motilal Banarsidass Publishers.

Wardle, J., & Wrightson, K. J. (1997). Cultural variation in health locus of control. *Ethnicity & health, 2*(1-2), 13-20.

Weber, T. (2002). Gandhian nonviolence and the salt march. *Social Alternatives, 21*(2), 46–51.

Whitehead-Pleaux, A., Donnenwerth, A., Robinson, B., Hardy, S., Oswanski, L., Forinash, M., ... & York, E. (2012). Lesbian, gay, bisexual, transgender, and questioning: Best practices in music therapy. *Music Therapy Perspectives, 30*(2), 158–166.

Wilkinson, S. I. (2015). *Army and nation: The military and Indian democracy since independence*. Cambridge, MA: Harvard University Press.

Yim, J. Y., & Mahalingam, R. (2006). Culture, masculinity, and psychological well-being in Punjab, India. *Sex Roles, 55*(9), 715–724.

Young, J. O. (2010). *Cultural appropriation and the arts*. West Sussex, UK: John Wiley & Sons.

Chapter 7
DISCOVERING ARAB/MIDDLE EASTERN CULTURE

Aksana Kavaliova-Moussi

In March 2014, I received an email inviting me to contribute to this important book by writing about the Arab/Middle Eastern culture. I was thrilled but worried that my knowledge would not be sufficient enough. Here is why:

I was born in Belarus, then part of the Soviet Union. We lived in a big country, where people spoke various languages (there were 15 Soviet republics and many autonomic regions, and each had its own language). My mother tongue was Russian, but we learned Belarusian as well. I studied French as a foreign language and used to be quite good at it. (I also had three years of German classes, but it was not "my" language at all).

My parents were musicians, and at the age of 15, I went into a music college for four years, receiving a degree in music theory and history. Then, I completed another bachelor of arts degree in cultural studies. My final research was focused on composers of Belarusian descent, but during those five years, we learned a lot about both Western and Eastern cultures and arts. However, I did not know much about the Arab world until my 20s, when I met my husband and joined him in one of the countries in the Arabian Gulf. My husband is originally Algerian Berber and has many close family members in Algeria.

Although Arabic is an official language of the Arabian Gulf, English is widely used. I have to admit that I began learning English just after I met my husband. Except for the three months of group classes, I have not had any other formal training. If I wanted to understand my new environment, I had to learn at least one language. English was everywhere; this is why I did not even think about studying Arabic. However, I fell in love with the culture, its hospitable people, and its rich musical traditions. After a few years, we moved to Canada, where I began studying music therapy at the University of Windsor, Ontario. During my clinical practice and internship, I felt very close to the Middle East, as many of my hospital and hospice patients originated from the Arab world. Windsor had 3.7% of its population who indicated Arabic as their mother tongue in 2011 (Statistics Canada, 2011). I think that my education and my experience of living in the Middle East have helped me professionally. I could recognize and understand cultural values of my clients and families. I had some knowledge of their musical heritage, and learning a few songs was not very difficult (except for the Arabic pronunciation, of course!).

I came back to the Arabian Gulf in 2008 and started a private practice, working with individuals with special needs. The majority of my students are Arabs, although they speak and/or understand English well. I must admit that I still have yet to find the time and courage to learn Arabic, a very rich and difficult language.

The society of the Arabian Gulf is multicultural, with people coming from all over the world. However, most of our close friends here are Arabs from various countries. I also have opportunities to see a family structure, and the relationships within, while visiting our Algerian family. Thus, I can see how diverse but interconnected the Arab world is. During the process of working on this chapter, I have found my own observations and conclusions being supported by those who wrote about Arabs, whether natives or foreigners. I hope it will be helpful for those professionals who work with the Arab/Middle Eastern/Arab-American population.

Introduction

The term "Arab" is associated with a particular region extending from the Atlantic coast of northern Africa to the Arabian Gulf. The term is not a racial classification but is based on a common language (Arabic) and a shared geographic, historical, and cultural identity (Hammad, Kysia, Rabah, Hassoun, & Connelly, 1999). The 22 Arab League countries are Algeria, Bahrain, Comoros, Djibouti, Egypt, Iraq, Jordan, Kuwait, Lebanon, Libya, Mauritania, Morocco, Oman, Palestine, Qatar, Saudi Arabia, Somalia, Sudan, Syria, Tunisia, United Arab Emirates, and Yemen. The total population of the Arab world was 369.8 million in 2013, according to the World Bank (http://data.worldbank.org/region/ARB).

Arab immigration to the United States began in the 1880s. The first wave of immigrants came from the Ottoman Turkish district of Syria, which is known as the Levant region and includes Syria, Lebanon, Jordan, and Palestine. The vast majority of these immigrants were Christians (90%) seeking better economic opportunities. In the late 1960s, another wave of immigration began, with a majority being Muslims who were forced to move due to political and social instabilities. These recent waves of Arab immigration paralleled political events in the region: the formation of Israel (1948), the occupation of the Palestinian West Bank and Gaza Strip (1967), the Lebanese war of 1977–1992, the Yemeni civil war (1990s), the persecution of the Shi'ite minority in Iraq (early 1980s), and the Gulf Wars of 1991 and 2003 (Hammad, Kysia, Rabah, Hassoun, & Connelly, 1999, p. 2).

According to the 2010 U.S. Census, there were at least 1.9 million Arab-Americans in the United States. However, according to the Arab-American Institute (AAI), the number was more than 3.5 million (Arab-American Institute Foundation, 2012). Arab-Americans live in all 50 states, but two-thirds are concentrated in 10 states: California, Michigan, New York, Florida, Texas, New Jersey, Illinois, Ohio, Massachusetts, and Pennsylvania. One-third of the total number lives in California, New York, and Michigan, with 94% living in metropolitan areas. Los Angeles, Detroit, New York, Chicago, and Washington, DC, are the top five cities of Arab-American concentration. Lebanese-Americans constitute 27% of the total number, with Egyptians coming second at 11%. Other nationalities include Syrians (8%); Somalis (6%); Palestinians, Iraqis, and Assyrians (5% each); Moroccans (4%); Jordanians (3%); Sudanese (2%); Yemenis (2%); and 7% other Arabs (Arab-American Institute, n.d.)

In this chapter, we will cover the Arab culture of the MENA region (Middle East/North Africa).

Historical Realities Versus Popular Myths

There are many myths and misconceptions about the Arab people, and the common ones will be discussed here. The first five myths were presented in *Arab Voices,* a book written by James Zogby, founder and president of the Arab-American Institute, and discussed in an article written by Elshinnawi (2011, January 19).

Myth 1: Arabs Are All the Same and Can Be Reduced to a "Type"

Just by looking at the world map, we can see a large area covered by the Arab world. For example, the distance between Morocco to the west and Oman to the east is more than 6,000 kilometers, or about 4,000 miles, according to www.distancefromto.net. That is more than 2,000 kilometers longer than the distance between San Francisco and New York, and 1,300 kilometers longer than a distance between Ireland and Teheran in Iran! Zogby says, "Culture in Morocco is different than culture in Lebanon, Saudi Arabia is different than Egypt" (Elshinnawi, 2011, January 19). Each country has its subcultures, but people show a sense of belonging to a greater Arab world. This brings us to the second myth listed by Zogby (Elshinnawi, 2011, January 19).

Myth 2: There Is No "Arab World"

Arabs are as diverse as any people; however, they share common beliefs that are derived from a common language and sensibility. As Zogby states, "When Iraq was invaded, they came together, when Palestine is hurting, they come together and they speak in one language and they feel and they resonate together with certain words that mean something powerful to them" (Elshinnawi, 2011, January 19).

Myth 3: Arabs Despise the West, the United States, and Their Values and Ways of Life

Like other people, Arabs have the same everyday concerns: their families, children, health, education, jobs, and so forth. They do not live their lives hating the West, as some media portrays it. According to Nydell (2006), Muslims and Arabs in general do not want to change Western culture. They might not want foreign values to enter their own societies, but many of them emigrate to the West "because they admire many of the social values and want to participate in a Western way of life. They want their children to grow up … with the possibility of prosperity" (Nydell, 2006, p. xvii).

Myth 4: Most Arabs Are Terrorists Driven by Religious Fanaticism

Zogby (Elshinnawi, 2011, January 19) states that this misrepresentation is due to Hollywood's portrayal of Arabs as either corrupt oil millionaires or terrorists. According to Middle Eastern public opinion surveys, mosque attendance rates over the past decade had been similar to church attendance rates in the United States (Elshinnawi, 2011, January 19). As for the misperception of Islam being an oppressive religion of terrorists, it is worth noting that Islam encourages kindness toward others, lifelong learning, and social welfare and charitable activities and is based on the same tenets as Christianity and Judaism (Erickson & Al-Tamimi, 2001).

Myth 5: Arabs Reject Reforms and Will Never Change Unless the West Pushes Them

Using polling data, Zogby (Elshinnawi, 2011, January 19) found that Arabs want social and political change but do not want it being imposed on them. "[The] reform they want is theirs, not the West's. … Most Arabs do not want the United States meddling in their internal affairs, but they would welcome assistance in helping their societies" (Zogby, 2010, October 24, p. 2).

Myth 6: All Arabs Are Muslims

While the majority of Arabs are Muslims, about 7% to 10% of them are Christians. Arab Christians generally follow Greek Orthodox and Greek Catholic Churches. In Egypt, there are 9 million Coptic Christians, and in Lebanon, about 25% to 30% of population is Christian, with the denominations including Maronites, Greek Orthodox, Catholics, and Protestants (Tristam, n.d.). The majority of Arab-Americans continue to be Christians (63%), followed by Muslims (24%), with 13% of people being other/Jewish/no affiliation (Arab-American, 2014).

Myth 7: All Muslims Are Arab

Arab Muslims constitute less than 15% of the total Muslim population worldwide. According to Pew Research Center's Forum on Religion and Public Life (2009, October), more than 60% of the world Muslim population is concentrated in Asia. The top four Muslim countries are Indonesia (12.9%), Pakistan (11.1%), India (10.3%), and Bangladesh (9.3%).

Myth 8: All People from the Arab World Are Arab

In reality, not every person who comes from Arab countries is an Arab. The Arabian Peninsula is the homeland of the ethnic Semitic Arabian people. It includes Saudi Arabia, Yemen, Kuwait, Qatar, United Arab Emirates, Oman, and Bahrain. However, Oman and Bahrain are less ethnically homogeneous. In Oman, 15% of citizens are non-Arabs (Nydell, 2006), and in Bahrain there are a large number of Persians, descendants from Iran. The rest of the Arab world is even more ethnically diverse. Maghreb in North Africa has been inhabited by Berbers for millennia, and today, more than 12 million people in Morocco, Algeria, Tunisia, and Libya speak Berber languages. Most Moroccans and almost all Algerians are of Berber ethnic origin, while Tunisians and Libyans ethnically are of mixed Berber and Arabian descent. Sudan is one of the most ethnically diverse populations in the world (Nydell, 2006), with more than 400 languages, 19 ethnic groups, and 597 subgroups. Northern Sudanese are Arabs in language, but only partially in ethnicity. Although Arabic is the only official language, it is spoken by only 60% of the population. People from Lebanon, Syria, and Palestine are mainly from non-Arabian Semitic origins, mostly Phoenician and Canaanite, but they speak Arabic (Nydell, 2006). Only 75% of Iraqis are Arabs, and 20% are Kurds; the rest are Turkmens, Assyrians, and Armenians. Jordanians are of northern Arabian Bedouin descent; however, 60% of Jordanian citizens are Palestinians.

Myth 9: The Middle East and Arab Nations Are Oil-Rich

According to the 2012–2013 data for crude oil production (Central Intelligence Agency, 2012–2013), only a few Arab countries were included in the list of the top 20 oil producers: Saudi Arabia (1), Iran (6), UAE (7), Iraq (8), Kuwait (10), Algeria (15), Qatar (18), and Libya (20). Most Arab countries have less income than developed economies (Nydell, 2006) and suffer from high inflation and unemployment rates.

Myth 10: All Arab Women Must Cover Themselves from Head to Toe

In reality, traditions and current trends differ from one country to another, from one family to another, and even within families. Of course, you will not find women in Saudi Arabia without their long black "cloak" (abaya) and head scarf (hijab), as these pieces of clothing are customary for this country and for many conservative women in the Arab world. For instance, more women wear veils in Algeria than in any other North African country (Nydell, 2006). What the West calls "burka" is in fact a veil found in Afghanistan (which is not an Arab country). Nevertheless, in many regions, one can see women wearing Western clothes with or without a hijab. Overall, the level of coverage depends on several factors: the country of residence, religious affiliations, personal choice, or social status (Traditional clothing, n.d.).

Myth 11: Arab Immigrants Are Used to Living in Deserts, Ride Camels, and Have No Education

For me, this myth stays in the same category as the myth that Russians are people who live in eternal snow, are always drunk, wear fur hats, and walk alongside bears! Deserts do occupy a large area in North Africa and the Middle East, but people tend to live in the areas suitable for living. Almost all Arab countries have a high percentage of urban population, with the majority falling between 73% and 98% (Central Intelligence Agency, 2011). Needless to say, we won't see any camels strolling down the streets. As for their education level, 85% of Arab-Americans have at least a high school diploma, with more than 4 out of 10 having at least a bachelor's degree. Seventeen percent of Arab-Americans have postgraduate degrees, and this is nearly twice the American average of 9% (Arab-Americans, n.d.).

Cultural Values and Norms

The Arab/Arab-American culture is very diverse. This diversity is based on people's countries of origin, religious affiliations, social status, and levels of education. We have to bear in mind that broad generalizations cannot apply to all individuals; however, there are some common values and norms that are shared across the Arab world, and we will talk about them in the following section.

Values, Social Norms, and Customs

According to Nydell (2006), all Arabs share basic beliefs and values. For instance, child-rearing practices are nearly universal, as well as views on the role of a family, class structure, patterns of living, and moral standards. Arabs believe that many things in life are controlled by fate; that everyone loves (and wants to have) children; that wisdom increases with age. Nydell (2006, p. 15) listed several basic social and religious values: It is important to behave at all times in order to make a good impression on others and to protect one's personal dignity, honor, and reputation, as they impact the entire family or group. Personal preferences are less important than loyalty to one's family. Social class and family background are the first to determine a personal status; individual achievements come later. Everyone should have a religious affiliation. God, or fate, controls many, if not all, life events. Piety is an important and admirable personal characteristic.

Now, let's look at the values and norms more closely.

The Social Structure, Norms, and Etiquette. Most Arab countries have three social classes: the upper class (royalty, influential families, some wealthy people), the middle class (merchants, teachers, government employees, military officers), and the lower class (poor people, peasants). There are nomadic Bedouins who do not fit into any of these classes and are independent of society. Arabs accept their social class; they can improve their status through education, professional position, and wealth, but their origins will be remembered (Nydell, 2006).

People from the upper class are expected to behave according to a set of rules. For example, they must not engage in manual work in front of others, unless it can be considered as a hobby (e.g., painting, crafts, sewing). Thus, even after immigrating to the West, these families will often employ domestic helpers at least on a part-time basis. Their appearance is also very important, because "the way a person dresses indicates his or her wealth and social standing" (Nydell, 2006, p. 69). From my experience, upper-class Arabs prefer to dress in Western clothing when they travel or live abroad. Moreover, one should not be deceived by the simple-looking abayas (long black dresses), as they may have been made by world-class designers and cost a small fortune!

Social rules of etiquette are very important, and people are judged according to their manners and behaviors. Arabs are very hospitable and generous people. In the office or at home, a guest will never be allowed to stay without being offered food or at least some tea or coffee. It is imperative to not decline, but to accept even a small quantity so as to not be viewed as disrespectful. Regarding visits, Arab people will not refuse entrance to a guest, no matter how inconvenient this may be for them. However, if a woman (or women) were home alone, and the visitor were a man, it would be inappropriate for him to enter the house (Nydell, 2006). We will talk more about this in the section of gender differences.

The concept of time is different from its counterpart in the West. Arabs are more relaxed in general and often can be late for their appointments. This is changing in business relations but is still considered acceptable for less formal events. I remember how rigid I was about the timing when I first came to the Arab world. In my European mind, if a dinner was scheduled for 8:00 P.M., we had to be there on time. Then we would wait for our local friends for 30 to 40 minutes at a restaurant, and I would get upset. Now I laugh at it, and we try to arrive at parties about 20 minutes later than the scheduled time, so as to not be the first ones to arrive and not impose ourselves on the hosts. As for the scheduling of private music therapy sessions, it is important to discuss your professional schedule in advance to avoid any problems and delays. I make sure to allot some extra after-session time for clients, just in case they get in late. I want to appear professional but not inflexible, because this helps in building my professional reputation with the people in my community.

The following are some rules of etiquette as provided by Nydell (2006, pp. 62–64):

It is important to sit properly when talking, not allowing the sole of one's shoe to face another person. While talking with someone, stand straight without leaning against the wall or holding hands in one's pockets.

In many countries in the Arab world, a guest removes shoes at the door; this is a sign of respect.

Failure to shake hands is considered rude. However, an Arab woman is free to choose not to shake hands with a Western man. Some Muslims may decline to shake hands with a woman.

Dress code is important. Dressing in too-casual clothes in public is considered rude. At social events, people are supposed to dress rather formally.

At the gatherings, everyone stands when new guests arrive and when high-ranking or elderly people leave. A host will accompany leaving guests to the door, or elevator, or gate.

Men offer their seats to women and open the doors for them.

Elderly people should be greeted first.

Gifts are given and accepted with both hands and are not opened immediately.

The left hand is considered unclean; therefore, always use the right hand when giving/passing something, for instance, an empty coffee cup.

At a restaurant, Arabs will almost always insist on paying. It is proper to ritually offer to pay, then accept their payment and return the favor later. Public calculation and division of the bill is regarded embarrassing (although within a group of close friends, it is more acceptable).

People should not be photographed without their permission.

Family Values. The family is at the core of Arabic society. Arabic family structure differs from the Western one. The entire society is built around the extended family. There is a strong affiliation with all relatives, no matter how close they are to the immediate family. This strength, of course, varies among families, but most Arabs have dozens of close relatives. It is interesting to note that an immediate, or nuclear, family is of least significance in the traditional family unit. The extended family consists of blood relatives and women who married into the family and is governed by the eldest male. (Hammad, Kysia, Rabah, Hassoun, & Connelly, 1999).

Family obligations and loyalty are more important than any other social responsibilities. Individual identity is less significant than the identity defined by the family affiliation. Members of a family are expected to support each other in front of other people; thus, internal conflicts rarely get to the point of being public. Family members depend on each other emotionally and feel very close to each other. Sisters, brothers, and cousins are often best friends. Families are expected to provide support, sometimes interfering in the private lives of spouses but not disclosing anything to nonrelatives so as to not "lose face." Erickson and Al-Tamimi (2001) write that talking about family or personal issues with a mental health professional may be seen as disloyalty and even a threat to family honor. Personal bad actions dishonor not only the individual, but also the entire family. Such "bad actions" include out-of-wedlock relations, drug and alcohol use, homosexual relations, and even mental illness (Hammad, Kysia, Rabah, Hassoun, & Connelly, 1999). Family honor also means being responsible for each other and making individual sacrifices for the benefit of the family. Of course, as in any society, competition among family members exists. Nevertheless, siblings are taught to love, support, and sacrifice their interests for the benefit of their sisters and brothers. In this "tension between competition and generosity, between love and power … the dynamics of family are often played out. The tension provides spaces for negotiation, maneuvering, direct and indirect empowerment" (Joseph, 1996, p. 200).

Arabs love children and express their love openly. The entire family surrounds young children, and it is not only acceptable but expected that they get raised and disciplined by all adult relatives. Thus, a new mother always gets help from her mother, sisters, and other female family members, which creates a great support system. Having children is imperative, unless, of course, it is impossible due to some health issues. Having many children is still considered a priority in some rural societies. Children are taught great respect for adults; as a person grows older, his or her status in a family rises. Nydell (2006) writes that all families have patriarchs or matriarchs, whose opinions weigh a lot in family decisions or disputes. Adult children, particularly sons, are responsible for their parents as they grow older. "It is shameful by Arab cultural standards to place a parent in a nursing home instead of providing the care for the parent within one's own home" (Hammad, Kysia, Rabah, Hassoun, & Connelly, 1999, p. 20). Another interesting note is that Arab parents do not push their children to be totally independent, like Western parents do. It is expected that children will accept parental influence throughout their lives, which means being emotionally and even economically tied to the parents, who often help their grown children financially. Unmarried daughters remain their father's responsibility.

I know a few women who, after getting separated or divorced, went back to live with their parents. The society does not approve of unmarried women living alone; thus, they have to stay in their parents' homes. Sometimes this can create problems for women, when they cannot find a job in their own countries, but cannot travel abroad and live alone. One must remember, of course, that this varies across different subcultures.

Having a happy family is of utmost importance in the Arab culture. "The peace and security offered by a stable family … is greatly valued and seen as essential for the spiritual growth of its members. … Strong families create strong communities" (Nydell, 2006, p. 72). Thus, any occasion calls for the presence of most, if not all family members. Being surrounded by one's family is emotionally supportive and important in happiness and in mourning. Therefore, professionals working with Arabs must remember that they are dealing not only with one person, but also with their family members, and should work on developing good and trusting relationships with them (Hammad, Kysia, Rabah, Hassoun, & Connelly, 1999).

More Notes on Customs. There are a few more things worth mentioning here. As Nydell (2006) points out, Arabs like to ask personal questions, which Westerners would consider as being improper or even intrusive. Thus, the subject of money is not taboo for many traditional people. If one doesn't want to discuss his salary, it is better to politely avoid giving a straight answer. People can expect to be asked why they are not married or why they do not have children or when they are going to have more children.

This is less common among Westernized people; however, tradition-oriented Arabs believe in strong families with many children. I used to get some strange looks when people heard me talking about not wanting to have children because I was studying back then. Now, with one daughter and a master's degree, I have to be really creative in answering questions about having more children, because one child is not sufficient in many people's view.

Another important point to mention is what Nydell (2006, p. 35) calls "social distance." Arabs tend to stand and sit more closely together; people of the same sex will kiss cheeks and hug each other several times when they meet and before they part. An acceptable social distance between two persons may be perceived as being too close and intimate to some foreigners, although men in general tend to stay away from women in public places.

Coming from a culture where it is normal to kiss cheeks three times, I always find it fascinating to see how many varieties of greetings there are in the Arab culture. My friends from Lebanon kiss cheeks two times; family and friends from Algeria tell me that it is either two or four times. With some friends from Bahrain, I simply lose count every time I see them, as they kiss one cheek many times!

I think it is essential to talk about Arabic names, as they can provide us with additional information about people's cultural heritages. Nydell (2006, pp. 40–41) gives the following guidelines: If the name sounds Western, this means that a person is Christian. If the name is of a known Islamic historical figure, it marks a Muslim (e.g., A'isha/Ayesha, Fatima, Mohammed/Muhammad, etc.). Most hyphenated names are Muslim ("Abdel-" means Servant, and the second part would be one of the attributes of God). Names with the second part containing "deen" (religion) also are Muslim. Other names are adjectives and don't mark any religion (e.g., Said: happy, Jameela: beautiful). However, Westernized families tend to give neutral-sounding names to their children.

Gender Differences

The nature of the interaction between women and men in Arab society differs from that in Western society and has some rules and restrictions that are important to talk about. There is a strong sense of paternalism, or male dominance. Females can be very powerful at home; however, males are seen as protectors of their families (Transcultural Nursing, 2012). By Western standards, professional interactions between males and females can be seen as reserved. Nydell (2006) writes that Arab men and women avoid being together alone, and it is improper to be in a room with closed doors. However, there are many females in top positions, working in various fields. One thing for sure is that Islamic companies (e.g., insurance, banks) have stricter regulations, even toward dress codes. In gender-segregated Saudi Arabia, normal business interactions between the genders are restricted. Leeth (2014, September 12) writes that the "rules limit face-to-face interactions, mandate separate offices and facilities, and limit direct oversight of work by male managers." Saudi Arabia has the Committee for the Propagation of Virtue and the Prevention of Vice, or so-called "religious police." This government agency inspects businesses and public places on a regular basis (Leeth, 2014, September 12).

Social interactions are controlled, and the level of control depends on the degree of conservatism of a country or a particular family. "The maintenance of family honor is one of the highest values in Arab society. Misbehavior by women is believed to do more damage to family honor than misbehavior by men" (Nydell, 2006, p. 43). To maintain family honor, it is imperative to follow strict social rules. Thus, to avoid false impressions and gossip, women interact freely only with other women and close male relatives. As stated earlier, it is improper for nonrelatives of opposite sexes to be alone in a room with closed doors, to have a date, or to travel together. Of course, the younger generations or people from Westernized families have different, perhaps more relaxed, views on these social norms. Abraham (2014) writes that while young Arab-Americans may oppose the traditions and try living a "Western" life, for example, meeting and dating freely, their families, however, will never approve of such a lifestyle and will interfere to stop it. Importantly, tradition-oriented people do not see these customs as restrictive, but as a form of protection for women "so that they need not be subjected to the stress, competition, temptations, and possible indignities found in outside society" (Nydell, 2006, p. 52).

Overall, Middle Eastern gender roles have long been governed by a patriarchal system, with some local variations on the status of women. Traditionally, men were providing for their families, while women took care of the house and children. Modernization of the society, as well as political and economic changes, resulted in some transformations of the traditional roles. According to Nydell (2006), in Morocco, for instance, half of university students and 20% of judges are women. In Algeria, half of university graduates are women; however, due to high unemployment, women made up only 12% of the workforce (Nydell, 2006). Tunisian women were the most liberated before the recent political turmoil; they were active in the fields of education, social services, health care, administration, and the judicial system (Nydell, 2006). It is important to note that women make up the majority of university populations in two-thirds of the Middle Eastern countries (e.g., Kuwait, 64%; Qatar, 63%; UAE, 60%; Palestine, 56%; Lebanon, 54%; Saudi Arabia, 52%; Jordan, 51%). In spite of this, unemployment and societal expectations in some countries result in women being underrepresented in the workforce (Davies, 2012).

As I noted earlier, all of these norms and customs vary depending on the country of origin, religious affiliation, and amount of time that a person has lived within a Western society. While working on this chapter, I asked my friends the following questions: "Would you go to a doctor of the opposite sex and discuss all your issues freely? If not, why? Would you be at ease to work with a therapist of the opposite sex?" Many females said that they would not mind seeing male doctors, except for the gynecologists. However, both males and females would prefer to have a same-sex therapist in order to feel comfortable discussing their private issues. This potential influence of gender differences has been mentioned by Erickson and Al-Tamimi (2001, p. 323), who said, "Clients from some cultures may be less comfortable with counselors of the opposite sex." However, gender seems not to be of any importance in working with young children. I would advise that professionals working with Arab-Americans of the opposite sex directly asked the patient, or his or her family, about the acceptable level of interaction. During my internship in Ontario, where there was a strong community of immigrants from various Arab countries, I frequently worked with male hospital patients. I was mindful about my appearance, kept some physical distance between patients and myself, and would initiate no bodily contact such as handshakes or gentle touches unless I could see that they were appropriate and acceptable. As a Western woman living in an Arab culture, I got used to the social norms and don't necessarily see them as being restrictive. It is expected of us to behave and dress properly, and, quite frankly, I don't find any problem in keeping my skirts at a knee length and minding my neckline when in public.

Generational Differences

As was mentioned before, Arab patriarchal and gerontocratic society gives privileges to elderly men and women. They have a special status in society due to their experience and are looked up to and listened to by younger people. According to Joseph (1996), females are taught to comply with their fathers, brothers, grandparents, and uncles; younger people are taught to defer to their older family members; men are expected to take responsibility for females and the elderly; and elders are there to protect and be responsible for the younger generation. Patriarchal rules are widely observed in Arab families; however, there are some variations. For example, a more successful younger brother can have authority over an older one, a sister can be more powerful than her brother, or an elderly father can lose his authority to his sons if he becomes unhealthy or loses his wealth. Generally, male elders in the father's kin group are more powerful, but, again, it all depends on the family situation, as in some cases maternal relatives may be more important politically, emotionally, or socially. Traditionally, young married couples lived close to the husband's family, what Joseph calls *partilocality* (1996, p. 196). Today, however, this kind of living arrangement is less preferred among young couples.

In the United States, Arab-Americans continue with their traditions in general. Families are patrilineal, which means that they descend from the father's side, and patriarchal. Women continue to belong to their paternal family after marriage. Aswad (n.d.) writes that women's fathers and brothers can be a defense against their husbands in cases of domestic violence or any dispute. However, this pattern may be breaking down, with men being less protective of their female family members after they marry. Younger generations born in the United States may be rejecting the cultural values and traditions of older family members who immigrated to the United States and kept a strong cultural and ethical identity (Erickson & Al-Tamimi, 2001).

In working with Arab-Americans, therapists must remember the important roles that families and especially older family members play in the Arab communities. According to Erickson and Al-Tamimi (2001), one of the reasons why Arab-Americans are hesitant to seek mental health services is the cultural practice of seeking out the guidance of an older family member of the same gender. It is advisable to involve family members in the treatment process to support clients' growth and progress. In cases of conflicts between a loyalty to one's family versus individual achievements, it is important to encourage clients' connection to families, generating possible solutions to meet the needs of both parties (Erickson & Al-Tamimi, 2001).

Acculturation and Assimilation

Arab-Americans are one of the most diverse groups in the United States. For instance, individuals from the Arabian Gulf are more likely to be Muslims with more conservative values and higher standards of living; those from Syria or Lebanon may identify more with Western values, be Christian, and have lower standards of living. Thus, the levels of the acculturation and assimilation vary among Arab-Americans. Among the influencing factors are religious affiliation, time spent in America, country of origin, reasons to emigrate, educational and economic status, English language proficiency, whether or not they have family still living abroad, and their ability to return to or visit their home country (Erickson & Al-Tamimi, 2001).

According to Abraham (2014), early Arab immigrants, who were predominantly Christians, assimilated easily into American society. They Anglicized their surnames (a practice very common among the immigrants from the Old World at the time) and did not hold strongly to their roots. The second wave of Arab immigrants, who arrived in the middle of the 20th century, retained some ethnical features, in part because many of the newcomers were Muslims. They assimilated into society, but maintained their cultural identity and political awareness by establishing Arabic language schools, cultural clubs, societies, and committees. These early Arab immigrants went to the West as professionals seeking better economic opportunities. However, conflicts in the Arab world in the 1970s–1980s resulted in a third wave of forced immigrants, who formed communities of refugees in some parts of the United States. These people were separated from their families, came in from war situations, and experienced a lot of economic and psychological pressure. Abraham (2014) states that these immigrants, in general, chose not to assimilate and became a driving force behind the establishment of Muslim schools, charities, mosques, and Arabic language classes.

Generally, Arabs, Muslims, and Middle Easterners in the United States experience cultural marginalization. Abraham (2014) points out that they coped with this in one of three different ways: (1) denying their ethnic identity, (2) withdrawing into their ethnic community, or (3) advocating for Arab-Americans through information campaigns involving media, book publishers, schools, and politicians. Those who deny their ethnic background include individuals who are newcomers, assimilated immigrants, or American-born. Some immigrants prefer to identify themselves as non-Arabs (e.g., Berbers from North Africa or Chaldeans from Iraq). Those born in the United States tend to break away from their ethnical heritage and adopt the American culture as their own. Those individuals who withdraw into their enclaves tend to think that their traditions are alien to American culture; they usually live in the ethnic neighborhoods or in suburban communities. Integrationists, or the third group, try to "win societal acceptance of Arab-Americans as an integral part of America's cultural plurality" (Abraham, 2014). They stress family ties as common values in both Arab/Islamic and American cultures and focus on the commonalities between Christianity and Islam. They confront racism and stereotyping while maintaining their ethnic identity.

Relocation to another country and culture is difficult and challenging. A study by Faragallah, Schumm, and Webb (1997) found that Arab-Americans who had a longer U.S. residency, were at a younger age at immigration, had fewer ties with and fewer visits to a home country, and were Christian experienced greater acculturation into U.S. society and a higher overall satisfaction with life. Another factor that plays a role in the Arab-Americans' cultural adjustment is families' "educational and economic status in their home country and the degree to which these have changed since coming to the United States" (Erickson & Al-Timimi, 2001, pp. 312–313), because the differences can add a significant level of stress. A study by Amer (Greer, 2005) on Arab-Americans' level of adjustment to life in the United States found that Muslim Arabs experienced more stress and health problems trying to fit into American society when compared with Christian Arabs. This may be due to several reasons. Traditions of Christian Arabs may be closer to those of the hosting country, and thus they need less time and effort to assimilate with a new culture. Muslim Arabs, on the other hand, may have different values and traditions, be more conservative, and experience more stereotyping and discrimination. This leads us to the next section of this chapter.

Minority Discrimination

Early immigrants had no problems fitting into American society. This, however, changed during the third immigration wave, beginning with the Arab-Israeli war of 1967. Due to political and economic reasons (e.g., the Arab oil embargo and an immediate increase in oil prices after the Arab-Israeli war of 1973), "Arabs and Muslims were vilified as bloodthirsty terrorists, greedy oil sheiks, and religious fanatics by the mass media, politicians, and political commentators" (Abraham,

2014). Abraham writes that in the 1960s, the FBI, the Immigration and Naturalization Service, and other federal and local law enforcement agencies began surveillance of Arab students and communities. The surveillance was code-named Operation Boulder, was signed by President Richard Nixon, and included such measures as restrictions on entry and Arab access to permanent resident status, surveillance, information-gathering on organizations, and political activities. These measures were designed to prevent Arab terrorists from operating in the country. Interestingly, there had not yet been any instances of Arab terrorism in the United States (Abraham, 2014). Moreover, the first terrorist act did not occur until the 1993 bombing of the World Trade Center.

The stereotypes and negative portrayal by the media fueled the general public perception of Arabs as terrorists. Following a bombing in Oklahoma City (1995), where White American terrorists were quickly identified as primary suspects, Arab-Americans across the United States reported increased harassment and intimidation. After the TWA Flight 800 explosion in 1996, which apparently was caused by a mechanical failure, the targeting of Muslim Americans and Arab-Americans became a constant problem, as airlines continued profiling people based on their Arab-sounding names or passport stamps from Arab countries (Saito, 2001). Among other acts of discrimination was the creation of a special court to use secret evidence to deport foreigners who were labeled as terrorists. As Saito states, "It made support for the peaceful humanitarian and political activities of selected foreign groups a crime." Deportation on so-called "national security grounds," according to Saito, is a human tragedy, as families get torn apart and careers ruined. The author cites Susan Akram from Boston University School of Law:

> The use of secret evidence in deportation proceedings is the most powerful tool in an apparently systematic attack by U.S. governmental agencies on the speech, association, and religious activities of a very defined group of people: Muslims, Arabs, and U.S. lawful permanent residents of Arab origin residing in this country. Evidence emerging from these cases indicates that the government is spending thousands of U.S. taxpayer dollars on prosecuting and attempting to deport Arabs and Muslims under the rubric of "terrorism," when the "classified evidence" used to charge them is apparently nothing more than hearsay, innuendo, and, at most, guilt by association. (Saito, 2001)

Faragallah et al. (1997) noted in their exploratory study on Arab-American acculturation that if the immigrants were recognized as Arabs, they might face more intense discrimination. According to the authors, the nonsignificant relationship between length of residence and discrimination showed that the latter was not declining over time. The

practice of discrimination, which began in the 1960s, has continued ever since. Ghazali (2012) states that racial profiling by U.S. law enforcement agencies increased after September 11, 2001. "Racial profiling is any use of race, religion, ethnicity, or national origin by law enforcement agents as a means of deciding who should be investigated, except where these characteristics are part of a specific suspect description" (Leadership Conference on Civil Rights Education Fund, n.d., p. 10). Authorities enforced minor violations by Arabs and Muslims, while ignoring similar cases by other ethnic groups. Air travel became a real psychological trauma for many. People were pulled out of security lines for additional screenings and investigations just because they appeared to be Arabs, were held without food or water for hours by Customs and Border Protection agents, and kicked off the flights or even separated from their families and deported. All these abuses and humiliations happened because they appeared to be Arabs or Muslims and therefore were being viewed as terrorists.

Ghazali also writes that "'driving while Arab or Muslim' has joined the profiling lexicon alongside 'driving while Black' and 'driving while Brown' since 9/11" (2001, p. 76). The book gives numerous examples of discrimination against Arab-Americans, stating that many innocent people were detained without due process and held without being formally charged. Moreover, Arabs and Arab-Americans were and are constantly subjected to the scrutiny of White and other groups of Americans, especially in public places, airports, and planes. For instance, during the first Gulf War of 1991, many major American cities had "terrorist hotlines" (Erickson & Al-Tamimi, 2001, p. 319) and were asking people to report any suspicious "Arab-looking" individuals; this led to numerous violent acts against Arab-Americans. While it is politically incorrect to make derogatory generalizations about Asian- or African-Americans, people are not so aware of their negative stereotypes about Arabs (Erickson & Al-Tamimi, 2001). People in the Arab-American community continuously deal with violence, threats, and employment discrimination, but they believe that such prejudice is based on a lack of knowledge and unbiased information about them (Nydell, 2006).

Meaning of Medicine and Well-Being

The system of Arab medicine and healing, formulated over a thousand years ago, started with the birth of the Islamic civilization in the 7th century. It was then that ancient Greek, Turkish, Indian, Persian, and Arab traditions were synthesized, producing a scientific system of healing (Hammad et al., 1999). Arab medical texts were among the foundations of the modern Western medicine. Arabic, or Islamic, medicine followed the healing system of Hippocrates, which saw the body in terms of four humors: blood, phlegm, yellow bile, and black bile. Traditional cures target either an excess or a deficiency in one of the humors, thereby rebalancing and healing the body.

The development of hospitals was a major achievement at that time. The first hospital was established in Damascus in the

7th century and was a prototype of the modern hospital. It was a place for curing diseases as well as for teaching students. The therapeutic approaches being used were typical of the Hippocrates system of healing: baths, exercise, and diets. However, by the 13th century, there were over 13,000 drugs, and many surgical techniques were utilized (Hammad et al., 1999). Today, the traditional healing system of Arabs is present mostly in rural areas, where modern medicine may be limited to basic primary care, whereas in the cities, Western medicine is used.

In addition to this, a folk belief system exists in the Middle East. One belief is the acceptance of outside, unseen forces that can affect a person's health. These unseen forces are "jinns," or evil spirits. Hammad et al. (1999) note that mental disorders are often attributed to the influence of those dark forces. Also, people can be negatively influenced by the thoughts and negative intentions of other people, and this can cause a disease. For protection of adults and children from the evil eye, traditional amulets are used, such as pendants with turquoise, "hamsa" or "Fatima's hand" (a palm of one hand), or a "Turkish eye," as well as verses from holy books. To prevent bad luck or illness, to speed up recovery, and to give comfort to patients and families, people burn incense (especially "oud," or agar tree) and offer prayers and readings from the Qur'an or the Bible.

Due to their cultural and religious traditions, Arabs may be perceived as fatalists. The will of God is "the mover of all actions and the originator of all fate and events" (Hammad et al., 1999, p. 14). One will often hear people saying "In sha Allah" ("God willing"), when referring to anything that might happen in the future. Sometimes, a cause of the disease may be viewed as God's punishment or a test. Arab Muslims, according to Hammad et al. (1999), often believe that their illness is the result of Divine Will and not their lifestyles or risky behavior. Thus, recovery is seen as a result of treatment and God's will combined. Hammad et al. (1999) advise health care professionals to not talk about the future with their Arab clients, but rather to use the same "God willing" assertions.

Another important characteristic of Arabs is their tendency to be less aware of the psychological part of one's health and well-being. Often, they describe mental, emotional problems in physical terms, for example, an aching body or gastrointestinal problems in place of anxiety or depression (Erickson & Al-Tamimi, 2001). There is also a lack of psychological terminology in the Arabic language. Mental issues are considered a taboo to talk about, and often people would prefer to hide them rather than expose themselves. It is imperative to reassure such clients about their mental stability and the confidential nature of the therapeutic relationship (Erickson & Al-Tamimi, 2001). Once in therapy, many Arabs may expect to be given detailed guidance and directions. Thus, it is advisable for mental health practitioners to offer a clear explanation of their role and the treatment process, as well as providing more structured therapies. Erickson and Al-Tamimi (2001) give excellent recommendations for implementing culturally relevant interventions. They explain that client-centered approaches may be useful in establishing therapeutic relationships; however, these may be too self-focused, thus creating confusion on the part of Arab-American clients. "Psychoeducational, cognitive, cognitive-behavioral approaches that involve more formal or didactic interactions are more similar to the helping approaches many Arab-American clients may be familiar with and therefore may be more easily accepted" (Erickson & Al-Tamimi, 2001, pp. 322–323).

A very important tradition in Arabic culture is visiting the sick in a hospital or at home. Family members, friends, and colleagues all come, bringing presents, flowers, sweets, tea, and coffee. This extensive social support is very important for patients' recovery. One can see sofas and chairs everywhere in hospitals' rooms and corridors. As has been mentioned several times in this chapter, the best way to work with Arab people, just as with anybody else, is to be aware of their cultural norms and to make the necessary accommodations.

This makes me think of my own experiences, first as a caregiver and later as a patient in Middle Eastern hospitals. The first time I spent at the bedside of my husband in a hospital, I got really dizzy and disoriented by the number of people visiting us! As I had no idea of what was expected from me, I felt fortunate to have caring friends who brought all the necessary items with them, such as thermoses of coffee and tea, with plates of traditional sweets and chocolates. Visiting hours extend to 9:00 p.m. This was absolutely impossible for me to imagine, as visits in my home country are usually limited to a couple of morning and evening hours! I lost count of the visitors and was wondering how locals with big families around were dealing with similar situations. However, the more I lived here, the more appreciative I became of such a custom. Once I experienced being on the "receiving end," I understood how much this social support, all this positive energy, all the chats and jokes really keep your spirits up. Instead of lying in bed alone, wondering about your health while taking pain medications, you are surrounded by people who love you and care about you! It is all about the power of positive thinking, which helps in the healing of bodies and souls.

Arab/Middle Eastern Music and Its Function

It is believed by some that music has no place in Arab society, as many presumably think that it is forbidden, or *"haram."* Contrary to this popular misconception, music plays a very important part in the lives of Arab/Middle Eastern people, regardless of their religious affiliations. Music is present everywhere in the Arab world: at home, at work, during the happy moments, during the Muslim holy month of Ramadan, and even in times of grief and mourning. Understanding of the therapeutic effects of music is becoming more widespread today.

Arabic Music in Therapy

During the early times of Islam, music was considered a branch of mathematics and philosophy. In the 9th century, Al-Kindi, an Arab Muslim philosopher, mathematician, physician, and musician, recognized music's therapeutic value and even tried to cure a boy with quadriplegia using music (Saoud, 2004). Al Farabi, a renowned philosopher, scientist, cosmologist, and music scholar, later wrote a treatise titled *Meaning of the Intellect,* in which he talked about the therapeutic effects of music on psychological disorders. According to Syed (2002), Arab/Muslim physicians were using music therapy in asylums for the mentally ill. Such asylums were built in Fez, Morocco, in the 8th century; in Baghdad in the year 705; in Cairo in 800; and in Damascus and Aleppo in 1270. In addition to treatments such as baths and drugs, patients were exposed to music-based therapy and occupational therapy. Special choirs and live bands were performing daily. Performances included singing, musical, and comical performances for patients (Syed, 2002). In the 13th century in Cairo, light music, narrated stories, and the singing of religious songs were used at the Al Mansuri Hospital, so that patients could forget their sufferings. As we can see, the early forms of music therapy were somewhat equivalent to what we now know as therapeutic music, or what the pioneers of American music therapy were doing in the 19th and early 20th centuries.

In the Ottoman period, music was included in medical education, along with mathematics, philosophy, and astronomy. Al Farabi, in his book *Musiki-ul-kebir,* described the effects of different microtonal scales, or *makamat* (singular: *makam*), on the soul. Hekimbaşı Gevrekzade Hasan Efendi, in the 18th century, outlined the effectiveness of each makam in the treatment of various diseases. According to Somakci (n.d.), makamat were not played randomly, but at certain times during the day. Some makamat were found to be most effective for certain nationalities: Huseyni makamat for Arabs, Irak makamat for Iranians, Uşşak makamat for Turks, and Buselik makamat for Greeks. Certain makamat were used to provoke certain feelings; they were also associated with a particular zodiac sign. According to Sari (n.d.), while specific makamat were prescribed for specific conditions, the temperament and reaction of each patient also had to be observed, so that the most suitable mode could be found in accordance with the individual response. However, music therapy still consisted solely of group listening sessions where musicians and players performed in front of the patients.

According to Tucek (2005, p. 211), "traditional oriental music therapy has Islamic roots. In a way, Islamic culture is a culture of listening. Nobody reacts with more enthusiasm than Muslims to the melodious sound of the divine word." Although no solid evidence has been found that would support the notion of the emotion- and organ-specific effects of makamat, the general idea of the medical, therapeutic effects of Arab music has remained consistent with time (Tucek, 2005, p. 213). Each makam is said to evoke a different emotion in listeners.

However, there seems to be no consensus on what the mood of each makam is. There has not been any research examining makamat effects on a diverse group of Arab and non-Arab listeners. Are these theories still used today? I don't think so, since there is no music in hospitals around the region at the moment, and the few music therapists who practice here have been educated in the West. Perhaps this could be a topic of exploration for locally educated music therapists. As for average patients, I don't think that they would have much knowledge of makamat.

Music, Its Elements, and Instruments

It is important to note that Arab/Middle Eastern music has several distinctive components, as described by Touma (Arab Culture, 2014). They include the above-mentioned microtonal, or makam system; a rich variety of rhythmic patterns; typical musical instruments; emphasis on melody and rhythm rather than harmony; the predominance of vocal music with long, ornamented, melismatic tunes; and the absence of polyphony. There are at least 24 makamat, and the notes of a scale often lie at what Westerners would call a quarter note apart. This helps in creating highly ornamented melodies, and only virtuoso singers can successfully perform some pieces. Middle Eastern music often contains overlapping rhythms, and playing a darbouka/tabla (drum) is a difficult task. Improvisation is an essential part of almost any musical performance, as is a technique of call-and-response between different instruments.

Among the essential Arabic musical instruments are the *tabla (darbouka, derbek, doumbek),* a gobletlike drum, a "heartbeat of Middle Eastern music" (Paulson, n.d.); *oud,* a pear-shape string instrument, which is similar to the European lute but with a smaller neck and no frets; violin; *sagat,* small finger cymbals; *nai,* a hollow reed flute with a very distinctive sound; *riq/daff,* a tambourine; and *tar,* a large-frame drum (Paulson, n.d.).

Music therapists working with the Arab/Middle Eastern population should make an effort to learn about Arabic music. One must recognize that some conservative Muslims still view music as being strictly secular and foreign. For instance, string and wind instruments are viewed as "producing hypocrisy in the heart" and therefore are considered forbidden (Islamhelpline, n.d.). Some even ban singing. This may appear to be a double standard, for the recitations of the Qur'an sound like music to the Western ear. Interestingly, no double standard exists, since recitations of Qur'an are not considered to be music. However, there is no verse in the Holy Qur'an that prohibits music (Islamawareness, n.d.). More information on this topic can be found in the chapter within this book on Muslim culture. It is important for professionals working with the Arab population to remember that a majority of Arabs don't hold the above-mentioned views. There is literally not a single Muslim country where music is banned, and, of course, as has been stated before, not all Arabs are Muslims, and only a small percentage of Muslims are really that conservative. In my music therapy practice, I have never encountered such a person.

Just as in any society, music plays an important role in the lives of Arabic people. Of course, in the modern world, where music and art are not confined to geographical borders, individual preferences may include music of various styles and cultures. For instance, Western classical musicians, although less widely known, perform sold-out concerts in the region. American and European pop music is recognized and performed often. Nevertheless, just a couple of songs in Arabic may help music therapists to establish a good therapeutic relationship between them and clients, as well as clients' families. A short "starter" list of famous Arabic singers can be found in Appendix A and some examples of the songs from various countries, in Appendix B. It is impossible to name just a few of the most popular songs, because of the diversity of Arab culture.

For children's music, I find that modern technology has eliminated all borders. While there are Arabic children's shows and music, almost all children know Barney, Dora the Explorer, Disney movies (2014 was a *Frozen* year!), and many English nursery rhymes. Music for children is used just as it is anywhere else in the world, by mothers singing lullabies and finger playing songs for child development and schools using nursery rhymes in teaching basics like the alphabet and numbers. My daughter had Arabic classes in her nursery and sang these songs at the age of three. A reader can find some useful sources of Arabic children songs in Appendix B.

During my undergraduate studies in Windsor, Ontario, I was one of the student music therapists in the "Music Therapy in Medicine" project, which provided services at the palliative care/oncology ward of the local hospital. In my music binder, I had songs in many languages, including two in Arabic. These two were"Tamalli Maak" ("Always with You") and "Habibi" ("Beloved"), sung by the Egyptian singer Amr Diab. As I mentioned before, Ontario, just like neighboring Michigan in the United States, has a large Arab/Middle Eastern population. I sang these songs numerous times, and they were really great icebreakers. I remember one Iraqi man who at first did not want any music. I asked him if I could sing for him in Arabic, and he obviously was very surprised to hear that from a Caucasian woman with a Slavic accent. The man had tears in his eyes throughout the song. It really helped me in establishing that necessary connection with him. We had a great session, where he talked about his home and family, his country, which he had to leave, and his hopes for a better future. Another young man, a cancer patient in the oncology ward, started by angrily refusing our services because they were of "no use to him." I simply asked him if he could help me with some Arabic pronunciation and began singing "Habibi." The nurse who came to check on him was very surprised to see this usually passive and sad young man sitting up in his bed, playing a hand drum and singing along. And let's not forget the empowering Arabic mini-lesson he provided to his therapist!

One of my internship sites was a hospice company in

Michigan. Sometime during my first month of observing the supervising MT-BC, we worked with a Lebanese woman, whose daughter was present. After several English songs, I proposed to sing my two favorites in Arabic. The daughter was not sure about "Habibi," as the song is usually sung at the weddings and other happy events. I assured her that by changing the tone of my voice and the tempo, I could sing a completely different song from the one she knew. So I did, and the song became a sad ballad about a loved one. A few weeks later, our company received a phone call from that nursing home, asking us to send the music therapist who came before and sang in Arabic. It was urgent, as the patient was actively dying. My supervisor rescheduled our visits of the day and brought me there. These songs became a hymn of love between a daughter and her dying mother.

Enabling Health and Well-Being: Recommendations for Music Therapists

When working with Arab-Americans, professionals must utilize as many resources as possible to learn about their clients' backgrounds. For instance, there are a number of newspapers and online resources; cultural events take place in many parts of the country. Connect to the cultural resources in your community; utilize the help of other music therapists by means of social media, networking live and online, and connecting with national and international music therapy associations and federations. Communicate with universities' language and ethnomusicology departments; find help in community centers and religious and nonprofit organizations; visit local stores. The sky is the limit in our era of technology. It is also crucial to learn about the individual worldview of each client; about his or her ethnic, cultural, and religious identity, political beliefs, and level of assimilation and acculturation; and about any negative experiences of minority discrimination, as these factors have a profound impact on a person's mental and physical health. Family history and interrelationships should be considered as well, to understand the amount of social support available to clients, as well as any obligations that clients might have to family members. Recognize the differences in acculturation experienced by first-generation immigrants versus Arab-Americans born in the United States and their relationship with their own culture.

Among other recommendations for implementing culturally relevant interventions, Ericson and Al-Tamimi (2001, pp. 323–324) listed the following: Be aware of gender differences and address them as they arise; some clients may feel uncomfortable in dealing with a therapist of the opposite sex. Don't expect clients to openly discuss emotional issues; a sense of trust and confidentiality needs to be developed. Involve family members in treatment planning or sessions; family support can play a great role in a client's recovery. Consider religious affiliation and if necessary, consult with religious leaders in the client's community. For clients with mental health issues, provide as much information as needed to counter their negative attitude toward mental illness; help them cope with their concerns about the social stigma of mental illness, which can be a serious issue for many Arab-Americans. Allow yourself to be educated by your clients about their individual cultural contexts, ethnic identity, family relationships, and religious and cultural beliefs. Assess their level of acculturation and assimilation.

I would like to add some more suggestions, which can be helpful in establishing a strong and positive therapeutic relationship. When visiting regular clients, don't say no to a small amount of food or drink being offered, as this may offend people. Arabs are very hospitable, and feeding a guest is very important to them. I know that in many American facilities it is forbidden to accept anything from the clients or their family members. However, if we want to be efficient, we must be culturally responsive and weigh the pros and cons of our attitude and strict rule-following (unless, of course, there is a written policy that forbids such actions). It would be advisable to explain your company or facility policies on this, so that the clients and their families do not take your refusal personally.

If you know absolutely nothing about your clients' culture and music, ask questions: Family members can be a great source of information in cases where clients have communication difficulties. Educate yourself on various topics related to your client's background. Be open-minded and remember that Arabs are very diverse; therefore, don't assume that you know them from one or two encounters.

Try to learn some basic Arabic words; this will help in creating a positive and trusting atmosphere. As Nydell noted, "Even the simplest phrases, no matter how poorly pronounced, will produce an immediate smile and comment of appreciation" (2006, p. 193). Arabs use many beautiful greetings and blessings, which are required by etiquette in many social situations (Nydell, 2006, pp. 201–202). For instance, meeting someone's small child calls for praise mixed with blessings, such as *Mashallah* (What God wills). Blessings such as *Mabrook* (Blessed) are used to congratulate on anything. Another highly used expression is *Inshallah* (If God wills): It is said when speaking of any future events or plans. *Alhamdu lillah* (Thanks be to God) is used as a response to any good news. *Hamdillah'ala ssalama* (Thanks be to God for your safety) is said when someone returns from a trip or recovers from an illness. *Naam* means yes, and *Lah* means no. Some predetermined situational expressions include the following: *Marhaba/Marhabtayn* (Hello/Hello); *Sabah alkhayr/Sabah annour* (Good morning/Good morning); *Assalamu' alaykum/Wa' alaykum assalam* (Peace be upon you/And upon you peace); *Shukran/'Afwan* (Thank you/You're welcome); congratulatory *Mabrook/Allah yibarik feek* (Blessed/May God bless you); and, when leaving, *Ma'a ssalama/Allah yisallimak* (Go with safety/May God make you safe).

Conclusion

For me personally, working with Arabic adults felt a bit like working with Slavs: Both can appear to be hiding in a shell, being emotionally reserved and careful. However, once you get their trust, they open up and show their true warm personalities. One last piece of advice for music therapists working with Arabs/Arab-Americans would be the following: Regardless of the level of education and modernization that your clients might have, be prepared to offer them a lot of explanations of why and how music therapy works. Some may not perceive you as an allied health professional, especially if you work in private practice. It would be important to explain to them the differences between music teaching and therapy, if you work with children, and between entertainment and therapy, if you work with adults. I know that this is an ongoing problem we all face, regardless of our location in the world, but music therapy is literally unknown by the majority of the Arabs. As an example, there is only one training program for music therapists, in Jordan, which is not really known outside the country. Therefore, we have to double our efforts in order to educate our current and future clients and their family members.

This chapter provides some useful information on the culture, social customs, values, and music of Arab/Middle Eastern people. Arab people are very kind and helpful by nature, and thus one should not be worried about his or her lack of knowledge or musical repertoire. Music therapists listening to and learning Arabic music might find themselves falling in love with oriental rhythms, beautiful melodies, and virtuoso voices. Just as with any other nation or ethnicity, working with Arabs requires learning about them, trying to understand them, and being open-minded, embracing new experiences that will enrich one's life.

References

Abraham, N. (2014). Arab-Americans. In Countries and their cultures. Retrieved from http://www.everyculture.com/multi/A-Br/Arab-Americans.html

Arab Culture. (n.d.). In Wikipedia. Retrieved from http://en.wikipedia.org/wiki/Arab_culture

Arab-American. (2014). In Wikipedia. Retrieved from http://en.wikipedia.org/wiki/Arab_American

Arab-American Institute. (n.d.). Demographics. Retrieved from http://www.aaiusa.org/pages/demographics/

Arab-American Institute Foundation. (2012). Retrieved from http://b.3cdn.net/aai/44b17815d8b386bf16_v0m6iv4b5.pdf

Arab-Americans. (n.d.). In Arab-America. Retrieved from http://www.arabamerica.com/arabamericans.php

Aswad, B. (2011, July 7). Social dynamics and identity: Family, gender and community organization. Wilson Center. Retrieved from http://www.wilsoncenter.org/sites/default/files/aswad.pdf

Central Intelligence Agency. (2011). *The World Factbook*. Urbanization. Retrieved from https://www.cia.gov/library/publications/the-world-factbook/fields/2212.html

Central Intelligence Agency. (2012–2013). *The World Factbook*. Country Comparison: crude oil production. Retrieved from https://www.cia.gov/library/publications/the-world-factbook/rankorder/2241rank.html

Davies, C. (2012, June 7). Mideast women beat men in education, lose out at work. *CNN: Inside the Middle East*. Retrieved from http://edition.cnn.com/2012/06/01/world/meast/middle-east-women-education/

Elshinnawi, M. (2011, January 19). New book busts myths about Arabs. *Voice of America*. Retrieved from http://www.voanews.com/content/new-book-busts-arab-myths-114273089/160193.html

Erickson, C. D., & Al-Tamimi, N. R. (2001). Providing mental health services to Arab-Americans: Recommendations and considerations. *Cultural Diversity and Ethnic Minority Psychology, 7*(4), 308–327.

Faragallah, M. H., Schumm, W. R., & Webb, F. J. (1999). Acculturation of Arab-American immigrants: An exploratory study. *Journal of Comparative Family Studies, 28*(3), 182–203.

Ghazali, A. S. (2012). *Islam and Muslims in Post-9/11 America*. Retrieved from http://www.ghazali.net/asghazali/Islam___Muslims_in_the_Post-9-11_America-Version_1.pdf

Greed, M. (2005, January). Investigating the pain of integration. *GradPSYCH Magazine, American Psychological Association*. Retrieved from http://www.apa.org/gradpsych/2005/01/integration.aspx

Hammad, A., Kysia, R., Rabah, R., Hassoun, R., & Connelly, M. (1999). Guide to Arab Culture: Health Care Delivery to the Arab-American Community. *ACCESS: Arab Community Center for Economic and Social Services*. Retrieved from http://www.naama.com/pdf/arab-american-culture-health-care.pdf

Islamawareness. (n.d.). *Is music prohibited in Islam?* Retrieved from http://www.islamawareness.net/Music/prohibited.html

Islamhelpline. (n.d.). *Why are string instruments forbidden in Islam?* Retrieved from http://www.islamhelpline.net/node/3700

Joseph, S. (1996). Gender and family in the Arab world. In S. Sabbagh (Ed.), *Arab women. Between defiance and restraint* (pp. 194–202). New York, NY: Olive Branch Press.

Leadership Conference on Civil Rights Education Fund. (n.d.). *Wrong then, wrong now. Racial profiling before & after September 11, 2001*. Retrieved from http://www.civilrights.org/publications/wrong-then/racial_profiling_report.pdf

Leeth, J. (2014, September 12). Integrating Saudi women into the workforce brings challenges. *Society for Human Resource Management*. Retrieved from http://www.shrm.org/hrdisciplines/global/articles/pages/saudi-women-workforce-challenges.aspx

Nydell, M. K. (2006). *Understanding Arabs: A Guide for Modern Times* (4th ed.). Boston, MA: Intercultural Press.

Paulson, L. (n.d.). *About the dance, about the music*. Retrieved from http://www.jawaahir.org/AboutTheDance,AboutTheMusic.htm#Instruments

Pew Research Center's Forum on Religion and Public Life. (2009, October). *Mapping the Global Muslim Population*. Retrieved from http://www.pewforum.org/2009/10/07/mapping-the-global-muslim-population/#map1

Saito, N. T. (2001, May). Symbolism under siege: Japanese American redress and the "racing" of Arab-Americans as "terrorists." *Asian-American Law Journal, 8*(1), 11–17, 24–26.

Saoud, R. (2004, March). *The Arab contribution to music of the Western world*. Foundation for Science, Technology, and Civilization. Retrieved from http://www.umich.edu/~hksa/rsix.pdf

Sari, N. (n.d.). Ottoman music therapy. *Muslim Heritage*. Retrieved from http://www.muslimheritage.com/article/ottoman-music-therapy

Somakci, P. (n.d.). Music therapy in Islamic culture. *Turkish Music Portal*. Retrieved from http://www.turkishmusicportal.org/article.php?id=12&lang2=en

Statistics Canada. (2012). *Census metropolitan area of Windsor, Ontario*. Retrieved from http://www12.statcan.gc.ca/census-recensement/2011/as-sa/fogs-spg/Facts-cma-eng.cfm?LANG=Eng&GK=CMA&GC=559

Syed, I. B. (2002). Music therapy. *The Fountain, 40,* October–December. Retrieved from http://www.fountainmagazine.com/Issue/detail/Music-Therapy

Traditional clothing. (n.d.). In *Canadian Arab Community*. Retrieved from http://www.canadianarabcommunity.com/traditionalclothing.php

Transcultural Nursing (2012). *The Middle Eastern community*. Retrieved from http://www.culturediversity.org/mide.htm

Tristam, P. (n.d.). *Five myths about the Middle East*. About.com. Middle East Issues. Retrieved from http://middleeast.about.com/od/middleeast101/tp/me080120.htm

Tucek, G. (2005). Traditional oriental music therapy in neurological rehabilitation. In D. Aldridge (Ed.), *Music therapy and neurological rehabilitation* (pp. 211–230). London, UK: Jessica Kingsley Publishers.

Zogby, J. (2010, October 24). Five pernicious myths the West holds about Arab world. *The National*. Retrieved from http://www.thenational.ae/the-national-conversation/analysis/five-pernicious-myths-the-west-holds-about-arab-world

Appendix A

Popular Singers in the Arab World
Om (Um) Kulthoum—Egypt (1898 or 1904–1975)
Mohammed Abdel Wahab—Egypt (1907–1991)
Farid al-Atrash—Syrian-Egyptian (1910–1974)
Layla Mourad—Egypt (1918–1995)
Abdel Halim Hafez—Egypt (1929–1977)
Fayrouz—Lebanon (1935)
Warda Al-Jazairia—Algerian-Lebanese (1939–2012)
Majida El Roumi—Lebanon (1957)
Amr Diab—Egypt (1961)
Nancy Ajram—Lebanon (1983)

There are many more popular singers across the Arab world, and it is best to ask and do an online search for their songs and lyrics.

A list of Arab musicians according to Wikipedia can be found here:
http://en.wikipedia.org/wiki/List_of_Arabic_pop_musicians

Appendix B

Song Resources in Arabic
"Teach children Arabic—Easy and fun!"
https://www.youtube.com/playlist?list=PL44F7F9175E41395 A

Mama Lisa's World, Arabic Children's Songs and Rhymes
http://www.mamalisa.com/?t=el&lang=Arabic

The Arabic Student: Top 15 Arabic Songs for Americans
http://www.thearabicstudent.com/2012/10/top-15-arabic-songs-for-americans.html

List of some popular Arabic songs
http://www.quora.com/What-are-the-best-Arabic-songs

It is nearly impossible to list the most popular Arabic songs, as there are so many countries with their own distinct musical cultures. Use search engines to search the Internet, including YouTube, and ask your clients for help.

Chapter 8
AFRICAN AMERICAN PERSPECTIVES
Karen Jean Reed & Darlene Brooks

Worldview of the Community

To address the worldview of the African American culture, one must first understand that all Blacks in America are not African Americans. Blacks often identify themselves by their countries of settlement. This could be anywhere from America to Spain, France, Italy, England, Cuba, and so forth. Another important consideration in understanding African Americans is the region where African Americans reside. Blacks from the South have a different worldview than Blacks from the North. It was commonly believed that Blacks from the South were more oppressed than Blacks who migrated to the North because there were more economic opportunities for African Americans who migrated to the North. Consequently, the ability to earn income and live a better material existence shifted the worldview between these two groups. Still an additional consideration is based on class among African Americans. By this, we are referencing European classifications of monetary groups such as the upper, middle, and lower classes, the last of which we now call poverty. All of these economic and life experiences influenced the worldview of African Americans. It is essential to keep this in mind when trying to understand the diversity of worldviews among African Americans. What will be presented here is a general worldview based on documented history and the life experiences of the authors.

It is agreed among historians that the singular influence that most shaped the worldview of African Americans was slavery. Because of the oppression that accompanied slavery, three primary factors in the African American worldview were then and are now crucial to the very survival of its people. Those are pride, family, and communication.

Pride

Despite being forced into subservience by the majority culture, African Americans were never ashamed of their heritage. They have always embraced it with dignity and a sense of pride that is so fierce that it may be perceived as angry. Through rituals brought from Africa, celebrations, and unity, the voices of Africans were never silent for too long. With the passing of the Civil Rights Act, the mask of subservience needed for survival was no longer necessary. They are speaking out, expressing their needs and beliefs, and appreciating the difference that exists between them and the majority culture. Today, Blacks say, "See me, respect me, and take the time to know me as a Black African American. See my beauty. I am different from you, and I love my difference. I wear my own unique hairstyle. I

dress differently! I am a proud person and embrace all that is my heritage. I don't want to be you! I want you to understand, respect, and appreciate all that is me! I walk differently. I talk differently. I am trying to help you know me and appreciate me. You embrace my music from blues to jazz to rhythm & blues to hip-hop and rap. Do you get the messages I'm trying to tell you? I am proud! I am Black! I am an African American!!!"

African Americans have choices now that were never afforded previously. Blacks can choose to embrace or reject the style of the majority culture. They can choose which values of the majority culture resonate with their own values and reject those that do not. Their music is mainstream and, while not appreciated by all, accepted as a form of expression that was seldom so globally embraced in the past, except in the Black community. African Americans have their own role models, who have finally been recognized for their contributions to the growth of the country. For the first time in recorded history, there has been an African American President of the United States. Pride reigns supreme among most African Americans residing in the United States.

Family

Possibly one of the concepts most misunderstood by the majority culture is the definition of family in the Black community. Regardless of how Black Americans address themselves (Jamaican, Haitian, Spanish, British, etc.), family is vital. The majority culture defines family as husband, wife, children, grandparents, aunts, uncles, cousins, and in-laws.

> Partially for survival reasons and partially due to African traditions, Blacks deeply value the strengths of the extended family. Grandmothers, grandfathers, aunts, uncles, and even so-called fictive kin all play a major role in raising children and providing support to parents. The term "fictive kin" refers to those people who are treated like blood relatives although they're really only close family friends. Members of African American families are taught to share their resources with other family members. Likewise, they are taught that when they are in need, they can ask "family" for help. (Janis, 2000, p. 15)

In the African American culture, each of those persons has influence. Each of those persons is valued and respected. Each has a thought and opinion on how the family should exist and coexist. The entire community is considered family. Exchanging and sharing support is central to the lives of African Americans (Waites, 2008). Perhaps the most revered among the kin is the grandmother. She represents wisdom and strength and is the keeper of family values, which include love, respect, community, and religion.

Celebrations are family affairs. Events like birthday parties, weddings, school graduations, or other special events include the entire family. In certain parts of America, these celebrations happen as block parties, where each member of that community takes part, offering food, music, games, and so on. In other areas of the country, community centers or church annexes are the gathering places. When sorrow hits the African American community, everyone grieves. Funeral services in the Black community include wake services where the community can collectively mourn the person who passed, sometimes viewing the body and recalling past times with the family and person who has passed. This is followed by funeral services, where, once again, the family is allowed to openly express their grief for the deceased.

Communication

Communication is highly valued among the African American community as vital for survival.

> African Americans enjoy a long-standing cultural tradition of valuing oral expression. Black families encourage even very young children to memorize songs and dialogues from movies, television, and books. This oral tradition began in slavery when African Americans were prohibited from reading and writing. Blacks learned to pass on family history, issue warnings, and share stories, songs, jokes, parables, and biblical passages via the spoken word. Blacks used this oral tradition to learn how to problem-solve and think quickly on their feet in case they were challenged by Whites or by other Blacks. African Americans have learned to be experts in oral activities like trading insults (as in "playing the dozens") and developing rap music. (Sanchez-Hucles, 2000, p. 20)

Through oral history, African Americans learn resilience and gain strength. Churches, porches, bars, and street corners are the main avenues for communication for the African American community. The main source of communication in churches was the minister or the head deacon or deaconess. On the porches, the grandparents, aunts, uncles, or other neighbors provided information. Bars, while considered social venues, were also important places to gather information. The street corner is often considered one of the more reliable places for communication. Hanging on the corner provided an eye on the community, current fashion trends, information about who was in trouble, information on who was moving, and knowledge of what to avoid. Because many African American households are

separated because of prison, it is common to see young African Americans on street corners, seeking allies, that is, others like themselves who have separated family, and using meeting on the corner as both a connection with family and a rite of passage. The corner represents the extended family.

Historical Realities Versus Popular Myths

When American history is viewed from the African American perspective, the interpretation of the historical realities is frequently different from the White American perspective of the same events. Historical realities are stories and records of actual facts or real things that happened to a person or nation that are known to be true, usually having explanation of what caused them to happen and the effects resulting (Barnhart & Barnhart, 1994). Reality has to do with the things that really exist—actuality. Reed (2000) defined True Reality as "a condition of the mind in which the individual is cognizant of what is real, genuine, and can distinguish fantasy from actuality concerning people, things, situations, spirituality, and events" (p. 159). Reed asserted that people can experience several types of reality that are not based in true reality, and the interpretation of reality can be differently viewed by the person who is the recipient of the experience. What society defines as a reality (actually), a truth, changes based upon what the majority decides to be truth at a particular time in history.

In this 21st century, the historical reality is that 149 years after the end of slavery, African Americans are not lynched in the streets, they are gunned down by licensed gun-bearing citizens and local police or murdered in manners just as cruel or even crueler than those of slavery times. On August 9, 2014, Michael Brown, an unarmed 18-year-old was gunned down by a police in Ferguson, Missouri. On July 12, 2014, in New York, Eric Garner, an unarmed African American, died after a White police officer put him in a choke hold. Officers were detaining him as they alleged him to be selling illegal cigarettes, which he adamantly denied before he was choked to death. On February 26, 2012, Trevon Martin, an unarmed 17-year-old returning to his father's fiancée's townhouse, was fatally shot by George Zimmerman, a neighborhood watch volunteer. On New Year's Day, 2009, Oscar Grant III, an African American homeless man, was shot in the back and killed by a BART (Bay Area [CA] Rapid Transit) police officer 25 seconds after he arrived in the area, without any life-threatening rationale; a lawsuit was won by the family. In 2010, Anthony Hill of Winnsboro, South Carolina, was shot and dragged behind a pickup truck for miles by a White American. On February 4, 1999, Amadou Diallo, an unarmed 22-year-old, was killed by police when they fired 41 bullets at him, with 19 hitting his body, in the Bronx, NY; New York City paid $3 million to settle the lawsuit. On the evening of June 7, 1998, James Byrd, Jr., 49 years old, was walking home from his parents' house when he was beaten, chained, and dragged behind a pickup truck for two miles by three White men in Jasper, Texas; two of the White men were involved with White supremacist groups

(Rosenblatt, 2013). Mr. Byrd's head, arms, and torso were found in different parts of the road over a mile-long stretch. In 1991, Rodney King was filmed receiving a beating from several cops simultaneously; as a result of the acquittal of officers involved, massive devastation and more violent acts occurred in Los Angeles, where fires were set by protesters displaying their disapproval of the verdict.

In this, the 21st century, several realities are still true with regard to African Americans (Black Americans). Black males are incarcerated at a higher rate than any other race and given longer sentences, particularly in the area of drug offenses. Black males and females are more likely to be follow around by store employees when Blacks examine merchandise, as they are presumed to be criminals and more likely to steal. When Black males drive a nice car, they are more frequently pulled over by the police, although they are not breaking the law. Additionally, if Blacks are driving through an affluent White neighborhood, they are more likely to be stopped by police because it is naturally presumed that they don't belong there. When they do buy nice cars, it is presumed that they did something illegal to acquire the funds for the purchase, such as drug-dealing. Even when the pinnacle of success is reached by Blacks such as James Brown and Michael Jackson, the media and society look for things to bring them down. Even when found innocent in a court of law, black celebrities like OJ. Simpson continued to be thought of as guilty the majority of society especially by Whites (Gillespie, 2004). This societal presumption that Blacks are guilty, enforces the stereotypical beliefs of many White people.

Stereotypes

These historical realities have often produced long-standing stereotypes regarding Black Americans as individuals, a race, and a culture and alter the overall perception of Black people, who are frequently vilified, degraded and depicted as inferior. In the United States, stereotypical views of Blacks have existed since colonial days, and many have continued to the present regarding their level of intelligence, food preferences, educational potential, religious needs, personality, emotional state, athletic ability, economic class status, and other areas.

After slavery ended, minstrel shows perpetuated the gross racial stereotypes of Black Americans as being ignorant, happy servants, superstitious, and naive (Koslow, 1999). Seven racial stereotypes developed during and after slavery and perpetuated by White Americans regarding African Americans were examined; it was found that although these stereotypes were not as powerful as in past times, they were still alive and thriving in the 21st century (Green, 1998–1999). The offensive term *Sambo* was used to refer to any Black American. Today, we still have the *Aunt Jemimah* stereotype, started in 1875, which is readily visible on stores shelves on syrup bottles and pancake mixes. The perception of Black women as more sexually promiscuous and available came with the title *Jezebelle*. These names and many other stereotypes have propelled the negative perceptions of Black Americans.

History reflects that Black Americans have incurred numerous stereotypes, many that still linger today, but the 21st century continues to spread such perceptions through movies, radio, television, the internet, and people in general. The movies have been very instrumental in promoting the stereotypic perception of Blacks. In 1915, David Llewelyn Wark ("D. W.") Griffith produced *The Clansman,* later called *The Birth of a Nation,* which illustrated slavery, the Ku Klux Klan, and race relations in the Civil War and the Reconstruction Era. Prior to the 1980s, most movies and television shows portrayed Blacks as thieves, household Mammies, butlers, and people of no education and low positions. The 1980s brought a change in television, with Bill Cosby and Phylicia Rashad playing a doctor and lawyer, respectively, on his eponymous show. Still, today African Americans are more often depicted in film as vulgar-talking, physically violent criminals; thugs; corrupted law officers; drug lords; crack victims; angry, drama-ridden women; uneducated domestic workers; and with little or no self-esteem. In 2009, Michael Lewis's movie *The Blind Side* portrayed the real-life story of NFL player Michael Oher, who was portrayed as an uneducated African American who hardly spoke and needed his White adoptive mom to tell him how to play football. These stereotypes are like the idea of slavery. The majority perception has changed with regard to most Blacks, but some minority groups still hold on to the old views.

Popular Myths

There are many myths regarding African Americans and eating, musical ability, sports ability, and many others. Many believe that African Americans have innate rhythms and musical, singing, and dance skills. The prevalence of African Americans in the music and dance industries often leaves people with the impression that the ability is innate. Like all people, some African Americans are born with the ability to play music by ear or dance extremely well while others are not. Despite stereotypes about African Americans espousing the belief that all African Americans are amazing dancers, this is not true. When video came out in the 1980s, Michael Jackson was immediately hailed for his amazing dancing skills, but Lionel Richie, also releasing videos in the 1980s, was viewed as having very little dance rhythm on the videos. In the African American culture, if a person does not have natural rhythm, the person may be ridiculed or teased by members of their own culture, even compared at times to the White race.

African American superiority in sports, due to a better athletic (and especially running) ability, is another popular assumption. Although African Americans are a smaller portion of the population, they dominate football, basketball, and track. In most of the other sports, like hockey, golf, and tennis, there may be a small handful of African Americans who have risen to the highest levels, but they are not the norm. P. K. Subban, Tiger Woods, and the Williams sisters are all exceptions.

The following is a list of some of the myths that African

American face on a daily basis: (1) All African Americans look alike. African American diversity in physical characteristics is vast; people of many shades, sizes, and heights exist. Thus, all African Americans don't look alike. (2) Blacks men are lazy. As in any ethnic group, there are some lazy people, and some happen to be men, but not all Black men are lazy. Many of them are hardworking providers in the family. (3) They are from the 'hood, the ghetto, or the projects and abuse the welfare system. Many African Americans do live in the 'hood, ghetto, or projects, but more live in middle-class neighborhoods and even upper-class neighborhoods. (4) African Americans are not the primary customers on welfare, contrary to popular belief. (5) The media, the courts, and various industries make everything about race. Other races tend to make everything focused on race. African American just seek to be seen as a human, not by their color. (6) When a Black person achieves a professional title, their color is always front-and-center. They are referred to as "the Black music therapist," "the African American dentist," or "the Black lawyer." African Americans would just like to be referred to as a professional, not distinguished by their color. (7) Affirmative Action unfairly provides them opportunities that are not afforded to other people. One of the advancements of Affirmative Action was that it to some degree leveled the playing field for African Americans, who were typically denied regular jobs for which they had the qualifications. Due to prejudices against their race, they were generally kept in domestic, subservient jobs (Genovese & Han, 2009). Most hiring selections did not afford African Americans the opportunities that were provided to other races, but Affirmative Action did provide a way for African Americans to have the same employment opportunities that were already being offered to other races. (8) African American men are more likely to marry a White woman over a black woman. Over the decades, African American men have certainly married White women. However, a greater number of them still marry within their own race. (9) They are not good businesspeople. This myth is compounded by another myth that African Americans commit more crimes than Whites. This myth grew out of the time after emancipation when there were many Black businesses established due to the fact that discrimination was still prevalent, so they provided commodities and services to their own race.

Throughout the 19th century, the historical realities and popular myths regarding the attitudes and beliefs at work within White America were reflected in the content of textbooks (Provenzo, 1986). The White race was clearly divided from other races and depicted as the most highly developed, civilized people. Blacks were depicted in an unflattering way, as being ugly and slow. These depictions of other races conveyed stereotypes to children. Before and after emancipation, African Americans were illustrated as uneducated, childlike, slow, inferior, and foolish beings who lacked intelligence.

Diversity Within the Culture

Possibly one of the richest aspects of the African American culture is its diversity. Blacks have diverse geographic backgrounds due to the slave trade routes (Sanchez-Hucles, 2000). On a recent CNN special, *New Revelations About Slaves and the Slave Trade,* presenters highlighted the work of Eltis and Richardson (2011) and their *Atlas of the Transatlantic Slave Trade.* In this documentary, it was found that "Angola supplied four out of every five captives to the southern cone region of South America (Brazil, Argentina, Uruguay)." Slaves sent to the United States primarily came from Senegambia south to Liberia. Amazonia drew its slaves from Guinea, and Jamaica drew heavily from Ghana and Benin. Africans were slaves and free men everywhere. In most countries, slavery ended much sooner than it did in the United States. The United States, however, was the richest nation in the world, with many opportunities for prosperity. Yet, its history was soiled by the abysmal treatment of slaves. Consequently, as these Africans who settled in other countries migrated to the United States, they maintained their identity associated with the particular country in which their ancestors were enslaved. Here in the United States, we have Africans who are Jamaican, Haitian, Cuban, South American, French, Portuguese, Canadian, and British, among others. Each of these groups brought traditions, foods, customs, and ways of being that echoed their country of origin. It was important for Blacks to maintain this distinction, primarily because while also sold into slavery in other countries, they did not experience the length or level of hatred and brutality experienced by African Americans who were brought to the United States, but instead saw themselves as persons who had sought the "American" way of life after that time of turmoil.

In thinking about regions, there is a marked difference between Blacks who are southern versus those who are northern (Mendez, 2011). Southern Blacks have a way about them that to many northern Blacks seems to resemble oppression. Many southern Blacks reside in the same homes as their grandparents or in the same neighborhoods and actively maintain the values that were passed down from generation to generation. These include cooking, communication and sense of community, patience, and inclusiveness. They are friendly, welcoming, and comfortable in their traditions. Northern Blacks, on the other hand, may maintain these values, but often narrow their community to close friends and relatives. Blacks originally migrated to the North seeking employment opportunities, 1976). While many were able to gain employment, many were not, and their sense of community narrowed. They are less welcoming of strangers, less inclusive, and more protective of their way of life. Possibly one of the reasons for the distinction between regions is because the South has maintained a slow, agriculturally based way of life, whereas the more industrial North has fostered a harder, faster, more impersonal way of life. Generally, since the Civil Rights Act, there seems to have been a heightened sense of suspicion among northern Blacks that is not as evident in southern Blacks. The South was the primary focus of discrimination leading to the Civil Rights movement. After its success, southern Blacks were finally able to gain some of the advantages of the majority culture. With those gains, southern Blacks strongly believed that they would benefit more from the peaceful movement established by Martin Luther King, Jr. Northern Blacks, on the other hand, were more aggressive in their demands for services than southern Blacks. Much of this difference could be attributed to the movement led by Malcolm X, who proposed that aggression, which was often practiced by the majority culture toward Blacks, was the primary way of getting needs met. What is interesting to note is that after an inability to gain the economic comfort that the North initially offered, there has been a shift among Blacks and many are returning to the South (Blocker, 1996; Dowden, 1993).

Culture Within the Race

What is an interesting factor among African Americans is the diversity within the race and the impact of that diversity on relationships. The majority of persons coming from Africa were of a medium to dark complexion. Depending on the country in which they resided and climate conditions, over time, hues began to change. Another factor that led to this change in complexion was the bedding of African women by their slave owners. During slavery, Africans were considered property, and it was not uncommon for slave owners to choose many African women as their liaisons, believing the misconception that African women were wild and would do whatever they were told to do in bed. Many of these women were raped, sodomized, beaten, and treated poorly. Far too frequently, children were sired as a result of these unwelcome unions. Often, these children were fairer-skinned than their birth mothers, called mulatto, and seemed to gain privileges that were not afforded to their own mothers. As children matured and became slaves themselves, they quickly learned that the fairer-skinned African had more privileges, was encouraged to dress better, had more duties in the home (rather than in the fields), and was among the first to gain emancipation. It was not uncommon, when slaves were finally freed, that the belief existed that to "pass" as White was the preferred way of existence. Mulattos had fairer skin, silky hair, and, in some cases, light eyes and general body shapes that seemed similar to those of the majority culture. If a Black person could "pass," they were granted privilege and status. Unfortunately, often the same prejudice demonstrated by Whites toward Blacks was seen by mulattos toward darker-skinned Blacks as well. Blacks who were a mixture of French and/or Spanish were called Creole. This group also had more privileges, thus further dividing the race. Unfortunately, this belief that fairer-skinned Blacks were the superior group prevailed for many years after slavery.

> In the history of African American vernacular, slogans and rhymes have been used to express the linkages among skin tone and Black self- and group

images. "If you're White, you're alright. If you're yellow, you're mellow. If you're Brown, stick around. If you're Black, get back." ... Individuals of different complexions have expressed the pain, dejection, or guilt associated with unjustified treatment by others because of their skin tone. (Brown et al., 1999, p. 191)

Darlene: *I am from New Orleans, Louisiana, a city made up of many mulatto and Creole African Americans. This city represents an example of a Black culture taking on the worldview of its oppressors. Lighter-skinned African Americans were favored. Fortunately for me, I never really knew that my very dark shade of black was not popular. Nor did I know that even among African Americans, the belief existed that if you were as black as I was, you were not meant to succeed. I am very grateful to my family for appreciating my blackness and having me appreciate it as well. In New Orleans at the time I was entering college, there were two Black universities—Dillard University and Xavier University. Because of my music skills, I was offered a scholarship to study at Xavier. It was a wonderful experience.*

> Skin tone, both immediately obvious and relatively stable as a characteristic, has been used by White and Black Americans alike to stereotype and discriminate against African Americans who fall on different ends of the color spectrum. Generally, light-skinned individuals have been associated with positive, favorable characteristics, while darker skin tone is more likely to be linked to derogatory attributes. (p. 194)

> Having a Black skin tone was more often associated with being the dumbest, the dirtiest, the person one would not like to marry, the person with bad hair, the person with the ugliest skin complexion, than the light-skinned. (p. 196)

Many years after completing my undergraduate degrees, I was told that in the late '60s, when I was in college, the majority of students who had dark complexions like mine went to Dillard, and the fairer skinned students went to Xavier. I learned that I was watched very closely throughout my education at Xavier because of a fear the nuns had that I would be ostracized. What they appreciated was my popularity among students of all complexions and my ability to hold my own. As I reflect on this period while writing this chapter, it is an excellent representation of the separation within culture that existed because of slavery, privilege, and oppression. What is noteworthy is that when the Black Power movement began, most of my fair-skinned Black friends with silky hair were desperate to somehow wear Afros, so they looked like me!

Unfortunately, this belief continues, and the impact of oppression left permanent marks on many African Americans.

Sadly, even today, there are many fair-skinned persons who reject their blackness and prefer to associate only with individuals who look like them.

Gender Differences Within the Culture

Culture signifies the system of shared meanings, perceptions, and beliefs maintained by a person belonging to some community or population (Smith & Bond, 1993). Culture influences the way one thinks, feels, and presumes and one's lifestyle. African American culture is influenced by socioeconomic status and psychological and biological needs, depending on their geographical location. Culture can be so ingrained that one does not realize that the behavior might be different from that of others.

For years, the American historical reality pertaining to culture was that if the person was culturally different from White Americans, then they were an inferior culture (Gollnick & Chinn, 1986). Since the end of slavery in the United States, White Americans have labeled this group as Negroid, Colored, Black, and African American. Although White America identifies the group as African Americans in this 21st century, the terms "Black American" and "African American" are often used interchangeably; which part of the country an African American hails from determines with which term they prefer to be labeled. Southern Blacks born prior to the 1970s prefer to be called Black Americans (Gollnick & Chinn, 1986). Western Blacks had a tendency to prefer African American, as they often experienced less discrimination than southerners. Northern Blacks tend to lean either way, due to the fact that many immigrated from the South, so they are aware of the significance of the race labeling history.

Culturally, African Americans may share some similarities of living in America. They are exposed to the same lifestyles, values, rules, and regulations, but they may have different dialects, depending on where they were mostly raised. They may share the common African American religions of Baptist; Methodist—AME or CME; or Pentecostal—Church of God in Christ, Apostolic, or Independent; or other variations of these three main denominations. Catholics are less common among African Americans, but they do exist. Also, Nation of Islam, Buddhism, and Santeria are some other religions of choice that some African Americans practice (Auerbach, 1994). Prayer is important in all these religions, with some praying more or on specific days. Prayer before going to bed is an expectation that had to be complied with at all times, young and old.

Culture impacts food selection. Many African Americans will eat bacon, but those who practice the Muslim religion will not eat pork. Some southern Blacks farmed and raised their own food, including meats. Many African Americans will eat at least three meals a day, often instilling in the children that breakfast is the most important meal of the day. Many families eat together at specific times. Some Blacks reared in Mississippi will separate the children from the adults, particularly when guests arrive for dinner, or have them eat after the guests. With other Blacks, reared in states like Arkansas, the children and adults eat together, and it is important to set the table with the right positioning of forks, spoons, and knives. Basic table manners are expected, such as no elbows on the table during the meals. Blessing the food before eating a meal is always expected.

Culturally, African Americans have specific ideals regarding females. There are standards regarding with whom females would spend their time and under what circumstances the female would spend time with them, particularly males. It is expected that girls should be around other girls. If a female is going to be in the company of a male, other females should also be present. Frequently, girls are taught, "If they are selling, don't advertise," which means that how the female dresses communicates what she is willing to give up sexually. This style of dress is associated with a "hoochie mamma," "slut," or promiscuous lifestyle. Most families expected females to carry themselves well. In some religious denominations, young Black southern girls were not permitted to whistle; the saying was, "The Devil don't like a clacking hen or a whistling woman. If the Devil don't want you, you're not good for nothing." Additionally, some Blacks believed that young women were not to cross their legs; this action was referred to as "A spirit of a whore." Neither were they to cross their legs high like men. The African American culture has many sayings and expectations for females which promote standards by which they should live, and many are tied to the past history of slavery (Degler, 1980).

The environment in which a Black male is raised determines what the expectations are for him. Most are taught that the man is the head of the house, the provider, the rule-setter, and the enforcer. It is often stated, "If a man does not work, he does not eat." He is expected to achieve greater levels than his parents did educationally, financially, and in overall status. The male is expected to have references for his parents and the elderly. He is expected to have control over his children and command respect. Black males are taught at an early age how to respond when they encounter White cops, in an effort to prevent a "cop killing."

For many African Americans in the South, a high school education was an expectation, as was even college. African Americans had been denied access all during slavery and even thereafter in some areas. Most of the previous generation wanted more for their kids, so education was pushed. In southern families, there were many first-time high school and college graduates. In the 1980s, the value of education in the North did not seem to be as valued as it was in the South, and children not completing their basic education did not seem to be a big deal for some parents. In the South, education was a point of pride, and parents advocated for their children to have the best education, even if this meant pushing for the integration of schools.

In the African American community, the cultural expectation is that a man and woman marry prior to sexual activity. Even when a child is conceived out of wedlock, it has been and still is the expectation that marriage occurs. Even if a woman got pregnant prior to marriage, many married prior to the birth of the child. Some attempted to conceal that they were already pregnant. In this 21st century, more Black couples live together or parent together as singles; more Black women have children and have never been married; more Black men are engaged in multiple relationships, often at the same time; and more men and women have babies by multiple partners and may never marry. Yet, the primarily expectation is that women marry men.

Many African Americans have family members and/or know someone (male or female) who identifies as gay, lesbian, bisexual, or transgender, but it is still less accepted in African American communities, particular in southern parts of the United States. Frequently, people, whether black or another color, are ostracized if they are not heterosexual. Most African American church denominations hold positions of opposition against homosexuality. Family members who hold strong religious belief are frequently impacted by how they perceive, differentiate, and deal with family and acquaintances who identify as gay, lesbian, bisexual, or transgender.

African-American gender differences are similar to those of traditional White Americans. The man is regarded as the head (the king) of the household, mostly based on the biblical perspective. The man is respected as the primary provider of the house. He can work all day, come home, and sit in front of the television. The man will be brought his food, if he chooses not to eat at the table. He will be allowed to watch whatever he wants, regardless of what others might want to view on the television. If he asks for a glass of water, a cup of coffee, or salt and pepper, someone will get up and get it for him. Even if the man is not employed, he is still regarded as the head of the home (castle).

From slavery to the 20th century, the gender roles of Black females were varied, from being field laborers working in the fields, just like Black men, and often right by their sides, to house laborers taking care of the plantation owner's children and home. Movies such as *Roots, 12 Years a Slave, Django Unchained,* and many others illustrate how the females were worked to the extreme without any regard to their gender orientation. Other slave women were used primarily for sexual pleasure and breeding more slaves. Each sexual act and/or sexual assault was often rendered by the slave owner. During slavery, many of the women also developed midwifery skills.

After slavery ended, most Black women in the South had rougher occupational roles than those of northern Black women, who worked more in domestic services. In the South, Black women were carrying out the same roles that they had had during slavery, working as sharecroppers, laborers, and domestic help (Auerbach, 1994). Over time in the northern states, White immigrants impacted the domestic service occupations once dominated by Black women (Auerbach, 1994).

Other Black women were able to become teachers, leaders, missionaries, social reformers, women's club founders, and members of the medical profession, including nurses (Auerbach, 1994). In 1864, Rebecca Lee Crump became the first Black female doctor. By the turn of the 20th century, 4,000 Black women had graduated from colleges and normal schools (Auerbach, 1994). In 1972, Charlotte E. Ray was admitted to the Washington, DC, bar.

The role of children in the African American culture can vary, depending on economic factors, geographical location, and the parents' religious practices. Some African Americans hold the old view that children are to be seen and not heard. Others believe that children are the church of tomorrow, so they must be loved and trained today, prompting church members and parents to spend much time on their moral and social development. Some think that children are there for their personal use as cleaners, field workers, and things related to work. In the southern states, the children often respond with "Yes, ma'am," "No, ma'am," "Yes, sir," or "No, sir" when responding to an adult; using any other types of response is a sign of disrespect, and the child will be verbally reprimanded for his response. The child is not to turn his/her head away from the adult when they are being corrected, which would aggravate the situation. The child is not to interrupt an adult conversation without saying "Excuse me" and getting the adults' approval to proceed with the interruption. A child is not to call an adult by their first name. Even children who are related to an adult are required to preface the name with some title for example, Ms. Carrie, Cousin Karen, Uncle Michael, or Aunt Helen. Most of all, a child is never to call an adult a liar or state something that implies that an adult has lied.

Up until the late 1970s, most African American families disciplined their children by whipping them with a switch (branch from a tree), belt, or sometimes an extension cord. Even though most states prohibit corporal punishment, it is still not uncommon today for African American children to physically discipline their children with a switch or belt. Some parents will use the "time out," but it is not a form of discipline used by most African Americans. Additionally, "grounding" is not a practice used by most African Americans.

The gender and cultural experiences of Black Americans have been extensive, from the labeling of their race constantly changing to variations in servitude jobs, to gender roles dictated or influenced more often than not by White American. Blacks have encountered changes from slavery through the 21st century but have prevailed in keeping elements of their culture in food, religion, and family.

Generational and Migrational Differences

As African Americans settled in the United States, they would often move to areas that provided a means of economic growth for them and their families. Black Cuban-Americans initially settled in Miami, only to find segregation worse than they had experienced in Cuba (Darlington, 2009), and many eventually migrated to New York. Many Black Haitian-Americans settled in New Orleans, where the Creole population was strong. Over time, however, and because of the Civil Rights Movement in the 60s, African Americans felt less restricted and moved to other parts of the United States. Some were connecting with family, while others were seeking new opportunities for growth. One thing that African Americans discovered in moving was that housing opportunities were limited to areas where other African Americans resided. As a result, the emergence of racial communities within the United States became a staple of life. In communities with like people there was safety and a sense of community. Many cities now have areas called "Little Haiti," "Little Cuba," and so forth.

A difference in this pattern began to emerge when schools became integrated. Young people in the 1970s and '80s were given educational opportunities that more closely resembled those of the majority culture. They mingled more with persons from the majority culture with each living in their respective communities, so they no longer felt the need to remain within the confines of their smaller communities. In many cases, parents sought environments that afforded their children a better education. Consequently, these young people became curious about life outside of that community. They felt they had earned the right to experience life and its opportunities. They shared classrooms, school activities, and music with their peers from the majority culture and, in some cases, began to date interracially. The majority culture seemed to embrace many of these young people, especially females, musicians, and athletes. In some cases, those individuals were able to excel and not experience the obvious oppression experienced by their parents. With the federal Affirmative Action law, more jobs were made available, and the development of a Black middle class was seen. Blacks were able to move into neighborhoods that were called middle class, in homes that were spacious, in communities that were initially integrated. Unfortunately, as more Black families moved in, there was a White exodus to suburban areas, and this continued until we had exclusive high-priced neighborhoods throughout the country that are beyond the economic reach of many Black Americans.

For many, this housing segregation was not initially recognized because they saw these new living conditions as a vast improvement over the impoverished conditions that had seemed to plague their parents' communities. They had better job offers and were becoming more prosperous, and there was a different view of life and work than that preached by parents and grandparents. Many young people found themselves in situations where the rejection they experienced because of their race was almost more painful than what they had experienced in their communities. This new rejection was subtle. There were events occurring all around them in which they were not able to partake, and promotions at work were given to a majority culture peer who did equal work. While appearing popular on the job, they were not invited to social events with their majority peers. They worked harder and earned less than an equal majority peer and began a downward spiral that was both unfamiliar and frightening. What made this particularly painful was that even though conditions appeared to improve on one level, these young people felt very ostracized. They didn't have a new community and had walked away from the one their parents worked so hard to provide. In

many cases, Blacks moved back into their original communities. In other cases, they brought their communities into their new environments. While they were happy to move from the oppressive conditions of previous neighborhoods, Blacks found that the new communities didn't provide the solutions that they had anticipated. Poverty appeared more pronounced, community traditions were not as prominent, and despair seemed to prevail.

These moves separated individuals not only from their families, but also from their cultures. Festivals and community happenings were not as common, mainly because there was a blending of African Americans that did not feel as natural as the communities from which they came. The original communities that developed when moving to various parts of the United States became more impoverished. Job descriptions were such that many African Americans would not qualify. The minimum-wage jobs that were available began to dwindle, and many African Americans had to depend on the welfare system to exist. It should be noted that this was known as the Social Security Act, created by President Franklin Roosevelt in 1939 to assist poor families after the great Depression. The Social Security Act was originally designed not to aid African Americans, but to help poor majority culture women who had immigrated to the United States and whose husbands were absent, either through war or death.

Acculturation/Assimilation

Assimilation

Assimilation is a manner by which a minority or subordinate group progressively blends into or becomes a part of the majority group's society and culture (Smith, 2003). Ivey (1986) stressed that when the majority acts on and forces their perspectives on the environment, then assimilation has occurred. In the United States, it has been the practice of White Americans to demand or expect that other cultures forsake their native languages and beliefs and assimilate into the White American mainstream. The minority group little by little attains the standards, tenets, and conduct patterns of the majority, either entirely or in part (Smith, 2003). Historically, Black Americans have been subjected to extreme assimilation, meaning that they were expected to completely accept the White American perspective, and all of what the Black culture is and/or had been was required to fade away. Their native name, belief system, language, religious practices, music, and sense of just being a person of value were compelled by White America to disappear.

There is a scene in Alex Haley's movie *Roots* where Kunta Kinte is caught after a failed attempt to escape to freedom (Haley, 1996a; Haley, 1996b). From the very beginning of his enslavement, Kunta Kinte is determined to preserve his Mandinka heritage and maintain his Mandinka roots, and he does not want to change his name. After his last attempt to find freedom fails, he is found and tied to a whipping post. The overseer proceeds to order another slave to beat Kunta until he acknowledges his new American name, "Toby." Kunta is asked, "What's your name?" Each time, he responds, "Kunta Kinte." The overseer wants him to say "Toby." Each time Kunta Kinte states his African name, he is whipped on the back. This continues until he cannot endure the pain anymore and responds, "Toby" (Haley, 1996b). Throughout the movie, Toby takes on his new name, and when he brings up his Mandinka heritage and the beliefs of his African heritage, he is often ridiculed for it. The movie *Roots* is a prime example of White America's expectation of a minority group to take on their norms, values, and behavior patterns and the inferior role which was paved for Black Americans. Additionally, movies such as *Django Unchained, The Butler,* and *The Help* are all examples of the assimilation of Blacks.

Education. In the United States, education served as a method of assimilation for other immigrants of Anglo-Saxon origin, but not for Black Americans. Historically, White Americans utilized education as a method of imposing a uniform set of political values on immigrants. Whether Blacks were free or slave, White Americans considered Blacks to be inferior, and for hundreds of years continued to forbid the education of that race, instituting compulsory ignorance. White Americans had very little interest in educating Black Americans. For many years, academically, Black Americans were not provided the opportunity to integrate into the dominant culture.

From the 1700s on, laws were instituted to prohibit Blacks from being educated. Black slaves were directed by Whites and not allowed to direct themselves. They were treated as objects, not subjects, and their creative abilities were smothered. The movie *Roots* illustrated how Kizzy learned to read by being a childhood playmate of the slave owner's daughter. The movie *12 Years a Slave* illustrated the threat of death to any Black male slave who knew how to read.

When African Americans were finally granted education, they were segregated and granted a separate inferior education in comparison to White Americans. The Fourteenth Amendment (1867) granted African Americans civil rights, but *Plessy v. Ferguson* (1896) continued education segregation, asserting the legitimacy of "separate but equal." Further discrimination continued in the decision of *Cumming v. Richmond County Board of Education* (1899), which allowed the African American high school to be closed and the White high school to remain open and to operate in segregation.

Most Blacks Americans are educated in how many White Americans perceive African Americans. The older Black generations who had educational goals for their children would indoctrinate the children with the following perspectives: (1) No matter how much education Blacks receive, Blacks are seen only by the color of their skin. (2) African Americans will have to work two or three times as hard to get the same job that a White person with less education or qualifications would get. (3) No matter what the obstacles, the pressure, the isolations, or the stumbling blocks encountered, the child is taught to pursue the dream, the education, or the job and endure whatever

persecutions may be dealt by White Americans. They may be reminded that Dr. Martin Luther King, Jr., wished for the day that African Americans would be judged by their character, not their color, but color is still a factor.

Additionally, education was used as a vehicle to continue educating Blacks to maintain an inferior mentally in their role as being subordinate to White Americans. Prompted by continued discrimination and opportunities of the new freedom, many African Americans established their own schools, colleges, and universities to educate their own race. These included Howard University, Spelman College, Morehouse College, Gambling State University, AM&N College (Arkansas), Fisk College, Tuskegee University, Hampton College, and many others. Although slavery had ended, many American-Americans still remained illiterate at the turn of the 20th century.

Educationally change began for African Americans when in 1954 the Supreme Court decision on *Brown v. Board of Education of Topeka* overruled the "separate but equal" policy and deemed segregated public school education unconstitutional, finding that they were inherently unequal. Thus, the 1960s expanded new possibilities that African Americans had never experienced, such as the possibility of genuine equality (Pendergast & Pendergast, 2003). Just 60 years ago, few African Americans had access to the same education as White Americans.

For many years, African American culture developed separately from mainstream American culture, because of slavery, laws designed specifically against African American, and the persistence of racial discrimination. Additionally, African American slave descendants desired to create and preserve their own traditions (Bennett, 1973). In the South, they experienced the passage of laws that systematically enforced the physical and social separation of Black Americans from Whites in all areas of public life, including schools, churches, hospitals, cemeteries, buses, restaurants, water fountains, housing, store accessibility, and restrooms (Kendall, 2004; Mapson, 1984). In the North, they experienced racial separation and inequality suffered by African Americans seeking northern factory jobs (Kendall, 2004).

Acculturation

Acculturation is variation of the culture of a group or individual resulting from interaction with a different culture (*Webster's II New College Dictionary,* 2005). Acculturation does not necessarily imply that the group or individual is forced to take on the modification, but it occurs as a result of the contact. It does not necessarily indicate peer, societal, or psychological pressures, although all of those may be experienced. In the United States, this process has led to the disappearance of cultural groups that are different from the dominant White culture.

For most groups, acculturation occurred after the group had been in the United States for at least one generation (Gollnick,

1986). Since African Americans have been present in United States since the 1600s, their families have created many generations, and their cultural patterns have changed to those of White Americans in areas such as family structure, basic living, education, work, seeking the American dream, physical appearance, clothing, food choices, moral standards, and religious preferences.

Acts of discrimination and prejudice displayed by White Americans do not necessarily subside because ethnic members acculturate (Gollnick, 1986). Particularly in the South after emancipation and even to this present day, the Ku Klux Klan targets Blacks and inflicts severe flogging, torture, and murder in an effort to keep them mentally submissive and in the same role as they had during slavery (Gottesman, 1999). No matter how much an African American has tried to placate by culturally adopting White America, they have been viewed differently. They are rarely viewed as just a person. They are always identified by "Black" or "African American," but never identified just as a person. If he is a lawyer, he is called the "Black lawyer"; similarly: the "Black nurse," the "Black music therapist," and the "Black Doctor." Their name may be stated, but somewhere in there, their race will be specified.

Most college-educated African American students assimilated in pledging to sororities and fraternities. Many come out of universities and colleges holding the values of White Americans. Frequently, many African American college students stop practicing their religious upbringing, lose their religious relationship, and question the reality of God after being exposed to theories and philosophies at school. The Pentecostal churches often say, "Get your learning, but don't lose your burning." This is to emphasize "Get your education, but don't abandon your religious faith."

Since integration and busing were implemented, many African American have attended educational school with multiracial students, but more often than not, Whites were the majority of the students (Gollnick, 1986). When an African American takes on attributes associated with White Americans, such as proper English speech, opinions, fashion, or lifestyle, he or she will sometimes be called by people of their own race "Little White Girl" or "White Boy" and are accused of trying to be White. In the 21st century, African American males who are perceived by other African Americans to be acting "too White" in their speech, behaviors, or dress will be labeled an "Uncle Tom," implying that they are submissive toward Whites (Pendergast & Pendergast, 2005).

Microaggression and Oppression

Microaggression

On the surface, microaggressions seem innocent, but they can indeed be quite harmful to the person who is the recipient of these aggressions. Examples of microinsults might be denying that a person who is intelligent could be African American. Or making a comment like "You are a credit to your race." A

popular microinsult occurs when the majority culture person says something that he feels resembles the African American's speech, over exaggerating their words and accents so that their words sound stereotypical of vaudevillian theater in their delivery. Another example might be color blindness, which is a way of denying the persons' race. And of course, one of the most common that I have heard is, "I have several Black friends." The message here is an implied immunity to racism because of these friendships. Sue (2010a) points out that the victims of microaggressions often feel the insults and lack of respect. Because of the way these aggressions are delivered and the denial from the person issuing the microaggression, victims begin to question themselves. Additionally, when confronted, the victims are accused of overreacting or being hypersensitive. Perpetrators will trivialize the impact of their comments to avoid feeing any guilt, thus adding to the victim's self-questioning. This is known as microinvalidation. The feelings, thoughts, or reality of the situation are negated or dismissed by the perpetrator.

Oppression

Five key types of oppression impacting the lives of African Americans have been identified in the literature. They are violence, exploitation, marginalization, powerlessness, and cultural imperialism (Heldke & O'Connor, 2004). Since the days of slavery, Blacks have been subjected to violence. Early in their history in America, there were beatings, hangings, shootings, and physical and sexual abuse. Since the onset of the Civil Rights Movement, through which both overt and covert acts of violence were deemed to be unlawful, oppression has taken center stage in the form of exploitation. Majority cultures have used the labors of the minority culture to make profits, yet have failed to compensate those minority citizens fairly. This exploitation has led to a larger culture of haves and have-nots, making the rich richer and the poor poorer, creating a greater separation of races and marginalization, where African Americans were at the lowest social standing and excluded from many of the benefits of the majority culture. Marginalization prevented Blacks from getting jobs, having a voice, or providing for their families and left them with a sense of powerlessness, apathy, and despondence that was and continues to be palpable.

With an education system that does not teach to the strengths of African Americans, increased poverty, community fragmentation, poor health, and dependence on the majority culture for financial assistance, which is disempowering in and of itself, became the state of the African American community. Black women were able to work in menial jobs making the minimum wage or less, while Black men were demeaned and often unable to get employment except at hard labor. The stress felt by Black Americans continued to rise, and families began to fragment. Over time, there was and continues to be an increase in anger, frustration, low self-esteem, and learned hopelessness among many African American families. Witnessing this struggle on a daily basis led many Black youths to find ways to combat this negativity. The family was not able to change, and, as a result, youth often turned to other disenfranchised youth to demonstrate their power and strength by forming gangs, which became a means of survival and a way to protect their fragile egos. They took it upon themselves to protect their environments and give the appearance of solidarity. Communities rarely complained about these groups of adolescents congregating, because they too felt a sense of protection with them present. Interestingly, the biggest social problems seen in spite of the above conditions were the occasional heroin addicts and alcoholics living in the community.

This seemed to be the future of the African American community that was not able benefit from Affirmative Action or other opportunities to get out of this oppression, until a sordid period in American history arose. In 1985, The United States became involved in a non-sanctioned action through which millions of dollars' worth of weapons were sold and routed to the Nicaraguan Contras in eventual exchange for American hostages held by Iranian terrorists (Sabato, 1998). What also occurred during that time was that the Contras were collaborating with drug traffickers and used this as an opportunity to flood the U.S. borders with cocaine from South America (White, 2001; Perry, 2004). Suddenly, minority communities in large cities like Los Angeles, New York City, Chicago, and Philadelphia were flooded with crack cocaine. Four things happened to the African American community. First, the high from crack cocaine provided a respite from the malaise that hung over the community. Second, unknown to the users, crack was a very addictive drug, and the addictions that followed reached epidemic proportions. The third was that the money made selling crack was impressive. The young gangs protecting their communities began to realize that they could become wealthy entrepreneurs, handing out creature comforts and drugs at will. The fourth was that along with crack cocaine, there was suddenly the availability of all kinds of weapons, thus enabling youth to further feel powerful, but at the same time causing loss of life for many young people and further separation in the community.

Being the best drug lord is the goal, and anyone in the way is often eliminated. This claiming of territory, crack addiction, and money led to a rise in violence in the African American communities that made many look like war zones. The youth who together protected their community and provided for their families began to split and claim territory. There was a disintegration of community and a rise in violence. For many young African Americans, the gang life, a way of trying to protect themselves from the microaggressions they were avoiding, became their vehicle to enact the same microaggressions onto members of their own community. The result of these horrors has left more poverty, broken families, oppression, and hopelessness in many communities. The number of Black-on-Black crimes has risen at an alarming rate because of drugs and weapons. Many African American communities are living in fear.

With a justice system that specifically targets African Americans and a prison system overflowing with a disproportionate number of young Black men, drugs, guns, and the justice system are the newest challenges facing African Americans today. Aggressions that were tempered following the Civil Rights Movement have once again become a focus, except that now the perpetrators of those aggressions seem to be the very people who pledged to keep them from happening—cases in point: the recent deaths of Brown and Garner. Minority stress has risen to epidemic proportions because now, in addition to worry about housing and feeding the family, drug use, gang violence, lack of education, and job opportunities, a new and equally frightening need—protection of self and family from law enforcement—has become an additional concern.

Meaning of Medicine and Well-Being

The quality of health among African Americans is impacted by socioeconomic status, access to health care services, and genetic background (Reyes, 2001). Typically, in receiving health care services, African Americans have fared poorer than other ethnic groups. However, with the passage of the Affordable Care Act and improvements in medical technology and public health practices, African Americans now have more access to health services than ever before in American history (Reyes, 2001). Prior to this health care act, more than 38.4 million Americans were uninsured and had no access to health care.

In recent times, the Census Bureau (2007) has estimated the African American population to be 40.7 million, 13.5% of the total population (Centers for Disease Control and Prevention, 2008). Previously, in 2000, the African American population had been estimated to be 12% of the American population, almost 35 million individuals. They project that by the year 2035, the African American population will be 50 million, or 14.3% of the population; by year 2050, 65.7 million, or 15% of the total population. Among the current 40.7 million African Americans, many experience significant health issues that could lead to death.

African American Health Concerns

History has shown that when people have health insurance, their health status improves. However, African Americans have been less likely to have health insurance, and their children have been more likely to be insured by Med-Cal and Medicare (Reyes, 2001). When a person possesses health insurance, then their ability to access vaccinations, preventative care, screenings, dental care, prescription drugs, medical attention to injuries, and continuous medical follow-up is more likely to occur (Reyes, 2001; Sykes, 2014). A primary indicator of access to health care services is a person having insurance and being able to pay the co-pay requirements as a prerequisite of care (Reyes, 2001).

The Affordable Care Act (aka "Obamacare") makes it

possible for every person, regardless of race or economic status, to have health insurance, which also makes available preventative medical services, vaccinations, and prenatal care. Typically, African American women have been less likely to receive adequate prenatal care. Their children lag behind in being updated on immunizations and the infant mortality rate of their children has exceeded that of White women (Reyes, 2001). Also, in the past, African American women experienced gender bias in acquiring access to quality health care for specific illnesses such as breast, cervical, and ovarian cancers. Plus, health issues resulting from violence against African American women had largely been ignored by the medical community. All of these deficient areas of health care hopefully will change under the Affordable Care Act.

In 2002, the leading causes of death in African Americans were (1) heart disease (26.8%, 76,694 individuals); (2) cancer (21.6%, 61,996); (3) stroke (6.5%, 18,691); (4) diabetes (4.4%, 12,583); (5) unintentional injury (4.3%, 12,285); (6) homicide (2.8%, 8,147); (7) chronic lower respiratory disease (2.7%, 7,730); (8) Human Immunodeficiency Virus (2.7%, 7,714); (9) nephritis (2.6%, 7,410); (10) septicemia (2.1%, 6,074); and (11) all others (23.5%, 67,249). Total deaths were 286,573 African Americans (Centers for Disease Control and Prevention, 2005). The Centers for Disease Control and Prevention found that hypertension, tuberculosis, smoking, obesity, cancer, and diabetes in African American continue to be significant areas of concern.

Hypertension is the term for high blood pressure. Blood pressure is a measurement of the force against the walls of a person's arteries as their heart pumps blood through their body. Hypertension occurs when a person's blood pressure is 140/90 mmHG or above most of the time. Systolic blood pressure is the top number, and the bottom number is the diastolic blood pressure. Normal blood pressure is when the blood pressure is lower than 120/80 mmHg most of the time. Prehypertension occurs when numbers are 120/80 or higher, but below 140/90 (Chen, Zieve, & Ogilvie, 2014).

In African Americans, hypertension is more severe and develops earlier life than in Whites (Cute, 1997). 43% of African American men and 45.7% of African American women are diagnosed with hypertension. Not only are more African American people diagnosed with hypertension, they are being diagnosed at earlier ages. Between 2007 to 2010, 37.6% of African American men who were 20 years of age and over were diagnosed with hypertension. Similarly, 44.4% of African American women who were 20 years of age and over were diagnosed with hypertension. Hypertension is two times more prevalent in African Americans than in Whites and has connections to kidney disease, kidney failure, atherosclerosis (hardening of the arteries), stroke, and heart attack (Cute, 1997).

The Centers for Disease Control and Prevention (2009) investigated tuberculosis (TB) in the United States for the year 2008 and found the following information: (1) Approximately 3,273 African Americans were diagnosed with TB, which represented 25% of total TB cases. (2) Overall, United States–born African Americans represented 42% of TB cases, and 14% of TB cases were in foreign-born persons. (3) Asian-Americans exceeded African Americans as the second largest racial or ethnic group with TB cases. (4) African Americans had a TB incidence rate approximately eight times greater than Caucasians (8.8 per 100,000, compared to 1.1 per 100,000, respectively). (5) African Americans had the third highest incidence rate of TB, behind Asian-Americans (25.6 per 100,000) and Native Hawaiians/Pacific Islanders (15.9 per 100,000). In 2007, 45% of African Americans are diagnosed with tuberculosis.

In the United States each year, about 45,000 African American die from smoking-related disease (e.g., lung cancer, cardiovascular disease). It is estimated that 1.6 million Black Americans under the age of 18 will become regular smokers, and a half million will die from smoking. From 2008 to 2010, 27.4% of male African Americans ages 18 and over were smokers. Similarly, 18% of African American women ages 18 and up were smokers. From 1999 to 2002, African American males and females ages 20 to 74 years had higher age-adjusted rates per 100,000 population of hypertension than their White counterparts (36.8 vs. 23.9 for males; 39.4 vs. 23.3 for females). From 2008 to 2010, the obesity rate at ages 20 years and over for men was 38.1%, and for women, 54.2%.

In African Americans, cancer is the second leading cause of death. In 2001, the age-adjusted incidence per 100,000 population was substantially higher for Black females than for White females for certain cancers, including colon/rectal (54.0 vs. 43.3), pancreatic (13.0 vs. 8.9), and stomach (9.0 vs. 4.5) cancers. Among males, the age-adjusted incidence was higher for Black males than for White males for certain cancers, including prostate (251.3 vs. 167.8), lung/bronchus (108.2 vs. 72.8), colon/rectal (68.3 vs. 58.9), and stomach (16.3 vs. 10.0) cancers (The Henry J. Kaiser Family Foundation, 2006). In 2001, the age-adjusted rate for all cancers was 25.4% higher for African Americans (243.1 per 100,000) than for White Americans (193.9), and the diabetes age-adjusted death rate for African Americans was more than twice that for White Americans (49.2 per 100,000 vs. 23.0).

Additionally, there are other areas that have posed severe threats to African Americans.

Heart disease refers to a range of conditions that affect the heart. From 2005 to 2008, African American women and men ages 45 to 75 had much higher heart disease death rates than women and men of other races. In 2001, the age-adjusted death rate for heart disease was 30.1% higher for African Americans (316.9 per 100,000) than for White American (243.5). Moreover, African American women younger than 75 years of age died more often from heart disease than White women of the same age. Similar patterns were found for Black men when compared with White men.

AIDS (Acquired Immune Deficiency Syndrome) is the final stage of HIV disease, which causes severe damage to the immune system. In 2009, the Centers for Disease Control and Prevention determined that while African Americans made up

14% of the U.S. population, they accounted for 44% of all new HIV infections (MMVR, 2010). Young African American gay and bisexual men are especially at risk of HIV infection. In 2009, Black men accounted for 70% of the estimated new HIV infections among all Blacks. The estimated rate of new HIV infection for Black men was more than 6.5 times as high as that of White men, and 2.5 times as high as that of Latino men or Black women (Office of National AIDS Policy, 2010).

Black men who have sex with men (MSM) represented an estimated 73% of new infections among all Black men, and 37% among all MSM. More new HIV infections occurred among young Black MSM (ages 13–29) than any other age and racial group of MSM. In addition, new HIV infections among young Black MSM increased by 48% from 2006–2009. Black women accounted for 30% of the estimated new HIV infections among all Blacks. Most (85%) Black women with HIV acquired HIV through heterosexual sex (Hall et al., 2008). The estimated rate of new HIV infections for Black women was more than 15 times as high as the rate for White women, and more than three times as high as that of Latina women (Office of National AIDS Policy, 2010). All of these health conditions affect African American men and women who are incarcerated and/or placed in state institutions.

African Americans in Prisons/State Hospitals

U.S. prisons now hold more Black men than were ever enslaved. African American men are disproportionately represented in the criminal justice system, seven times more so than Whites (Pitterson, 2011). In 2011, about 40% of incarcerated individuals were Black (APA, October 2014). As of 2008, the U. S. Department of Justice estimated that there were over 846,000 Black men in prison, making up 40.2% of all inmates in the system at large (U.S. Department of Justice, 2009). Moreover, African American women are eight times more likely to go to prison and receive longer sentences that White women (Vassall, 2003). Blacks are less likely to post bail money and thus more likely to remain incarcerated before trial. They receive harsher sentencing in plea agreements and often receive prison time for the same crimes for which a White person would serve no time (APA, October 2014). Frequently, Blacks incur drug charges, which automatically incur stiff mandatory sentences, and more Black receive the death penalty (APA, October 2014).

One of the factors increasing the number of African Americans in prison in the United States is that the murder rate of Blacks is four times the national average. In 2011, the Black homicide victimization rate was 17.51 per 100,000. In 2011, there 6,309 homicide victims; 5,452 (86%) were male (31. 67 per 100,000) and 854 (14%) were female (4.54 per 100,000), compared with 1.45 per 100,000 for White females. Overall, the national homicide victimization rate was 4.44 per 100,000; among White Americans, the homicide rate was 2.64 per 100,000. Young Black men die at a rate that is at least 1.5 times the rate of young Whites, and more of their deaths are due to homicide.

African American men make up over 30% of the males in state hospital institutions. An excessive number of African Americans experience discriminatory policies and practices such as excessive use of medications, excessive use of restraints, unequal access to emergency care, a lack of continuity of care, and excessive wait times to address basic request (Reyes, 2001; Sykes, 2014). Frequently, policies and practices disproportionately affect racial and ethnic minorities, particularly African Americans. In state hospitals, many employees are not culturally competent (able to effectively function in a culturally diverse setting). They lack good comprehension of the languages, religions, beliefs, history, cultures, and traditions of patients, and all of these areas can impact the quality of treatment. African American men experience gender and ethnic bias.

Many in the African American group did not have the luxury of insurance or doctors for years. They often had home remedies that had has been passed down through generations in order to address their mental illnesses. They had their own doctors and midwives to treat them because they were segregated from the White populations due Jim Crow laws in the South. Many of the older generations were born in their homes, with no available medical facilities.

Religion and Medicine

Depending upon in which decade African American were born and in which locations in the United States, there was a strong belief that God was the healer, and not a real belief in medicine. Many African Americans were not receptive to medical intervention, due to belief and lack of money.

Music of African Americans

Whether secular and sacred or combination of both, music is the fabric of every African American household. It ranges from songs in the cotton fields during slavery, to the March on Washington, D.C., to performing for presidents, kings, and queens. Whether in the form of singing in the choir, playing music around the piano in the homes, dancing to music in the home and clubs, or, as in some Pentecostal churches, even praise-dance during services, music is an essential element of life. Music has been the fabric of American-Americans, in the forms of composing, singing, playing, and performance.

"African American music" is an umbrella term given to a range of music and musical genres emerging from influence by African Americans, who have long constituted a large and significant ethnic minority of the population of the United States (Estell, 1994). Many of their ancestors were originally brought to North America to work as enslaved people, bringing with them polyrhythmic songs from hundreds of Black African ethnic groups across West and sub-Saharan Africa (Estell, 1994). The convergence in the Americas of African people from different regions and from multiple cultural traditions merged their music with influences from polka, waltzes, and other

European styles. Later periods saw considerable innovation and change. Their experience in the United States produced several genres of music, both religious and secular, which are credited as originating from African Americans. These genres have been highly influential and popular across socioeconomic and racial groupings internationally.

Religious Music

Religious songs were composed through religious influence, and often performed for religious use (Southhall, 1997). African Americans have invented and/or influenced the development of various forms of religious music originating in the United States. In the southern part of the United States, Negro spirituals were often called America's "first true folk music" (Broughton et al., 1994). Negro spirituals could relay several meanings to slaves, informing them of plans to escape, directions to take, or other Underground Railroad plans.

Eventually, after the United States abolished slavery in 1863, The Fisk Jubilee toured all over the United States and Europe and was credited with spreading spirituals throughout the world. The Tuskegee Institute Choir, Loudin's Jubilee Singers, and Stinton's Jubilee Singers had Negro spirituals singers and others form of entertainment.

American entertainment came in the form of minstrels. They were predominantly black-faced White men who used Black songs, dance, and comic skits in musical theater and propagated racial stereotypes that slaves had experienced for decades, which then reinforced inaccurate images of African Americans such as the slave dandy, Mammy, Sambo, Aunt Jemimah, Jim Crow, and other characters displayed as inferior, shuffling, and childlike slaves. They also reinforced the idea of White supremacy. Throughout the lifespan of minstrels, Black American minstrels mainly performed spirituals. It was the minstrel, vaudeville, and chorus groups that paved the way for Gospel music.

Gospel Music

Gospel music developed from the Negro spiritual music of the African slaves, and the South is credited as the birthplace of gospel music (Broughton et al., 1994). It is estimated that 4 million slaves existed in the South at the time of Emancipation, and it was through ex-slaves that gospel music first developed. As the minstrel, vaudeville, and chorus groups spread Negro Spirituals to White Americans and Europe, so too they would spread gospel music to White America.

With freedom came new experiences in religious worship and new music that was holiness-based. In the 1890s, Charles Harrison Mason founded the Church of God in Christ, Inc. (COGIC), with a predominantly African American membership based on holiness-sanctified pentecostalism; today, its membership numbers more than six million in 63 countries (Lippy & Williams, 1988). In this holiness denomination and others of the sort, African influence and traditions were observable through the call-and-response jubilee songs, shouts, foot-stomping, hand clapping, and dance, as in that of the plantation "praise houses." Vocally, the singers would sometimes suddenly shout, moan, or give falsetto cries. Initially, they used drums, guitars, washboards, and tambourines. Over time, the piano was added. In the present day, the main instruments are the B3 Hammond organ, drums, keyboard, guitar, bass, and brass and woodwind instruments. The gospel area has been greatly influenced by the following people: singers Thomas Andrew Dorsey, Sallie Martin, Mahalia Jackson, Roberta Martin Singers, Clara Ward Singers, the Caravans, Marion Williams, Sister Rosetta Tharpe, Dorthy L. Coates, Ernestine Washington, Davis Sisters, Staples Singers, Albertina Walker, Shirley Caesar, Dorothy Norwood, Inez Andrews, Andrea Crouch, James Edward Cleveland, Rev. Milton Brunson, Edwin Hawkins, Walter Hawkins, Tramine Hawkins, John P. Kee, Kirk Franklin, Fred Hammond, Smokie Norfolk, and Marvin Sapp, and instrumentalists Dr. Vernard Johnson, Steve Fry, Kirk Whalum, Karen J. Reed, Kevin Moore, and Dennis Reed.

Many choirs and singers have contributed to gospel music popularity, including The Angelic Choir of Nutley, New Jersey, Mass Choir; The Florida Mass Choir; Love Center Choir; The Southern California Community; The Mississippi Mass Choir; The West Angeles Church of God in Christ; Hezekiah Walker; Sounds of Blackness; New Life; Full Gospel Choir; National Church of God in Christ Choir; and many others.

Detroit, Michigan, has produced some of the greatest gospel singers in the world: Dr. Mattie Moss-Clark; The Clark Sisters—Jacky, Twinkie, Dorinda, and Karen; Kierra "KiKi" Sheard and J Moss; James Moore; Vanessa Bell-Armstrong; The Winans (brothers Ronald, Marvin, Carvin, and Michael); Vickie Winans; The Winans family (Delores "Mom" and David "Pop" Wininas); duet Benjamin (Bebe) and Priscilla (CeCe) Winans; sister duet Angie and Debbie Winans; and David Winans, Furthermore, artists such as Aretha Franklin, Anita Baker, and many Motown greats had their beginnings in gospel music.

Secular Music

Secular music is nonreligious music, and it signifies being disconnected from religion. For years, secular music was not condoned by the holiness-sanctified churches and other denominations as music that could be listened to by their members, and this continues to be the standard for traditional holiness believers. Secular music was labeled as "worldly music" or "the devil's music," and born-again believers were not to associate with secular music. To this day, secular music is a conflict-ridden topic among religious believers. Gospel musicians were not permitted to intermix with secular musicians because darkness was not to seek fellowship with light, and secular music was regarded as darkness. Some of the African American secular singers and musicians who have made an exceptional impact on music throughout the world include Michael Jackson, Aretha Franklin, Diana Ross, Stevie Wonder, Marian Anderson, Louis Armstrong, Duke Ellington, Harry

Belafonte, Chuck Berry, Ray Charles, Nat King Cole, Billie Holiday, Miles Davis, Dizzy Gillespie, Duke Ellington, Jimi Hendrix, and Robert Johnson.

Jazz

African Americans are credited with the origination of jazz music. Scott Joplin, the African American composer, is credited with creating ragtime in the 1800s, (Clarke, 1989). He combined newly introduced European compositional styles with the rhythmic and melodic music of the Black community, creating a syncopation or "ragged" rhythm. Ragtime was popular from 1895 to 1918 was performed by pianists such as Scott Joplin, James Scott, Tom Turpin, Charles Lamb, James P. Johnson, Lucky Roberts, and others (Mehegan, 1964). Jazz took many forms. New Orleans style (1910–1919) utilized brass bands to perform gospel songs and marches. After 1917 came the evolution of the Chicago style of jazz music. From 1920 to 1930, boogie-woogie was a jazz-related piano solo form. The Big Bands and the Swing Era from 1930s to 1940 originated in small group jazz played in the clubs on New York's 52nd Street by African American musicians (Carr, Fairweather, & Priestley, 1995). Bebop and the Jazz Schism of the 1940s originated during World War II in Harlem, New York, at Minton's Playhouse, where Dizzy Gillespie (trumpet), Charlie Parker (alto saxophone), and Kenny Clarke (drum) played together (Berendt, 1982). Charlie Christian (guitar) and Thelonious Monk (piano) also played at Milton's. It was a fast, upbeat tempo, combining dissonance, elaborate melodies, and abstract chording with rhythmic patterns. Bebop has a greater emphasis on a solo performer. Cool Jazz, attributed to Miles Davis (trumpet), John Lewis (piano), and Tadd Dameron (piano), had a laid-back beat. Hard bop (a modern form of bebop) was created as a description of the consolidation of bop, and Consolidation was the jazz genre that dominated the 1950s. In 1959, the Free Jazz movement was started in New York by Ornette Coleman. It was improvisation not based on predetermined chords, underlying harmonic structure, and with no predetermined structural length (Carr, Fairweather, & Priestley, 1995). The more extreme Free Jazz became known as "Black Music" and was associated with racial protests of the African American community, illustrating the impact of the Civil Rights Movement on jazz music. In the 1970s, jazz evolved to take on a new form called fusion or jazz rock, a combination of rock rhythm, jazz improvisation, and electronics derived from non-Western music and extended to instrumental compositions with a jazz approach (Berendt, 1982). Usually, the wind and brass instruments used a high level of instrumental technique. Major innovators Miles Davis and Ornette Coleman were the artists whose music led to fusion (Koslow, 1999). Fusion albums show a variety of styles. In the summer of 1980, Wynton Marsalis joined Art Blakey's Jazz Messengers Band, where he and other musicians spearheaded a resurgence of more traditional jazz styles, thus producing an extraordinary range of choices (Koslow, 1999). By the early 1980s, much of the original fusion genre had been incorporated into other divisions of jazz and rock, especially smooth jazz, a subgenre of jazz which is influenced stylistically by R&B, funk, and pop. Smooth jazz can be traced to at least the late 1960s and Marsalis. In the 1990s, musicians continued to acknowledge their (distant) heritage as an influence, with a new generation examining in detail what happened during the previous jazz decades and, in the process, bringing the past to life.

Blues

Blues is considered the first Black secular music originating in the United States in the 1900s (Clarke, 1989). Blues was the first solely secular form of African American–based music, with the birth of ragtime and jazz following closely behind. Hart Wand's "Dallas Blues" is considered the first publication of blues sheet music, coming in 1912 (Clarke, 1989). That same year, W. C. Handy's "The Memphis Blues" was published. Mamie Smith was the first African American recording singer, making in 1920 a rendition of Perry Bradford's "Crazy Blues" (Randel 1986). Ethel Waters had a clear voice. Rainey, Ida Cox, Victoria Spivey, and Bessie Smith had a roughness and concomitant directness to their styles (Randel, 1986).

Like the Negro spirituals, the blues was heard by a diverse variety of people, including White listeners. Because of the Great Depression in the United States, African Americans migrated north along the route of the Illinois Central Railroad toward Chicago, bringing blues music with them. As a result, urban nightclubs filled with blues, and the Chicago blues formed as a more powerful style than all types before. In the late 1950s, blues music became popular. In 1958, #1 hit "Tom Dooley," recorded by The Kingston Trio, gave birth to the folk revival. From 1959–1966, the Newport Folk Festival reintroduced folk and blues music to a mainstream White American audience. After this time, blues was increasingly merged with rock music to form the rock blues bands of the 1960s and '70s. The Rolling Stones, John Mayall, Led Zeppelin, and others carried on the noble tradition of their forefathers, the blues minstrels.

Rhythm and Blues

In the 1940s, "rhythm and blues" (R&B) was the term used to describe popular African American music; the style was adopted to replace race recordings in the United States record industry (Clarke, 1989). R&B, representing jazz and blues elements, was utilized by small combos and the "doo-wop" sound to produce a strong dance rhythm (Koslow, 1999). Artists in the 1950s included Chuck Berry and Fats Domino; in the 1960s, Motown artists, The Supremes, The Temptations, Aretha Franklin, and Otis Redding. New-style R&B developed from the 1960s to 1980s and incorporated funk and disco. More changes occurred in the mid-1990s, with artists TLC, Mary J. Blige, Usher, R. Kelly and others. The 21st century has a variety of styles incorporating dance, pop, rap, and hip-hop.

Soul

Soul is a genre in African American popular music in which Motown dominated both the pop and R&B charts and to some extent Billboard's R&B chart. The 1960s was the first time in American history when African American and Whites purchased the same records. African Americans also started their own recording companies, such as Motown. In the late 1960s, Aretha Franklin was not at Motown, but she recorded hits such as "Baby I Love You," "Chain of Fools," and "Respect" (Pendergast & Pendergast, 2003). Some of the R&B artists included Ray Charles, Little Richard, Sam Cook, James Brown, Otis Redding, Isaac Hayes, Sam & Dave, Wilson Pickett, Joe Tex, Percy Sledge, Lionel Richie, Al Green, Peabo Bryson, Al Jarreau, The Platters, The Jackson Five, and many others (Clarke, 1989).

Motown was one corporation that impacted the dispensation of soul music throughout the world. In 1960, Barry Gordy, Jr., founded Motown Record Corporation, which eventually became the single most profitable African American–owned corporation in the United States (Pendergast & Pendergast, 2003). Some of Motown's artists included Little Stevie Wonder, Diana Ross, The Four Tops, Martha and the Vandellas, Marvin Gaye, Gladys Knight, Smokey Robinson, The Marvelettes, Barrett Strong, The Miracles, Mary Wells, The Contours, and The Jackson Five.

Rap

Started by disc jockeys and urban African Americans in late 1970s, rap originated as a music form that had a background recurring beat pattern in which the vocalist uttered boastful, slangy lyrics. The lyrics address politics, discrimination, and all types of life events. Over the decades, rap has developed several different types and continues to flourish as an industry.

There have been several forms of rap, including old school rap (1979–1984; Fab Five Freddy, The Cold Crush Brothers, Afrika Bambaataa, The Sugarhill Gang, Lovebug Starski); Grandmaster Flash, Spoonie Gee, Newcleus, Treacherous Three, Funky Four Plus One, Kurtis Blow, and Busy Bee Starski; hip-hop (late '80s into '90s; Run DMC, Public Enemy, Beastie Boys, Boogie Down Productions, Eric B. & Rakim, Big Daddy Kane, De La Soul, Gang Starr, Pete Rock & CL Smooth, EPMD, A Tribe Called Quest, Slick Rick and Jungle Brothers); early gangsta rap (Ice-T, Geto Boys, and N.W.A); sex rap (2 Live Crew and Too Short); party-oriented music (M.C. Hammer, Kid 'n Play, The Fat Boys, DJ Jazzy Jeff, and The Fresh Prince); gangsta rap (1980s, political; Public Enemy, led by Chuck D and Flavor Flav); alternative (East Coast rappers include De La Soul, Pete Rock & CL Smooth, Jungle Brothers, A Tribe Called Quest, Brand Nubian, and Digable Planets; West Coast rappers include The Pharcyde, Del Funkee Homosapien, Digital Underground, Freestyle Fellowship, and Jurassic Five; Southern rappers include Arrested Development, Goodie Mob, and Outcast); and crank (1990s into early 2000s). Lil Jon and the Eastside Boyz popularized crank with releases like "Put Yo Hood Up."

Other Music Genres

Although the previously listed music genres are areas in which African Americans have been the originators, rock (Jimi Hendrix, Prince), pop (Michael Jackson), country (Charlie Pride), classical music, and other music genres also are areas where African Americans have had great influence and contributions.

African American music has played a pivotal role in the area of music development in the United States and the world at large. From slavery to the 21st century, from Negro spirituals to rap music, much has been the creation of African Americans. This music has touched every corner of the world, reaching across cultural boundaries, stereotypes, and century-long prejudices to create a musical language that has overcome all three.

Conclusion

This chapter attempts to provide the reader with an understanding of the history of the African American in the United States. It would have been impossible within the scope of this chapter to cover all of the rich history of African Americans. As evidenced in this chapter, African Americans are very diverse and present many challenges for the music therapist. We have tried to present a history of the journey of African Americans, along with the struggles, desires, and countless achievements of Blacks in America. We felt it important that the reader understand this brief history of African Americans, the cultural environment from which they come and live, the attitudes and sensitivities they present, the relationship patterns of these rich and diverse people, to enable the therapist to have a clearer sense of the difficulties the African American culture has endured and, in many circumstances, continues to endure. As evidenced in this chapter, music is very important in the African American community for communication, self-expression, and celebration.

Our hope is that therapists are more empowered to treat African Americans with a new lens to aid in understanding treatment needs and the diversity within the culture. Of primary significance in working with and understanding the African American client is self-reflection by the therapist. Being sensitive to microaggressions that are a common part of the majority vernacular is important prior to working with this population. Along those same lines, the sometimes active aggression of clients toward the majority therapist should be taken into consideration. In many cases, the aggression is a combination of fear and mistrust. Therapists should be aware of both the client's and their own fear and mistrust to successfully treat the African American client. Open honest communication, and the appropriate use of music will enhance treatment, communication, and relationships.

References

American Heart Association. (2014, August 4). *High blood pressure and African Americans*. Retrieved from http://www.heart.org/HEARTORG/Conditions/HighBloodP ressure/UnderstandYourRiskforHighBloodPressure/High-Blood-Pressure-and-African%20Americans_UCM_301832_Article.jsp#

American Psychological Association. (2014). The United States leads the world in incarceration. A new report explores why—and offers recommendations for fixing the system. *Monitor on Psychology, 45*(9). Retrieved from http://www.apa.org/monitor/2014/10/incarceration.aspx

Atkins, Ronald. (Ed.). (1996). *All that jazz: The illustrated story of jazz music*. Dubai: Carlton Books Limited.

Auerbach, S. (1994). *Encyclopedia of multiculturalism: Ethnic and minority group names - inner city* (Vol. 3). New York, NY: Marshall Cavendish.

Barnhart, C. L., & Barnhart, R. K. (Eds.). (1994). *The World Book Dictionary* (Vol. 1, A–K, p. 1004). Chicago, IL: World Book, Inc.

Barnhart, C. L., & Barnhart, R. K. (Eds.). (1994). *The World Book Dictionary* (Vol. 2, L–Z, p. 1798). Chicago, IL: World Book, Inc.

Bennett, L. (1973). *Ebony Pictorial History of Black Americans* (Vols. 1–4). Chicago, IL: Johnson Publishing Company.

Berendt, J. E. (1982). *The jazz book: From ragtime to fusion and beyond*. Westport, CT: Lawrence Hill & Company.

Blocker, J. S. (1996). Black migration to Muncie, 1860-1930. *Indiana Magazine of History, 92*(4), 297-320.

Boskin, J. (1986). *Sambo: The rise and demise of an American jester*. New York, NY: Oxford University Press.

Broughton, S., Ellingham, M., Muddyman, D., & Trillo, R. (Eds.). (1994). *World music: The rough guide*. New York, NY: Penguin Books.

Brown, K. T., Ward, G. K., Lightborn, T., & Jackson, J. (1999). Skin tone and racial identity among African Americans: A theoretical research framework. In R. Jones (Ed.), *Advances in African American perspectives*. Hampton, VA: Cobb & Henry Publishers.

Carr, I., Fairweather, D., & Priestley, B. (1995). *Jazz, the rough guide: The essential companion to artists and albums*. New York, NY: Penguin Books.

Centers for Disease Control and Prevention. *Morbidity and mortality weekly report* (2005, January 13). Retrieved from http://www.cdc.gov/mmwr/preview/mmwrhtml/mm5401 a1.htm

Centers for Disease Control and Prevention. (2006). Subpopulation estimates from the HIV incidence surveillance system—United States. MMWR, 57, 985–989.

Centers for Disease Control and Prevention. (2008). *Reported Tuberculosis in the United States, 2008*. Atlanta, GA: U.S. Department of Health and Human Services, CDC.

Centers for Disease Control and Prevention. (2010). Prevalence and awareness of HIV infection among men who have sex with men—21 cities, United States, 2008. *MMWR, 59,* 1201–1207.

Chen, M. A., Zieve, D., & Ogilvie, I. (Eds.). (2014). *High blood pressure. Medline Plus Trusted Health Information for You*. U.S. National Library of Medicine. National Institutes of Health. Retrieved from http://www.nlm.nih.gov/medlineplus/ency/article/000468.htm

Clarke, D. (Ed.). (1989). *The Penguin encyclopedia of popular music*. New York, NY: Viking Penguin.

Clinton, C. (2004). *Harriet Tubman: The road to freedom*. New York, NY: Little, Brown & Company.

Degler, C. N. (1980). *At odds: Women and the family in America from the revolution to the present*. New York, NY: Oxford University Press.

Dowden, P. A. (1993). The great migration in historical perspective: New dimensions of race, class, and gender. *Indiana Magazine of History, 89*(1), 75-76.

Estell, K. (1994). *African American: Celebrating 400 years of achievement*. Detroit, MI: Visible Ink Press.

Eltis, D., & Richardson, D. (2011, January 5). New revelations about slaves and slave trade. *CNN*. Retrieved from http://www.cnn.com/2011/OPINION/01/05/eltis.richards on.slave.trade/

Fargis, P. (1997). *The New York Public Library American History Desk Reference*. New York, NY: John Wiley & Sons.

Gaines, K. K. (2010). "Racial Uplift Ideology in the Era of 'the Negro Problem.'" Freedom's Story, TeacherServe©. National Humanities Center. Retrieved from http://nationalhumanitiescenter.org/tserve/freedom/186 5-1917/essays/racialuplift.htm

Gates, H. L., & Yacovone, D. (2013). *The African Americans: Many rivers to cross*. New York, NY: SmileyBooks.

Genovese, M. A., & Han, L. C. (2009). *Encyclopedia of American government and civics*. New York, NY: Facts on File.

Gillespie, M. (2004, June 17). Americans still believe O.J. Simpson is guilty. Retrieved from http://www.gallup.com/poll/12046/americans-still-believe-oj-simpson-guilty.aspx

Goings, K. W. (1994). *Mammy and Uncle Mose: Black collectibles and American stereotyping*. Bloomington, IN: University Press.

Gollnick, D. M., & Chinn, P. C. (1986). *Multicultural education in a pluralistic society* (2nd ed.). Columbus, OH: Charles E. Merrill.

Gottesman, R. (Ed.). (1999). *Violence in America, an encyclopedia*. New York, NY: Charles Scribner's Sons.

Green, L. (1998, Winter). Stereotypes: Negative racial stereotypes and their effect on attitudes toward African Americans. *Perspectives on Multiculturism and Cultural Diversity, 11*(1). Retrieved from http://www.ferris.edu/jimcrow/links/VCU.htm

Greene, J. (2013). *10 common causes of hypertension*. Retrieved from http://www.activebeat.co/your-health/women/10-common-causes-of-hypertension/?utm_source=google&utm_campaign=adwo

rds&utm_medium=cpc&utm_keyword=hypertension%20s
ymptoms&gclid=CN3xzMqO58ECFZFhfgodWVIAKQ

Haley, A. (1996a). *Roots: The saga of an American family.* New York, NY: Vanguard Press.

Haley, A. (1996b). *Roots: The saga of an American family (TV series).* Los Angeles, CA: Warner Bros. Television.

Hall, H. I., Song, R., Rhodes, P., Prejean, J., An, Q., Lee, L. M., … & Janssen, R. S. (2008). Estimation of HIV incidence in the United States. *JAMA, 300*(5), 520–529.

Harris, W. H. (1976). Black migration: Movement North, 1900–1920. *Indiana Magazine of History, 72*(1), 85-86.

Henderson, R. (1997). *QPB encyclopedia of word and phrase origins.* New York, NY: Facts on File.

Hip-hop. (2016). In Wikipedia. Retrieved from http://en.wikipedia.org/wiki/Hip_hop_music

Ivey, A. (1986). *Development therapy: Theory into practice.* San Francisco, CA: Jossey-Bass.

Jewell, S. K. (1993). *From Mammy to Miss America and beyond: Cultural images and the shaping of U.S. policy.* New York, NY: Routledge.

Jones, R. (Ed.). (1999). *Advances in African American psychology.* Hampton, VA: Cobb & Henry Publishers.

Kendall, D. (2004). *Social problems in a diverse society* (3rd ed.). Boston, MA: A Pearson Education Company.

Koslow, P. (1999). *The New York public library African American desk reference: The ultimate source for essential information about history, culture, and contemporary life.* New York, NY: John Wiley & Sons.

Lippy, C. H., & Williams, P. W. (Eds.). (1988). *Encyclopedia of the American religious experience: Studies traditions and movements.* New York, NY: Charles Scribner's Sons.

Mapson, J. W., Jr., (1984). *The ministry of music in the black church.* Valley Forge, PA: Judson Press.

Mehegan, J. (1964). *Swing and early progressive piano styles: Jazz improvisation III.* New York, NY: Watson-Guptill Publications.

Mendez, J. G. (2011). *A great sacrifice: Northern Black families and their civil war experiences.* Chicago, IL: University of Illinois at Chicago. Retrieved from INDIGO (http://hdl.handle.net/10027/12787).

Morris, K. (1977). *Choir directors' guide.* Chicago, IL: Martin & Morris Music, Inc.

National Center for HIV/AIDS, Viral Hepatitis, STD, and TB Prevention. (2011, November). Retrieved from www.cdc.gov/hiv

Office of National AIDS Policy. (2010, November 1). *National HIV/AIDS Strategy.* Retrieved from http://www.whitehouse.gov/administration/eop/onap/nhas

Parham, T. (Ed.). (2002). *Counseling persons of African descent: Raising the bar of practitioner competence.* Thousand Oaks, CA: SAGE Publications.

Parry, R. (2004, October 25). How John Kerry exposed the Contra-cocaine scandal. *Salon.* Retrieved from http://www.salon.com/2004/10/25/contra/

Pendergast, T., & Pendergast, S. (Eds.). (2003). *U-X-L American Decades, 1960–1969.* Farmington Hills, MI: The Gale Group, Inc.

Pendergast, T., & Pendergast, S. (Eds.). (2005). *The Sixties in American Biographies.* Farmington Hills, MI: The Gale Group, Inc.

Pitterson, L. (2011, March 28). U.S. prisons now hold more black men than slavery ever did. *Clutch Magazine.* Retrieved from http://www.clutchmagonline.com/2011/03/u-s-prisons-now-hold-more-black-men-than-slavery-ever-did/

Randel, D. M. (Ed.). (1986). *The New Harvard dictionary of music.* Cambridge, MA: The Belknap Press of Harvard University Press.

Rasheed, J., & Rasheed, M. (1999). *Social work practice with African American men: The invisible presence.* Thousand Oaks, CA: SAGE Publications.

Reed, K. J. (2000). *Music is the master key.* Orlando, FL: Rivercross Publishing.

Reed, K. J. (2002). Music therapy treatment groups for mentally disordered offenders (MDO) in a state hospital setting: Atascadero State Hospital, California. *Music Therapy Perspectives, 22*(2), 98–116.

Reyes, B. I. (Ed.). (2001). *A portrait of race and ethnicity in California: An assessment of social and economic well-being.* San Francisco, CA: Public Policy Institute of CA.

Rosenblatt, J. (2013, July, 25). Long road out of Jasper: A documentary chronicles James Byrd Jr.'s life and tragic death. *Texas Observer.* Retrieved from https://www.texasobserver.org/long-road-out-of-jasper/

Sabato, L. (1998). Iran Contra Affair – 1986-1987. *Washington Post.* Retrieved from http://www.washingtonpost.com/wp-srv/politics/special/clinton/frenzy/iran.htm

Smith, P. B., & Bond, M. H. (1993). *Social psychology across cultures.* Boston, MA: Allyn & Bacon.

Smith, R. C. (2003). *Encyclopedia of African American politics.* New York, NY: Facts on File.

Southern, E. (1997). *The music of Black America: A history.* New York, NY: W. W. Norton & Company.

Sue, D., Capodilupo, C., Torino, G., Bucceri, J., Holder, A., Nadal, K., & Esquilin, M. (2007). Racial microaggressions in everyday life: Implications for clinical practice. *American Psychologist, 62*(4), 271–286.

Sykes, K. (Ed.). (2014). *ProQuest statistical abstract of the United States, 2014.* New York, NY: Berman Press.

The Henry J. Kaiser Family Foundation (2006, July). *Race, ethnicity & health care fact sheet: Young African American men in the United States.* Washington, DC: Kaiser Family Foundation. Retrieved from https://kaiserfamilyfoundation.files.wordpress.com/2013/01/7541.pdf

Thomas, V. M. (2001). *No man can hinder me: The journey from slavery to emancipation through song.* New York, NY: Crown Publishers.

Turner, S. (2010). *An illustrated history of gospel: Gospel music from early spirituals to contemporary urban.* Grand Rapids, MI: Lion Hudson.

U.S. Department of Justice. (2009, December). Prisoners in 2008. *Bureau of Justice Statistics Bulletin, NCJ 228417.* Washington, DC: U.S. Department of Justice.

Vassall-Fall, D. A. (2003, August). Not to be ignored: African American women and the prison system. *Urban Journal.* Nashville, TN: Urban Communications.

Violence Policy Center. (2014, January). *Black homicide victimization in the United States: An analysis of 2011 homicide data.* Retrieved from http://www.vpc.org/studies/blackhomicide14.pdf

Waites, C. (Ed.). (2008). *Social work practice with African American families: An intergenerational perspective.* New York, NY: Routledge.

Webster's II New College Dictionary (3rd ed.). (2005). Boston, MA: Houghton Mifflin.

Welch, C. A., & Parlin, T. (2003). *Frederick Douglass.* New York, NY: Barnes and Noble.

White, J. (2001, June 24). Crack, Contras, and cyberspace. *Time.* Retrieved from http://content.time.com/time/magazine/article/0%2c9171%2c136590%2c00.html

Chapter 9

THE CULTURES OF NATIVE AMERICANS/ FIRST PEOPLES: THE VOICES OF TWO INDIGENOUS WOMAN SCHOLARS

Therese M. West & Carolyn Kenny

Carolyn's Story

I feel so blessed to have a rich cultural background. My mother was a Mississippi Choctaw with a tiny bit of Irish thrown into the mix. My father was a first-generation Ukrainian-American. Equally treasured are my Haida relatives. Many years ago, Dorothy Bell, one of the great matriarchs of the Haida Nation, formally adopted me. My story is long. So I want to focus mainly on how I can help the readers of this book when they come in contact with Indigenous peoples. I use the term Indigenous, meaning people of the land, because this term is all-embracing and connotes the International expansiveness of tribes around the world. It is also the term of preference for most Indigenous scholars these days.

My two professional passions are music therapy, which I have been practicing since 1969, and Indigenous studies, which I have been studying and experiencing since 1970. I have written books and many articles in these two areas, as well as presented at conferences around the world in the spirit of connecting my two worlds—West and East—through my life, my practice, and my scholarship.

Another great blessing for me is that I have been able to live, work, learn, and generally experience life with many different Native peoples around the world. Since my mother was abandoned by her Native mother when she was three years old, I did not know very much about life on the reservation or Native life in general until 1970, when I made friends with the Musqueam people as we played spontaneous music together in the Longhouse on a grant from the Canadian government. I have also taught many Native students in programs at universities and traveled to many Native nations around the world. It always surprises me that there is such a small presence of Native people in music therapy programs, since the use of the arts is so important for healing in traditional societies.

Therese's Story

My grandmother was a storyteller who grew up in Kalispell, Montana. I loved her creativity and expressiveness and could listen to her for hours. Grandma told how her mother and father had settled in Montana, spoke fluent Blackfoot and Flathead dialects, and traded with the Indians, and she proudly shared how her father won a tomahawk-throwing contest at a gathering. She said that her mother scolded her for playing outside in the sun, because it would make her skin dark. But in

a photo of her playing outdoors with children of other settlers, she is clearly several shades darker than the other children. A photo of her mother in long braids looks quite a bit like that of an Indigenous woman. But when someone said that she must be Native, citing the distinctive features, Grandma denied being an "Injun." She identified as White, "French Canuck and a little Scotch." Grandma had been sent to a convent school after her mother died. She had been born before women in the United States had the right to vote, and she grew up during a time when Native Americans were still being stripped of their language, religion, and culture. If a person of color could pass for White, they could avoid a lot of persecution and have better economic opportunities. Grandma was married to a man of English and German ancestry, who often made very derogatory comments about members of minorities, including Indians, whom he considered to be lazy, stupid, and inferior beings. Grandma was skilled at avoiding her husband's temper and seemed unruffled by his bigotry. She was proud about maintaining her own secret beliefs, which she shared with me in special private times together. She explained that she put up with a lot because her husband was a good provider.

Was my grandmother a Native American passing for White? The census records don't say. In a census, peoples' ethnicity could be variously identified according to what they looked like and who was reporting. Contemplating the inconsistencies in my grandmother's story has led me to better appreciate the ways that oppressed peoples survive, maintaining and even transmitting their values, while living among (but holding some things secret and sacred from) the dominating culture.

Eventually, following my heart led me to spend a good deal of time with members of various tribes: Creek, Lakota, Apache, Purepecha, Pomo, and others. As I spent time with Native Elders such as Marcellus Bear-Heart Williams, Oh Shinnah Fast Wolf, and Chief Luciano Perez and learned from the teachings of Wallace Black Elk and Essie Parrish, I was struck by how deeply comfortable and familiar it felt to be immersed in Native culture, in the sacred and healing ways. Grandfather Bear Heart, a Creek Elder, adopted me and named me, which is a sign of being family. I am grateful for what he taught me about the ways of the Indigenous healer and how he modeled a compassionate embrace of both Indigenous and "Western" peoples.

A lot of things I experienced with Native Elders resonated with what I had learned from my grandmother: harmony with nature and each other, the following of cycles and seasons, what we can learn from the birds and the animals, where to find the healing plants. There was a cadence to the Elder's speech, a certain sense of humor, and a way of spinning the story that reminded me of my grandmother. I also explored threads of deep resonant connections with Hawaiian native, Maori, and Sami peoples, following a call of Indigenous wisdom that continues to give me hope for our shared future.

In my graduate studies, I focused on developing multicultural competencies and was mentored by a Native-Mexican-American scholar in winning a grant to support underrepresented minorities in developing research skills. I continued to grow in and teach about cultural competency as an educator of music therapists. Multicultural competency is not an arrival point; it is a process of self- and other-discovery that continues for a lifetime.

My grandmother and the Indigenous Elders taught me to see, and hear, and care for the Creator's created. I am grateful for all my mentors who helped me develop some skills to walk in balance between the worlds of academic/scholarly rigor and Indigenous/experiential ways of knowing and being. I am honored to share some of these gifts here, to support music therapists in a process of growth and service.

Introduction

Therese: It is an honor and a daunting task to be asked to speak to music therapists on behalf of the Native Americans or American Indians. Referred to by various Native and non-Native names, the Indigenous peoples of the North American continent include many different tribes, languages, cultural and regional groups, and living situations. In U.S. Census data from 2010 (United States Census Bureau, 2010), 564 different American Indian and Alaska Native tribal entities are identified as qualifying for Bureau of Indian Affairs (BIA) funding and services. Data from the 2010 Census reveals that of the 5.2 million people (1.7% of the total U.S. population) identifying themselves as American Indian or Alaska Native, 2.3 million, or nearly half, report being Native in combination with one or more other races. The 2010 census found that a majority (78%) of alone or in combination Native people live outside of designated tribal lands or reservations. As therapists, particularly if we are non-Native, we cannot predict the level of acculturation or assimilation, values, family history, or current experience of any Native or part-native individual we hope to serve. We must enter each encounter with a respectful openness, a readiness to listen and learn. We must patiently face our limitations, utilize our strengths, and enlist the aid of tribal people who have experience and knowledge that can help us be of service in a good way.

While there is tremendous diversity among Native peoples, there are shared values, historical experiences, and current health, education, and socioeconomic challenges that resonate across this vast continent, from the reservations to the urban dwelling places of today's Native American peoples. It is only realistic here to try to provide a broad overview, a jumping-off point, if you will. You will need to go much further in your own

personal and professional development if you are to become competent to deliver music therapy services in the context of Native cultures.

Worldview

Humankind has not woven the web of life. We are but one thread within it. Whatever we do to the web, we do to ourselves. All things are bound together. All things connect.
—Chief Seattle

Therese: This quote, attributed to Chief Seattle, is simple and eloquent, beautiful in the use of language; these are common qualities found in the speech of Native Elders. It expresses a core value in the Indigenous worldview, which is the essential unity of all Creation, at every level, from the smallest stone or living thing to the family, tribal, national, and universal levels.

Carolyn: Let's start with four embodied concepts that guide the lives of tribal peoples—land, ancestors, Elders, and story (Kenny & Fraser, 2012). The land is so important to Indigenous people that it serves as an embodied metaphor for existence itself. This intimate relationship with Mother Earth reflects the spiritual principle of the interconnectivity of all things.

As First Nations peoples, we experience and define beauty in relation to the way we live. Our relationship to Mother Earth and to each other, the way we live together in a place, and our appreciation of holistic aspects of life all coalesce to give a sense of coherence to our worlds. It is our ability to sense this coherence that can give us the confidence to express ourselves fully, define ourselves authentically, and assist ourselves in the creation of our own stories. Through this sense of coherence, we know who we are and we can see the visions of who we might become in the future. This landscape is rich in image, metaphor, and symbol. It is punctuated by texture, song, color, story, and prose. It is implied in the patterns of a basket and the shape of a carving and reflects the land that we inhabit, our experience on it, and the knowledge that we acquire because of our respect for place (Kenny, 1998).

We rely on Elders, who transmit sacred knowledge through their stories. Thus ancestors, Elders, and story are also at the foundation of a healthy and good life in Indian country.

When I listen to an Elder, I do not always understand what is said. Yet there is a presence that holds me in aesthetic arrest. I do not move. I attempt a deep listening. I sense qualities. I perceive the many lines on a face. I open my heart to voice, to tone. I watch arms move and laughter flash. I pay attention to regalia. When Elders depart, not only have I gained information on practical things, but also I feel rejuvenated by their qualities, the echo of their spirits. No one can steal this from me, and this sense does not diminish over time, nor is it altered by new ideas, new technology. It is constant and persists (Kenny, 1998).

Therese: Flowing from the Native understanding of the interrelatedness of all things is a belief in the importance of the family, the extended family, and the community. This value is directly opposite from the American dominant cultural value of individualism as holding primary importance, a perspective from which it was impossible to understand why a Native person would put the good of the group before personal ambitions. Some non-Native settlers, on encountering Native traditions such as "give-away" (or in the Northwest tribal tradition, the potlatch), considered them stupid, foolish, or primitive. But the Native American values of gratitude, generosity, and self-sacrifice are seen as essential for the survival of all.

Native spirituality also flows out of the direct experience of connectedness with and interdependence among all Creation. Spiritual values provide the foundation for Indigenous societies.

> *Out of the Indian approach to existence there came a great freedom, an intense and absorbing love for nature ... enriching faith in a Supreme Power; and principles of truth, honesty, generosity, equity, and brotherhood as a guide to mundane relations.*
> —Luther Standing Bear, ca. 1868–1939
> (Fuller, 2012, p. 59)

The Native appreciation of our essential connectedness can be seen as the root of a great tree of life. Branching from that basic unity come the values of respect for all peoples, all life, and all elements of our environment and the idea that we do not own the earth but are stewards who must think ahead for the next seven generations, asking ourselves how each action will affect those coming after us.

Carolyn: If you work in music therapy with Native people, you will notice that they often speak in a storied voice. This is traditional and one of the embodied practices that have been transmitted across thousands of years from ancestors and Elders.

Historical Realities Versus Popular Myths

Carolyn: Since the arrival of the settlers in North America, Native peoples have suffered tremendously at the hands of government agents and religious authorities. Residential schools were established to purge the so-called savages of their wayward beliefs and lifestyles. Settlers were greedy for the rich resources in what they thought was a new land inhabited by human beings they considered to be more like worrisome animals getting in their way. They generally thought that the only way to possess such rich resources was not to share them with the original people of the land, but instead to dominate and subjugate those people (Alfred, 1999; DeLoria, 1969). If you decide to really understand the history of Native peoples, you will discover many atrocities. Children were punished (and worse) for speaking their own language. Many were abused physically and sexually in the residential schools that existed throughout Canada and the United States and even around the world in places like Australia and New Zealand. Consequently, the legacy of colonization has left many intergenerational social

problems. Native people who were forced into residential schools did not learn how to parent their own children when they became adults. The suffering in these schools and anomie or depression due to loss of culture was soul-numbing. Often victims turned to substance abuse so that they could forget the bad memories (Brown, 1989; Brownlie & Korinek, 2012; Churchill, 2004; Grant, 1996; Haig-Brown, 2002).

On a more global level, treaties were made and broken. Time and time again, many Indigenous peoples offered to work with the settlers and to share the territory. Most of these treaties were broken in the face of atrocities (DeLoria, 1969; Neihardt, 1972; Wilson, 1998).

Today, Native nations are slowly on the mend through claiming their identities and sovereignty (Regan, 2010). There is a lot of healing going on. Native peoples are striving not only to survive the past, but also to thrive. Still, there is a lot of work to be done—many situations in which music therapists can engage, both on- and off-reservation. The Maori people were able to have a quiet revolution in the 1960s by starting fresh with Kohunga Reo's language nests. They took charge of the education of their youngest children in order to save their language and culture by refusing to accept funding from the government. From these bare beginnings of Elders educating the youngest children in garages with no government support, they built an entire Maori school system, from preschools to higher education, with language and cultural immersion.

There are still many areas that need help and healing. But the image of the lazy, dirty Indian is a thing of the past. There are many Native professional nurses, social workers, lawyers, doctors, educators, and more. Now Indigenous people strive to heal themselves and their nations through education and social action.

Therese: Until fairly recently, books, movies, and television shows have tended to popularize and perpetuate largely derogatory stereotypes of the American Indian. Growing up, I heard my grandmother use story and humor to counter such ideas as the "dumb Injun." "Dumb like a fox," Grandma quipped, with respect for the fox's cleverness and camouflage. She appreciated the ability to keep one's integrity by keeping the important things hidden from those who do not understand and who might persecute one for certain beliefs. Within any oppressed group, there will be ways of surviving through behaviors that are not understood or accepted by the dominant culture. If we as therapists are not aware of these patterns, we can easily misinterpret adaptive coping behaviors as resistance to treatment. We may be looking for eye contact and verbalizations as signs of engagement. But particularly with acculturated Native persons, we may actually be experienced as intrusive, disrespectful, or threatening by doing what we think is "right." We may misinterpret cryptic humor as evasive, when it may actually be a test to see if we will engage with the person by meeting them in their story. Our way of relating to the construct of time may be very different from that of the Native who lives on "Indian time," which is not divided into minutes and tied to a clock.

When I went through my own process of looking at the biases that came from what I heard as a young person, it was painful but important to realize that along with my grandmother's moderating input, I had also heard from others that "Indians are too lazy and stupid to get an education. They're just a bunch of falling down drunks who don't even appreciate the reservation lands they were given." The tragic ignorance of such attitudes unfortunately continues to this day, contributing to a poor self-image and ongoing oppression of the First Peoples of our land.

Negative stereotypes can be understood as a natural psychological defense serving to buffer the impact of the sad truths about how our first Americans were treated. This kind of defense, known as blaming the victim, is found wherever there is oppression. Many Americans do not know very much at all about the history of the Native American. But ignorance does not help us become instruments of change, and the truth of what happened is *real living history* for many modern Native Americans. They live with the results of the intentional, systematic efforts by non-Natives and the U.S. government to eradicate Native American languages, religion, sacred and social traditions, culture, and society and to take their ancestral lands and resources from them.

> At a time when Black Elk was lamenting the broken hoop of his people's nations, it was generally believed, even by the specialists, that it would be only a matter of time—very little time, in fact— until the Indians, with their seemingly archaic and anachronistic cultures, would be completely assimilated into a larger American society which was convinced of its superiority and the validity of its goals. We are still very far from being aware of the dimensions and ramifications of our ethnocentric illusions. (Brown, 1989, p. xv)

American Indians participate in annual commemorations on the very land where their ancestors fought American troops led by General Custer. They remember the ancestors, men, women and children, who were killed by U.S. soldiers in the 1890 massacre at Wounded Knee, South Dakota. Others live far from their ancestors' homelands and may have little knowledge of their heritage. Entire tribes and languages have been annihilated; others depend on a small number of Elders to transmit the language, traditions, and stories to future generations. Many are working hard to preserve dying languages or to resurrect and strengthen traditional and sacred ways that in some cases were banned by our government for a long time, traditions that harmed no one, but that were misunderstood, perceived as a threat, and subject to systematic persecution by the dominant American society.

Therapists need to be sensitive to the deep undercurrents that result from oppression. In the late 1990s, I was blessed to be invited to participate as a supporter in a traditional Sun Dance ceremony on the land of Lakota Chief Leonard Crow Dog, who had been a spiritual leader during the time of the 1973 Wounded Knee conflict between the American Indian Movement and the federal government. Our group, consisting of both Native and non-Native persons, was led by a Native Elder who put us through rigorous preparation to participate in this very traditional sacred ceremony and to conduct ourselves with a respect of traditional values and societal norms as guests of the Lakota people. I came to appreciate that various Indigenous peoples have experienced a kind of spiritual wounding and breach of trust because ignorant or unscrupulous non-Natives have appropriated Native spiritual practices and then used that knowledge for individual commercial gain outside of and apart from the Native society. We were advised that in addition to these issues, there were ongoing tensions among the tribe related to federal agents monitoring and harassing Crow Dog, such that we needed to be prepared to leave the camp on a moment's notice if the tribal people required it. I was shocked to learn that these tensions were still so high decades after the Wounded Knee incident. Most Americans are not aware of the continuing political and social tensions that are a reality for many modern Indigenous peoples who are still suffering the effects of oppression. It is encouraging to observe what happened in New Zealand, where the indigenous Maori language, values, and culture have been appreciated and integrated with European cultural elements, strengthening the society as a whole and resulting in a nation known for the way it honors and protects the land and its peoples.

We are all subject to our own ethnocentric and personal "illusions" or perspectives. Often we are unaware of deeply embedded biases received from those who raised or influenced us. Multicultural competence requires that we honestly examine our own biases and beliefs and fearlessly challenge any distortions of truth, if we are to become part of a process of healing the wounds of oppression by contributing to societal change.

As therapists, we are trained in observation skills and often lean heavily on those skills when we are in new territory. But it is important to remember that observations are influenced by who is doing the observing and the assumptions the observer brings to the situation. The scholar Paula Gunn Allen reminds us that even the research can be distorted by bias. In her Native American feminist work, she says, "… the White collectors of Indian myths and ritual stories are also subject to patriarchal assumptions. Perhaps the questions scholarly investigators ask as well as the fact that it is they who ask the questions about a particular tribe's spiritual teachings influence the responses they receive" (Allen, 1991, p. 31).

To become more culturally competent, we must suspend our need to be "right" and be willing to follow the guidance of Elders. It helps to have an open, childlike attitude that receives without trying to make "sense" in relation to our own preconceptions and biases. We also need to engage in multiple ways, listening with all of our senses. When I joined the line of women modestly dressed in long skirts, dancing barefoot in the hot dusty arbor, my learning went to a new depth as I experienced something that transcends spoken language: an essential unity among the voices, the drumbeats, the moving body, the people, the earth, and the Creator.

Diversity Within the Culture

Carolyn: If you have the good fortune to travel across the many lands on this Earth and to visit the tribal peoples of every single continent, you will see great differences in land, language, culture, and philosophy. There is no pan-Indian identity. I have traveled with the Ainu, the native tribal people of Japan, in their traditional territory in the Ainu Arts Project and learned from their music and art. I have spent many weeks with the Maori in New Zealand, having taken my graduate students there to study the initiatives in the revitalization of Maori language and culture. In New Zealand, an Elder told me that the Maori surround their children with arts because the arts provide the aesthetic environment that is essential for the growth of healthy children (Kenny, 2006). I have conducted policy research with Indigenous women across Canada (Kenny, 2002a/2002b). I have attended ceremonies of the Cree, the Salish, and my own tribe, the Haida, many times. Also, I have had the great fortune to get to know other tribal peoples like the Apache, Choctaw, Cherokee, Sami, Hawaiian, Secwepmec, Chumash, Mi'kmaq, Sioux, Anishnabee, Ojibway, Sto:lo, Tseil-Waututh, Squamish, Tong, Tsimshian, Nis'ga, P:aute, Muckleshoot, Navaho, Okanagan, Coleville, Tlingat, Pachamama, Sami, and many more. The diversity is stunning!

When you are working as a music therapist, it is important to remember that artificial borders between the United States and Canada and the United States and Mexico do not exist in the minds and hearts of many tribal people even today. In 1974, the United States and Great Britain passed The Jay Treaty (Pine Tree Legal Assistance, 2003). In Article III of the Jay Treaty, the U. S and Great Britain sealed their own relations but, in particular, demonstrated to First Nations that First Nations were an essential element in diplomatic relations between these two governments.

This treaty between two European nations acknowledged that protection of First Nations' rights was an important part of the non-Indian reality. The signatories to the Jay Treaty were aware of the rights and freedoms that First Nations people utilized and expected, especially for unimpeded travel throughout their Aboriginal territories. These systems and relationships developed to include European nations, who further cultivated and encouraged the precontact relationships and utilized the pre-existing networks and systems for their own use, benefit, and profit.

The Jay Treaty includes provisions recognizing and acknowledging the existence and right of certain long-established "Indian" systems and practices. These are contained in Article III of the Jay Treaty. Aboriginal practices and systems of trade, commerce, and mobility between territories existed long before European arrival in North America. The Jay Treaty, by way of Article III, was the European mechanism by which they were able to reiterate and recognize particular independent and pre-existing rights of Aboriginal peoples. Therefore, Article III of the Jay Treaty, as well as numerous other treaties and treaty councils, are not the source of Aboriginal rights but instead examples of European recognition of a range of Aboriginal rights, and as such must constitute treaty rights and produce treaty protections. But try quoting her proclamation to border guards these days, and you won't have much success.

There is a generalized romanticism about Native peoples as "the noble savage." This notion is portrayed in films such as *Dances with Wolves.* It is also found in English and French literature as a rhetorical reference. This concept has served to emphasize the homogenization of tribal peoples. When you are working with Native people, it is important to put this romanticism aside and to listen deeply to the unique stories and qualities of each person and culture. In addition to being able to provide more respectful music therapy, you will find that you are learning many useful things.

Therese: The diversity within Native American and Alaska Native peoples is tremendous. Even related tribes and bands within tribes may differ in linguistic and cultural ways. Individual persons may have many different layers contributing to the totality of their identity. It is not enough just to ask about tribal heritage. Who in their family has lived on a reservation? Who speaks the language? What religion(s) are important in the family? There are any number of variations in spiritual practices, from very conservative traditional practices to the Native American Church (which blends traditional and Christian elements), to the practice of any of the many religions taken to Native peoples by missionaries or found in modern society.

The fact that our most recent U. S. Census showed that nearly one-half of the people identifying as Native American indicated a combination with other race or ethnic elements speaks in itself to the level of complexity we face when trying to understand whom we are serving. The numbers of Elders who speak no English is rapidly dwindling, and some dialects are dying out for lack of skilled speakers. Native language programs on reservations and in educational facilities serving Native youth are trying to counter this and also helping to keep the traditions alive. There are wide ranges of tribal, governmental, NGO, and church-sponsored resources and organizations serving Native peoples. Multitribal groups support Native traditions by bringing together different peoples for sharing in dance, honoring Native arts and crafts, information-sharing, sharing food, and socializing at local and regional powwows. Some Natives are completely involved in traditional ways of life; others have never experienced any of these ways. So we have to ask. But it helps to have a sense of some of the specific questions to explore and some of the organizations and resources in your area.

Gender Differences Within the Culture

Therese: When I was first allowed to attend traditional Native American ceremonies, I was surprised to encounter some very distinct differences in behavior and dress expectations for women and men in ceremonies, as compared to expectations in modern American society. It helped me a great deal that I was told to expect these things, and it also helped that the Elders taught us why these things were important in the culture. In traditional societies, the roles for men and for women were well defined and honored both male and female contributions to the welfare of all. Regardless of our personal preferences and beliefs, whenever we are guests at any traditional event in any culture, it is very important that we show respect and appreciation for our hosts by dressing and behaving as expected.

Carolyn: In tribal societies, on the surface, it seems like the men dominate. However, appearances can be deceiving. Traditionally, the men may have the formal leadership roles. However, there is always a strong circle of women surrounding these men—mothers, grandmothers, wives, daughters, and a host of female extended family members. These women are considered to be the moral guardians of the tribe. They observe everything the men do as leaders. They listen intently to all conversations, dialogues, and formal and informal meetings in the community. In quieter moments, the women give the men their marching orders. If the male leaders do not perform as the women instruct, they are accountable to the women. This means that the women can deprive them of status; esteem in the community; sex, including pleasure and progeny; companionship; food; and other important things that sustain life. This traditional norm still exists in many tribes (Kenny, 2002a/2002b).

Some tribes, like the Navajo, are matrilineal, meaning that women are the holders of property and goods. This gives them a tremendous amount of power when it comes to major and minor decisions about the life and practices in the community.

In contemporary society, these gender roles have been decimated, to an extent, by the crippling effects of interference by settlers. With Native nations in disarray, the traditional formal and informal governance practices have been replaced by non-Native policies like the imposition of so-called democratic processes, as opposed to traditional ways of choosing leaders. In some cases, governance is now a hybrid system because of faulty policies, like the Indian Act and Bill C-31 in Canada, and the relocation of whole tribes to unfamiliar lands by the U.S. government. Violence against Native women is epidemic and perpetrated by both Native and non-Native men. Available statistics consistently point to a greatly disproportionate incidence of violence against Indigenous women in Canada.

In a 2009 government survey of the 10 provinces, Aboriginal women were nearly three times more likely than non-Aboriginal women to report being a victim of a violent crime; this was true regardless of whether the violence was perpetrated by a stranger or by a spouse.

Not only do Indigenous women face more frequent incidence of violence, but also the violence is much more severe. A recent Statistics Canada report suggests that the national homicide rate for Indigenous women is at least seven times higher than that for non-Indigenous women.

Indigenous women are far more likely than non-Indigenous women to experience violence. In a 2009 government survey of the 10 provinces, Aboriginal women were nearly three times more likely than non-Aboriginal women to report being a victim of a violent crime.

The violence experienced by Indigenous women is more severe. RCMP statistics released in 2014 show that Indigenous women are four times more likely to be murdered than non-Indigenous women.

The high rates of violence threaten the lives of Indigenous women and girls from all walks of life, in every region of the country, on reserve, and in major Canadian cities. The perpetrators include Aboriginal and non-Aboriginal men alike.

Some patterns of violence facing Indigenous women and girls are different from those facing non-Indigenous women. For example, according to the RCMP report released in May 2014, Indigenous women are more likely than non-Indigenous women to be murdered by what the police call acquaintances—friends, colleagues, neighbors, and other men who are not intimate partners or spouses.

A report released by the RCMP in May 2014 states that 1,017 Indigenous women and girls were murdered from 1980 to 2012. Because of gaps in police and government reporting, the actual numbers may be much higher (Amnesty International, n.d.).

Music therapists are working with Native women in hospitals, community health centers, and shelters across Canada and the United States. Veteran music therapist Colleen Purdon has worked in a shelter in Owen Sound, Ontario, for many years. The shelter there includes both Native and non-Native women. Purdon and Ostertag (1999) describe their approach to music therapy in these settings in the *Canadian Journal of Music Therapy*. In their work, they adapted the Domestic Abuse Intervention Project originally used in cases of domestic violence in Duluth, Minnesota, as their theoretical model. At the core of this theory is the Power and Control Wheel, which articulates the many abusive tactics employed by abusers against victims (Purdon, 2006; Purdon & Ostertag, 1999). After conducting workshops with music therapists based on their work with clients, Purdon and Ostertag (1999) recommended special training for music therapists who were also working with victims of abuse.

Therese: A good friend of mine introduced me to the "Two-Spirit" community in San Francisco. "Two-Spirit" is a modern term used by contemporary urban lesbian, gay, bisexual and transgender (LGBT) Native Americans, who look to historical evidence that a respected place was afforded in some tribal societies for persons manifesting a sacred balance of male and female qualities (Bay Area American Indian Two-Spirits, 2010). However, this is a fairly recently developed movement, and some individuals, particularly older Native Americans, may not share the attitudes supported by the Two-Spirit community.

Generational and Migrational Differences Within the Culture

Therese: As in any group or people, we encounter age cohort differences in Native Americans. It is more common to find more traditional ways among older individuals, but this is not always the case.

Carolyn: Intergenerational learning was and in many cases still is front-and-center in Native societies. Indeed, a great deal of the healing and revitalizing initiatives across nations centers on this learning. It is often said among Native peoples that when one generation of children has not been taught their language and customs through grandparents, especially grandmothers, the culture is lost. This saying is passed around most Native nations, who must learn their own language now from books written by non-Native scholars or non-Native anthropologists who have documented the customs of the people in text.

Parents are too busy doing the practical work of keeping the home together. So, the grandparents take on a lot of "raising up" responsibility. In general, grandparents and aunties have a permissive parenting style. By nature, Native nations are collective rather than individualistic. But children are closely watched for the unique talents the Creator has given to each one. These individual talents are nurtured and encouraged.

Therese: Unfortunately, younger Native Americans are more likely now to be affected by drug abuse and suicide within their circle of friends. There are no overarching generalizations to be made, but there are some important traditional values to appreciate.

As alcohol and drug abuse problems has claimed more and more Native adults, the job of raising the children has increasingly been passed to the grandparents. Because the extended family is very important, especially where poverty is a factor, it is not uncommon for several generations and both close and distant relatives to live in the same household. The cohesiveness of family is very important to Native cultures. It is also common to hear younger Native Americans addressing older ones as "Grandfather, Grandmother, Uncle, or Auntie" as a way of showing respect, even in situations where there is no blood relationship. We are all relations. "Mitakue Oyasin," meaning "All my Relations," is a prayerful response one says in certain sacred Native American ceremonies. It reminds us that we are truly all related.

Carolyn: Grandmothers play a particularly important role in the raising of children. Often children are taught that they have many grandmothers and that grandmothers are determined not only by blood relation, but also by the status of older women in the community. For example, when I visit my village in the Haida Gwaii, the children call me Naanii ("Grandmother"), even though I have no formal blood relations there, having been adopted (Kenny & Fraser, 2012; Schaefer, 2006).

Therese: Native American cultures respect their Elders. The Elders are keepers of the history, skills, language, songs, and stories of their people. They are the heart and the wisdom of their community. The role of the Elder in traditional groups is one of great importance. I was taught to serve the Elders first and to show them every possible respect and consideration. Unfortunately, this is not always done in modern environments. The elder Native Americans we encounter may carry memories of being dishonored by the dominant culture. Elder Native men have likely served in the U.S. military and are proud of their service. Native American powwows always include public honoring of veterans and display of the American flag.

Some Native Elders are eager to share their ways with nontribal people, but I have also encountered Elders living on reservations who are more cautious and reluctant to interact with outsiders. You must be invited in; in some situations, as an outsider you may not be trusted until that trust is earned.

Acculturation and Assimilation

Carolyn: Certainly, throughout the years since the settlers arrived in North America and on other tribal shores throughout the world, a large percentage of Native peoples went along with complete or partial acculturation just to survive the intrusion. The East met the West. But the West usually did not meet the East in a respectful way. When I attended the Mescalero Apache lsd. isin the same household. The cohesiveness of family into their community, the beautiful traditional dances, songs, and rituals of this ceremony were honored. As well, one could observe the migration of non-Native elements like the Catholic rosary beads the young women wore with their White buckskin dresses. This is certainly normal in the exchange of cultures.

Yet many Native people today are still traumatized in one way or another from wholesale assimilation policies that were intended to tame the wild savage or steal the resources of the land from Native peoples as previously noted. We know as therapists that identity is a precious and fragile thing. We need a sense of belonging, and we need to develop and know our identities including our cultural roots.

Therese: In order to understand the cultural context in which an individual lives, we must consider both the level of acculturation and the degree of assimilation or pressures to assimilate. The fact that we have Indian reservations in the United States also creates a set of conditions known to no other racial or ethnic group in our country. Reservation land, as part of a sovereign nation, has its own laws and law enforcement. Poverty is a long-standing problem on most reservations. We also must realize that during the past century, many Native Americans were subjected to a brutal forced process of assimilation and punished for speaking their language, singing their songs, or speaking of their ancestors. Today, the reservations may function as enclaves for the preservation of the culture, places where acculturation can take place; they may also be experienced as places of desperate poverty and suffering. This suffering has led to ambivalence or shame about living on the reservation for some modern tribal people. For others, it feeds motivation to obtain higher education and skills and return to the reservation to serve and strengthen the tribe.

After Native Americans were subjected by the dominant society to a kind of cultural genocide, many never had the opportunity to become acculturated in the first place and then faced additional assimilation pressures by living among the dominant culture. Lack of fluency in Native languages today poses a serious limit to the acquisition of the culture. Many of the songs and stories exist only in aural form, in the memories of very old people. Some tribal groups have too few members to maintain the language and traditions, and in places like California, large numbers of tribal bands and their languages have been wiped out completely. Many urban Native Americans have little access to traditional learning, but, increasingly, tribal and intertribal groups are offering opportunities to learn Native languages, arts, and cultural heritage.

Microaggression and Oppression

Carolyn: The oppression of Native peoples around the world is one of the serious crimes against humanity. This is an old problem, but also a contemporary one. The lingering prejudice against Native peoples exists in both micro and macro aggressions. Examples are the continuous breaking of treaties and negative stereotypes that inhibit Native peoples from getting good jobs or extending their learning into higher education (Kenny, 2002a/2002b; Kenny & Fraser, 2012). However, there are also many positive changes taking place in which Native people strive tenaciously and succeed in challenging and overcoming the negative stereotypes. Now there are many Native people who serve in all professions. But their struggles have not always been easy.

Therese: While the true story of the oppression of Native Americans is seen much more now in television, film, print, and online media, Natives' ongoing experience of oppression is largely out of the view of the average American today. To the outsider, oppression might be only history. But many minority individuals have a very personal and direct sense of oppression as ongoing in their lives today. Sources of minority stress include dominant society attitudes toward Native Americans, continued tensions related to broken treaties, conflicts around land and resource usage, poverty, health problems, substance abuse, and crime problems pervasive in many Native communities. For example, in the 2010 census, it was found that nearly half of those living on the Pine Ridge Reservation in South Dakota lived at or below the poverty rate, and per capita income was only $9,728, as compared to $27,334 for the United States; life expectancy was less than 67 years (versus. the average of 76.5 years for Americans overall); infant mortality was nearly three times the national average; and suicides at were more than three times the national average (as cited in Fuller, 2012, pp. 38, 48, 51).

Carolyn: My concern is for one of the more heinous forms of oppression, called "internalized oppression." Here we often see that Native people have internalized these negative stereotypes and maintain a sense of self-hatred that not only prevents them from fulfilling their human potential but also surfaces in tribal corruption. Such corruption often exists because of the shunning of traditional Indigenous values. One example is the disenrollment of tribal members motivated by greed in the casinos. Tribal members who have been enrolled in their tribes since birth are suddenly disenrolled because corrupt families who want to dominate the funds received in casinos of sovereign Native nations are finding ways to shun them and take away their rights (Nogueras, 2014).

Meaning of Medicine and Well-Being

In our Native American way, medicine is not just a bunch of herbs or the training a physician receives. It's helping people attain that which is good in life. If you can point them in a new direction, saying this is the path, this is the way to go, that's a form of healing. When you give a lifting hand and make someone feel better for it, you have given that person medicine. (Bear Heart, 1996, p. 117)

Therese: Bear Heart taught me many things over the years. He also "doctored" me on more than one occasion. He says, "Native people of every continent go through their rituals—shaking gourds, chanting, drumming, dancing—trying to connect with the One who can heal. … There are many factors involved, but the belief of the patient also must be there because that's what initiates the healing process" (Bear Heart, 1996, p. 88). Native Americans speak of "carrying medicine." One is a caretaker of the good that makes up the "medicine." Some medicine is personal and private, while others are for specific purposes or for the good and welfare of the whole tribe, even for the Mother Earth herself. From my own experience in watching Native healers at work, I have come to appreciate certain qualities and experiences, which I believe made them effective as medicine people: (1) absolute dedication to serving their people, willingness to sacrifice, to be uncomfortable; (2) long and often arduous periods of training and preparation, integrity, trustworthiness; (3) skill and the ability to focus intently for long periods if necessary; (4) extensive knowledge of traditional prayers, songs, and rituals, foods, and plants; and (5) the understanding that they are not personally the source of the help

In most traditions, the medicine person never asks for anything in return for their services. But it is understood that people coming to them for help are to bring a gift that signifies the value of the help for which they are asking. The tribe took care of the medicine people, who took care of them.

It is only a modern phenomenon to hang out a shingle announcing "shamanic healing." That would never have been done in Native American tribes. A healer's skill spoke for itself, and the people recognized whom they could trust to go to for medicine. The role of shaman, or healer, was earned through significant dedication and carried with it a sense of responsibility to those served. In some traditions, the medicine person needed to be willing to give their own life for the good of the tribe.

Different tribes had different ways of talking about "medicine," or healing. The Navajo talk of "walking in beauty." I have heard others speak of walking in balance. The Indigenous concept of medicine is the original holistic approach, because it looks at the person or the problem as related to everything else. What is their relationship with themselves, their family, and their community? With everything? Returning to balance, to wholeness (or health), very often requires a willingness to make changes in one's life, but that is not done alone or in a doctor's office. In Native American traditional medicine, the community comes together to pray and to support the individual. As with everything else, there is an understanding of our basic interconnectedness in the healing process.

Carolyn: "Medicine" is an all-encompassing term in most tribal societies (Kenny, 2015). It usually includes cleansings, prayers, medicine plants from local lands, songs, arts, dances, and, in some cases, elaborate rituals, as in the case of the Salish Guardian Spirit Dance Ceremonials. In these ceremonies, songs come to the initiate from ancestors and animals in the spirit world and are expressed in public. Members of the audience also participate in these rituals with drumming and full attention. But the ceremonials are also social occasions in which family members come from near and far to support the initiates and visit each other. Food is also an important part of the ceremonies. Although the initiates have usually been fasting for days, the attendees come and go from the hall behind the Longhouse, a ceremonial house, as they partake of traditional foods and gather in small groups for breaks during the 24-hour-long ceremony (Kenny, 2006).

The Salish Guardian Spirit Dance Ceremonials went underground for many years when the settlers attempted to ban such healing ceremonies. In the 1970s, when standard Western medicine had failed to be effective with Native youth suffering from substance abuse, the Elders brought this Indigenous medicine to the communities once again. In some cases, the medicine people were able to work successfully with Western medicine practitioners who understood the value of traditional Indian medicine. This partnership, which brought the best of both worlds together in a respectful manner, provided for much healing of youth and other community members (Jilek, 1972; Kenny, 2006).

Meaning and Function of Music

Carolyn: One cannot underestimate the role of music and song in Native societies and cultures. Songs are considered to be intellectual property and belong to individuals, families, and tribes. When you are working as a music therapist, you must ask permission to sing a song that does not belong to you. Most often, your client or friend will "gift" the song to you and allow you to share it with others. However, we must remember that a tremendous amount of trust has been violated over the years; songs have been stolen, and intellectual property rights have been violated. Songs are holy expressions and must be treated with respect.

Therese: Native American music is as diverse as its peoples. It is beyond the scope of this chapter to cover this diversity, but some important concepts may help. Native American traditional music does not follow the rules of Western classical music and does not translate easily to Western notation or melodic or rhythmic structural expectations. As a music therapist, it is not your job to come up with a harmonic accompaniment for a traditional song. But your good aural training will serve well as you listen and learn the music.

A "drum" not only is the instrument, but also designates a group of people dedicated to maintaining Native American traditions by singing together as they drum in unison on a large group drum under the direction of the drum leader. This style is very structured; there is no improvisation. These drums are constructed in the traditional manner and treated as sacred objects. These drums are not used for other purposes. It would be offensive for a visitor to step up to play on the drum, uninvited. Membership on the drum requires a commitment to attend practices and learn traditional songs.

As music therapists, we may feel a need to lead. Sometimes it is much more important to follow. I once worked with a six-year-old Native American boy who was being evaluated for emotional disturbance following multiple traumas and losses suffered both during and after living on the reservation. He walked with a tough-guy swagger and avoided all the staff. He would not speak or make eye contact, but I could tell he was carefully checking me out. He signaled, indicating that my straight hair was like his.

He was willing to go to the music room, but continued to avert his eyes. Silence or avoidance of eye contact can be ways of trying to maintain autonomy. (In many traditional cultures, direct eye contact is considered intrusive or a sign of intent to challenge or dominate. I had been taught never to approach an Elder or spiritual leader with direct eye contact, and women in traditional culture did not initiate eye contact with men on first meeting. Eye contact would naturally arise as the relationship developed.) I respectfully averted my gaze from the boy to signal that I understood and would not push my way into his sacred space.

He was in a small group with two non-Native peers. I simply presented the boys with a large drum surrounded with chairs, positioned like a traditional group drum. Because his tribal experience may have been of men-only drums (not all tribes have mixed-gender drum groups), I did not sit at the drum myself, but handed him the mallets to distribute. This also signaled that I was not going to sit in the role of the dominant culture or take a power position. I sat nearby, as an attentive listener. He immediately began to lead the drumming. The boys did not speak, but drummed together for a long time, with an intense quality of listening and connecting. It was a first step in building trust and tremendously gratifying to witness.

Native music has been an aural tradition, learned by memory and passed from generation to generation for eons. The voice is often used, especially in group singing, in a way that might sound harsh to musically trained ears. Try not to judge, but just listen. Native language and music are intimately interwoven within the larger fabric of the culture.

Meanings are difficult to fully comprehend if one has had little exposure to the culture and has no understanding of the language. There is music that is highly sacred and used only in certain situations. Other music serves social functions such as group dancing or dance competitions at powwows and other tribal or intertribal gatherings. Although an unfamiliar ear might think that a sacred Sundance song and a powwow song sound similar, they are not the same thing. Unlike Western sacred music, which might be heard in a concert setting as well as during a religious service, Native American sacred music is not used for multiple purposes. Sacred song is not a performance. It is an offering, a prayer, a gift. Respect it as you would your own prayers.

On the other hand, you may attend and participate in a powwow, as nontribal guests are often welcome. Listen carefully to the announcer and follow his directions. Only certain dances are appropriate for both men and women, so pay close attention to the directions. Some dances are performed only by trained dancers who exhibit skill in a particular type of traditional dance. You may be invited to join in a traditional group dance, which is a structured social experience and not a place for improvisation or individualistic self-expression. Listen, watch, and follow.

Any Native American person may have exposure to and preferences for any kind of music. Urban Natives listen to the same kinds of music as non-Native urban dwellers. There are many recordings available now for those interested in contemporary Native American music. If you are working with traditional people, be aware that much of what is on the market is not strictly traditional. Canyon Records' *Voices Across the Canyon* introduces the listener to a broad spectrum of styles in contemporary Native music. It offers a way to hear many different kinds of music by Native artists. The first volume in this series includes a new style of vocal chant from the Native American Church, modern versions of older songs, original compositions blending traditional and non-Native musical elements, a Native flute playing the hymn "Amazing Grace," social types of music from the powwow circuit, and Waila, a social dance music heard at weddings and parties in southern Arizona (Various artists, 1996).

On the reservations, look for recordings for sale in the little stores found along the roadside. There one may find recordings of local people singing social or sacred ceremonial songs.

Carolyn: In 1997, when I did my research in the role of the arts in the revitalization of Haida culture, my little brother Ernie Collison told me:

I've felt songs of mourning, of celebration, of

closure, of social commentary, of spirituality, and of good old fun. Songs are important. They bring generations together. They bring us, as a people from other villages, together. Songs give us a common feeling of strength and power. A person can learn a lot about another from sharing a song. Our songs in common vary a lot in tempo and relationships in life. Drums have a life in the songs that generate emotions and evoke spirituality and (the) meaning of life that we honor with artworks and prayer. I love songs and doing them. I think everybody has music in them, and when people learn one song in Haida, you get thirsty to learn more. (Kenny, 2006, p. 90)

Many friends and relatives that I interviewed for this research project also spoke about playing jazz and blues and even about playing in jazz bands in their youth. So, the worlds meet.

Once, after I had attended the one-year anniversary of the death of a great Haida chief, I wrote about the singing and dancing of the Spirit Song:

When I turned to the back of the hall to look for the Spirit Singers, to my great surprise, I did not see singers but one magnificent Blue Wolf. Our chief belonged to the Wolf Clan. … Blue Wolf moved slowly. Something between a dance and a slow walk, punctuated by turning of shoulders and head. When he stepped, he dipped and rose, dipped and rose. Blue Wolf was a spirit. He walked in this slow fashion accompanied by the Spirit Song, through the hall, taking time to gaze at people in the crowd, turning his proud and beautiful countenance to see us. Everyone was still. … It took a long time for the wolf to walk throughout the hall with his penetrating gaze. No one was crying now. We were all part of an aesthetic moment, which, for the Haida, is a spiritual moment. We could experience both sides of the veil of life and death at the same time. In this moment, time did not exist. (Kenny, 2006, p. 151)

After learning about the Salish Guardian Spirit Dances and Blue Wolf's ceremony, perhaps you can understand why, when people ask me if I do music therapy in my own Haida community, I say no. The traditional ceremonies and rituals were medicine and designed to do the therapeutic work of assuaging grief, curing substance abuse, and a host of other human conditions that we see in the practice of music therapy. Sometimes when I'm participating in Haida ceremonies, I imagine that if only the settlers had left well enough alone, we might not have needed "therapies."

Enabling Health and Well-Being

Carolyn: In general, Indigenous philosophy is embedded in a mandate to "live a good life." My own mother, who was raised by her Comanche auntie after her mother had left the family, always told me, "Be a good human being first. The rest comes later." In general, a good life meant to always act on behalf of the other members of your family and community; to help others and contribute to life-sustaining actions; to appreciate the beauty that the Great Creator has bestowed upon us; to be careful not to waste or take more than you need; to be happy and laugh a lot; and to be kind.

The Navajo have many wonderful ways to express what it means to live a good life. They tell us to walk in beauty. Here is a Navajo Blessing Way:

> With beauty before me, I walk.
> With beauty behind me, I walk.
> With beauty above me, I walk.
> With beauty below me, I walk.
> From the East, beauty has been restored.
> From the South, beauty has been restored.
> From the West, beauty has been restored.
> From the North, beauty has been restored.
> From the zenith in the sky, beauty has been restored.
> From the nadir of the earth, beauty has been restored.
> From all around me, beauty has been restored.
> (Witherspoon, 1977)

In fact, when I spent time with the Navajo peoples on their land in Canyon de Chelly, I embraced their worldview (with permission) in my own theory of music therapy because I recognized the Navajo ideas of beauty and wholeness, thus defining the human person as a form of beauty. This Blessing Way also teaches us about healing. We are all always needing to "be restored." We can always grow. Also, studying Navajo philosophy helped me to understand the critical connection between healing, our senses, and the entire notion of beauty and its central role in a good human life (Kenny, 2006).

In most traditional societies, healing rituals were practiced in a consistent way year-round not only because we all need healing, but also because, at times, the earth needs healing. When I asked the Musqueam Elder Walker Stogan why the Salish people performed the Salish Guardian Spirit Dance ceremonials in the winter, he said, "In the winter, the earth's reserves are low. So we must dance to help the earth's energy to sustain itself." These dances are also healing dances for community members. They include singing, dancing, and trance states for those who have behavior problems in the community (Kenny, 2006).

Native nations had clear and effective as well as ongoing practices to keep their members healthy and in a state of awe at the wonders of the universe. Because of the settlers' imperialistic practices, many of these important rituals were lost. However, today, many Native nations strive to recover their health through returning to these practices, sometimes combining them with modern medicine and therapies.

Therese: When working with traditional Native Americans, non-Native helping professionals need to connect with local Native groups and resources. Sometimes it might mean consulting with an Elder or an Indigenous healer. We want to help the individual reconnect with the sources of healing that have meaning and power for them. We need to locate the locus of support within that person's community.

Southcentral Foundation in Anchorage offers a successful model for cutting health care costs while improving the lives of Alaska Natives through using an innovative holistic care system they call Nuka, a Native word for strong living things. Native clients are served with understanding and sensitivity to their issues, in an environment conducive to building trusting relationships with health care providers. The results so far have been both cost-effective and positive, with reductions in suicides, binge drinking, strokes, deaths from heart disease and cancer, and emergency room visits and hospital admissions. Other hospitals are taking a good look at the Southcentral model (Graves, 2012).

It is encouraging to think that the efforts of Native groups may lead us to better health as individuals and as a society.

Conclusion

Carolyn: Today, most Indigenous people prefer not to be perceived as vulnerable populations. A very active stage of healing and revitalization is occurring in many, many tribes and bands. As music therapists, we must be sensitive these internal efforts and join them instead of imposing our protocols and procedures onto Native peoples. This can be difficult. There is a general norm called the "principle of noninterference" among many tribal peoples. As music therapist, we are trained to do interventions, a sister concept to interference. The principle of noninterference means that we let things take their natural course even if it means that someone must die. In Indigenous spirituality, dying might mean a healing of the spirit. This is difficult to understand when we work in hospital systems that strive at all costs to keep a person alive through artificial means.

For my entire scholarly career, I have worked to craft a theoretical model that marries East and West. This journey began in 1970 and culminated in a model that I call The Field of Play, which, for me, integrates my understanding of both East and West and attempts to bring these two worlds together both within myself and for my patients, clients, and music therapy colleagues who are interested in learning from the Native world. This has been a satisfying journey for me and has helped me to understand music therapy processes within a broad context (Kenny, 2006).

Therese: I would like to echo Carolyn's message of sensitive and respectful noninterference. I also do not claim to specialize in music therapy for tribal people. I believe that the traditional ways can support the needed healing. But my practice as a music therapist has been blessed and strengthened by my learning and participation in the Indigenous world. As a member of the dominant culture, music therapists may feel a desire to do something to help repair the damage. But it is humbling and freeing to face what we cannot "fix." In relation to the Indigenous world, we may need much more to be the student rather than the teacher. I am convinced that Indigenous wisdom holds vital keys for the future survival and thriving of all peoples and our planet. Indigenous wisdom knows how to care for the land, the growing things, the animals, and the people. We can each benefit on personal, social, and transpersonal levels by listening, taking in the wisdom, and becoming partners in our shared healing.

References

Alfred, T. (1999). *Peace, power, and righteousness: An indigenous manifesto.* London, UK: Oxford University Press.

Allen, P. G. (1991). *Grandmothers of the light: A medicine woman's sourcebook.* Boston, MA: Beacon Press.

Amnesty International. (n.d.). *No more stolen sisters.* Retrieved from http://www.amnesty.ca/our-work/campaigns/no-more-stolen-sisters

Bay Area American Indian Two Spirits. (2010). *Who are "Two-Spirits"?* Retrieved from http://www.baaits.org/two-spirits

Bear Heart, with Larkin, M. (1996). *The wind is my mother: The life and teachings of a Native American Shaman.* New York, NY: Berkley Books.

Brown, J. E. (1989). *The sacred pipe: Black Elk's account of the Seven Rites of the Oglala Sioux.* Norman, OK: University of Oklahoma Press.

Brownlie, J., & Korinek, V. J. (Eds.). (2012). *Finding a way to the heart: Feminist writings on Aboriginal and women's history in Canada.* Winnipeg, MB: University of Manitoba Press.

Churchill, W. (2004*). Kill the Indian, save the man: The genocidal impact of American Indian residential schools.* San Francisco, CA: City Lights Publisher.

DeLoria, V. (1969). *Custer died for your sins: An Indian manifesto.* New York, NY: Macmillan Ltd.

Erdoes, R., & Ortiz, A. (1984). *American Indian myths and legends.* New York, NY: Pantheon Books.

Fuller. A. (2012, August). Life after wounded knee. *National Geographic, 22*(2), 30–67.

Grant, A. (1996). *No end of grief: Indian residential schools in Canada.* Winnipeg, MB: Pemmican Publishing.

Graves, B. (2012, July 22). Holistic approach helps heal gaps in Native health system. *The Sunday Oregonian,* A1, A9.

Haig-Brown, C. (2002*). Resistance and renewal: Surviving the Indian residential school.* Vancouver, BC: Arsenal Pulp Press.

Jilek, W. (1972). *Indian healing.* Surrey, BC: Hancock House Publishers, Ltd.

Kenny, C. (1998). The sense of art: A First Nations view. *Canadian Journal of Native Education, 22*(1), 77–84.

Kenny, C. (2002a). *North American Indian, Morth and Inuit women speak about culture, education, and work.* Ottawa, ON: Status of Women Canada Policy Document.

Kenny, C. (2002b). Keeping the world in balance: Music Therapy in a ritual context. *Voices: A world forum for music therapy, 2*(2). Retrieved from https://voices.no/index.php/voices/article/view/84/66)

Kenny, C. (2006). *Music and life in the field of play: An anthology.* Gilsum, NH: Barcelona Publishers.

Kenny, C., & Fraser, T. N. (2012). *Living Indigenous leadership: Native narratives on building strong communities.* Vancouver, BC: UBC Press.

Mohawk Council of Akwesasne. (1999). *Jay Treaty 1794.* Retrieved from http://www.akwesasne.ca/node/119

Neihardt, J. G. (1972). *Black Elk speaks.* Lincoln, NE: University of Nebraska Press.

Nogueras, D. (2014). *For Native Americans, losing tribal membership tests identity.* Retrieved from http://www.npr.org/blogs/codeswitch/2014/04/01/295798832/for-native-americans-losing-tribal-membership-tests-identity

Pine Tree Legal Assistance (2003). *Border crossing rights under the Jay Treaty.* Retrieved from http://ptla.org/border-crossing-rights-jay-treaty

Purdon, C. (2006). Feminist music therapy with abused teen girls. In S. Hadley (Ed.), *Feminist music therapy* (pp. 205–226). Gilsum, NH: Barcelona Publishers.

Purdon, C., & Ostertag, J. (1999). Understanding abuse: Clinical and training implications for music therapists. *Canadian Journal of Music Therapy, 6,* 9–28.

Regan, P. (2010). *Unsettling the settler within: Indian residential schools, truth telling, and reconciliation in Canada.* Vancouver, BC: UBC Press.

Schaefer, C. (2006). *Grandmothers counsel the world: Women elders offer their vision for our planet.* Boston, MA: Trumpeter Books.

United States Census Bureau. (2010). *Census briefs and reports: The American Indian and Alaska Native population: 2010.* Retrieved from http://2010.census.gov/2010census/

Various artists. (1996). *Voices Across the Canyon, Vol. 1: Collection of Native American Music* [CD: CR-7051]. Phoenix, AZ: Canyon Records.

Wilson, J. (1998). *The Earth shall weep: A history of Native America.* London. UK: Macmillan Ltd.

Witherspoon, G. (1977). *Language and arts in the Navajo universe.* Ann Arbor, MI: University of Michigan Press.

Chapter 10

"32 FLAVORS" (AND THEN SOME): REFLECTIONS ON IDENTITIES THAT FALL SOMEWHERE IN BETWEEN

Roia Rafieyan

Why am I suddenly so uncertain, so hyperaware about how I am trying to describe my mixed heritage?

I've been explaining where I'm from and how I got here ever since I can remember speaking. It's not new to me to tell people that I'm half-American and half-Iranian and that I lived in the southern part of Iran with my Jewish mother, Muslim father, and younger brother until 1978, just before the Iranian Revolution. My parents decided to send my brother and me to the United States to live with my American grandparents, hoping the political unrest would settle down soon, and we could go on with our lives. It didn't. My mother came to join us in 1979, and my father, feeling terribly torn between love for his family and love for his country, finally came to the United States to stay in 1981.

Our community in Abadan, where we lived for the first 12 years of my life, where I'd learned to be more or less Iranian, was destroyed during the subsequent Iran-Iraq war. As much as there was a part of us that hoped we'd someday go back, it became less and less likely. So we settled into our lives in Connecticut, and we worked at becoming more or less American.

Again, I must pause in the retelling of this story to wonder what it is about this particular retelling that doesn't feel okay to me. Why, in this particular context, does it seem somehow to be … lacking?

The only answer I can offer myself is that I've been asked to write about being multi-ethnic and about being multiracial. Now, then. Being multi-ethnic is an identity I own. I haven't called it that, because I usually refer to myself as bicultural, but, yes, multi-ethnic. Yes, I've got that. But talking about being multiracial? That frightens me. That stops me.

I find that each time I'm asked to think and write about who I am, where I come from, which identities I have chosen for myself, and how I situate myself in this world, I have to reconsider the questions from an entirely new perspective, depending on the context and who happens to be asking. When Susan Hadley invited me to think about myself in terms of race, I explored my mixed Iranian and American heritage through the lens of Whiteness (Rafieyan & Hadley, 2013). Even as I write this, I'm aware that, now that I've spent months immersed in the literature and writings about being multiracial and multiethnic, what I really need to say is that she was asking me to think in terms of my race, which, from what I've since discovered, now that I've finally read the United States Census descriptions of racial categories, is considered to be "White."

"White" refers to a person having origins in any of

the original peoples of Europe, the Middle East, or North Africa. It includes people who indicated their race(s) as "White" or reported entries such as Irish, German, Italian, Lebanese, Arab, Moroccan, or Caucasian. (Jones & Bullock, 2012)

In some ways, it's a little deflating to realize that I've never been anything but White, because I have not always felt myself as "only" White. When faced with boxes to check in order to identify myself on various forms, I used to stare at them for a while, not sure which one to mark (because until recently we've been allowed to check only one). I mean, I've never seen a box for "Half-____ and half-____ (Please insert your answers here)," which, to me, would have been the most accurate description of who I am. Usually, in frustration, I just check "Caucasian/White." My brother, who, unlike me, was born in Iran, also struggled to figure out which box described him, and for years he resorted to checking off the box marked "Asian," figuring that Iran is in the Asian continent.

But, yes, as a half-Iranian and half-American, I'm decidedly designated as White, and on a lot of different levels I have a great deal of privilege (McIntosh, 1988). As far as immigrants go, Iranians have had about the easiest time of just about any ethnic group with regard to finding their way in the United States. This is not to say that our family didn't struggle when we arrived in this country. My father, who had years of experience as a chemical engineer and was highly respected in his position at the oil company in Abadan, wasn't able to get a job in his professional field, because anti-Iranian sentiment was so high during and after the Iranian hostage crisis. He put aside his pride and his differences with my American grandfather and went to work with him.

For me, living in the United States was entirely different from just visiting for the summer, and I found myself feeling awkward as I tried to negotiate the social experience of going to school in a "new" country. While the schoolwork wasn't too difficult, I was teased because of how I dressed and because I didn't know a lot of slang. I was horrified at how rude students were to their teachers (which was not tolerated at all in Iran). I also recall thinking how bizarre it was that almost everyone seemed to have a comb sticking out of a back pocket of their jeans.

We lived in a largely Jewish community, and, having grown up without any religion, I found it unsettling when my classmates at school demanded to know whether or not I was Jewish. I answered, explaining I was technically half-Jewish and half-Muslim. Invariably, they'd argue with me that my mother being a Jew made me, by default, Jewish. Standing my ground firmly, I argued back, explaining that my father being a Muslim actually made me Muslim, and therefore I was half- and half-. It may have been foolish to argue an unnecessary point (given that we didn't practice either faith), but I felt strongly that I needed to defend my full heritage and not have someone else's ideas about who I was defining me or my family.

As it happened, my mother's two sisters also married outside of the Jewish faith, one marrying a man whose family was Swedish and the other a man whose family was Jamaican. When our family got together for the holidays, we looked (and probably sounded) like the United Nations. There was a hodgepodge of multiracial and multi-ethnic cousins, a lot of food, and a lot of noise when the political "discussions" began.

Eventually, I managed to find my place. I found friends. I got used to the cultural clashes that came along with trying to be something of an American teenager in a house with an Iranian father.

Although I now feel settled into being American, I have never fully lost the experience of being simultaneously a foreigner, and I comfortably switch from the role of American to Iranian (in spite of not having lived in Iran for decades). This happens most often, I find, when I'm interacting with people who are also foreigners or of mixed parentage.

And so, again, I wonder, how dare I, from this privileged White perspective, talk about the experience of being multiracial? Who am I to even begin to address the complexity of living life in between different races?

Yet, as I keep reading through narratives in order to familiarize myself with the lived experiences of multiracial and multi-ethnic people, I'm struck by some of the similarities in our stories.

In the United States, I've been mistakenly thought of as Arabic (and thought to speak Arabic and Urdu, which I don't) and Israeli (and thought to speak Hebrew, which I don't). The two languages I do speak are English and Farsi. When I've indicated my mixed status, I've frequently been asked how I learned "to speak English so well," and I've had to re-explain the fact that my mother is American and spoke to me in English (although she is extremely capable of conducting a conversation in Farsi with Iranian friends and relatives).

The stories of other multiracial/multi-ethnic people are, in some ways, just like mine. They include the wish to self-identify and to be included as some kind of a category on the numerous forms we fill out in our lives, the need for a community of other "others," having a "chameleon-like" identity to suit different situations, and dealing with people's assumptions about who and/or what we are. These descriptions resonate deeply within me and speak to my life as a person who has lived in between cultures.

But, even having witnessed racism first- and secondhand, when I dated and lived with a Black man for three years, I can't pretend to know what it is to not be White in America.

And so, for the purpose of this chapter, I situate myself and write as a White, bi-ethnic, binational, bicultural, half-Iranian and half-American, half-Jewish and half-Muslim woman. Not "32 Flavors" (DiFranco, 1995), but quite a few nonetheless.

Introduction

As I searched for clarity, I found ambiguity. I longed for something that I could not produce—a neat and tidy category into which I could place myself ... and I found none. I ... discovered that being multiracial meant challenging existing categories due to their incapacity to define me. (Bruner, 2014, p. 146)

In order to begin to understand people who are multiracial/multi-ethnic, it is necessary to find ways to listen to stories that share complexity and uncertainty rather than relying on descriptions by way of numbers, statistics, and categorization. Indeed, society's attempts at fitting people who are of mixed race/ethnicity into check-one-or-the-other-group designations, often placing them into those associated with marginalization and discrimination, has been an ongoing challenge to those whose identities fall somewhere in between officially preassigned Census boxes (Harris & Durodoye, 2006; Qian, 2004).

A theme that emerges over and over is the need for time, space, and an accepting community within which to become aware of and fully discover the various aspects of an identity made up of each person's particular cultural, racial, and ethnic blend. Significant people who are willing to be present at crucial developmental periods, particularly those who are willing to look at their own preconceived ideas about race and ethnicity, support positive identity development in young people of mixed heritage (Harris & Durodoye, 2006; Maxwell & Henriksen, 2012; Miville, Constantine, Baysden, & So-Lloyd, 2005).

"Who am I? How do I articulate my chosen identity? With whom, when and where am I willing to share the fullness of who I am?" Underneath and behind these often prickly questions lie perhaps one of the strengths of multiracial/multi-ethnic people: the ability to interrogate the impreciseness of a constructed racial/ethnic identity (Bruner, 2014; Jackson, 2010).

Worldview

"What are you?" Almost without fail, each multiracial/multi-ethnic person's story begins with this often-asked question (Swanson, 2013). Families are met with curious uncertainty. Mothers, whose skin tone may be darker than that of their children, are thought to be nannies. People from older generations shake their heads and pity children born of their parents' irresponsible decision to marry and procreate. Don't they care about how confusing it will be for the child? Yet, in the next breath, they note how remarkably beautiful mixed race children are.

Nowhere are divided ideas about race and ethnicity more keenly felt than in the person of one who is multiracial/multi-ethnic. From the start, they learn that their identity will be questioned, even challenged, and assumptions will be made. They discover the intimate connection between how others see them and how they will come to see and understand themselves (Khanna, 2010).

Historical Realities

Readers may be surprised to learn that marriage, and other liaisons, between people of different racial and ethnic backgrounds not only existed, but was fairly common in what was then referred to as the New World. At this point in history, people distinguished themselves from each other by religion, nationality, and class. Marriage between people of different skin colors was not cause for concern, and children of mixed heritage were of little consequence (Smedley, 2007). It was natural for European and African servants, who worked and struggled together in close quarters, to marry and have children, then commonly referred to as mulattos.

While it would be inaccurate to say that prejudice didn't exist in 1676, powerful landowners were motivated more by their need for a consistent supply of laborers than by their skin color. They took note of the fact that African settlers had better farming skills, and the native Indians (whose land they had unceremoniously usurped) were dying from newly introduced European diseases. Dissatisfied with the costs associated with maintaining indentured servants, who were not legally bound to stay once their debts were paid, they began to pass laws. Over a period of time, they gradually and systematically began to restrict the rights of African settlers while simultaneously according specific privileges to Europeans, regardless of social or economic standing (Smedley, 2007).

Anti-Miscegenation and Hypodescent

The first *anti-miscegenation* laws came into being in 1691. These were designed to render unlawful marriage between European settlers and those of African, Indian, or mixed heritage. Thus was inaugurated a legal and social system of identifying people by the color of their skin, firmly establishing White privilege and perpetrating a racial divide in the United States that continues to the present day (Smedley, 2007).

Closely linked to anti-miscegenation was the notion of *hypodescent*, often referred to informally as the "one-drop rule." At that time in history, any person with so much as one drop of African blood was to be considered Black (Khanna, 2010, p. 98). As with most statutes of the time, the driving force behind the initiative was social and economic advantage. The law significantly benefited White slave owners by designating any children born to enslaved Black women as part of the owner's property. It also effectively absolved them of their unfortunate predilection for raping their Black female slaves. Thus, a great many multiracial children were born into slavery and identified as Black (Hollinger, 2003, para. 17).

When slavery was finally abolished almost a century later, there was still a great deal of concern, particularly in southern states, with regard to maintaining segregation. With the advent of Jim Crow (referring to the laws enacted to ensure the continued division between Blacks and Whites), the "one-drop rule" was formally adopted into law.

The Multiracial Movement

The 1950s and 1960s brought a radical shift in the way the United States government, if not the general population, treated Blacks. Schools were integrated, and the 1964 Civil Rights Act made discrimination on the basis of race, color, national origin, and religion illegal. In 1967, deciding the landmark case of *Loving v. Virginia*, the Supreme Court unanimously declared anti-miscegenation laws unconstitutional (Hollinger, 2003; Nagai, 2010). At the time, multiracial people, finding more support within the Black community, simply identified as Black. This was partly an outcome of the lingering "one-drop rule," but it was also an expression of solidarity with the Black Power movement (Khanna, 2010, p. 99).

While people in the United States were gradually getting used to the idea of intermarriage, families began to seek and create communities within which to raise their multiracial/multi-ethnic children. Groups such as Interracial Intercultural Pride (IPride), Biracial Family Network (BFN), Interracial Family Circle (IFC), and Multiracial Americans of Southern California (MASC) emerged between 1978 and 1987. While the majority had social agendas, newer groups, such as Project RACE (Reclassify All Children Equally) and the Hapa Issues Forum (HIF), began to focus more specifically on education and advocacy. Recognizing the need for a unified voice, they eventually joined forces in 1988, calling themselves the Association of Multi-Ethnic Americans (AMEA). The multiracial movement, as it came to be called, mainly advocated accurate representation of mixed race/ethnicity on school and government documents. A related focus was acknowledgment that a person of mixed heritage would be equally protected by the Civil Rights Act. Advocates also hoped to emphasize the need for awareness within the medical arena. This referred to the need to collect more thorough medical data on people of mixed heritage. The tendency to assume a monoracial/mono-ethnic identity, based largely on physical appearance, often prevented appropriate screenings for genetic diseases associated with particular ethnicities (Douglass, 2003; Wardle, 2013).

Because AMEA represented a rather large and diverse group, there was strong disagreement as to how the movement should proceed and what the preferred outcome ought to be. Additionally, the African-American academic community expressed strong opposition with regard to moving toward multiracial identity (Douglass, 2003; Spencer, 2011; Wardle, 2013). The objections were, and continue to be, based on the belief that a multiracial focus perpetuates a biological notion of race and avoids confronting long-held beliefs and discriminatory practices toward Black people (Spencer, 2011). The movement was seen as anti-Black, one in which an attempt was being made to place people of mixed parentage above

Blacks within the racial hierarchy instead of challenging that it existed in the first place (Wardle, 2013, Spencer's Critique section, para. 2).

Spencer's (2011) assertions regarding the racial status of Black people seem credible. Non-European immigrants who began to come to the United States in large numbers (especially Asians and Hispanic/Latinos/as) perceived the strong racial divide and thus actively sought ways to distance themselves from identification with Blacks (Lee & Bean, 2004). It is not unusual for people of mixed Asian and White heritage, as well as Hispanic/Latino and White origins, to gradually, over time, begin to simply identify as White (Lee & Bean, 2007, 2010). In stark contrast, people of mixed Black and White heritage continue to be perceived as Black, making it more difficult to identify as multiracial (Herman, 2004; Ho, Sidanius, Levin, & Banaji, 2011; Lee & Bean, 2007). This also holds true for people whose heritage includes Asian-Black and/or Hispanic/Latino-Black ancestry (Jackson, Wolven, & Aguilera, 2013; Lee & Bean, 2010).

In spite of significant challenges and numerous differences of opinion, the year 2000 marked the first time in the history of the United States Census in which multiracial/multi-ethnic people were able to "check all that apply" in the section on race. Although this approach required a great deal of compromise, activists within the multiracial movement perceive this change as a positive step toward political presence (Douglass, 2003). As of the completion of the 2010 Census, nine million U. S. citizens identified themselves as belonging to two or more racial categories. People who are multiracial/multi-ethnic are found throughout the United States; however, the state with by far the largest mixed heritage population is California, followed by Texas and New York (Jones & Bullock, 2012).

Myths and Stereotypes

People of mixed heritage are no more immune to stereotyping and myths than those who are monoracial/mono-ethnic. Multiracial/multi-ethnic people are sometimes heralded as representing the beginning of a "raceless" society (Nittle, n.d., Section 4). Although some eschew racial/ethnic classification, recognizing race as a social construct rather than a fact, they are not without race (Rockquemore & Brunsma, 2008). They are simply a mix of the races that make up their parentage. Sadly, racism and discrimination continue to be significant social and economic factors in the United States, often profoundly affecting those who are racially/ethnically mixed.

Perspective, of course, is everything. This becomes uncomfortably evident when comparing narratives about multiracial/multi-ethnic people as presented in White versus Black news outlets. White news media tend to advance the idea that multiracial people are ushering in a "new race era" (Thornton, 2009, p. 121), symbolizing a move toward a "color-blind" society (p. 119). Although articles in these newspapers celebrate the power to choose racial identity, they rarely acknowledge the effect of White privilege in the making of this choice. Conversely, Black newspapers remind readers that being Black is inherently multiracial. Identifying as multiracial is seen as a deliberate effort at distancing oneself from the Black community (p. 115).

Another way that perspective can affect the way in which multiracial/multi-ethnic people are viewed is connected to geographic location. For instance, a person whose ethnic mix includes being part Mexican will more likely experience stereotyping and bias living in a border state such as Arizona (Jackson, Wolven, & Aguilera, 2013). Generational differences also come into play. A woman whose Japanese parents spent time in an internment camp in the United States will have a completely different frame of reference from one whose mother moved to the United States as a Japanese war bride with her American GI husband after World War II (Alexander, 2014; Ries, personal communication, July 12, 2015). A man who has lived through segregation and remembers the "one-drop rule" is more likely to assume that people who are Black-White biracial identify as Black (Khanna, 2010).

Hypodescent continues to be a large factor in the ongoing assumption that Black-White biracial people automatically identify as Black. Likewise, a person who is Asian and White, especially if male, is often perceived as Asian (Ho, Sidanius, Levin, & Banaji, 2011). How a person who is multiracial/multi-ethnic self-identifies is usually related to a number of factors. These include, among others, the race/ethnicity of their minority parent (Root, 1998/2002; Xian, 2004), how they feel they appear to others (Khanna, 2010), knowledge about their family cultures, language(s) they speak at home, their peer group (Renn, 2008), the ethnic makeup of their neighborhood, and social class (Townsend, Wilkins, Fryberg, & Markus, 2012).

Multiracial/multi-ethnic people in general, and women in particular, are frequently described as possessing attractive physical features. This happens to such an extent that Sims (2012) calls this phenomenon the "Biracial Beauty Stereotype" (p. 64; see also Hall, 2004; Root, 2004). Depending on when they were born, women of mixed race, situated within different social and political time periods, have had to navigate the complex matrices of race, gender, power, and sexuality (Root, 2004).

A frustrating misperception is that people who are multiracial/multi-ethnic experience confusion and identity problems, causing emotional difficulties and self-hatred. Although the identity development of a multiracial/multi-ethnic person is a complex process, it is certainly not an impossible task (Cheng & Lee, 2009; Rockquemore, Brunsma, & Delgado, 2009). With family, peer group, and community support, children and adolescents can, and do, successfully negotiate their multiracial/multi-ethnic identity (Herman, 2004; Jackson et al., 2013; Kelley, 2006; Stone, 2009). Resilient multiracial/multi-ethnic people sometimes choose to adopt more than one identity. This is referred to as a *both/and* identity, such as Black *and* multiracial (Ayo, 2014; Brunsma, 2004).

Identity confusion is more likely to occur as a result of expectations and assumptions based on stereotypes and misperceptions. For the most part, multiracial/multi-ethnic people successfully negotiate adolescence and grow up to be psychologically well adjusted (Chen, 2013; Kelley, 2006; Mok & Morris, 2009). Positive attributes associated with being mixed include the ability to be flexible, creativity, and the ability to take the perspective of others in difficult situations (Chang, Hsu, Shih, & Chen, 2014; Jackson et al., 2013; Paxton & Wade, 2011).

Describing Diverse People

Multiracial/multi-ethnic people, as a community, embody diversity. Even people within the same family and with the same racial/ethnic mix may identify differently from each other. It is, therefore, difficult to make generalizations. An issue pertinent to one person of mixed heritage will not necessarily have the same impact on the life of another. Further complicating matters, the identity a person chooses shifts in different contexts, depending on numerous other factors and influences.

Language, Cultural Connotations, and Mixed Identity

It is helpful to learn some of the language used to describe people whose parents are of different racial, ethnic, and cultural backgrounds. A number of terms have been proposed at various points in history, and some are not included here because they are no longer in use and may be considered offensive. One such word, *mulatto,* was first used in the late 1500s to describe people who had a specific percentage of Black-White racial mix. In 1850, the United States Census incorporated it as a racial grouping, along with other words that measured varying levels of racial mixture, and continued to do so until 1920 (Nagai, 2010). Some find it disrespectful, believing that it comes from the Spanish term for mule, *mulo.* Spencer (2004) corrects this misperception, though, identifying it more accurately as having Arabic roots, based on the word *muwallad,* describing someone who is part Arab (p. 376).

The words *mestizo/a, hapa,* and *hafu* refer to specific racial/ethnic mixes. While not necessarily unfavorable, they each carry cultural connotations. It is best to wait until the person of mixed heritage initiates and clearly invites the use of these terms. *Mestizo/a* is used in a variety of ways, not always respectfully, by people of Hispanic/Latino/a descent to indicate mixed Latino/a heritage. Multiracial/multi-ethnic people of Hispanic/Latino/a origin represent a particularly large portion of the population in the United States, yet little has been written about their experiences (Jackson, Wolven, & Aguilera, 2013). Part of the reason for this may be that racial/ethnic mixture is extremely common in this community (Humes, Jones, & Ramirez, 2011). Another aspect to consider is how a person whose heritage includes being part Hispanic/Latino/a identifies can be rather complex. In addition to race, national origin factors into how parents identify their racially/ethnically mixed children. By way of example:

Latinos identified racially as Black or other are over three times as likely as White Latinos to identify their children as Latino. Latino-White couples in which the Latino spouse is White are not as inclined to characterize their children as Latino because of the shared race with the White spouse. National origin variation is strong. Mexican-White couples are most likely to identify their children as Mexican rather than White. Puerto Rican-White couples are 74% as likely to identify their children as Puerto Rican as are Mexican-White couples to identify their children as Mexican. In contrast, other Latino-White couples are much less likely to indicate their children's Latino national origin (Cuban, Central, or South American). (Qian, 2004, p. 760)

In a similar vein, *hapa* originated in Hawaii as a derogatory term for a person of mixed parentage who was part Asian or Pacific Islander and part White. Over time, Hawaii has become one of the most ethnically diverse states in the country, with the largest proportion of people living there being of mixed heritage (Jones & Bullock, 2012). The word *hapa* has evolved to include anyone whose racial/ethnic ancestry is partly Asian or Pacific Islander (Laughlin, 2014).

In Japan, *hafu* means "half." Asian cultures, in general, are less accepting of people who are "half," but especially so when the person lacks cultural knowledge. Those who are both Japanese and White are well aware that Japan is a monoculture, and those of mixed heritage feel less welcome (Khanna, 2004). As such, the word *hafu* has strong implications and not just for people designated as such. It also marks their family member as having made the choice to partner with a person who was not Japanese (Ries, personal communication, July 13, 2015).

People of mixed Asian heritage who choose a primarily White identity frequently feel alienated from their Asian family members, especially when they have difficulty speaking the language. Those who are more familiar with their Asian parent's language and culture, however, are still more likely to identify as Asian. Another important consideration within this community is one's generational status. Mixed Asians born and living in the late 1940s and early 1950s in the United States were, at the time, more likely to be identified by others as Asian. Those coming of age now, two generations later, have parents who grew up identifying as American, and they tend to have available a wider range of identity options (Khanna, 2004; Wijeyesinghe, 2012).

More Commonly Used Language

Commonly accepted words are: *bi-* and *multiracial* and *bi-* and *multi-ethnic.* A person can also be described as being of *mixed heritage*, *mixed race*, or *mixed ethnicity.* People who identify as bi- or multiracial have parents who are each a different race. Although the word "ethnicity" is sometimes used to refer to race, it is used here to describe a person whose country of origin or cultural heritage is not the United States.

A person can be both multiracial *and* multi-ethnic (for example, someone who is both Black and Asian), multiracial and *mono*-ethnic (such as someone who has one Black and one White parent, both of whom identify as U.S. citizens), or multi-ethnic and *monoracial* (for example, someone whose family makeup is White European-American and Iranian). Some individuals create entirely new language, blending words to honor their diverse racial/ethnic mix. Golfer Tiger Woods, for example, identifies himself as "Cablinasian," a contraction of the Caucasian, Black, American Indian, and Asian backgrounds passed down to him through his family (Nagai, 2010). David Hollinger (2003) suggests the term *ethnoracial* as fully inclusive and descriptive of all forms of ethnic/racial mixture.

In some multiracial families, both parents are part of racial/ethnic minority groups. Their offspring may identify as *dual* or *double minorities*, which can present a number of additional challenges (Romo, 2008). A case in point would be a person who has both Asian and Black heritage and may be regarded with suspicion by Asian family members. Although the Black community may be more welcoming, individuals who have spent time in an Asian culture can still find it difficult to fit in (Fackler, 2015; Lee & Bean, 2010).

How a person of dual mixed heritage identifies depends a great deal on the types of family, peer, and community support they receive while growing up. This, in turn, affects the extent to which they are able to integrate aspects of both their parents' cultures. A person for whom both cultures have been affirmed may choose a fully mixed identity, such as a person of Black and Mexican origins living in California who self-identifies as Blaxican (Romo, 2008, p. 67). A person's identity can be as much a function of geography as one's support system. A person with exactly the same Black/Mexican heritage growing up in a southwestern state and stereotyped as a "criminal other" may experience significant stress related to their dual minority status (Jackson, Wolven, & Aguilera, 2013, p. 213).

People who have one United States–born and one foreign-born parent sometimes refer to themselves as *bi-* or *multinational* or simply as *bicultural*. These words describe individuals who have, to a greater or lesser extent, incorporated aspects of more than one culture into their lives (Nguyen & Benet-Martinez, 2007; Schwartz & Unger, 2010). Distinguishing aspects of this group are the likelihood of having spent time living abroad, as well as the ability to speak more than one language (Cross & Gilly, 2013; Paxton & Wade, 2011). Both language and cultural learning may take place simultaneously or successively, and each may become more pertinent at various significant points in a person's life (Grosjean, 2014; Nguyen & Ahmadpanah, 2014).

International travel provides opportunities to interact with and learn from people in other cultures, a fact that binational people feel serves them well (Paxton & Wade, 2011). They often develop a "contextual" (Paxton & Wade, 2011, p. 327) understanding of race rather than thinking of it as a fixed entity.

This comes about as a result of observing, and sometimes living firsthand, the effects of racism in the United States and contrasting this with their experiences of race in other countries (Paxton & Wade, 2011).

People who are mixed frequently engage in *code switching*. A concept that comes from linguistics, this has come to be associated with those who are multicultural/multiracial. It is used to describe the ability to easily switch between languages and/or cultural customs and norms. It relates closely to the idea of having a fluid identity, in that people who are bicultural/biracial have the ability to situationally suppress the habits of one culture and incorporate the behavioral expectations and norms of another (Grosjean, 2014).

In spite of this ability, when parents come from remarkably different cultures, there are inevitable challenges. Binghalib (2011) offers a thought-provoking example by providing a glimpse into the lives of young people living in the United States who have Arab Muslim fathers and American mothers who convert to Islam. It is customary in Islamic cultures for children to take on the father's religion, and they are expected to "be respectful, honest, modest, and hardworking" (Pipes & Duran, 2002, para. 2). Family honor, particularly as it relates to the role of young Muslim women, is of utmost importance to Arab Muslim fathers; however, a complicated dynamic is set up when mothers side with their daughters, who, immersed in Western culture, wish to have the freedom to pursue romantic relationships. Other forms of tension are experienced when young Muslim Arab-Americans, expected to adhere to strict Islamic customs, struggle to be understood by their White, non-Muslim friends. At the same time, mono-ethnic Muslim contemporaries may accuse them of behaving in a Westernized manner, leading to further feelings of isolation (Binghalib, 2011).

Diverse Identity Patterns

In an effort to understand mixed identity, various theorists have presented stage-based models of identity development (Poston, 1990). These approaches, however, typically assumed a linear progression, and, because they were based on monoracial models, were apt to pathologize fluid identity patterns (Rockquemore et al., 2009). Thus, it was of some relief to the multiracial/multi-ethnic community when Maria Root (2002), herself a woman of mixed race and ethnicity, put forth the, now more commonly accepted Ecological Framework for Understanding Multiracial Identity Development (see Resources section). This inclusive model acknowledges the myriad elements that go into how, why, and under what circumstances the identity of a person who is multiracial/multi-ethnic gradually takes shape and evolves. These include physical appearance, how a person is socialized within their family and neighborhood, and where they live in the United States, as well as the types of people who make up their social networks. Just as important, and having as profound an impact, are the effects of gender, class, and sexual orientation, factors which occur within the larger historical and sociopolitical climate happening within a person's lifetime (Rockquemore & Brunsma, 2008; Rockquemore, Brunsma, & Delgado, 2009; Root, 2002; see also Wijeyesinghe, 2012).

Rockquemore and Brunsma (2008) elaborate Dr. Root's work, enumerating the common ways in which people bring together their racial and ethnic parentage to form an identity. Generally, there are four ways people are likely to incorporate their particular racial/ethnic mix. Those adopting a *border identity* see themselves as fully, and more or less equally, expressing each of the aspects of their parental heritage, while others choose to identify exclusively with the heritage of one parent, or, put another way, they prefer a *singular identity*. People with a *protean identity* are those who comfortably switch back and forth between racial/ethnic identities as situations may warrant. Still others entirely reject the notion of race as a means of social categorization and take on a *transcendent identity*, preferring instead to be identified by personal characteristics and qualities having nothing to do with race (pp. 62–74; see also Jackson, 2010; Miville et al., 2005; Renn, 2008).

Microaggression and Discrimination

Microaggression

Everybody comes in contact with microaggression in some form or another. What sets apart the experiences of people who are multiracial/multi-ethnic is that the microaggressive behavior comes from all sides, so to speak. Aside from "What are you?," a person whose family includes both a Black and a White parent, for example, may simultaneously feel pressure from both the Black and White communities to identify as Black; listen to people who are unaware of their racial heritage make comments that stereotype Black people; be perceived as "exotic" and fetishized; be seen as an underachiever, as not Black enough, as not White enough; and deal with rejection from family members who may have cut off ties with the individual's parents for having broken what they perceive as a cultural taboo by marrying outside their race (Greig, 2013; Herman, 2004; Nadal, Wong, Griffin, Sriken, Vargas, Wideman, & Kolawole, 2011; Qian, 2004; Remedios, Chasteen, & Oey, 2012; Root, 2003; Sims, 2012; Swanson, 2013). These infractions are startlingly common, and many of them stem from a default presumption that being monoracial/mono-ethnic is the standard, and even preferred, way to be (Nadal et al., 2011; Orloff, 2012; Root, 2003). Is it any wonder that racially/ethnically mixed people quickly learn to adapt to different situations by shifting their identity?

Multiracial/multi-ethnic families face reactions ranging from inquisitive and confused stares to blatant contempt (Greig, 2013; Root, 2003). Young people are put in the position of having to prove or "authenticate" their membership in the various racial/ethnic groups to which they belong (Hall, 2004, p. 240; Jackson et al., 2013, p. 46). Even more discouraging, though, is the exposure to microaggression within one's own family (Jackson et al., 2013; Jhangiani, 2013; Nadal, Sriken, Davidoff, Wong, & McLean, 2013; Orloff, 2012). Experiences within this realm are similar to those described above, in that relatives may also assert the need to choose a monoracial/mono-ethnic identity. On the other hand, some multiracial/multi-ethnic individuals feel alienated and unwelcome, a sense of not quite belonging to either side of their parents' families (Fackler, 2015). Some, especially girls and women, endure uncomfortable attention because of relatives' responses, favorable and unfavorable, to their mixed features (Nadal et al., 2013, pp. 195–197; Sims, 2012). The fact that insensitive treatment originates in one's family may have a particularly painful impact on the multiracial/multi-ethnic person.

Discrimination

There are no specific laws protecting people of mixed heritage from experiencing discrimination, in spite of the frequency with which it occurs (Campbell & Herman, 2010). Young White and Hispanic/Latino/a students who identify as Hispanic in school tend not to perform as well academically, because of teachers' perceptions of them as underachievers (Wilkinson, 2008). Male job applicants of mixed Black-White heritage earn less than their White male counterparts. They are also more likely to be stereotyped as lacking adequate social skills and seen as not presenting themselves well in job interviews (Remedios et al., 2012). Workplace discrimination can also be seen in the insidious practice of using people of mixed Asian and White heritage as the public face of workplace diversity, regardless of how the individual identifies (Leong, 2013).

Health and Well-Being

Families and Caregivers

Families play a crucial role in the psychological and emotional development and well-being of multiracial/multi-ethnic children. There are plenty of ways through which parents can instill a sense of racial, ethnic, and cultural pride. A good first step is intentionally choosing ethnically and racially diverse neighborhoods, schools, and places of worship (Jhangiani, 2013; Kennedy & Romo, 2013; Lee, 2004; Orloff, 2012; Stone, 2009). Another way that families model diversity is by having friends of various races/ethnicities and demonstrating a curiosity and willingness to understand other cultures (Jhangiani, 2013; Lee, 2004).

Even when one parent is absent, families can learn about and celebrate the customs, traditions, and foods of both parents' heritage (Bruner, 2014; Crawford & Alaggia, 2008; Jhangiani, 2013; Kennedy & Romo, 2013; Lee, 2004; Stone, 2009). These experiences can be further strengthened by connecting socially with other mixed families and helping children find positive adult role models who are also multiracial/multi-ethnic (Lee, 2004).

Parents who acknowledge the likelihood that their multiracial/multi-ethnic children will face discrimination, misperceptions, and stereotypes will be more effective at helping them learn ways to respond to microaggressions (Crawford & Alaggia, 2008; Jhangiani, 2013; Lee, 2004; Stone, 2009). Speaking openly about race/ethnicity, racism/ethnocentrism, and prejudice creates a safe space where children can begin to talk about confusing and upsetting experiences (Jhangiani, 2013; Lee, 2004; Stone, 2009).

Parents send a powerful message when they accept the racial/ethnic identity/identities their children choose for themselves. A key to this acceptance is in recognizing that these may change over time and their siblings may choose to identify in different ways (Root, 1998). Parental advocacy can take the form of speaking out on behalf of their mixed-heritage children when they receive discriminatory or racist messages from other family members, in schools, or in community groups (Crawford & Alaggia, 2008; Jhangiani, 2013; Lee, 2004). Families who lack resources may be able to gain support from the wider community, such as extended family members, clergy, health care providers, and even online groups for people of mixed heritage (see Resources section).

Creating a Welcoming Therapeutic Space

Being of mixed heritage is not necessarily the reason a person decides to engage in therapy (Harris & Durodoye, 2006; Moss & Davis, 2008; Stone, 2009); however, the cumulative effects of microaggressions, feeling marginalized within one's family, discrimination, isolation, and struggles with one's identity can present as therapy issues. People of mixed race/ethnicity, and all people, are best served by those who have made a point of asking themselves difficult and often uncomfortable questions. Those in support roles need to be aware of the stereotyped narratives, ideas, beliefs, and biases that they may hold with regard to individuals whose race, ethnicity, and/or religion are different from their own as well as considering thoughts and reactions to those whose families are multiracial/multi-ethnic (Hadley, 2013; Harris & Durodoye, 2006; Jackson & Samuels, 2011; Kahn, 2011; Maxwell & Henriksen, 2012; Stone, 2009).

Culturally informed therapists make a point of being aware of the ways in which they occupy intersecting positions of privilege and power—or lack thereof—associated with race, ethnicity, gender, religious affiliation, sexual orientation, dis/ability, class, and socioeconomic status. They also recognize and, more specifically, name these elements as being present in all our lives, and, by extension, as a part of every therapy relationship, especially in work with clients of mixed heritage. Some clinicians, following a social justice model, advocate "location of [the] self" of the therapist, as well as that of the client, during the initial phases of therapy as a way of recognizing and attending to potential areas of misunderstanding and encouraging ongoing reflection with regard to the internalized effects of marginalization and oppression (Watts-Jones, 2010; see also Wyatt, 2008). This

further underscores rejection of the notion that one can be "color-blind" within the therapy context and unable to "see" race or difference (Williams, 2011). (Readers will find Monnica Williams' post, "Colorblind Ideology is a Form of Racism," illuminating in this regard: https://www.psychologytoday.com/blog/culturally-speaking/201112/colorblind-ideology-is-form-racism.) Not only does this stance negate the real experiences of multiracial/multi-ethnic clients, but also it creates a therapy space in which specific topics, such as those around race, racism, difference, and discrimination, are subtly discouraged and avoided (Kahn, 2011).

Therapists' self-awareness with regard to the largely Western cultural views and values they frequently bring to the therapy situation is also a pertinent factor, especially when counseling a person of binational heritage whose familial cultural norms may differ significantly from their own (Binghalib, 2011; Suyemoto, 2004). Asnaani and Hofmann (2012) outline a series of guidelines to assist in cross-cultural work, highlights of which include starting with a "culturally informed but person-specific" assessment and working with "culturally related strengths and resources" ("Features of Effective Collaboration in Multicultural Therapy" section). The authors emphasize the need to be conscious of the ways in which therapy, as well as the therapy relationship, are perceived within a patient's culture and community. Psychiatric care may be viewed with mistrust or seen as a source of shame, stigmatizing those who go to therapy as having somehow failed or not lived up to cultural standards ("Guideline #4" section). For a person of mixed parentage, this can present an added challenge to negotiate when making an effort to find support. Conscientious clinicians need to be prepared to check assumptions and respectfully work through these issues as they emerge in the course of therapy ("Guideline #1" and "Guideline #5" sections).

There is still another reason for practitioners to culturally situate themselves and maintain consistent awareness of the power they hold in their position as therapists. People of mixed heritage, again, have a natural ability to move between identities, potentially predisposing them to seamlessly adapt to the therapist's dominant cultural view (Rockquemore & Brunsma, 2008). Although fluid identity patterns are now more commonly recognized as adaptive, therapists can still easily miss what, in some cases, may be a form of reenactment. When this occurs, it can be helpful to work together to identify and clarify what has happened and invite multiracial/multi-ethnic clients to reflect on how easily they may find themselves in situations where they feel compelled to adapt themselves to fit others' expectations.

Meaning and Function of Music

Music is an important part of cultural identity and learning. Accordingly, taking part in musical experiences and rituals as a family helps children of mixed heritage learn about each parent's cultural traditions. It also provides a basis on which to build an identity as part of a multiracial/multi-ethnic family (Boer & Abubakar, 2014; Miranda, 2012). One unique aspect of growing up within a mixed family is the possibility for exposure to a wider range of music than one might have growing up in a monoracial/mono-ethnic family.

Multiracial/multi-ethnic adolescents use music in the same ways all young people use music: as a way to develop a sense of who they are, to differentiate themselves from their parents, to connect with their friends, and to relieve stress (Boer & Abubakar, 2014; Miranda, 2012; Ruud, 2010). Each of these elements has the potential to take on increased significance for youngsters negotiating a mixed identity, depending on how affirmed and supported they have felt in asserting their blended heritage.

Young people of mixed heritage usually find ways to work around and within constraints in order to fit in with peers and yet remain respectful of and connected to their families' cultural values and expectations. O'Brien (2013) provides a compelling example of how this might look in action in his thick description of a period of time he spent observing and interacting with a Muslim hip-hop group made up of five mono-ethnic (representing African, Arab, and South Asian nationalities), religiously observant, Muslim adolescent boys growing up in the United States. He describes, in fascinating detail, the ways in which this bicultural group (referring here to those who have internalized and integrated two different cultures) goes about the process of taking "advantage of the symbolic power and flexibility of both hip-hop music and religious Islam to manage the cultural tension between the two and produce a complex local identity that assists them in feeling—and seeming—both religiously observant and secularly cool" (pp. 104–105). He specifically acknowledges the fact that, for these young men, and for all people who are bicultural or of mixed race/ethnicity, rather than being a single event, managing the marked differences between the two cultures is an ongoing process that takes some creative effort (p. 117). An especially positive outgrowth is that, in the end, these individuals will have a deeper and more thoughtful understanding of both cultures as well as the ability to function within each of them in a meaningful way.

Another hip-hop proponent, Searle (n.d.), conveys the benefits of subgenres, specifically "conscious hip-hop," noting that they have a great deal to offer youth of all hues by highlighting issues surrounding race, class, and gender. Disclosing his own struggles with low self-esteem and discrimination as a young man of mixed race, Searle shares the following thoughts:

> Socially conscious hip-hop can … be very important in providing young people with role models. Indeed, "mixed-race" people can often have a different relationship with their parents or guardians and siblings than people in "same-race" families. In a "mixed-race" family, it can often be more difficult for a young person to see

themselves in their parents, or elder siblings, who may look quite different to them. … Therefore, young "mixed-race" people may find that traditional nonfamilial, role-model figures, such as sports personalities and musicians, may be more influential in their lives. ("Conclusion" section, para. 3; see also O'Brien, 2013)

Artistic endeavors of varied sorts and genres provide opportunities to creatively articulate, illuminate, explore, and perhaps come to terms with identity, oppression, racism, and discrimination. Music, in its many forms, provides a rich narrative through which to express the varying experiences of people of mixed race/ethnicity (Fulbeck, 2011; Jackson, Wolven, & Aguilera, 2013; Mayor, 2012; O'Brien, 2013; Searle, n.d.).

Implications for Music Therapy

A respectful approach to learning about how music functions in the life of an individual of mixed heritage is to simply ask the person and to invite the sharing of important pieces of music and songs as a way of beginning to establish a relationship. Jackson and Samuels (2011), presenting a social work perspective, make a series of recommendations for providing "multiracially attuned" therapy ("Multiraciality and the NASW Standards for Cultural Competence in Social Work Practice" section, para. 1) that are easily adaptable in a music therapy setting. They favor approaches that recognize people of mixed heritage as holding within them the knowledge they need to develop strong identities, and they find narrative therapy to be especially effective in this respect ("Multiracial Skills" section, para. 4). (Two helpful websites with information about Narrative Therapy, each with a number of resources and articles, are http://www.narrativeapproaches.com and http://dulwichcentre.com.au.) Music therapists have long recognized the value of exploring life stories through the creation of song and sound collages, improvised music, and songwriting. These music therapy techniques help multiracial/multi-ethnic clients recognize, sort through, and remusic the expectations and stereotypes that have cluttered their narratives (Amir, 2012; Austin, 2008; Bruscia, 1987; De Backer & Sutton, 2014; Eyre, 2007; Kenny, 1989; Montello, 1999; Rolvsjord, 2010; Stige, 2002).

Learning to stand firm in one's preferred identity and developing ways to safely and effectively respond to microaggression, particularly pressure to choose only one race/ethnicity, is another helpful strategy (Jackson & Samuels, 2011, "Multiracial Skills" section, para. 4). Group music therapy can provide a space to play with ideas around having one's voice heard within musical and nonmusical contexts. Participants can work specifically on negotiating the volume, intensity, and message of their musical voice, thus building ego strength while looking at group and personal experiences of power. Extending this idea, participants can practice musically standing up for themselves, which can serve as a multilayered metaphor for establishing healthier family and peer dynamics (Wyatt, 2008). Ultimately, music therapy experiences can fortify multiracial/multi-ethnic people's responses to discriminatory behavior and help to establish a feeling of belonging along with a positive identity (Richards & Davies, 2002).

Conclusion

In summary, people of mixed race/ethnicity bring a fresh and unique point of view that counters the societal tendency to rely on categories and fixed identities as a means of sorting through and organizing the masses. They invite reflection and a willingness to question, perhaps even to reconsider, long-held notions regarding the social and political constructions of race and ethnicity. By creatively working through the complex experiences that go along with being multiracial/multi-ethnic, most come to a conclusion similar to that of Marie Bruner (2014):

> Rather than seeking acceptance from others and fitting a mold that they assign to me, I choose to embrace all that I am and share what I have learned from my journey with others. For me, it is about connection to the people who matter most to me rather than connection to the people who try to label me. I do not need to struggle to "fit in" or "find my place" in this world, I can be me—a woman who grew up on burritos and black-eyed peas. (p. 157)

References

Alexander, L. (2014, October 5). *Daughters tell stories of "war brides" despised back home and in the U.S.* (Blog post). Retrieved from http://www.japantimes.co.jp/community/2014/10/05/how-tos/daughters-tell-stories-war-brides-despised-back-home-u-s/#.VaUOAng-Cu5

Amir, D. (2012). "My music is me": Musical presentation as a way of forming and sharing identity in music therapy group. *Nordic Journal of Music Therapy, 21*(2), 176–193.

Asnaani, A., & Hofmann, S. G. (2012). Collaboration in culturally responsive therapy: Establishing a strong therapeutic alliance across cultural lines. *Journal of Clinical Psychology, 68*(2), 187–197. Retrieved from http://www.ncbi.nlm.nih.gov/pmc/articles/PMC3641707/

Austin, D. (2008). *The theory and practice of vocal psychotherapy: Songs of the self.* London, UK: Jessica Kingsley Publishers.

Ayo, D. (2014, February 4). Becoming multiracial. Re: Defining Black History [Audio podcast episode]. In Letson, A., Host/Exec. Prod., *State of the Re:Union*. Retrieved from http://stateofthereunion.com/redefining-black-history/

Binghalib, Y. (2011). *Family dynamics between Arab Muslim parents, Western parents and their bi-ethnic children.*

Unpublished master's thesis. Retrieved from http://csus-dspace.calstate.edu/handle/10211.9/1104?show=full

Boer, D., & Abubakar, A. (2014). Music listening in families and peer groups: Benefits for young people's social cohesion and emotional well-being across four cultures. *Frontiers in Psychology, 5,* 1–15. doi:10.3389/fpsyg.2014.00392

Bruner, M. (2014). *Growing up on burritos and black-eyed peas: An autoethnography of multiracial identity development* (Doctoral dissertation). Retrieved August 8, 2014, from http://scholarworks.gsu.edu/msit_diss/127

Brunsma, D. L. (2004). Public categories, private identities: Exploring regional differences in biracial experience. *Social Science Research, 35,* 555–576.

Bruscia, K. E. (1987). *Improvisational models of music therapy.* Springfield, IL: Charles C. Thomas.

Campbell, M. E., & Herman, M. R. (2010). Politics and policies: Attitudes toward multiracial Americans. *Ethnic and Racial Studies, 33*(9), 1511–1536.

Chang, J-H., Hsu, C-C., Shih, N-H., & Chen, H-C. (2014). Multicultural families and creative children. *Journal of Cross-Cultural Psychology, 45*(8), 1288–1296.

Chen, T. S. (2013). *The positive and negative experiences of multiracial* identities (Doctoral dissertation, Massachusetts School of Professional Psychology). Abstract retrieved from http://gradworks.umi.com/36/10/3610189.html#returntop

Cheng, C-Y., & Lee, F. (2009). Multiracial identity integration: Perceptions of conflict and distance among multiracial individuals. *Journal of Social Issues, 65*(1), 51–68.

Crawford, S. E., & Alaggia, R. (2008). The best of both worlds? Family influences on mixed race youth identity development. *Qualitative Social Work, 7,* 81–98. doi:10.1177/1473325007086417

Cross, S. N. N., & Gilly, M. C. (2013). Navigating the diversity within. In R. W. Belk, L. Price, & L. Peñaloza (Eds.), *Consumer Culture Theory (Research in Consumer Behavior, Volume 15)* (pp. 57–72). doi:10.1108/S0885-2111(2013)0000015004

De Backer, J., & Sutton, J. (2014). Therapeutic interventions in psychodynamic music therapy: The music in music therapy. In J. De Backer & J. Sutton (Eds.), *The music in music therapy: Psychodynamic music therapy in Europe: Clinical, theoretical and research approaches* (pp. 338–349). London, UK: Jessica Kingsley Publishers.

DiFranco, A. (1995). 32 Flavors. On *Not a Pretty Girl* (CD). Buffalo, NY: Righteous Babe Records.

Douglass, R. E. (2003). The evolution of the multiracial movement. In M. P. P. Root & M. Kelley (Eds.), *The multiracial child sourcebook.* Seattle, WA: Mavin Foundation.

Eyre, L. (2007). The marriage of music and narrative: Explorations in art, therapy, and research. *Voices: A World Forum for Music Therapy, 7*(3). Retrieved from https://normt.uib.no/index.php/voices/article/view/549/410

Fackler, M. (2015, May 29). Biracial beauty queen challenges Japan's self-image. Retrieved from http://www.nytimes.com/2015/05/30/world/asia/biracial-beauty-queen-strives-for-change-in-mono-ethnic-japan.html?_r=0

Fulbeck, K. (2011). *The hapa project* (Website). Retrieved from http://kipfulbeck.com/the-hapa-project/

Greig, A. (2013, August). Seven essential facts about multiracial youth. *American Psychological Association*. Retrieved from http://www.apa.org/pi/families/resources/newsletter/2013/08/multiracial-youth.aspx

Grosjean, F. (2014). Bicultural bilinguals. *International Journal of Bilingualism*. Advance online publication. doi:10.1177/1367006914526297. Retrieved from http://ijb.sagepub.com/content/early/2014/03/31/1367006914526297.full.pdf

Hadley, S. (2013). *Experiencing race as a music therapist: Personal narratives*. Gilsum, NH: Barcelona Publishers.

Hall, C. C. I. (2004). Mixed-race women. *Women and Therapy, 27*(1), 237–246. doi:10.1300/J015v27n01_16

Harris, H. L., & Durodoye, B. A. (2006). School counselor perceptions of multiracial students. *Research in the Schools, 13*(2), 13–23.

Herman, M. (2004). Forced to choose: Some determinants of racial identification in multiracial adolescents. *Child Development, 75*(3), 730–748.

Ho, A. K., Sidanius, J., Levin, D. T., & Banaji, M. R. (2011). Evidence for hypodescent and racial hierarchy in the categorization and perception of biracial individuals. *Journal of Personality and Social Psychology, 100*(3), 492–506. doi:10.1037/a0021562

Hollinger, D. A. (2003). Amalgamation and hypodescent: The question of ethnoracial mixture in the history of the United States. *The American Historical Review, 108*(5), 1363–1390. Retrieved from http://history.berkeley.edu/sites/default/files/amalgamation_and_hypodescent.pdf

Humes, K. R., Jones, N. A., & Ramirez, R. R. (2011, March). *Overview of Race and Hispanic Origin: 2010*. 2010 Census Briefs. Retrieved from http://www.census.gov/prod/cen2010/briefs/c2010br-02.pdf

Jackson, K. F. (2010). Living the multiracial experience: Shifting racial expressions, resisting race, and seeking community. *Qualitative Social Work, 11*(1), 42–60. doi:10.1177/1473325010375646

Jackson, K. F., & Samuels, G. M. (2011). Multiracial competence in social work: Recommendations for culturally attuned work with multiracial people. *Social Work, 56*(3), 235–245.

Jackson, K. F., Wolven, T., & Aguilera, K. (2013). Mixed resilience: A study of multi-ethnic Mexican-American stress and coping in Arizona. *Family Relations, 62*(1), 212–225.

Jhangiani, C. A. (2013). *"What are you, anyway?" How parents help their multiracial children live in a world of singular racial categories* (Master's thesis). Retrieved from https://dspace.smith.edu/handle/11020/24214?show=full

Jones, N. A., & Bullock, J. (2012). *The two or more races population: 2010*. 2010 Census Briefs. United States Census Bureau. Retrieved from https://www.census.gov/prod/cen2010/briefs/c2010br-13.pdf

Kahn, V. D. (2011). *The social negotiation of ambiguous in-between stigmatized identities: Investigating identity processes in multiracial and bisexual people* (Doctoral dissertation). Paper 59. Retrieved from http://scholarworks.umb.edu/doctoral_dissertations/59

Kelley, W. (2006). *Psychological adjustment, behavior and health problems in multiracial young adults* (Doctoral dissertation). Retrieved from http://drum.lib.umd.edu/bitstream/1903/4224/1/umi-umd-4046.pdf

Kennedy, K. D., & Romo, H. D. (2013). "All colors and hues": An autoethnography of a multi-ethnic family's strategies for bilingualism and multiculturalism. *Family Relations, 62*(1), 109–124. Retrieved from http://colfa.utsa.edu/sociology/docs/publication_romo_colors.pdf

Kenny, C. B. (1989). *The field of play: A guide for the theory and practice of music therapy*. Atascadero, CA: Ridgeview Publishing.

Khanna, N. (2004). The role of reflected appraisals in racial identity: The case of multiracial Asians. *Social Psychology Quarterly, 67*(2), 115–131.

Khanna, N. (2010). "If you're half-black, you're just black": Reflected appraisals and the persistence of the one-drop rule. *The Sociological Quarterly, 51,* 96–121.

Laughlin, A. (2014, December 15). *"Half-Asian?" "Half-White?" No—"Hapa"* (Blog post). Retrieved from http://www.npr.org/sections/codeswitch/2014/12/15/370416571/half-asian-half-white-no-hapa

Lee, J., & Bean, F. D. (2004). America's changing color lines: Immigration, race/ethnicity, and multiracial identification. *Annual Review of Sociology, 30,* 221–242. doi:10.1146/annurev.soc.30.012703.110519

Lee, J., & Bean, F. D. (2007). Reinventing the color line: Immigration and America's new racial/ethnic divide. *Social Forces, 86*(2), 561–586.

Lee, J., & Bean, F. D. (2010). *The diversity paradox: Immigration and the color line in twenty-first century America*. New York, NY: Russell Sage Foundation.

Lee, W. M. L. (2004). Therapeutic considerations in work with biracial girls. *Women & Therapy, 27*(1–2), 203–216. doi:10.1300/J015v27n01_14

Leong, N. (2013). Half/Full. *Irvine Law Review*, 1125–1149. Retrieved from http://ssm.com/abstract=2246546

Maxwell, M. J., & Henriksen, Jr., R. C. (2012). Counseling multiple heritage adolescents: A phenomenological study of experiences and practices of middle school counselors. *Professional School Counseling, 16*(1), 18–28. doi:10.5330/PSC.n.2012-16.18

Mayor, C. (2012). Playing with race: A theoretical framework and approach for creative arts therapists. *The Arts in Psychotherapy, 39,* 214–219.

Miranda, D. (2012). The role of music in adolescent development: Much more than the same old song. *International Journal of Adolescence and Youth, 18*(1), 5–22. doi:10.1080/02673843.2011.650182

Miville, M. L., Constantine, M. G., Baysden, M. F., & So-Lloyd, G. (2005). Chameleon changes: An exploration of racial identity themes of multiracial people. *Journal of Counseling Psychology, 52*(4), 507–516. doi:10.1037/0022-0167.52.4.507

Mok, A., & Morris, M. W. (2009). Cultural chameleons and iconoclasts: Assimilation and reactance to cultural cues in biculturals' expressed personalities as a function of identity conflict. *Journal of Experimental Social Psychology, 45*(4), 884–889.

Montello, L. (1999). A psychoanalytic music therapy approach to treating adults traumatized as children. *Music Therapy Perspectives, 17*(2), 74–81. doi:10.1093/mtp/17.2.74

Moss, R. C., & Davis, D. (2008). Counseling biracial students: A review of issues and interventions. *Journal of Multicultural Counseling and Development, 36*(4), 219–230.

Nadal, K. L., Sriken, J., Davidoff, K. C., Wong, Y., & McLean, K. (2013). Microaggressions within families: Experiences of multiracial people. *Family Relations, 62*(1), 190–201.

Nadal, K. L., Wong, Y., Griffin, K., Sriken, J., Vargas, V., Wideman, M., & Kolawole, A. (2011). Microaggressions and the multiracial experience. *International Journal of Humanities and Social Science, 1*(7), 36–44.

Nagai, T. (2010). *Multiracial Identity and the U.S. Census.* ProQuest Discovery Guides. Retrieved from http://www.csa.com/discoveryguides/census/review.pdf

Nguyen, A. T. D., & Ahmadpanah, S. S. (2014). The interplay between bicultural blending and dual language acquisition. *Journal of Cross-Cultural Psychology, 45*(8), 1215–1220. doi:10.1177/0022022114542849

Nguyen, A. T. D., & Benet-Martinez, V. (2007). Biculturalism unpacked: Components, measurement, individual differences, and outcomes. *Social and Personality Psychology Compass, 1*(1), 101–114. doi:10.1111/j.1751-9004.2007.00029.x

Nittle, N. K. (n.d.). Five myths about multiracial people in the U.S. Retrieved from http://racerelations.about.com/od/understandingrac1/a/Five-Myths-About-Multiracial-People-In-The-U-S.htm

O'Brien, J. (2013). Muslim American youth and secular hip-hop: Manifesting "cool piety" through musical practices. *Poetics, 41*(2), 99–121.

Orloff, M. J. (2012). *The experience of community among biracial Americans identifying as Filipino and white* (Doctoral dissertation). Available from ProQuest Dissertations and Theses Database. (UMI No. 3539729)

Paxton, A., & Wade, P. (2011). Binational Americans: In their own words. *Global Public Health, 6*(3), 320–333.

Pipes, D., & Duran, K. (2002). Faces of American Islam: Muslim Immigrants. *Middle East Forum.* Retrieved from http://www.meforum.org/4104/faces-of-american-islam-muslim-immigration

Poston, W. S. C. (1990). The biracial identity development model: A needed addition. *Journal of Counseling & Development, 69,* 152–155.

Qian, Z. (2004). Options: Racial/ethnic identification of children of intermarried couples. *Social Sciences Quarterly, 85*(3), 746–766.

Rafieyan, R., & Hadley, S. (2013). "Does your family drive camels?" In S. Hadley (Ed.), *Experiencing race as a music therapist: Personal narratives.* Gilsum, NH: Barcelona Publishers.

Remedios, J. D., Chasteen, A. L., & Oey, E. (2012). "Unskilled" workers: Social skills stereotypes affect evaluations of biracial job applicants. *Basic and Applied Social Psychology, 34,* 204–211. doi:10.1080/01973533.2012.674451

Renn, K. A. (2008). Research on biracial and multiracial identity development: An overview and synthesis. *New Directions for Student Services, 123,* 13–21. doi:10.1002/ss.282

Richards, E., & Davies, A. (2002). Introduction. In A. Davies & E. Richards (Eds.), *Music therapy and group work: Sound company* (pp. 15–26). London, UK: Jessica Kingsley Publishers.

Rockquemore, K. A., & Brunsma, D. L. (2008). *Beyond Black: Biracial identity in America* (2nd ed.). Lanham, MD: Rowman & Littlefield.

Rockquemore, K. A., Brunsma, D. L., & Delgado, D. J. (2009). Racing to theory or theorizing race? Understanding the struggle to build a multiracial identity theory. *Journal of Social Issues, 65*(1), 13–34.

Rolvsjord, R. (2010). *Resource-oriented music therapy in mental health care.* Gilsum, NH: Barcelona Publishers.

Romo, R. (2008, April). *Blaxican identity: An exploratory study of Blacks/Chicanas/os in California.* Paper presented at the meeting of the National Association for Chicana and Chicano Studies Annual Conference, Austin, TX. Retrieved from http://scholarworks.sjsu.edu/naccs/2008/Proceedings/9/

Root, M. P. P. (1998). Experiences and processes affecting racial identity development: Preliminary results from the biracial sibling project. *Cultural Diversity and Mental Health, 4*(3), 237–247.

Root, M. P. P. (2002). *Ecological framework for understanding multiracial identity development.* Retrieved from http://www.drmariaroot.com/doc/EcologicalFramework.pdf

Root, M. P. P. (2003). 50 Experiences of racially mixed people. In M. P. P. Root & M. Kelley (Eds.), *The Multiracial Child Resource Book.* Seattle, WA: Mavin Foundation. Retrieved from http://www.drmariaroot.com/doc/50Experiences.pdf

Root, M. P. P. (2004). From exotic to a dime a dozen. *Women & Therapy, 27*(1), 19–31. Retrieved from http://search.proquest.com/docview/215890226?accountid=12536

Ruud, E. (2010). *Music therapy: A perspective from the humanities*. Gilsum, NH: Barcelona Publishers.

Schwartz, S. J., & Unger, J. B. (2010). Biculturalism and context: What is biculturalism, and when is it adaptive? Commentary on Mistry and Wu. *Human Development, 53*(1), 26–32. doi:10.1159/000268137

Searle, K. (n.d.). "A yellow-ass nigga"? Hip-hop and the "mixed race" experience. Retrieved from http://www.intermix.org.uk/academic/dr%20kevin%20searle.asp

Sims, J. P. (2012). Beautiful stereotypes: The relationship between physical attractiveness and mixed race identity. *Identities: Global Studies in Culture and Power, 19*(1), 61–80. doi:10.1080/1070289X.2012.672838

Smedley, A. (2007). *The History of the Idea of Race … and Why It Matters*. Paper presented at conference "Race, Human Variation and Disease: Consensus and Frontiers" (American Anthropological Association). Retrieved from http://www.understandingrace.org/resources/pdf/disease/smedley.pdf

Spencer, R. (2004). Assessing multiracial identity theory and politics: The challenge of hypodescent. *Ethnicities, 4*, 357–379.

Spencer, R. (2011). *Reproducing race: The paradox of Generation Mix*. Boulder, CO: Lynne Rienner Publishers. Retrieved from https://faculty.unlv.edu/spencer/Pages%20from%20ReproducingRace.pdf

Stige, B. (2002). *Culture-centered music therapy*. Gilsum, NH: Barcelona Publishers.

Stone, D. J. (2009). *Parent and child influences on the development of a black-white biracial identity* (Doctoral dissertation). Retrieved from http://scholar.lib.vt.edu/theses/available/etd-11162009-035955/unrestricted/Stone_DJ_D_2009.pdf

Suyemoto, K. L. (2004). Racial/ethnic identities and related attributed experiences of multiracial Japanese European-Americans. *Journal of Multicultural Counseling and Development, 32*(4), 206–221.

Swanson, M. L. (2013). So what are you anyway? *American Psychological Association*. Retrieved from http://www.apa.org/pi/families/resources/newsletter/2013/08/biracial-identity.aspx

Thornton, M. C. (2009). Policing the borderlands: White- and Black-American newspaper perceptions of multiracial heritage and the idea of race, 1996–2006. *Journal of Social Issues, 65*(1), 105–127. Retrieved from http://global.wisc.edu/multiracial/docs/josi_1590.pdf

Townsend, S. S. M., Wilkins, C. L., Fryberg, S. A., & Markus, H. R. (2012). Being mixed: Who claims a biracial identity? *Cultural Diversity and Ethnic Minority Psychology, 18*(1), 91–96. doi:10.1037/a0026845

Wardle, F. (2013, December 4). *Pushback of the pushback (Critiquing the recent attacks on the multiracial movement and multiracial people)* (Weblog post). Retrieved from http://csbchome.org/?p=45

Watts-Jones, T. D. (2010). Location of self: Opening the door to dialogue on intersectionality in the therapy process. *Family Process, 49*(3), 405–420.

Wijeyesinghe, C. (2012). The intersectional model of multiracial identity: Integrating multiracial identity theories and intersectional perspectives on social identity. In C. L. Wijeyesinghe & B. W. Jackson (Eds.), *New perspectives on racial identity development: Integrating emerging frameworks* (2nd ed., pp. 81–107). New York, NY: New York University Press.

Wilkinson, L. (2008, April). *Ethnic self-identification selectivity and educational progress among Latino adolescents*. Paper presented at the Population Association of America Annual Meeting, New Orleans, LA. Retrieved from http://paa2008.princeton.edu/papers/81559

Williams, M. T. (2011, December 27). *Color-blind ideology is a form of racism* (Weblog post). Retrieved from https://www.psychologytoday.com/blog/culturally-speaking/201112/colorblind-ideology-is-form-racism

Wyatt, R. C. (2008, June). *Kenneth V. Hardy on multiculturalism and psychotherapy*. Retrieved from https://www.psychotherapy.net/interview/kenneth-hardy

Resources

Blended People of America: http://blendedpeopleamerica.com

Blog post by Anna Stirling: "Dark-Skinned White Girls?" (May 6, 2010; http://feministing.com/2010/05/06/dark-skinned-white-girls/)

Ecological Framework for Understanding Multiracial Identity Development (Dr. Maria Root): http://www.drmariaroot.com/publications.php

Family Diversity Projects: http://familydiv.org/

Interracial Voice : http://www.interracialvoice.com/

IPride—Interracial, Intercultural Pride: http://www.ipride.org/

Jews in All Hues: http://www.jewsinallhues.org/about/

MAVIN: http://www.mavinfoundation.org/new/

Metisse Magazine: http://www.metisse.com/

Mixed Heritage Center—Information and Resources for People of Mixed Heritage: http://www.mixedheritagecenter.org/

Mixed Race Studies—Scholarly perspectives on the mixed race experience: http://www.mixedracestudies.org/

Mixed Remixed Festival: http://www.mixedremixed.org/about-mixed-remixed/

Project RACE—The national advocates for multiracial children, teens, adults, and our families: http://www.projectrace.com/

Swirl—A National Multi-Ethnic Organization: http://www.swirlinc.org/

The Asian-American Donor Program—Serving the Multi-Ethnic Communities: http://www.aadp.org/

The Center for the Study of Biracial Children: http://csbchome.org/

The Hapa Project (Kip Fulbeck): http://kipfulbeck.com/the-hapa-project/hapa-about/

The Multiracial Activist: http://multiracial.com/site/

Visualizing Race, Identity, and Change (Michelle Norris): http://proof.nationalgeographic.com/2013/09/17/visualizing-change/(Original article: http://ngm.nationalgeographic.com/2013/10/changing-faces/funderburg-text)

Glossary of Terms

Anti-miscegenation: The first anti-miscegenation laws came into being in 1691. These were designed to render unlawfumarriage between European settlers and those of African, Indian, or mixed heritage. In 1967, deciding the landmark case of *Loving v. Virginia,* the Supreme Court unanimously declared anti-miscegenation laws unconstitutional. Multicultural families in the United States celebrate Loving Day to commemorate this important decision.

Bi- or multicultural: Primarily refers to people who have incorporated core elements of more than one culture into their lives, such as languages, social norms, customs, and values.

Binational: May be a person or family of mixed heritage with one United States–born and one foreign-born parent or a person or family who moves from their country of origin to a new country and incorporates important aspects of the new culture into their life. May also be referred to as bi- or multicultural.

Border identity: People of mixed race/ethnicity who see themselves as fully, and more or less equally, expressing each of the aspects of their parental heritage.

Code switching: A concept that comes from linguistics, it has come to be associated with those who are multicultural/multiracial. It is used to describe the ability to easily switch between languages and/or cultural customs and norms. It relates closely to the idea of having a fluid identity.

Dual minority: A person whose mixed heritage includes two or more socially marginalized groups.

Fluid identity: Refers to an ability to identify and adopt the habits, languages, customs, behavioral expectations and norms of more than one culture or ethnicity.

Hafu: Hafu means "half" in Japanese. The word has various implications, both for people who are of mixed Japanese

heritage as well as for their families. Many who are half-Japanese self-identify as hafu; however, the term may also be used as a way of negatively singling out those who are not fully Japanese. Although the number of mixed-race children born in Japan are increasing rapidly, they are not fully accepted within the culture.

Hapa: Similar to "hafu," this word, identifying a person who is half–Pacific Islander or half-Hawaiian, has been used both as a racial slur and as a way to self-identify as being of mixed, or blended, heritage. Many do find the term offensive, so it needs to be used only with the individual's consent.

Hypodescent: More commonly known as the "one-drop rule." Starting in the late 1600s, any person with so much as one drop of African blood was to be considered Black. As with most statutes of the time, the driving force behind the initiative was social and economic advantage. The law significantly benefited White slave owners by designating any children born to enslaved Black women as part of the owner's property.

Mestizo/a: Mestizo/a is used in a variety of ways by people of Hispanic/Latino/a descent to indicate an ethnoracial mix of White and indigenous Latino/a heritage. Some prefer it and identify as such, while others do not.

Mulatto or mulato: "Mulatto" was first used in the late 1500s to describe people who had a specific percentage of Black-White racial mix. Some find it disrespectful, believing it comes from the Spanish term for mule, *mulo.* Spencer (2004) corrects this misperception, though, identifying it more accurately as having Arabic roots, based on the word *muwallad,* describing someone who is part Arab (p. 376). Racially mixed people who are of Hispanic/Latino/a and Black African heritage may also refer to themselves as mulato.

Passing: This is a term used to indicate a person whose skin tone may enable them to identify privately as one race but publicly as another. This may, for various reasons, be done for the purpose of fitting in with a particular racial/ethnic group with whom one prefers to identify or with a racial/ethnic group associated with greater privilege. Passing can be a source of guilt and remorse for some people who may feel they are pretending to be someone they are not. People who are of mixed heritage can often "pass" in a variety of circumstances.

Protean identity: People of mixed race/ethnicity who comfortably switch back and forth between racial/ethnic identities as situations warrant.

Reflected appraisal: This is the tendency of people to begin to look at themselves as others see them. In the case of people who are racially/ethnically mixed, this may mean, for example, racially, as the race other people perceive them to be.

Singular identity: People of mixed race/ethnicity who choose to identify exclusively with the heritage of one parent.

Transcendent identity: People of mixed race who reject the notion of race as a means of social categorization, preferring instead to be identified by personal characteristics and qualities having nothing to do with race.

Chapter 11

MUSLIM CULTURES

Paige A. Robbins Elwafi

The Beginning of My Journey

I was introduced to Islam when I was in college. Initially, I was intrigued by the Arabic language, the rich culture, and deeply spiritual beliefs of my Muslim friends. After spending seven years learning about the religion, meeting many Muslims, living in a Muslim country, and asking a lot of questions, I converted to Islam in 2006. Looking back, I see the seven years between learning about Islam and accepting the faith as a slow but deliberate journey. I have faced many myths about Islam and Muslim cultures. I have tried to ask a lot of questions and even experienced some stereotypes personally. Some of the experiences were very difficult, but within each trial is an opportunity to grow.

My music therapy practice and spiritual journey have been closely related to one another. Even though I made a decision to separate my spirituality from my music at one point in my journey, somehow they came back together again. I am finding that my spiritual journey and my work inspire one another. In this chapter, I hope to provide an overview of Islam and the general faith culture that accompanies Muslims worldwide. I hope to present an authentic introduction to the worldview, stereotypes, and cultural issues associated with the cultures of Muslims. By sharing my own experiences, as well as research and religious texts, I strive to educate the reader on the truth behind the stereotypes and the meaning of health and music in Muslim cultures.

The Basics of Islam

Islam means "submission" and comes from the root word of *salam,* meaning "peace." A person who submits to the will of Allah and believes in the five pillars of Islam is a *Muslim.* Muslims pray to God, or *Allah.* One becomes Muslim by saying the *Shahada,* or the declaration of faith. The five pillars of Islam are the foundation for the Muslim's faith, spirituality, and religious practice. The five pillars are (1) *Shahada,* the declaration of faith: belief in one God and that Muhammad, peace be upon him (PBUH), was the last Prophet of God; (2) *Salat:* praying five times per day; (3) *Sawm:* fasting during the holy month of Ramadan; (4) *Zakat:* purifying wealth by almsgiving; and (5) *Hajj:* completing the pilgrimage to Mecca at least one time during a specified time of the year. (PBUH is the abbreviation for "Peace be upon him." When Muslims mention the name of the Prophet Muhammad [PBUH], they are encouraged to say this small prayer to Allah to send peace and blessings to the Prophet [PBUH]. This is translated from the Arabic *Sahll Allahu nslated from the Ar* meaning, "May

Allah honor him and grant him peace". Allah to send peace and blessings to the Prophet [PBUH], not as a prayer to the Prophet Muhammad [PBUH].)

Muslims are provided with two primary guides in Islam to help them through life, the Qu'ran and the Sunnah of the Prophet Muhammad (PBUH). These guides help Muslims to grow personally and spiritually, as well as strive to attain lasting peace in this life and in the afterlife. The Qur'an (also spelled as Koran) is the heart of Islam. It is a guidance and one way Muslims can grow closer to Allah and attain peace in their lives. The Qur'an is the holy book of Islam and was revealed to the Prophet Muhammad (PBUH) by the Angel Gabriel (*Gibreel,* in Arabic) over a period of 23 years. The Qur'an has been preserved through recitation and transcription in its original form, with no changes made to the original Arabic. The Qur'an was not written by a human being. The author of the Qur'an is Allah (God), therefore it is a very sacred book and should be treated as such. Out of respect, non-Muslims should treat the actual book and the recitation with respect, even if it is something in which one does not personally believe. Many translations of the meaning of the Qur'an are available in various languages, so it is common to see the name of someone who has translated the meaning of the original Arabic. Because of the complexity and richness of the Arabic language, these translations of the Qur'an are only a translation of the meaning and not a literal, word for word, translation.

A word in Arabic can sometimes have many meanings, and sometimes the word in Arabic may not even have an English equivalent. When interpreting the meaning of the Qur'an, the context of the original revelation to the Prophet Muhammad (PBUH) needs to be taken into account when interpreting the meaning. Taking a verse of the Qur'an out of context from its original revelation can lead to poisoning rhetoric from all sides, including from inside Islam with uneducated or politically motivated Muslims to non-Muslims looking to villainize Islam. This reckless practice leads only to misunderstanding. Some translations of the Qur'an are far superior to others because they are thoughtfully written and take into account the context in which the *ayah,* or verse, (literally meaning "evidence" or "sign") was initially revealed to Muhammad (PBUH). It is an honored accomplishment for a Muslim to memorize all 114 chapters of the Qur'an, and millions of people have done this. Research shows that memorizing the Qur'an has a positive sociocultural impact on the individual's life, as well as augers enhanced academic achievement (Jahangir & Nawaz, 2014).

Muhammad (PBUH) had many companions in his lifetime,

because he was known as a trusted, loving, and gentle man. People came from all over the Arabian Peninsula and farther away to learn from him. Many of his companions observed and recorded his interactions with others, the things that he said, and his actions. The recordings of these things are known as *hadith*. The large collection of hadith make up the *Sunnah* or "path" of the Prophet Muhammad (PBUH). They are examples from his daily life. The Sunnah of Muhammad (PBUH) is very important for Muslims to learn because he is viewed as the best of mankind. Muslims only pray to God or *Allah,* so they do not pray to Muhammad (PBUH). In general, Muslims strive to live their lives according to Muhammad's (PBUH) most excellent character. Each hadith is categorized based on the person who related it and the strength of its validity. While this system dates back to the beginning of the religion more than 1,400 years ago, its scientific methodology is quite similar to research techniques used in modern times.

Islam encourages the remembrance of God or *Allah* at all times. As part of this remembrance, there is a special language that is used among Muslims. Sometimes, the language might be shared with those outside the faith, depending upon the situation, but it is typically reserved for interaction between Muslims. Some prominent phrases that Muslims use are *Inshallah,* which is a way of saying that if God wills something to happen it will happen, and *Alhamdulilah,* meaning "Thanks be to God." *Subhanallah* is another phrase used by many Muslims as a way to show wonder and amazement. One might say *subhanallah* at the sight of a beautiful rainbow or upon getting a nice surprise.

Worldview

The Worldview of a Muslim

The worldview of a Muslim will vary, depending upon his or her spirituality, religious practice, culture of heritage, regional culture, sect or branch of Islam (Sunni, Shia, Sufi, etc.) and family culture. Generally, the worldview of a Muslim is one that is focused on God and doing what is pleasing to Allah because He sees all and hears all. This can be seen as a strong theme in the Muslim's worldview. Whether the person is practicing or not practicing, one will typically remain steadfast to this principle of pleasing Allah. In general, Muslims strive not only to submit to the will of Allah in their lives but also to avoid evil. Like followers of other monotheistic religions, Muslims believe in the Devil or *Shaytan* (Satan). The Qur'an and Sunnah warn about Shaytan's strategies to get the believer to stray from the straight path of Islam. Each Muslim's personal battle between good and evil in his or her own self can influence worldview. This is also a way to define *jihad,* as one's personal struggle to overcome weaknesses and become a better person.

Family is a very important part of a Muslim's life. Much like pleasing Allah is a value, pleasing and serving one's family, particularly the mother and father, is paramount. There are verses in the Qur'an and hadith that state the importance of serving and pleasing one's parents, especially the mother. The Prophet Muhammad (PBUH) said that Paradise (heaven) lies at the feet of your mother. One of my favorite hadiths states:

> A man thus addressed the Prophet (PBUH):
> "O Messenger of Allah, who rightfully deserves the best treatment from me?"
> "Your mother," the Prophet (PBUH) said.
> "Then who?" the man asked again.
> "Your mother," replied the Prophet (PBUH).
> "Then who?" asked the man once again.
> "Your mother," said the Prophet (PBUH).
> The man asked once more, "Then who?"
> "Your father," said the noble Prophet (PBUH).
> (Al-Bukhari and Muslim)

Maintaining the ties of kinship is a responsibility for all Muslims. This may be challenging for converts, especially those whose families are not open to their change of religion and new way of life. As a new Muslim, I often felt estranged from my family. I felt that my decision to convert had disappointed them and changed our relationship. But, because I understood that maintaining ties to my family was my responsibility as a Muslim, I tried hard through the years to maintain my relationships to my family members. However, this was not an easy task because our beliefs and faith practices were different. Instead of dwelling on our differences, I learned to focus on our similarities, which helped us continue to build our relationship and eventually create new traditions that not only bridged the space between, but also embraced their faith and my new faith.

Another religious practice that influences the worldview of Muslims are the concepts of *halal* (ha-LAHL) and *haram* (ha-ROM). Halal is something that is "permissible," while haram is "forbidden." Certain things like food, clothing, and other activities are considered either halal or haram for Muslims to partake of or to participate in. The Qur'an and the hadith of the Prophet (PBUH) are guides for Muslims to know what is permissible and what is forbidden. Muslims should try their best to stay away from those things that are haram in order to please God and follow the Sunnah of the Prophet Muhammad (PBUH). Muslims believe that staying with the halal and avoiding the haram will help them to be better people and earn more good deeds. It can be difficult for Muslims living in or visiting Western countries, such as the United States, to stay away from forbidden things like drinking alcohol or being alone with members of the opposite sex. Being accepted in a Western culture as a practicing Muslim can be a challenge because his or her behavior could be seen as counter to the majority culture. The effects of globalization and increased availability of technology can also pose these same challenges in predominantly Muslim countries.

Historical Realities Versus Popular Myths

Stereotypes and Myths

Islam is a religion that is widely misunderstood in the United States. Many stereotypes and myths are pervasive within our culture. I have observed these in other people as well as within myself. After I put on the *hijab,* or the traditional Islamic head covering, I imagined that everyone who I came into contact with me judged me negatively. I would say to myself, "I bet they think I'm a terrorist" and "They probably assume my husband makes me cover my hair." I've experienced all of these myths, some bordering on microaggressions. Being a product of my culture, I believed the very same stereotypes before I took the time to educate myself. That is when I discovered how I had misjudged. Reflecting on my own journey, as well as consulting with family and friends, I will present seven myths that I feel cover several stereotypes facing Muslims.

Myth 1: Muslims Worship One of Many Gods Called Allah

Islam shares much history with other monotheistic religions, such as Judaism and Christianity. Muslims believe in all of the prophets and messengers sent to the Jews and the Christians, including Jesus (AS), or in Arabic, *'Isa;* Moses (AS), or *Musa,* and Noah (AS), or *Nuh.* (AS is an acronym for *'Alayhi Asalaam,* said after the names of the prophets who came before the Prophet Muhammad [PBUH] to pay respect to them.) Judaism, Christianity, and Islam are three of the monotheistic religions that share the same father, Abraham, or *Ibrahim* (AS) as he is known by Muslims. Muslims believe in one God and pray to only one God, or *Allah,* meaning "God" in Arabic. They do not pray to Muhammad (PBUH) or any other prophets. Just like Muslims, Arab Christians use the word *Allah* to call on God in their worship. Monotheism and not associating any other being or part of Creation with Allah is of monumental importance for Muslims. Associating others with Allah is called *shirk,* and it is a very serious sin for Muslims.

Myth 2: All Muslims Are Arab

Out of the estimated 1.6 billion Muslims worldwide, no more than 20% live in the Arab world (CAIR, 2012). It is true that the religion was initially revealed in early Arabia, known today as Saudi Arabia, to a man whose language and culture was Arabic. However, as Islam spread, people who were not Arab joined the religion, including those from other lands and cultures. The Prophet Muhammad (PBUH) honored the cultures of non-Arabs and encouraged them to celebrate and share their traditions that were beneficial, while altering only those that were clearly detrimental (Abd-Allah, 2004). Today, the Arabs are the growing minority among Muslims, unlike popular stereotypes lead us to believe. In fact, Indonesia has the largest Muslim population in the world (CAIR, 2012). Indonesia is followed in second place by India; third, Pakistan; fourth, Bangladesh; and fifth, Nigeria (Pew Research Center, 2012b). The top three regions of the world in which Muslims live are Asia Pacific, Middle East and North Africa, and sub-Saharan Africa. Europe, Latin America and the Caribbean, and North America hold the next three smaller populations of Muslims in the world.

Myth 3: Islam Oppresses Women and Favors Men

This was one myth of which it took a long time for me to let go when I was learning about Islam. My thoughts had been influenced by what I had read and seen in the media and entertainment. It was difficult for me to put on the hijab because I couldn't understand it for a long time. I never thought I would wear it. When I converted to Islam, I went through an identity crisis. When I started wearing the hijab to religious events, I noticed how much more at ease I felt. The protection that the hijab offers is like nothing I have ever experienced. Putting on the hijab was the most outward step I could take to help me merge my new identity with the old identity I had known all of my life.

I believe a common myth is that Muslim women are oppressed. The modest dress, head scarf, and misunderstood roles as a wife, mother, or daughter can contribute to prejudice. Women have long been oppressed by men in the history of the world. Prior to the beginning of Islam, the society of Arabia was full of oppressive practices against women, such as treating them as property, prostitution, and female infanticide (Rahman, 1989). Islam gave rights to women and put an end to these oppressive practices.

For centuries, women have covered their bodies and valued modesty, no matter their religion or beliefs. It is just been in the past 15 to 20 years that women have started "uncovering," by wearing more revealing clothing and fashions. Now it seems that society views women as more liberated and feminine when they uncover their bodies. Mary, the mother of Jesus, is always depicted as being covered. Orthodox and observant Jewish women typically cover their hair. In the past, Catholic nuns covered, and they still continue to dress modestly. The Muslim woman's *hijab* is not only a head covering, but also a way of dressing and a behavior that honors her modesty and uniqueness. The hijab is worn only in front of men with whom a woman does not share a blood relation or her *mahraam.* A woman is not required to cover in front of her brothers, father, uncles, and father-in-law, and therefore most women do not wear the hijab when they are at home or when they are in the company of other women. The hijab is typically not viewed as a requirement for Muslim women, but it is encouraged.

While the Prophet Muhammad (PBUH) is scrutinized for having multiple wives, the fact is that this was common practice at the time. The practice of polygamy served many different purposes at that time. First, and most important, polygamy gave widowed or divorced women protection and sustenance. Otherwise, women without a husband would have no income to live by and raise their children, as it was not common for women to work outside of the home at that time. Some of Muhammad's (PBUH) marriages were made for political reasons and to create peace with another group. In addition, his marriages provided many examples of how to deal with conflicts, educate one another, raise children, and support the community at large. The Prophet (PBUH) valued women; he warned men to be fair and loving to their wives and families. A'isha, one of the Prophet's (PBUH) wives, reported that he said, "Among the believers who show most perfect faith are those who have the best disposition and are kindest to their families" (Al-Sufi, n.d.). Islam teaches that women and men are equal in the sight of Allah. It is a man's responsibility to be good to his wife and treat her as a partner, not as a servant. Any oppression we see of Muslim women today can be attributed to corrupt government, cultures of heritage, regional cultures, and misuse of power.

Myth 4: Islam Is a Religion That Does Not Accept Other Faiths

Islam shares a rich history with Jews and Christians. Muslims are told by Allah in the Qur'an to honor the People of the Book. Examples from the Prophet Muhammad's (PBUH) life show that he taught Muslims to respect people of other faiths, particularly the Jews and Christians . The Qur'an shares stories from the Jewish and Christian beliefs. The Qur'an speaks at length about Moses (AS), Jesus (AS), and Mary, the mother of Jesus (AS). The Qur'an includes the story of Jesus' birth, in Surah Mariam, although it is different from the version familiar to Christians. Muslims believe that from Abraham to Muhammad (PBUH), all of the prophets and messengers were teaching the same message, to worship God, and only God. Muslims believe that Islam is God's final message, building upon what was sent to the Jews and the Christians. Unity with other believers is an important aspect of Islam.

The first man to confirm Muhammad's (PBUH) prophethood was a Christian. Receiving the first revelation of the Qur'an was very distressing for Muhammad (PBUH) because he had had a close interaction with the archangel Gabriel. He was afraid he was losing his mind because of what he had heard and experienced. After the revelation, he immediately went to his wife Khadija and told her what had happened. She suggested they talk to her cousin Waraqa ibn Nawfal, who was a Christian scholar and priest, and explain what had happened. Based on his knowledge of the holy books, Waraqa ibn Nawfal confirmed the revelation and Muhammad's (PBUH) prophethood.

As Islam spread, Jews and Christians were consulted and even provided protection by Muslims. If they did not convert to Islam, the Prophet (PBUH) accepted their decision, gave them respect, and encouraged them to follow their holy books and not compromise their faith (Zain, 2012). One hadith from the Prophet Muhammad (PBUH) states, "He who wrongs a Jew or a Christian will have myself as his accuser on the Day of Judgment" (Al-Bukhari). The moral responsibility that accompanies this statement describes the true nature of the religion and the example that Muslims should follow. Dialogue between Muslims and people from other faiths is valuable. This is especially true in diverse societies such as the United States. I have found that most Muslims respect the beliefs of non-Muslims, even though there may be some practices that they do not share.

Myth 5: Islam Is a Religion That Promotes Violence, Terrorism, and War

In 2007, someone forwarded me an email from a friend condemning Islam. After researching the name of the man mentioned in the email, I found that the claims were a fabrication. I addressed the accusations as best as I could with the little knowledge I had as a new Muslim. Then, in 2011, the same email was forwarded to me from a family friend, claiming that Islam is a religion of violence and that the Qur'an tells Muslims to kill the infidels. I wasn't accustomed to having my faith and identity attacked so blatantly. It was difficult to adjust to, especially because I had such a love for the faith that I had embraced. Nadal et al. (2012) give six themes that were synthesized from two focus groups they conducted with American Muslims. One theme they discuss is the topic, "Endorsing religious stereotypes of Muslims as terrorists." The researchers give examples of how the participants or people close to them were assumed to be linked to terrorists. One participant who was a convert reported that her brother had asked if she heard about when the next bombing would happen when she went to the mosque.

Many verses of the Qur'an warn of the evils of murder. If anyone kills a person unjustly, it is as if he killed all of mankind. There are verses in the Qur'an that justify killing for retribution of an injustice. When confusion arises, it is best to return to the human example for Muslims, the Prophet Muhammad (PBUH). It is true that the first Muslims were required to fight in battles against their enemies, but this was not the first response to the ridicule and abuse they experienced. Muhammad (PBUH) and his followers patiently endured 13 long years of public condemnation, torture, and death; an embargo that resulted in many starving to death; and exile from their homeland. Only after the Muslims had dealt with these many hardships and tried everything in their power to negotiate with their enemies to no positive end were they were given the order by Allah to rise up and fight. If we look at the verses of the Qur'an about fighting and killing in context with the history of the religion, it provides the whole picture, doesn't serve one political agenda or another, and reaffirms the general nonviolence of the faith. This context-based interpretation of the Qur'an and the life of the Prophet Muhammad (PBUH) shows Islam to be a religion that is above ethnic or regional cultural interpretations.

Myth 6: Muhammad (PBUH) Was a Violent Man Who Spread Islam by the Sword

As someone who was new to the religion, it was difficult for me to gain a true understanding of the Prophet Muhammad (PBUH). Before I became interested in Islam, I had learned myths about Muhammad (PBUH): that he was a violent man, murderer, and oppressor of women. These false depictions of the Prophet (PBUH) clouded my view. Since I had been raised as a Christian, it was challenging for me to connect with Muhammad (PBUH) as I had with Jesus (AS), because Muhammad (PBUH) is not viewed as a deity or the son of God in Islam.

The absence of a visual representation of the Prophet (PBUH) also made it difficult for me to connect with him. Muhammad (PBUH) taught his followers to avoid drawing pictures of him or creating statues. This was taught to differentiate Islam from the idol worshipers of Mecca at the time when Islam was revealed. It was also practiced to prevent Muslims from worshiping Muhammad (PBUH). As a Christian, I was a very visual believer. Some of my most deeply spiritual moments in my Christian journey were when I was praying and looking at the crucifix or religious statues. Muslims are encouraged to read the Qur'an and meditate upon Allah's Creation to feel closer to him, for Allah is all around us. There are many beautiful, detailed poems describing Muhammad's (PBUH) appearance. Some of these poems have been put into songs, such as the *Burda*. I have found these to be a meaningful way of knowing him. In this way, I don't rely on an artist's visual depiction of him; instead, I use my imagination. One of my favorite stories describes the Prophet (PBUH) as more beautiful and radiant than the full moon.

Sacred music and chants called "nasheeds" were another way I learned more about the Prophet (PBUH). These are special songs about Muhammad (PBUH) that are sung and can be accompanied by percussion. Modern Muslim musicians and artists have contributed to my growing connection with the Prophet Muhammad (PBUH). CelebrateMercy.com is an organization that was founded to teach people about Muhammad (PBUH) and to tell the story of his life. Celebrate Mercy's educational webcasts have helped me in this process of learning more about the Prophet Muhammad (PBUH). It is a very good resource for non-Muslims as well to learn more about him.

Muhammad (PBUH) was a truly magnificent man. Before being given prophethood, Muhammad (PBUH) was known as *Al-Amin*, the trusted one. Muhammad (PBUH) was faced with so much hardship and sadness in his life, yet he remained steadfast to his purpose and mission. He was an orphan, losing his mother and father in childhood. Later, he had seven children, all of whom died in his lifetime except for one daughter, Fatima, who survived her father. The ways in which he (PBUH) persevered through many trials and tribulations have helped me in difficult times because his suffering gives mine perspective.

Myth 7: The Crescent Moon Is a Symbol of Islam

While the crescent moon is sometimes associated as a symbol of Islam, there is no universal symbol or banner of the religion. Especially in the time of Muhammad (PBUH), there was explicitly no symbol associated with Islam, to distinguish the Muslims from the Jews and Christians, who did have religious symbols. However, the majority of mosques or masjids in the United States do often have a crescent moon on the *minaret* or tower. One will typically see this only in North America; this may be practiced as a way to distinguish these places of worship for the Muslims, but this is not from a Sunnah of the Prophet Muhammad (PBUH).

There are 12 months in the Islamic calendar, which is a lunar calendar. The Islamic calendar is approximately 11 days shorter than the Gregorian calendar, so it changes every year (Islamicity, n.d.). The sighting of the new moon signifies the start of the new lunar month and can be difficult to do with the naked eye. The crescent moon is associated with the new lunar month in Islam, especially the month of Ramadan. The lunar calendar requires a Muslim to be in touch with nature and the stages of the moon.

Some countries and Islamic organizations, such as the Islamic Association of North America (ISNA), will accept if the new moon has been sighted in another country to begin the new month or end the month. This is especially important during the time of Ramadan. Due to waiting for the moon sighting, the new holy month may be projected to begin or end on a certain day, but if the moon is not sighted, the month will not commence. The two Islamic holidays, or *Eids* (meaning "Day of Celebration"), are always on a different day each year and depend on the moon sighting. Although I was accustomed to the set days of Christian holidays, I have adjusted to the lunar calendar with this natural element of the crescent moon sighting. It makes me pay more attention to Creation and the natural cycle of time, yet it is deeply connected to the earth. It gives me a greater respect for the beauty of nature. It also helps me to remember Allah through His Creation, which contributes to my worship.

Diversity Within Muslim Cultures

In the following section, I will do my best to touch upon the diversity of cultures among Muslims and some of the inherent challenges. Islam is the second largest religion in the world. According to the Pew Research Center (2012b), it is estimated that there is a total of 1.6 billion Muslims worldwide. Muslims live all over the world, and each ethnicity brings its own special cultural richness to the Islam it practices. Some of these cultural practices may go against the teachings of Islam. Abd-Allah (2004) courageously gets to the heart of the many cultural issues that Muslims encounter. Abd-Allah explains that culture is successful when it creates social cohesion and identity. Unfortunately, these are two aspects missing from many Muslim cultures, especially for those living in the West. For

Muslims today, cultural discord and confusion are irritated by the clash of Old World expectations with the complex needs and opportunities of our modern society.

When looking at these cultural issues, it is important to note that culture plays a dynamic role in Islam, especially since the cultural diversity among Muslims is so wide. This was an important issue that the Prophet Muhammad (PBUH) dealt with. He encouraged the cultural traditions that were good or beneficial for people, while decrying those that were clearly detrimental (Abd-Allah, 2004).

Gender Differences Within the Cultures

The role of men and women in Muslim cultures is one of much controversy. The laws of Islam (shari'a), the Qur'an, and Sunnah support a society in which Muslim women and men are equal. The nature of this ideal society on a macro level and family on a micro level is collectivistic, valuing the group above the individual. Viewing these gender roles from an individualistic perspective, as most Western cultures are oriented, can create the image that the roles of men and women in Islam are unequal. When the bigger picture is taken into account and one is able to look at it with awareness of his or her biases, gender roles in Muslim cultures fit the needs of the general culture well. There are cases in which this is taken to an extreme, especially in societies where the shari'a is taken as the law of the land. Shari'a is a very full and complicated subject (also called Fiqh), so much so that Muslim scholars spend years navigating the laws and how they should be applied to modern day. Shari'a, or Fiqh, is not a topic to be taken lightly and by someone who is not a scholar. Thus it will not be discussed further within this chapter.

Gender differences regarding the treatment of women in marriage and their role in the community are often a subject of controversy. Females have the same rights that males do, including those to an education and independent income, yet some women struggle with getting permission from their family or husband to work. When a Muslim girl reaches the age of puberty, she may cover her hair and dress modestly, if she so desires. The hijab is not compulsory in the religion. It is encouraged as a protection and a way to honor women. Still, many Western women see these practices in Muslim cultures as oppressive and unfair. Esposito and Mogahed (2007) found that Western women felt that Muslim women did not have equal status in their societies, while the Muslim women surveyed said that their rights were equal and were not concerned about their status. Interestingly, the Muslim women surveyed felt that promiscuity, pornography, and public indecency in Western societies were a sign of women's degraded status in those cultures.

A Muslim woman has the right to marry any man whom she chooses, with guidance from her family. Her husband should be Muslim or agree to convert to Islam. Unfortunately, it is common to hear of families pressuring their daughter to marry a certain person, not allowing her to actually choose her partner. Not all families practice this, but it is a common problem. Arranged marriages are a problem all over the world, especially in developing countries. It is an issue not only among Muslims, but also for other faiths as well. There are specific rites and responsibilities in Islam for both men and women when looking for a partner and in marriage. Unfortunately, the family may try to take away a person's right to choose a partner based on the ideal social status, education, and salary or occupation of the prospective spouse.

Domestic violence is a serious problem worldwide, and Muslims are no different. Violence in any form between a man and his wife is not acceptable in Islam. Muslims believe that children, spouses, and even our own bodies are an Amana, or trust, from Allah. If one harms another person unjustly (emotionally, psychologically, or physically), it is a grave sin and highly disrespectful. Unfortunately, the intersection of Islam and the dominant culture does not always allow these positive beliefs to shine through. Through the lens of the ethnic and regional culture, domestic violence can be ignored, or, worse, the victim is told to be patient, or have sabr. This unfortunate interpretation is accepted by many Muslims. One possible reason for this acceptance may be that Muslims believe that everything, the good and bad, comes from Allah. Yasmin Mogahed (2012), a Muslim writer and speaker in the United States, has spoken on this topic. She reminds Muslims that it is important to stop someone who is oppressing others, as in a domestic situation. The reminder comes from a hadith of the Prophet Muhammad (PBUH). The Prophet (PBUH) said:

> "Help your brother if he is an oppressor or oppressed." A man said, "Messenger of Allah, I can help him if he is oppressed but tell me how I can help him if he is the oppressor?" He said, "Prevent him from oppressing. That is helping him." (Sahih Bukhari)

Being outside of the home is a role typically reserved for men in Muslim cultures, although this is changing. A number of rulings regarding the mixing of males and females exist, so a Muslim may feel more comfortable talking to someone of the same sex. When interacting with a person of the opposite sex, a Muslim is encouraged to lower his or her gaze, as well as avoid shaking hands or hugging. Also, men and women who are not blood relatives or married should not be alone together. These things should be kept in mind for the music therapist working with a Muslim client.

Traditionally, Muslim women have one of the most important roles in the community, which is to care for the children and home. This may not seem important from an individualistic worldview, but many Muslims see it as essential to a balanced family. This is not to say that women should not be given the opportunity to be leaders or contribute to society in ways outside of raising children and keeping the home. They certainly do deserve that opportunity, and there is support for women contributing in these ways. However, in Islam, a woman's primary responsibility is to her children and family.

Generational and Migrational Differences

The migration of Muslims throughout the world, as well as generational differences, contributes to even more of the diversity and complexity of Muslim cultures. There are significant differences between generations of Muslims in their commitment to religious practice. The Pew Research Center (2012a) recently conducted a study looking at the diversity among practicing Muslims worldwide. The survey found that the older generations were more religiously committed than people 18 to 34 years of age.

As Abd-Allah (2004) explained, one of the primary conflicts for Muslims is the clash between Old World attitudes and the ever-changing needs of modern society. Modern issues like drug abuse, pornography, and alcoholism affect Muslim communities in the United States just as much as the majority culture. Unfortunately, there is a high degree of avoidance and denial of the effects of these issues in Muslim communities. The moral parameters of the religion are often seen as an automatic protection from the *haram* or forbidden, but there are many problems with this type of logic. Muslim communities need to work together to help both younger and older Muslims deal with these issues. There is natural support within the religion to deal with these issues, as long as communities look at it realistically, especially for young people. Goforth et al. (2014) looked at acculturative stress for Muslim Arab-American adolescents. They found that Muslim Arab-American adolescents who associated with Islam experienced less acculturative stress. Religious coping and community support could contribute to the experience of less stress.

Migration differences within Muslim cultures are generally well accepted. The wide diversity of Muslims just in my small community was surprising to me when I first accepted Islam. I had not realized how international Islam is and has been for centuries. I assumed that the Middle East was the primary place where Muslims lived. I was surprised to meet Muslims from many countries in Africa and eastern Europe, Indonesia, Malaysia, and China. My mind was opened when I went to the mosque for my first Eid celebration and experienced the diversity and richness of different types of clothing, ethnicities, and languages. I really loved feeling connected to something that was able to reach so many different people and cultures.

The Prophet Muhammad (PBUH) was committed to preserving the cultural diversity of the Muslims, and especially those from different cultures than his own. Abd-Allah (2004) shares a story about something that happened during the Prophet's (PBUH) time. In a religious celebration, a group of African converts to Islam started to dance with spears in the mosque. One of the close companions to the Prophet Muhammad (PBUH) tried to stop the dance, but the Prophet (PBUH) intervened. He even brought his wife A'isha to watch the dance and encouraged them by saying, "Play your games, sons of Arfida, so the Jews and Christians know there is latitude in our religion" (Abd-Allah, 2004).

Assimilation

Since I have put on the head scarf, I am often asked, "So, where are you from?" I have learned to reply with a smile and say, "I'm American, from Indiana." When the assuming person's surprise is evident with "Oh, really? Wow, that's nice," I then follow up with "Yes, I'm American. I was born here in America." I never had these experiences as a Caucasian girl from the Midwest, so they were at first a little annoying, but now I'm just happy that someone feels comfortable enough to ask questions.

Assimilation is defined by Maki and Kitano (2002, p. 113) as "... the process of acculturation and becoming 'Americanized'." Acculturation can be viewed as the degree to which a person identifies with his or her native culture. This can be a complicated issue for Muslims, depending upon generation, location, migration, immigration, and commitment to the religion. Whether or not the person is born into the religion or is a convert may also affect the process of assimilation. With the infiltration of Western ideals and globalization, many native cultures of Muslims are becoming mixed. I used to believe that Muslims living in the Islamic world face less challenges in navigating and defining culture, but this is changing with the influx of technology, social media, and the growing divide between the older generation and the needs of the younger generation, as Abd-Allah (2004) discusses.

Minority Stress and Discrimination

When I converted to Islam, not only did my worldview begin to change, but my status in society did as well. The reality of this shift hit me all at once, but the actual effects have taken longer to settle. Putting on the hijab made that shift from a majority culture member to an American minority physically clear. The hijab was the link to a new role in society for me. It would shape my behavior, give new dynamics to my relationships, alter my physical appearance, and influence how others perceive me. These changes affected every aspect of my life, including my work as a music therapist. In an attempt to adjust to this shift and new way of life, I pursued avenues of research and practice to connect my past with my present. I was also trying to bring about peace with my family and friends, who did not fully understand these changes in my life.

I struggled with finding a job, which I attribute in part to my head scarf. In searching for services for myself and my family, I found it necessary to protect my Muslim American identity, especially for my daughter. I had to be on guard at all times to avoid the influence of the majority culture that holds conflicting values from mine as a Muslim. The most troubling part was when I went to the Muslim community for help. I found the resources to be quite limited. On more than one occasion I was given advice that was not helpful for my personal situation and not contextual. I finally began to navigate my way with the help of Muslim friends who listened to me tell of my struggles. They worked to find help for me from other resources, but this affected the process of assimilation to my new culture.

There has been a noted increase in discrimination and hate crimes toward Muslims since the 9/11 attacks and the wars in Iraq and Afghanistan (Nadal et al., 2012). Any time there is a terrorist attack in the world, discrimination and hate crimes against Muslims also increase. These include the burning of mosques, bomb threats, physical and verbal assaults, profiling, and employment discrimination. Those Muslims who blend in and "pass" for majority culture members may not experience as much discrimination and microaggressions. Blatant religious discrimination is detrimental to the identity, health, and well-being of Muslim Americans and their communities (Nadal et al., 2012). While many studies look at stereotypes and microaggressions against American Muslims, few if any look at the actual psychological impact of that stress on the population.

The discrimination that minorities feel is real and painful. On top of that, the intensity of the hatred and aggression that Muslims experienced after September 11 created a whole new layer of stress. For me, that stress is always present and can arise at any time, even with an unintended comment or action. Those moments are sometimes the hardest, when I realize how much more work needs to be done for the sake of understanding and peace. As time passes, it heals wounds, but these wounds are re-opened easily with any negative action made by people who are Muslims or claim to be "Muslims," yet demonstrate no respect for human life. The media contributes to this as well, especially those who are so quick to blame Islamic extremists or Muslims for any violence committed in the world. This all contributes to the continuation of the cycle of ignorance, violence, and stereotypes that adds to the complexity of minority stress for Muslims.

Meaning of Medicine and Well-Being

In Islam, balance between emotional, mental, and physical health is valued and promoted through many different aspects of the religion. Muslims follow the Qur'an and examples from the life of the Prophet Muhammad (PBUH) to strive toward a path of well-being and balance. This includes staying away from things that are haram or forbidden and taking part in things that are halal or permissible. The religion provides support and guidance in matters related to everyday life, including things such as cleaning one's body, eating, going to the bathroom, and sleeping. Fasting during Ramadan and throughout the year provides a special cleansing for the body as well. It also provides a guide for spiritual, physical, psychological, and emotional wellness.

Muslims believe in Allah's qadr or predestination. In the Qur'an, Allah says that all things come from him, including the good and the bad. Because Muslims believe that Allah is The Merciful, The Healer, and The Protector, we try our best to trust

in His plan for us. If that plan includes illness or good health, we try to accept what comes from Allah and better ourselves through what He has given us. Muslims are told by Allah in the Qur'an that with difficulty and trials also comes ease. This attitude connects life experiences, including health, with the spiritual world for a Muslim. The daily prayer that is prescribed for Muslims is an opportunity for Muslims to maintain their mental, physical, emotional, and spiritual health (Rahman, 1989). Du'a, or personal prayers to Allah, can be another way to deal with hardship and illness. Muslims believe that enduring pain or sickness atones for sins (Al-Qarni, 2003). This comes from a hadith of the Prophet Muhammad (PBUH) in which he said: "Worry, anxiety, pain, fatigue, sickness, or even a thorn that pricks him— when a believer is afflicted with any of these, Allah grants him pardon for some of his sins (through or because of those afflictions)" (Al-Qarni, 2003).

The Muslim afflicted with an illness or pain can receive blessings from patiently dealing with that affliction. I was surprised when my friends asked me to remember them in du'a during the labor and birth of my first child. But it is well known among Muslims that the du'a of a woman in labor is very special and accepted by Allah. Muslims are also encouraged to visit the ill and imprisoned. Hadiths exist that explain that a person is accompanied by angels on his or her way to visit a sick person. The Prophet Muhammad (PBUH) would regularly visit people in their homes after the third day of their illness (Rahman, 1989). Visiting the sick is important for many Muslims.

Necessary medical or psychological treatment is not typically discouraged for Muslims. In fact, if one has access to medical technology or treatment, he or she should utilize it because Allah has provided that access (Rahman, 1989). Many traditional healing techniques are practiced worldwide in Muslim cultures. Most of these healing practices date back to the time of the Prophet Muhammad (PBUH) and are typically accompanied by reciting certain verses of the Qur'an. This is sometimes referred to as prophetic medicine. Some Muslims may be resistant or suspicious of Western medical treatments and medicine. These situations should be handled delicately by health care professionals as well as family or community members who can support the patient spiritually (Tuell, 2011).

The Meaning of Music in Muslim Cultures

Music is a controversial topic in Islam and among Muslims. When I worked in the Persian Gulf as a music therapist, I learned that listening to music and playing musical instruments is not widely accepted in many Muslim cultures, especially in this part of the world. The diverse thought on the topic can be traced back to the hadith of the Prophet Muhammad (PBUH) and some verses from the Qur'an. One stance on the restrictions of music is that the use of wind and string instruments is haram or forbidden (Elwafi, 2007). This dates back to the time of the Prophet Muhammad (PBUH). When Islam was revealed, the society of Mecca was corrupt and violent. Prostitution, gambling, and intoxicants were used heavily, mainly in establishments where music was played. Music often accompanied the immoral behavior, so as a way to stop those behaviors, musical instruments were discouraged.

Another approach to this issue encourages Muslims to avoid music that contains themes that are profane, immoral, or degrading to the human spirit (Elwafi, 2007). This covers a large amount of popular music today. This line of thought focuses less on the instruments used in the music and more on the messages in the music. Muslims, who avoid this kind of music, feel that listening to the messages that are degrading and immoral will affect the heart and soul, influencing them to follow a path that is not focused on pleasing Allah.

Likewise, music that uplifts the human soul, containing ethical and noble messages, is considered permissible or halal by some Muslims (Elwafi, 2007). There is much gray area between those holding the stance that all music is haram and should be avoided and those who focus more on the message of the music. Culture, religious practice, and personal preferences all come into play when defining the role of music in Muslim cultures. The geographical area can also influence a culture's acceptance of music if it is highly integrated into the cultural landscape. Morocco and Turkey are good examples of this, due to the influence from Sufism and its central role of music in worship (Elwafi, 2011).

A Muslim's acceptance of music and the role it plays in his or her life is often an independent choice, so music therapists should try to understand the issues and respect the client's choice. Muslims are encouraged to read, recite, and listen to the Qur'an. The most meaningful and beautiful sounds and words on Earth come from the Qur'an, so Muslims are encouraged to listen to the Qur'an instead of music. Nasheeds (also known as *annasheed*) are songs about Islam and the Prophet Muhammad (PBUH). These songs are performed with voice only and at other times with voice and drumming. While nasheeds are widely recognized, the type of instrumentation that is accepted will vary (Elwafi, 2007). Many nasheed artists will provide recordings of all of the songs on an album with voice only as well as percussion with voice to respect the differences on the topic. "Music" as it is known in the West can be seen by some Muslim cultures as secular and should therefore not be connected to the Qur'an in any way. However, there is a growing movement among Muslim musicians to create a positive alternative to mainstream popular music for those looking for a creative outlet to add to their spiritual practice. In a way, some see this movement as returning to the traditional roots of healing musical forms in some practices of Islam.

The recitation of the holy Qur'an is a unique style of chanting that contains certain melodic traits. The techniques used in recitation of the Qur'an are called *tajweed*. There are a variety of tajweed techniques, creating several different styles of recitation and sound. It is very important to understand that Qur'an recitation is not considered music (Elwafi, 2011). It would be disrespectful to say that the recitation of the Qur'an is music, so making this type of statement should be avoided. Musical instruments and singing are not permitted in the mosque for worship and prayer services. This was a foreign idea for me as a convert from Christianity, where worship services are often filled with music and singing. It is also not permissible for a Muslim woman to sing publicly in front of men. This is another practice that is very different from those of other faith cultures.

Enabling Health and Well-Being

Because Islam is an all-encompassing religion that touches on all aspects of life, when it is practiced properly, it should result in a well-balanced society and people. Unfortunately, this is not the reality for the Muslim community worldwide. Education of the public, assessment of the needs of Muslims, and development of programs and organizations in the community can help to support a healthy cultural identity to improve health and well-being for Muslims.

First, it is essential that Muslims accept the responsibility to educate the public, both non-Muslims and Muslims, about Islam. Much ignorance exists in the public as well as Muslim communities, so this must be addressed and education must be taken seriously. Interfaith cooperation, promoting mutual understanding, and cross-cultural communication can facilitate internal diversity for Muslim communities (Abd-Allah, 2004).

Second, the needs of Muslim communities should be assessed and a plan made that meets these needs. This assessment will likely be unique to each community's location, demographics, and resources. Minority stress and access to resources such as affordable housing, health care, education, and employment should be seriously considered. Is the community open to exploring what the real needs of its members are, even if they doesn't meet their traditional expectations? Abd-Allah (2004) stresses the importance of identifying problems honestly and seeking viable solutions that are based in the foundation of Islam and looking to the future with intelligence as well as creativity.

Seeking mental health treatment has long been associated with stigma in the United States. This has been a major problem for Muslims as well. Many Muslims pretend that mental illness doesn't exist in their communities (Eshmawi, 2007). Some cultures believe that mental illness is caused by evil spirits, and they often do not accept the role of genetics as a factor (Ciftci, Jones, & Corrigan, 2013). However, domestic violence, dysfunctional families, drug addiction, and mental illness are rapidly rising in American Muslim communities. Organizations such as MentalHealth4Muslims.com promote understanding and acceptance of mental health issues in Muslim communities. The *Journal of Muslim Mental Health* is an online, interdisciplinary, peer-reviewed journal seeking to provide culturally and religiously relevant research for professionals serving Muslims. Also, American Muslim Health Professionals is a nonprofit organization that is working to address health issues for Americans, especially those who are underserved and minorities. All of these groups could be good resources for music therapists who work with Muslim clients.

Developing programs and organizations that can meet the emerging needs of Muslim minorities is essential. Abd-Allah (2004) recommends the development of special medical clinics, political involvement, establishing educational institutions, investing in the arts, and translating Islamic texts to English. Abd-Allah points to the importance of counseling and working to find solutions for domestic violence, substance abuse, and psychological disorders among Muslims. These proposed solutions should involve religious leaders and imams in Muslim communities. Ali and Milstein (2012) found that imams of mosques in the United States whom they surveyed would be able to recognize the severity of a mental health problem for someone in their community. They also found that imams would be willing to refer a congregant to a mental health provider while continuing to counsel that person themselves.

Suggestions for Music Therapists

As Bradt (1997) recommends, the importance of assessing the role of music in the client's culture is essential for the music therapist, especially when working with a client from a different culture than his or her own. Given the controversial role of music in Islam, as well as compounding minority stress, issues of assimilation, and the process of acculturation, music therapists working with Muslim clients should pay special attention to these matters. The role of music in a Muslim's life is often a personal choice. When a referral is made, talking with the client or his/her guardian about the role of music in their lives is important. Music therapy services may not be recommended for the client due to religious beliefs and cultural limitations. In my experience, when music is used as a type of medicine to help the Muslim client, its use may be permissible, but this is truly a personal choice (Elwafi, 2007). Some clients may wish to consult with their imam or other religious leader.

Other cultural differences should be given attention, especially interaction between men and women. As described earlier in the chapter, a Muslim man should not be alone with a woman and vice versa. If the music therapist is working with a Muslim client of the opposite sex, it is recommended to ask the client or guardian if they are comfortable with this type of professional arrangement. It is also good for the music therapist to keep in mind that the Muslim client of the opposite sex may not feel comfortable in working together with the therapist. Physical contact should be kept to a minimum, unless the Muslim client indicates that he or she does not follow that ruling. This includes refraining from handshakes, hugs, or simple touches on the shoulder or back between opposite sexes. If you are unsure, I suggest asking the client about his or her comfort level.

The music therapist working with a Muslim client who is a child, adolescent, teenager, or young adult may find that many of the cultural differences mentioned in this chapter may very well not be an issue. Given the role of family and respecting one's parents, dealing with the cultural differences of the

parents or family may be more challenging. Of course, each client's case will be different. In addition, the music therapist working with an elderly Muslim client should be prepared to work with his or her family and adjust to any cultural differences that arise. Respect for cultural differences and acknowledgment of cultural biases should always be observed and checked by the music therapist. Clinical supervision is a good way to monitor biases. Collaboration with spiritual leaders, religious teachers, and imams of mosques is encouraged for the music therapist and other mental health providers.

Working with Muslims in a Music Therapy Setting

After my conversion to Islam, I had several opportunities to present on music and Islam. This was the first of my attempts to bridge the cultural gap between my life before Islam and the life I aspired to as a Muslim. I was encouraged by a colleague and mentor to reflect on my experiences and the available research to develop some guidelines for music therapists in working with a Muslim client. Based on work by Maki and Kitano (2002) on counseling Asian-Americans, I created a very basic cross-cultural music therapy plan for working with Muslim clients. The plan is based on the client's level of assimilation and ethnic/religious identity (Elwafi, 2007).

The cross-cultural music therapy plan provides general suggestions on the use of music therapy techniques, instrument choices, and musical idioms for the following categories of clients: (1) low ethnic/religious identity and high assimilation, (2) high ethnic/religious identity and high assimilation, (3) low ethnic/religious identity and low assimilation, and (4) high ethnic/religious identity and low assimilation (Elwafi, 2007). An illustration of the plan is included in Appendix A of this chapter and should be followed with the therapist's and team's discretion. These are broad suggestions and should be used primarily for assessment and to bring awareness to issues that may arise for music therapists working with Muslim clients. One example from the cross-cultural music therapy plan is for a more liberal use of music therapy techniques and musical instruments that can be implemented with clients who have lower ethnic/religious or cultural identity and high assimilation. Conversely, the conservative use of music therapy techniques, as well as minimal to no use of wind or string instruments, is suggested for clients with high ethnic/religious identity and low assimilation.

Conclusion

Islam is a religion of submission to the will of Allah. It is derived from the word *peace* and encourages balance, equality, and responsibility in all aspects of life. Muslims believe in one God and that Muhammad (PBUH) was the last Prophet of God. Muslims strive to live according to Allah's laws and guidance and by following the Sunnah and hadith from the Prophet Muhammad's (PBUH) life. Seeking peace in submission as well as balance between worldly existence and heavenly goals are some of the spiritual challenges for Muslims. One's knowledge, understanding of the religion and the spiritual aspects of Islam, and interpretation of those aspects are also important in determining the Muslim's worldview.

As a music therapist, I was met with challenges that threatened my clinical identity but pushed me to grow. Music had always been a way for me to connect with God. When I accepted Islam, I discovered a new way to connect with God that didn't directly involve music. I left behind the music I had known before Islam to try to understand my Creator and my role in this world as a new Muslim. Turning off the radio, putting my entire personal music library in storage, and concluding my aspirations to perform publicly was very difficult, but they were steps I pushed myself to take so that I could grow spiritually. I committed much of my energy to discovering and navigating the different cultures in my life as my worldview and status in society shifted. As I slowly reintroduce popular culture and changing spiritual norms for Muslims back into my life, I hope for more balance between my personal, spiritual, and professional sides.

References

Abd-Allah, U. F. (2004). Islam and the cultural imperative; A Nawawi foundation paper. Retrieved from http://www.nawawi.org/downloads/article3.pdf

Al-Qarni, A. (2003). *Don't be sad*. (F. Shafeeq, Trans.). Riyadh, Saudi Arabia: International Islamic Publishing House. (Original work published 2003).

Al-Sufi, M. I. (n.d.). The rights and virtues of women in Islam. Retrieved from http://spa.qibla.com/issue_view.asp?HD=10&ID=1497&CATE=89

Ali, O., & Milstein, G. (2012). Mental illness recognition and referral practices among imams in the United States. *Journal of Muslim Mental Health, 6*(2), 3–13.

Ansari, Z. (n.d.). Does the Koran teach to kill, tax, or convert infidels? Retrieved from http://spa.qibla.com/issue_view.asp?CATE=1426&HD=7&ID=9801

Bradt, J. (1997). Ethical issues in multicultural counseling: Implications for the field of music therapy. *The Arts in Psychotherapy, 24*(2), 137–143.

CAIR. (2012). About Islam and American Muslims. *Council on American-Islamic Relations (CAIR)*. Retrieved from http://www.cair.com/AboutIslam/IslamBasics.aspx

Ciftci, A., Jones, N., & Corrigan, P. (2013). Mental health stigma in the Muslim community. *Journal of Muslim Mental Health, 7*(1), 17–32.

Elwafi, P. (2007, June). *Islam and music therapy; Controversy and beauty*. Music Therapy Association of Kentucky, Louisville, Kentucky.

Elwafi, P. (2011). The impact of music therapists' religious beliefs on clinical identity and professional practice. In S. Gardstrom (Ed.), *Qualitative inquiries in music therapy: A monograph series. Volume Six* (pp. 155–191). Gilsum, NH: Barcelona Publishers.

Esposito, J., & Mogahed, D. (2007). *Who speaks for Islam? What a billion Muslims really think*. New York, NY: Gallup Press.

Goforth, A., Oka, E., Leong, F., & Denis, D. (2014). Acculturation, acculturative stress, religiosity, and psychological adjustment among Muslim Arab-American adolescents. *Journal of Muslim Mental Health, 8*(2), 3–19.

Islamicity. (n.d.). The Islamic calendar. Retrieved from http://www.islamicity.com/science/islamic_calendar.shtml

Jahangir, S., & Nawaz, N. (2014). Effects of memorizing Qur'an by heart (hifz) on later academic achievement. *Journal of Muslim Mental Health, 8*(2), 75.

Maki, M., & Kitano, H. (2002). Counseling Asian-Americans. In P. Pedersen, J. Draguns, W. Lonner, & J. Trimble (Eds.), *Counseling across cultures* (5th ed., pp. 109–131). Thousand Oaks, CA: SAGE.

Mogahed, Y. (2012). Islam does not accept domestic abuse. Retrieved from http://www.yasminmogahed.com/2012/03/20/islam-does-not-accept-domestic-abuse/

Nadal, K., Griffin, K., Hamit, S., Leon, J., Tobio, M., & Rivera, D. (2012). Subtle and overt forms of Islamophobia: Microaggressions toward Muslim Americans. *Journal of Muslim Mental Health, 6*(2), 15–37.

Pew Research Center. (2012a). The world's Muslims: Unity and Diversity. Retrieved from http://www.pewforum.org/Muslim/the-worlds-muslims-unity-and-diversity-executive-summary.aspx#generational

Pew Research Center. (2012b). The global religious landscape: Muslims. Retrieved from http://www.pewforum.org/2012/12/18/global-religious-landscape-muslim/

Rahman, F. (1989). *Health and medicine in the Islamic tradition: Change and identity*. New York, NY: Crossroad Publishing.

Tuell, R. S. (2011). *Islamic approaches to patient care: Muslim beliefs and health care practices for caregivers*. Beltsville, MD: Amana Publications.

Zain, M. (2012). The Prophet's kindness towards people of the book. Retrieved from http://www.onislam.net/english/reading-islam/about-muhammad/his-character/457717-the-prophets-kindness-towards-people-of-the-book.html

Appendix A

Cross-Cultural Music Therapy Guide—Muslim Cultures (Adapted from Maki & Kitano, 2002)

Low Ethnic/Religious Identity and High Assimilation •Most liberal use of variety of music therapy techniques •Wide selection of music techniques for use • *Use variety of instruments and variety of music genres*	**High Ethnic/Religious Identity and High Assimilation** • Monitor use of music and nonmusic techniques • Mix of Western and Eastern musical idioms • *Improvisation, drumming, traditional songs, careful use of instruments*
Low Ethnic/Religious Identity and Low Assimilation • Conservative use of music therapy techniques • Explore/assess client's comfort level with music • Nonmusic techniques • *Careful use of instruments; music listening may be appropriate*	**High Ethnic/Religious Identity and Low Assimilation** • Use of very conservative music therapy techniques • Nonmusic techniques, depending upon therapist's comfort level, including spiritual reflection or poetry • *No string or wind instruments. Therapist should rely on voice and percussion.*

Chapter 12

TWO JEWS, THREE OPINIONS

Rebecca J. Froman & Debra Jelinek Gombert

Becky: *An older man at a senior center where I lead a music therapy group approached me and asked if I was coming in for the* Yiddish *conversation group. I politely declined, telling him, "Oh, I don't know if you need another person in the group. You know what they say: 'two Jews, three opinions.'" He laughed and told a classic joke:*

A Jewish man was stranded on a deserted island for several years. The island was very remote, nothing around for miles. One day, the man spotted a boat in the distance, so he worked quickly to build a bonfire to send a signal to the boat. The boat made its way to the island, and the captain was the first off the boat. "So," said the captain to the man, "you've been alone on this island for many years?" "Yes, all alone," replied the man. "So tell me, what is it you've built over there?" asked the captain, pointing to a structure off in the distance. "Oh, that is my *synagogue*. I go there to say my prayers and observe the holidays," the man proudly explained to the captain. The captain nodded, then, peering in opposite direction, asked, "and what about over there?" The man exclaimed, "Oh, that? That is the other *synagogue*. I would never go there."

Becky and Debbie: *As the gentleman's joke suggests, diversity of beliefs, customs, and practices exist among Jewish people and may exist even for a single Jewish person. Our own connections to Judaism have evolved as we welcome new interpretations and ask new questions. We are two women who each emphatically include "Jewish" in our self-definitions. We are both* Ashkenazi *Jews who both had grandparents who left Europe because of the* Holocaust. *However, neither of us is Orthodox and neither of us keeps* kosher. *We are secular in some ways and observant in others: Debbie is currently a member of a Reconstructionist congregation. Becky is not currently affiliated, although she finds herself aligning with Reform. Becky grew up going to a Conservative synagogue; Debbie grew up in a non-practicing home. In this chapter, we attempt to explain a variety of Jewish practices and beliefs in the United States, yet we are aware of our biases. As we relay our own knowledge and opinions, we acknowledge that perhaps one synagogue would not have sufficed for either of us on a desert island.*

We are both practicing music therapists who work with clients from a variety of backgrounds and with various cultural and group affiliations. Each of us has been asked by clients or coworkers questions about Judaism and what it means to be Jewish; each of us has been asked to share what a music therapist should know when working with Jewish clients. This chapter is our attempt to begin to answer these broad and vast questions. The personal stories we use in this chapter are combinations of our own experiences, client experiences, and experiences of our friends or family. When appropriate, we have obtained permission to use stories; often names or identities have intentionally been changed. The stories are true in the sense that they represent truths and are based on true stories, but they may not report the events with 100% accuracy.

A note to our readers: Throughout this chapter and in many of the appendices, we have used italics in the text when one of us is telling a story. We also use italics in the text, or plain font in the italicized sections, to identify Hebrew *words,* Yiddish *words, or words that have a particular meaning in Jewish culture. If the italicized words are not defined in the context of the text, they can be found in Appendix A, the glossary. Appendix A also includes words that a music therapist might find helpful in clinical practice. We have not used italics for names of Jewish holidays because they are not in the glossary. Please refer to the chart in Appendix B for information about holidays. Spellings of the English transliteration of prayer and song titles are taken from Pasternak (1997) when possible. For information about transliteration in general, please see Appendix A.*

Worldview

Becky: *"What are you?" It is an awkward question. Many of my adult clients would answer that they are American and Jewish, as if the labels belong to different but equally important categories. During an occupational therapy co-treatment session, I was singing "G-d Bless America" with a client who was born in Europe and lived in Israel prior to coming to the United States. As the client's arms were raised by the occupational therapist in time with the music, the client emphatically proclaimed, "America is mine home, sweet, home. I am now America[n]. An America[n] Jew!" It seemed important to this client to include Jewish in her self-description.*

What can be said of "American Jews"? What kind of label is "Jewish"? Referring to Jews' shared ancestry, some identify "Jewish" as a race, ethnic group, or nation (Froman, 2009; Goldstein, 2006; Steinsaltz, 2005), although the validity of this definition is questionable, and it is cautioned against because in the past a racial identity has led to *anti-Semitism* (Schlossberger & Hecker, 1998). Many people have suggested that Judaism can be considered to be both a religion and a culture (Froman, 2009; Kessler, 2007; Steinsalz, 2005) and thus define it as a spiritual system, a blueprint for living, or an ethical civilization (Cohen, Gorvine, & Gorvine, 2013).

Jewish people live in all 50 of the United States (Saxe & Tighe, 2013) and represent a tremendous diversity based on different denominations of Judaism, different cultural and historical factors, different expressions and experiences with Judaism, and differences in Jewish culture and music (Froman, 2009). Historically and today, both Jews and non-Jews use terms and definitions inconsistently, indicating that perhaps there is just as much variation in how Jews see themselves as there is in how others see them. The only consensuses are that there is a Jewish religion, that people practice "Judaism," and that there are people who call themselves Jews or Jewish, whether they identify with the culture and customs or follow the religion (Froman, 2009).

If monolithic definitions of Judaism can be refuted by another person who identifies as Jewish, what, then, are the basic "facts" that can be said of Judaism or of Jews? Keller (2000) suggests that most Jews fall somewhere on a spectrum between tradition and modernity, while Kessler (2007) suggests that each Jewish person creates a self-definition with respect to three aspects: a religion, a culture, and a people (see Appendix C for further explanation).

Religion

The Jewish religion is a monotheistic religion. However, Jews may differ in their basic conception of the nature of *G-d,* and some reject a supernatural view of *G-d* (Cohen et al., 2013). Judaism does not emphasize belief as other religions do; much variation in belief is permitted, and debate is encouraged. Rather, Judaism emphasizes "participating in and continuing the arc of Jewish history, defined by the community's relationship with *G-d*" (Cohen et al., 2013, p. 666). Thus, Jewish life and community may be more important than belief to some. Traditionally, a person is Jewish based on matrilineal descent: A person who is born to a Jewish mother is considered to be Jewish, regardless of the extent to which he or she practices or observes any of the religion (Cohen et al., 2013). In the United States today, two denominations, Reform and Reconstructionist, additionally recognize patrilineal descent (personal communication, A. Ahuvia, August 15, 2015).

There are collections of sacred texts central to Judaism. The *Torah* is understood to be the law of *G-d.* The *Tanakh,* Jewish Bible, contains the *Torah* or *Pentateuch* (the five books of Moses), the *Nevi'im* (books of the Prophets), and the *Ketuvim* (other writings). The *Talmud* is a compilation of ancient *rabbinic* writings, which includes the *Mishna* and the *Gemara.* Judaism shares a common ancestry with Christianity and Islam, as all three monotheistic religions trace their lineage to Abraham. Figures such as Jesus and Muhammad are not part of Jewish liturgy or culture.

Several life cycle events include specific Jewish liturgy, customs, and rituals (see Appendix D for further information).

The Jewish year primarily follows a lunar calendar and includes several holidays and festivals (see Appendix B for further information).

Debbie: *The holidays were explained by a six-year-old with whom I worked: "They are like Thanksgiving. We have a big feast, and there are special foods, and my cousins come, and people I don't know come. Except that it is Jewish, and instead of watching football, we sing and read all about the holiday. But it is the same, because we want to be with family and to say 'Thank you' to* G-d."

Culture

Jewish culture can be understood to include celebrations, foods, music, traditions, and Jewish values. The Public Religion Research Institute conducted a survey designed to understand distinctive Jewish values (Jones & Cox, 2012) and found the following: More than 8 in 10 American Jews place a high value on pursuing justice, and more than 7 in 10 value *tikkun olam,* sharing responsibility to repair the world and seek social justice. When asked what qualities are most important to their Jewish identity, nearly half cited a commitment to social equality. Only 20% of American Jews cited support for Israel as being most important to their Jewish identity. Seventeen percent cited religious observance as being most important (Jones & Cox, 2012).

Cardin (2005) notes the pervasive role of community in Judaism: Certain prayers are recited only when in the company of others. Likewise, the home is emphasized as the place where festivals are celebrated and where one learns about Judaism (Miller & Lovinger, 2000). Steinsaltz (2005) describes a kinship that exists among Jews regardless of religious practice, akin to belonging to a large family.

People

How many Jewish people currently live in the United States? Saxe and Tighe (2013) at the Steinhardt Social Research Institute found that as of 2012, approximately 2% of the U.S. population was Jewish, either by religion or by criteria other than religion. Of these approximately 6.8 million individuals, 4.2 million adults consider Judaism to be their religion, one million adults consider themselves to be Jewish by other criteria, and 1.6 million are children under the age of 18 who are being raised exclusively as Jewish. Sax and Tighe further found that the Jewish population is concentrated primarily in metropolitan areas, with 97% living near a major city. One third (33%) of the Jewish population resides in New York, New Jersey, Massachusetts, and Pennsylvania. It is worth noting that one quarter (24%) of all adults who are Jewish by religion are age 65 years and older, compared to 18% of the general U.S. adult population. As Sheskin (2001) noted at the turn of the millennium, this trend of general aging of the Jewish population suggests that a number of Jewish clients may have increasing need for health care and end-of-life services.

Diversity Within the Culture

Becky: *Around the end of December, close to the celebration of Hanukkah, I visited one music therapy client in a skilled nursing facility. I was stunned to find a small Christmas tree in the corner of her room, adorned with tinsel and shiny ornaments, as Christmas is not a Jewish holiday. While the client identified herself as Jewish, she always had the front row center seat at the facility's Christmas service, and sang the Christian hymns with enthusiasm from the bottom of her heart. A few years later, I found myself in a different client's living room, leafing over her old* synagogue *choir music folder. This client's son informed me that although his mother was an avid member of her* synagogue's *choir in later adulthood, she had maintained a very secular home absent of Jewish traditions and practices when her children were at home. A third music therapy client repeatedly declared that while he had grown up in a very observant home, attending weekly Jewish worship services, he wanted nothing to do with prayer in his later years. Yet, he fretted over whether or not anyone would say "Kaddish," a Jewish prayer of mourning, on his behalf at his funeral. Each of these Jewish clients had differing connections to aspects of Jewish faith, observance, culture and tradition.*

Debbie: *I grew up in a town where there was one* synagogue *but no churches. To my grade-school mind, most of the town was Jewish, although my father was not. My family had a Christmas tree at home and celebrated Christmas with Dad's side of the family. We celebrated Hanukkah with Mom's side. I never questioned that I was Jewish, even though we rarely attended services or celebrated* Shabbat. *My grandparents were Jewish; my mother is Jewish; so I am Jewish. Today, I belong to and regularly attend services with a Reconstructionist congregation, where I am among others who find tradition and community to be more important than belief in* G-d.

My siblings and I each have chosen our own expression of Judaism. My husband is not Jewish; together he and I celebrate both Jewish and Christian holidays. My brother-in-law converted to Judaism. He and my elder sister belong to a Conservative synagogue. They have an observant household, do not miss Yom Kippur services, and have a fairly observant home devoid of secular or religious decorations for non-Jewish holidays in the house. My youngest sister is "just Jewish"; although she was married by a rabbi *and had a* ketubah *(Jewish marriage contract), she is not observant. My brother avoids religion all together and does not include Jewish in his self-definition.*

History of Denominations

In the Jewish Bible, Jewish history begins with Abraham, who recognized that the universe was the work of a single *G-d* (Kessler, 2007). Later in the Bible, Moses received the laws and commandments of the *Torah*. In the post-Biblical period, Judaism was practiced in the *Temple* in Jerusalem, and Jewish priests mediated between the people and *G-d*. In 70 CE, the second *Temple* was destroyed and Jews were exiled from Israel. Judaism evolved into *Rabbinic Judaism,* a portable religion that could be practiced in *diaspora* outside of Israel and without the *Temple* in Jerusalem (Kessler, 2007). *Rabbis* replaced the priests responsible for the *Temple* rituals, *synagogues* replaced the *Temple,* and prayer replaced sacrifice. A *rabbi* taught and passed on the religion, history, and laws; his role was akin to that of "teacher" or "judge" (Miller & Lovinger, 2000). Contemporary Judaism is derived from *Rabbinic Judaism.*

During the Middle Ages and the Renaissance, many European Jews lived in *ghettos* and were barred from owning land or becoming citizens (Limor, 1997; Robinson, 2001). However, within their own communities, they had complete autonomy to establish their own leadership and govern their own education and institutions (Robinson, 2001). In the late 17th and early 18th centuries, the European Enlightenment introduced the concepts of individual freedom and citizenship, contradicting the view of Jews being a separate nation within a country. One could be both Jewish and French, English, or German, and for the first time in history there was the possibility of being a secular Jew. Issues of nationalism sparked forced conversions, expulsions, and exterminations amidst the Jews' struggle to find their place in these societies (Robinson, 2001). France was the first to emancipate the Jews, but slowly across Europe, Jewish people were allowed to become citizens of the countries where they lived (Robinson, 2001).

The 17th century saw the beginnings of separation into today's Jewish denominations. The desire to assimilate into mainstream society sparked the development of Reform Judaism in Germany in the early part of the 19th century, as Jews adapted their traditions and customs to match those of their fellow citizens (Miller & Lovinger, 2000; Robinson, 2001). Reform Jewish services mirrored aspects of church services, such as using the vernacular language instead of *Hebrew,* scheduling worship on Sundays (instead of Saturday, the Jewish *Sabbath*), playing the organ, and using Protestant chorales (Wigoder, 2002). Today, some of the most assimilated practices of early Reform Judaism have modulated back toward more traditional Jewish customs; *Hebrew,* liturgy, and rituals have been re-incorporated, services have returned to Saturday, and more uniquely Jewish music is used in services.

The first Jews arrived in the United States in 1654. The roughly 2,000 Jews living in the United States by the time of the American Revolution were granted the same rights as other citizens when the country was formed (Cohen et al., 2013). Over time, Jews of all denominations came to live in the United States (Cohen et al., 2013), and Reconstructionist Judaism was developed (Alpert & Staub, 2000). According to the Pew Research Center, (Lugo, Cooperman, & Smith, 2013), there are several denominations practiced in the United States today. While the denominations share some central commonalities, there are significant differences.

Orthodox Judaism

A central Orthodox belief is that the *Torah*'s written laws have divine origin and that the oral laws are divinely influenced (Schnall, 2006; Wigoder, 2002). Orthodox Jews practice the most literal observance of the Jewish laws, traditions, and holidays, and have rules that strictly regulate interactions between men and women (e.g., only men are permitted to read ritually from the *Torah,* and men and women cannot sit together in a *synagogue*). Within the denomination of Orthodox Judaism, there are subdivisions, each of which has specific practices and interpretations of Judaism. Ultra-Orthodox groups follow the Jewish laws and liturgy with the most traditional adherence (Wigoder, 2002). *Hasidic* Judaism, one of the stricter Orthodox groups, emphasizes the intensity of prayer and aims to bring the mystical into daily practice (Sorkin, 1997). These Jews are quite recognizable as men may have long beards, hair curls by their ears, and wear long black coats; women may dress in modest clothing and cover their hair in public after marriage. Modern Orthodox is the most acculturated group of Orthodox Jews. A central tenet of this group is the maintenance of and some flexibility with strict laws and the teachings of the religious traditions while still participating in general secular society (Wasserstein, 1997; Wigoder, 2002). Most Modern Orthodox Jews dress in modern clothing and live modern life styles.

Both inside and outside the Orthodox community, there is an emerging debate about using the terms "ultra-Orthodox" and "Modern Orthodox." To some, the prefix "ultra-" has a negative association with extremism, and others find the use of the word "Modern" problematic (Goldschmidt, 2014). However, groups within Orthodoxy represent a spectrum of differences related to worldview, religious practice, dress, diet, and language, and Orthodox Jews may oppose general categorizations (Schnall, 2006).

Conservative Judaism

The American-based denomination of Conservative Judaism follows the belief that Jewish law is important and central to Jewish practice, but its interpretations are not as strict as Orthodox Judaism's adherences (Rabinowitz, 2000). Although following Jewish law is the ideal, Conservative Jews recognize that Judaism has changed over time in response to events in the past and thus generally believe that it is realistic to permit change in practice and interpretation of Judaism (Terry, 2000; The United Synagogue for Conservative Judaism, 2012). Therefore, a person who is a Conservative Jew may be very observant, but the laws and religion he or she is following have been adapted to reflect modern society (Wigoder, 2002). Cornerstones of Conservative Judaism include contribution to Jewish life through the *synagogue,* charity, family centrality, study, and observation of holidays and of the *Sabbath* (The United Synagogue for Conservative Judaism, 2012).

Reform Judaism

Like Conservative Judaism, the Reform denomination maintains traditions and takes current societal influences into account (Union for Reform Judaism, 2011). This denomination has the largest following of American Jewry. Whereas Conservative and Orthodox services use more *Hebrew,* Reform Jewish worship services tend to use more vernacular language in their services.

While Reform Judaism agrees with the main tenets of Judaism, it acknowledges diversity in expression and interpretation of laws, customs, and beliefs and embraces the idea of Jewish thought and practice meeting with contemporary society (Wigoder, 2002). Just as an observant Conservative Jew adheres to Jewish law that has been adapted to modern society, a Reform Jew can be strictly observant; he or she is observing law according to a Reform interpretation. The Reform movement emphasizes egalitarianism and social justice. Names of Jewish matriarchs are incorporated into prayers that were originally written with only the Jewish patriarchs' names. A woman's role may be the same as a man's in religious prayer, rituals, and leadership as *rabbis* and *cantors.* The Conservative movement has since adopted many of these practices (Wasserstein, 1997).

Becky: *Observing and upholding Jewish customs connects me to my family's history and my roots. It honors my past and my family members who were persecuted for being Jewish. The idea that Reform Judaism allows for fluidity as long as changes are made purposefully and are based on Jewish history resonates with me strongly, as does Reform Judaism's strong commitment to social action, justice, and inclusion.*

Reconstructionist Judaism

Mordechai Kaplan created Reconstructionist Judaism in the 1920s and '30s as an outgrowth of Conservative Judaism (Albert & Staub, 2000). Kaplan suggested that Judaism is an evolving religious civilization of the Jewish people and that every generation is responsible for guiding the evolution of Judaism to meet the needs of contemporary Jews (Reconstructionist Rabbinical College, 2014). Reconstructionist Judaism rejects the idea of a supernatural origin of *Torah;* thus it retains the traditional language of Jewish prayer, but not necessarily the literal understanding of its meaning and function (Bronstein, 2014). A key to understanding the pattern of observance in Reconstructionist Judaism is that "the past gets a vote, but not a veto" (Albert & Staub, 2000, p. 39). Reconstructionism has often been at the forefront of social issues: In 1922, a Reconstructionist *rabbi* performed the first *Bat Mitzvah* (coming-of-age ceremony previously only for boys); in 1984, the Reconstructionist Rabbinical College was the first *rabbinical* school in history to admit openly gay and lesbian students (Alpert & Staub, 2000).

Debbie: *When I returned to Judaism as an adult, I wanted to reconstruct what it means for me to be Jewish, to keep traditions and interpretations that are meaningful for me without conflicting with social progressiveness. While this might sound like a recipe for arbitrary rules, it in fact causes me to examine my faith and observance more carefully. For me, Reconstructionist Judaism provides a way to assimilate parts of Judaism into the rest of my mainstream life.*

Diversity Transcending Denominations

Differences between the Jewish denominations account for some of the diversity of religious and cultural expression found in the Jewish population in the United States (Froman, 2009). According to the Pew Research Center (Lugo et al., 2013), the denomination with the largest affiliation is Reform Judaism (35%), followed by Conservative Judaism (18%), and then Orthodox Judaism (10%). The remaining 6% classify themselves as "other," which includes smaller sects of Judaism, such as Reconstructionist and Humanistic Judaism. Although some people may consider themselves to be Jewish because of an affiliation with Jews for Jesus or with Messianic Judaism, these individuals were not included in this research. These groups are not considered to be Jewish by the major denominations of Judaism and instead are considered to be Christian with some Jewish practices (Fox, 2012).

Those people who affiliate with no particular denomination or only with some aspects of Judaism and consider themselves to be "just Jewish" comprise 30% of the United States Jewish population (Lugo et al., 2013). Some in the group who identify as "just Jewish" may consider themselves to be secular. Others may classify themselves as nondenominational and have no affiliation with any particular denomination. Secular and unaffiliated Jews tend to observe Jewish religious and cultural practices and traditions the least (Cohen, 2005). However, according to Cohen, since the 1960s there has been an increasing trend toward post-denominational or trans-denominational Judaism. These Jews tend to be committed to Judaism and may gather specifically to form community, work toward Jewish causes, practice Jewish religion, and partake in traditions in a way that goes across or beyond denominational customs, guidelines, and definitions (Cohen, 2005). Gathering together as an independent *minyan* is a related trend, particularly among younger Jews. These groups tend to avoid the terms *synagogue* and congregation, gather in places where they are welcome to use the space rather than in *synagogues,* and make decisions as a group with regard to ritual, observance, and *halakhah.* Some have *rabbis,* while others may have lay leaders, and all offer Jewish community (Cohen, Landres, Kaunfer, & Shain, 2007).

Denomination is not the only marker of diversity within Judaism. According to Saxe and Tighe (2013), 2% of Jewish people are not Caucasian. Jewish people have come to the United States from all parts of the world, including India, China, Ethiopia, and other parts of Africa (Miller & Lovinger, 2000). Jewish communities have existed in Ethiopia and India since roughly the 2nd or 3rd century, in Egypt since biblical times,

and in China since the 12th century. Today, Jewish communities exist in at least 100 countries, spanning six continents (World Jewish Congress, 2014).

Conversion or adoption into a Jewish family also accounts for some diversity of heritage (Steinsaltz, 2005). Orthodox and Conservative Judaism require the conversion of adopted children for them to be considered Jewish; each denomination has different criteria for conversion.

Debbie: *When I faced difficulty in conceiving, I was relieved to learn that Reform and Reconstructionist Judaism do consider a child to be Jewish if he or she was adopted by or conceived via egg donation for Jewish parents, regardless of the religion of the biological mother (Jotkowitz, 2011).*

Whereas the underlying difference among the various denominations can be seen as a continuum of less strict to most strict observance or practice of historically grounded rules and laws (Keller, 2000), the denominations may also be seen to represent a continuum of assimilation into American culture (Robinson, 2001). In this continuum, Reform would be seen on one end and Orthodox on the other. Gender roles follow a similar continuum, with more liberal interpretations often coinciding with less insistence on traditional gender roles and more gender equality.

Gender Differences Within the Culture

Becky: *When my mother's parents arrived in the United States from Poland after the* Holocaust, *my grandfather immediately resumed attending services at an Orthodox synagogue. He would come home in midafternoon on Fridays in order to prepare for the walk to his synagogue at sunset. My grandmother refused to go with him, as she disagreed with the Orthodox tradition of separating men and women. My mother recalled her explanation: "Why should I sit in a small box for the women and children, away from my husband, on the second floor where I can't even hear what is happening? Feh!" With that, she took her three children (my mother, aunt, and uncle) down the street to a Conservative synagogue.*

Debbie: *My grandfather (Opa) was the idealist, the scholar. My grandmother (Omi) was the pragmatist. Opa studied and read, always asking questions, always learning. Omi was practical; she said she "simply did what needed to be done": Get a job outside the home, keep food on the table, take care of the family. I always thought that their division of labor reflected their personalities, but I now realize that it also followed traditional Jewish gender roles: The man studies and provides for his family; the woman takes care of the home, even if that means working outside of the home.*

A woman of valor, who can find? For her
price is beyond rubies.
—Proverbs 31:10–13
"Blessed are thou … who has not made me a woman."
—Morning prayers

"A Woman of Valor" is a long text of praise, traditionally sung by a man to his wife on *Shabbat* each Friday evening; yet, every morning, a Jewish man who says the morning prayers thanks *G-d* that he is not a woman (Baker, 1993). Although not all Jewish men recite these traditional texts, the passages point to the historical gender differences in Judaism. While women are respected and revered in Orthodox Judaism and there are women of note in Jewish religious texts, they cannot lead prayer and in most groups are not ordained as rabbis (Baker, 1993). Gender roles and expectations follow a continuum from very traditional in Orthodox *synagogues* and families to more egalitarian among Conservative, Reform, and Reconstructionist congregations and families. The inclusion of gay, lesbian, bisexual, and transgender people follows a similar continuum (Union for Reform Judaism, 2011). The most traditional laws are described here.

Gender Roles in Religious Observance

Baker (1993) notes that some modern prayer books explain that the morning prayer is not meant to degrade women, but to thank *G-d* that as a man, one has the privilege of performing all of the laws of *Torah*, some of which women are not obliged to follow. While men are traditionally required to pray in *synagogue* or to study religious law, women are not required to do so (Baker, 1993). This requirement starts when a boy reaches the age of 13 and becomes a *Bar Mitzvah*, a "son of the commandment." A parallel recognition of a girl's reaching the age of Jewish majority has been observed only in the last century (Goldman, 2000; Robinson, 2001). According to Robinson, today the ceremony is celebrated for both boys and girls in most *synagogues*, including Orthodox *synagogues*. In Reform, Conservative, and Reconstructionist Judaism, adult women have the same responsibilities and privileges as men; in most Orthodox *synagogues*, there is still a separation of the genders during prayer, and men and women have different responsibilities (Vorspan & Saperstein, 1998).

Perhaps the most important privilege and responsibility is to be counted toward a *minyan*, which is the quorum of 10 Jewish adults required to say certain prayers. Orthodox *synagogues* count only men (a male who is post-*Bar Mitzvah*) toward a *minyan* (Vorspan & Saperstein, 1998). The Reform movement has counted women toward a *minyan* since 1845, and the Conservative movement has counted women since 1973 (Telushkin, 2008). Gradually, equality followed in religious prayer, rituals, and leadership as *rabbis* and *cantors*. Women have been ordained as *rabbis* since 1972 in the Reform movement, and since 1985 in the Conservative movement (Baker, 1993; Vorspan & Saperstein, 1998). As of 2013, four Orthodox women had been ordained (Stone, 2013). The introduction of female *cantors* followed a similar path: The first female Reform *cantor* was ordained in 1975 and the Conservative movement followed suit in the 1980s (Heskes, 2009).

Gender Roles in the Jewish Family

The *Shabbat* song from Proverbs goes on to state many of the traditional responsibilities for a "Woman of Valor." These revolve around women's responsibility to make the home a "Jewish home" by observing *Shabbat* and the holidays, keeping *kosher*, and creating a way of life that facilitates family cohesion. Women are the glue that holds everything together and are supposed to demonstrate strength and resourcefulness to help their family survive (Baker, 1993). Baker suggests that although women were not equal in traditional Jewish law, they have never been passive and oppressed, and their role is viewed as vital. Some argue that aspects of traditional Judaism encourage feminism (Ingall, 2005).

Parts of Jewish marriage law serve to protect the rights of wives (Robinson, 2001). Robinson further explains that the *Talmud* makes it clear that a wife is not property, that a woman has the right to reject her fiancé, and that a woman is not required to marry. Under Jewish law, Jewish men are required to provide their wives with food, clothing, medical care, conjugal relations, and financial support. Jewish law explicitly proscribes husbands from beating their wives, restricting their free movement, or forcing sex (Robinson, 2001).

Baker (1993) states that the majority of Orthodox women whom she interviewed did not feel inequality and instead emphasized that they are respected in a way that women in the secular world are rarely afforded. While appreciating the choice of women who choose to enter Orthodoxy after living in a more secular world, Baker examines the possibility that it is not always as ideal a picture as it seems, expressing concern that for some families, religious observance may mask family dysfunction.

Divorce has always has been possible in Judaism (Baker, 1993; Robinson, 2001; Teulshkin, 2008). In Orthodox Judaism, however, a woman needs her husband to issue a *get*, a divorce document, in order to remarry (Baker, 1993; Robinson, 2001; Vorspan & Saperstein, 1998). In some unfortunate cases, this can result in the woman becoming an *agunah*, a "chained" woman. The Jewish Orthodox Feminist Alliance (Jewish Orthodox Feminist Alliance, n.d.) is one of several organizations that are working to address this particular inequity.

Debbie: *I never had any difficulty including "Jewish" and "Feminist" together in my self-definition. From Bella Abzug and Ruth Bader Ginsburg to Gertrude Stein, Judy Blume, Judy Chicago, and, of course, Gloria Steinem, I grew up associating "Jewish" with "Feminist" in politics, literature, art, and popular culture.*

Becky: *My sister and I grew up hearing names like Golda Meir, Hannah Solomon, Hannah Senesh, and Henrietta Szold at the dinner table. When we visited the National Women's Hall of Fame and Women's Rights National Historical Park in Seneca Falls, NY, we felt pride in seeing the inclusion of many amazing Jewish women leaders.*

Generational and Migration Differences

Becky: *"Do you have the exact time?" These are not words that typically strike fear into a family of four on vacation in Washington, DC, about to tour the U.S. Capitol. In line behind my family was a tall, young man with icy blue eyes and pale blond hair. We were so enamored with our surroundings that we had not realized that the line had grown behind us. Upon hearing the tourist's simple question spoken with an extremely heavy German accent, all four of us turned suddenly, shoulders tense, eyebrows raised, and short of breath. Once we told him the time, he started telling us something about his watch being broken. As he spoke, our shoulders relaxed, and we all breathed a sigh of relief. We went on with the tour and wound up having a lovely conversation with the watchless German traveler behind us.*

What was that visceral reaction to hearing a German accent? It made no sense. My father's parents were German Jewish, and their English was coated in a thick German accent. They spoke in German when they did not want my sister and me to understand, and our shoulders remained perfectly calm, eyebrows never budging, our breath ever steady. The type of gut reaction that my family had at the Capitol mirrors that of someone who has posttraumatic stress disorder (PTSD).

It would make sense for Jewish survivors of the *Holocaust* in Europe to have this reaction to the German tourist's inquiry, as it is very well established that many survivors of the *Holocaust* suffer from posttraumatic stress disorder (Baranowsky, Young, Johnson-Douglas, Williams-Keeler, & McCarrey, 1998; Rykov, 2001). In addition, the literature describes other issues and patterns of *Holocaust* survivors: anxiety, depression, emotional numbness, sleep disturbances, dissociation, survivor guilt, fierce concern for social justice, family enmeshment, and communication dysfunction, to name a few (Berger & Berger, 2001; Hass, 1990; Rykov, 2001).

Becky: *Several* Holocaust *survivors with whom I have worked in music therapy have been overly suspicious of authority, mistrusting, withdrawn, and anxious, and have horrific flashbacks triggered by seemingly mundane tasks in health care, such as finding a line outside their facility's dining room or hearing a nurse announce that it is their shower time. In sessions, I have facilitated coping with unresolved grief as well as survivor's guilt, which is feelings of remorse over surviving or living when other family members have perished (Meyerstein, 2004; Rykov, 2001). Even those far away from Europe during the* Holocaust *may have lost family members and experience these difficult feelings. I certainly see the lasting impact of enduring and surviving this trauma in the* Holocaust *survivors with whom I have worked, but I have also noticed particular issues and patterns in their children and grandchildren. I am not alone in my observation.*

Studies have focused on the issue of intergenerational transmission of trauma and the characteristics and psychological issues found in *Holocaust* survivors' children and grandchildren (Chaitin, 2002; Meyerstein, 2004; Russell,

Plotkin, & Heapy, 1985). Although they did not live through the event, the experience of the *Holocaust* is passed on to the next generations via awareness of their elders' trauma and how it affected their interactions (or lack thereof) with their offspring (Abrams, 1999; Baranowsky et al., 1998; Chaitin, 2002; Hass, 1990; Russell et al., 1985). The impacts include their outlook on life, connectivity to Judaism, life goals or need for achievement, stress and anxiety, trust, guilt, hypervigilance, relationships with others, and psychological health and well-being (Hass, 1990; Meyerstein, 2004; Russell et al., 1985). Although studies of the Jewish population conducted in the United States have found a strong link between Jewish identity and generational status (Sheskin, 2001), fear of outsiders and mistrust of authority have roots in the history of *anti-Semitism* and are observed in both older and younger Jews (Miller & Lovinger, 2000).

Becky: *My best friend growing up thought that my family's behaviors and oddities, such as my mother's well-stocked pantry "just in case" or my parents' hypervigilance in large crowds, were quite strange. Although Jewish, her family had been in the United States for several generations, whereas my grandparents were all European and all* Holocaust *survivors. The experience of my grandparents impacted the way in which they parented their children. My parents grew up aware of the terrible pasts that their parents had endured and are able to acknowledge that it had significant influence over decisions they made throughout their lives; "They suffered enough; we didn't want to cause any trouble." My parents strove to bring happiness to their parents through their own successes and did what they could to ease their parents' lives in the United States. These lifelong patterns permeated their role as caregivers at the end of my grandparents' lives. "Haven't they been through enough?" This is often echoed by the children of* Holocaust *survivors with whom I work in music therapy, who convey guilt over failing to protect their parents from more pain.*

I realize that some aspects of my parents' characteristics, habits, fears, and outlooks became ingrained in my psyche. My husband is very supportive; he understands that keeping the refrigerator full assuages my nervousness about scarcity. However, he struggles to understand my lack of deeply rooted American identity and often reminds me that I am a second-generation American and was not born in a shtetl.

It is important to note that *Holocaust* survivors are not the only Jewish cohort who has survived trauma or is impacted by *anti-Semitism* (Levitt & Balkin, 2003). Anticipating and enduring *anti-Semitism* have become parts of the fabric of being Jewish, even for those who did not experience the *Holocaust* (Miller & Lovinger, 2000; Rykov, 2001). As the *Holocaust* unfolded in Europe, Jews in the United States faced systematic antagonism and *anti-Semitism* (Takaki, 1993). For some, religious persecution was lurking in the very places to which they had immigrated to seek a safe haven. Those who came after the *Holocaust* sometimes chose to avoid association with Jewish community institutions, choosing to remain secular and instilling strong American identities in their children in hope that this would prevent further *anti-Semitism* (Chaitin, 2002).

Although the *Holocaust* brought Jews to the United States, there have been waves of Jewish immigration to the United States at various times for over 350 years (Miller & Lovinger, 2000). Thriving Jewish communities developed as Jewish immigrants settled near large cities over time (Takaki, 1993). The largest wave of Jewish immigration in the late 19th century originated as a reaction to *pogroms,* targeted attacks against Jews, in Eastern Europe (Miller & Lovinger, 2000). The most recent wave of immigration was in the late 1970s through the early 1990s, when thousands of Jews from the former Soviet Union relocated to the United States (Kosmin, 1990; Wasserstein, 1997). A study of Jews who emigrated from the former Soviet Union between 1977 and 1981 showed that approximately 10 years after their arrival in the United States, the majority had a strong Jewish identity but lacked a strong religious affiliation (Kosmin, 1990). The author reported that although only about 4% had received a Jewish education in the Soviet Union, 79% of their children were receiving one in the United States. As with many other immigrant groups, the descendants had access to new opportunities.

Just as generation and cohort impact expression of Jewish culture and religion, differences in familial origin must also be taken into account (Amir, 1997; Froman, 2009; Levitt & Balkin, 2003). The majority of Jews in North America can trace their family origins to northern and eastern Europe and are called *Ashkenazim,* a term that comes from the *Hebrew* word for Germany. Jews whose lineage descends from the Iberian Peninsula (Spain and Portugal) and from Morocco are known as *Sephardim* (Rykov, 2001). Although some people use *Sephardic* to also include all Jews who are from the Middle East or North Africa, Jews whose lineage comes from Persia (modern-day Iraq and Iran) are known as *Mizrahim* (Khazzoom, 2016). Khazzoom noted that even though the *Mizrahim* are a minority in the United States, they account for half of the Jewish population in Israel, resulting in a strong cultural influence that is felt in the United States.

When considered according to lineage, whether from Europe, Africa, the Middle East, India, or China, each group has distinct practices of Judaism and different cultural nuances, including holiday foods, traditions in celebrations, and music (Froman, 2009; Miller & Lovinger, 2000; Rykov, 2001). They also each have their own languages: *Yiddish* is the language that combined medieval German, *Hebrew,* and other eastern European languages (Wigoder, 2002); *Ladino* is the language that combined medieval Spanish and *Hebrew* (Wassserstein, 1997); *Judeo-Arabic* blended *Hebrew* and an Arabic dialect (Khazzoom, 2016). Although these languages are not widely spoken today, they are still spoken within families and found in Jewish song repertoires. Differences in the liturgical and sacred music and melodies are maintained among people from these different heritages (Rykov, 2001), as are differences in *Hebrew* pronunciation.

Becky: *When singing with* Ashkenazi *older adults in* Hebrew, *I try to remember to change my "t" sounds to "s" sounds. At my*

own family celebrations, I sometimes forget to switch my letters back, which is always met with roaring laughter from my father. "You've been spending too much time with your 95-year-olds!" I smile, fully aware that my pronunciation reflects my clients' generational and geographic differences.*

Acculturation and Assimilation

Becky: *Every year when I was in high school, I spent Christmas Eve with my Catholic friend and her family. We had a delicious dinner, and I took part in their Christmas Eve tradition of singing Christmas carols and exchanging gifts. I loved spending Christmas Eve with my friend's family, although I felt very much like an outsider, dabbling in Catholicism and Christianity from a spectator's viewpoint. This was "theirs" and not "mine." My Jewishness has always been more about being culturally Jewish than about being religious or following all of the Jewish laws; I could celebrate Christmas with my friend and her family without threatening my Jewish identity because I was an observer and not a participant.*

Debbie: *My father is not Jewish; neither is my husband. Although I have always "celebrated" both Jewish and Christian holidays, they have different meanings to me. My family's Passover and Hanukkah celebrations are part of my personal Jewish culture; they have religious meaning for me and connect me to a shared history. On the other hand, the Christmas tree in my house in December is a newer part of my family's traditions and has no religious meaning to me. One Sunday last spring, I asked the father of my son's friend if it was okay for the boys to decorate Easter eggs together after Hebrew school. The father responded, "I have no problem with art projects." Like me, he was willing to participate in this part of the "other" culture without absorbing its religious significance. My current traditions include an acculturated mix of Jewish customs along with foods and rituals that have been adopted from my father's family, my husband's family, and the culture around me. Yet I have not assimilated completely; I have maintained aspects of my Jewish culture in my life and in my home.*

> Indeed, America's Jews witness two contradictory trends operating simultaneously in their community: assimilation and revitalization. Nobody knows which will predominate and what the future holds. That will be determined day by day, community by community, and Jew by Jew (Sarna, 2005, p. 7).

Jews have been asking questions and making conscious decisions about acculturation and assimilation for several hundred years. Divergent denominations arose in the 17th century, during the Age of Enlightenment, developing as Jews chose how much to assimilate as citizens of the their countries (Robinson, 2001). Today's denominations of Judaism can be distinguished, in large part, by how much the group assimilates with the rest of society and where the line is drawn between tradition and modern culture. For example, the very observant Orthodox group of *Hasidic* Jews rejects association with mainstream American society, separates themselves by their dress, and isolates themselves from those outside of the *Hasidic* community (Wasserstein, 1997). This group's culture has changed very little and is seeing population revitalization. Secular Jews, on the other end of the spectrum, might seem to be completely assimilated, indistinguishable from any other American, which results in a perceived Jewish population loss (Wasserstein, 1997). Yet, even among more assimilated communities, Jews often have their own Jewish community centers, philanthropic associations, social groups, and other types of Jewish-affiliated organizations (Kosmin, 1990; Levin & Price, 2010).

As each wave of Jewish immigrants came to the United States, previously settled Jews often encouraged different types of assimilation. When the European Jews came to the United States fleeing pre-*Holocaust* Europe and again when arriving post-World War II, there was pressure from the established American Jewish community to assimilate quickly. Survivors of the *Holocaust* were discouraged from discussing their experiences (Chaitin, 2002; Haas, 1990). Jewish immigrants often bestowed their children with "American-sounding" names. However, more recently, when Jews from the Soviet Union arrived in the United States, many found pressure from American Jews to assimilate into the American Jewish community rather than into the non-Jewish American community (Kosmin, 1990).

Debbie: *My grandparents wanted their children's names to sound American. They chose the English name "Jane" for their daughter and "Franklin" as a middle name for their son, to honor Franklin D. Roosevelt, who was president upon their arrival in the United States. Yet, they lived in a town that had one synagogue and no churches. I grew up in the same town with Jewish values and tradition as part of our daily lives. As an adult living in other cities, I consciously drew parts of that culture back into my own life.*

Becky: *My parents often speak about growing up in the 1950s in the era of cowboys and comic superheroes. They describe the general sentiment of the era shared by Jews in the United States to either hide or to separate from the perceived image of the emaciated, weak Holocaust survivor. Growing up in an area with a significant Jewish population, I never felt pressure to change or adapt my cultural identity, nor to assimilate to secular society. The family with which I spent every Christmas Eve in high school certainly understood and respected this about me, and I was always happy to share my holidays with them.*

Historical Realities Versus Popular Myths

Debbie: *Every day, Opa (my grandfather) asked me, "So, what did you learn today?" He instilled the idea that you should always be asking questions, that you should learn something from every moment. Mom always said, "They can take everything away, but they cannot take our education." Yes,*

there is a stereotype of Jewish people being "bookish," but in my mind it was positive, based on our traditions, our history, and our identity as "People of the Book."

Becky: *When my sister was in elementary school, she was puzzled when one of her friends asked if there was blood in the* matzah *(unleavened bread) that she was eating for snack time during the Passover holiday. Eating the blood of any animal (or human) is against traditional Jewish law. Yet, the falsehood about blood in* matzah, *along with other fabrications about ritual murder and cannibalism, collectively known as* blood libel, *have been used historically to blame Jews for Christian deaths; to exclude, marginalize, and dehumanize Jews; and to justify the torture and murder of Jews (Dinnerstein, 1994; Limor, 1997).*

The Anti-Defamation League (2001) defines *anti-Semitism* as a belief or behavior that is hostile toward Jews just because they are Jewish. They further explain that *anti- Semitism* may include religious teachings proclaiming the inferiority of Judaism, efforts to isolate or oppress Jews, or spreading or maintaining prejudices and stereotypes about Jewish people. According to the Anti-Defamation League, the three most common *anti-Semitic* beliefs are: (1) that Jews were responsible for the death of Jesus Christ, (2) that Jews are more loyal to Israel than to the United States, and (3) that Jews have too much power in the United States. More generally, these and other *anti-Semitic* beliefs can be characterized as religious *anti-Semitism*, allegiance to Israel, and stereotypes about Jewish people (Foxman, 2005; Nadal, Issa, Griffin, Hamit, & Lyons, 2010).

Religious Anti-Semitism

Robinson (2001) differentiates between religious *anti-Semitism*, hating Jews for what Jews believe, and racial *anti-Semitism*, hating Jews for who they are understood to be. Religious *anti-Semitism* emerged from intolerance for those Jewish religious beliefs and practices that made the Jews "other" (Prager & Telushkin, 2003). According to Prager and Telushkin, early church fathers felt that Judaism's theological connection to Christianity threatened to weaken Christianity, so they denied the validity of Jews and Judaism. Rather than depicting the Crucifixion as a Roman execution, the New Testament placed the blame for Jesus' death on the Jews, in part to encourage and promote rejection of Judaism (Limor, 1997). The accusation of Jews as "Christ-killers" gave legitimacy for brutalizing Jews. Chrysostom, who was highly influential in the formation of the Church during the 4th century, reinforced this accusation against the Jews and stated that Christians have divine sanctioning for beating or murdering Jews. Several centuries later, in medieval courts, Jews were frequently accused of mass murders. The only evidence needed for a conviction was the fact that Jews do not believe in the Trinity, a belief that is viewed in Judaism as a violation of the commandment of monotheism (Prager & Telushkin, 2003).

Just as the Jews persisted in their religious beliefs and

practices with the emergence of Christianity, they did not adopt Muslim religious tenets at the dawning of Islam. Muhammad's discontent was recorded in the Koran, which gave those Muslims who sought it a divinely sanctioned reason for *anti-Semitism* (Prager & Telushkin, 2003). King Faisal of Saudi Arabia incited the *blood libel* in the 1960s and 1970s. False accusations appeared again in a Jordanian newspaper in 2001 (Prager & Telushkin). Prager and Telushkin note the irony that Jewish law forbids human sacrifice and the consumption of blood. Jews, by their own definition, are not permitted to commit such an act.

Becky: *My grandfather's aunt returned to Poland after the concentration camps were liberated in 1945, only to witness attacks against fellow survivors. These* pogroms *were justified by* blood libel—*more false accusations.*

Allegiance to Israel

Jews have lived continuously in the contested sliver of land currently known as Israel since 1200 *BCE*. Today, Jewish people may refer to being Israelites or The Children of Israel. Although this may refer to the state of Israel, it may also refer to the Jewish people as descendants of Jacob, who was also named Israel ("he who wrestles with *G-d*"), in the *Torah*. While many Jews agree that having a Jewish homeland is important, some Orthodox Jews actually opposed the creation of the state of Israel (Wasserstein, 1997). Today, Jews who support the existence of Israel may nonetheless disapprove of Israeli politics (Vorspan & Saperstein, 1998). According to the Pew survey (Lugo, Cooperman & Smith, 2013), 89% of American Jews agree that a person can be both Jewish and strongly critical of Israel (Lugo et al., 2013).

Debbie: *When one colleague learned that I am Jewish, she immediately brought up Israeli politics. As she launched into complaints about Israel's policies, she said, "I don't have a problem with you, but the problem with Judaism is …." She did not separate my religion from the policies of another country. In fact, my Jewish Israeli cousins have openly expressed dissatisfaction or disagreement with their own government's actions. Being Jewish (whether one is Israeli or American) does not imply consistent agreement with Israeli policies any more than being American implies agreement with every single American political action. The Jewish people I know hold a wide range of opinions about both American and Israeli politics.*

Stereotypes About Jewish People

Just as the *blood libel* has its roots in the Middle Ages, myths about Jewish affinity toward specific professional fields are rooted in historical prejudice and exclusion of Jews from mainstream society. At many different points in history, restrictions have been placed upon Jews regarding what professions they were allowed to enter and what services they could provide. For example, Jews have been barred from owning property and businesses, military service, and labor. Jewish history is sprinkled with incidents of Jews being forced

to leave their dwellings and having restrictions placed upon where they could and could not live. Jews adapted by entering trade and commerce, intellectual work, and the arts. The importance of "study" in the Jewish religion historically bolstered the Jewish literacy rate, which enhanced the professions that Jews could pursue. This was passed down from generation to generation, as were family businesses and lines of work (Limor, 1997). However, this also fueled discrimination and drove stereotypes of the intellectual and professional pursuits of Jewish people (Miller & Lovinger, 2000; Takaki, 1993). During the Middle Ages, the church forbade Christians to lend money, opening the door for Jews to fill this niche in society. Although moneylending enabled economic growth and development, it also fueled hatred as interest rates became high, reflecting both the risk of loaning money and the high taxation placed on Jews (Limor, 1997). This fed negative views of Jews involving money that have remained over time.

Harmful propaganda falsely insinuating Jewish conspiracy for political control and global domination points to another deleterious stereotype about Jews. *Anti-Semitic* literature such as *Protocols of the Elders of Zion* (citation: see Appendix A), which outlines a fictitious plan of Jewish world domination, began mass circulation in the early 1900s (Dinnerstein, 1994; Steinsaltz, 2005). Although it was proven to be a fabrication, it was translated into several languages and circulates where *anti-Semitism* is rampant (Dinnerstein, 1994). The worst myths about Jews come to life in this widely distributed publication, and unfortunately, the reality of their falsehood remains overlooked by many.

Debbie: *I once had a prolonged conversation with a friend who angrily declared, "Jews have too much power in this country." When I asked him to substantiate this claim, he spent several hours doing research in an attempt to do so, ultimately admitting that his claim was based on unsubstantiated stereotypes.*

Historically, *anti-Semitic* beliefs and other current popular myths have fueled repeated expulsions and systematic genocides throughout history (Prager & Telushkin, 2003). Looking at more recent history, it was not uncommon in the United States for a Jewish person to be restricted from public organizations of facilities. Around the time of World War II, signs reading "no dogs or Jews allowed" were seen in parks in the United States, *anti-Semitic* songs were sung in the American military, and hearing *anti-Semitic* speech from political, religious, and business leaders was common plac (Dinnerstein, 1994).

In the late 20th century, Jews continued to experience *anti-Semitism* at the hands of neo-Nazis and within communities' political and social institutions (Dinnerstein, 1994). More recently, research by Kosmin and Keysar (2014) revealed the startling fact that more than half of all Jewish college students in the United States personally experienced or witnessed *anti-Semitism* during the 2013-2014 academic year. *Anti-Semitism* has been carried into the 21st century and is trending upward (Foxman, 2005; Prager & Telushkin, 2003).

Becky: *As a carpenter in the United States during the 1950s through the 1980s, my grandfather was told not to let Jews buy houses in particular Chicago suburbs. He felt as if* anti-Semitism *had followed him to America. Fueled by his anger, I used research assignments in school as opportunities to learn more about* anti-Semitism *in the United States. At a young age, I understood that* anti-Semitism *has shown up in history as a convenient scapegoat, backlash against social progressivism, and when immigration is a contested political topic. It is horrifying as a politically engaged adult to see these patterns reemerging, and to bare witness to* anti-Semitism *reclaiming a prominent and legitimate place on the political and social stages of America's story.*

Microaggressions

Debbie: *A few years ago, I hired a contractor to complete a project. While we were discussing the work to be done, he noticed a* menorah *on my shelf. "That's okay," he assured me. "I understand. I have had other Jewish clients." While I believe his statement was made in the name of political correctness, I was left wondering exactly what it was that he understood, what was okay, why it might not have been okay, and why my religion had anything to do with the work he was hired to complete.*

Sue (2010) suggests that more overt and deliberate forms of oppression are easier to deal with than unconscious and unintentional forms. According to Sue, the greatest harm comes from well-meaning people who consider their values egalitarian but have unknowingly inherited and perpetuate the biased values of our society. In many cases, people are not aware of their prejudices, especially if they hold beliefs that are held by their families, the media, or other circles of influence. No one is immune from inheriting the racial biases of the previous generation (Sue, 2010). "Denial of religious prejudices" (Nadal et al., 2010, p. 304) may be embedded in the "politically correct" phrases a person uses, especially when these phrases are often learned without understanding their origin or meaning (Sue, 2010). Furthermore, these "politically correct" phrases may not be perceived by all to actually be inclusive.

Debbie: *One year, I ran into a store the day before Christmas. As I left, the clerk wished me "Happy Holidays!" I returned her greeting as I walked out of the store. The excitement of Christmas Eve was palpable, and I think that the salesperson actually meant to wish me a Merry Christmas. I wish she had said that; it would have seemed more heartfelt and genuine to me (although, I know, not to others!). As I walked through the mall, I noticed that "Season's Greetings" was written next to the nativity scene. Did they think that writing "Season's Greetings" somehow neutralized the fact that a nativity scene is related to Christmas? While I love the joy conveyed during this time of year, I feel like there is an attempt to include me where I don't actually belong. The constant message is that the norm is Christian, or at least that the norm*

is to have a major holiday during the winter solstice. Hanukkah is not a major holiday. Wishing me "Season's Greetings" does not negate my "otherness."

The assumption that one's own religious identity is the norm is another common microaggression (Nadal et al., 2010, p. 302). Likewise, viewing the practices, music, or actions of Jews as wrong, or pathological, instead of understanding that the practice is an expression of religion or tradition, is a form of microaggression (Nadal et al.). This may take the form of telling someone that they are wrong for writing *G-d* without the vowel or not considering Jewish holidays when making appointments. Therapists may commit this microaggression if they fail to understand the importance of family, community, and tradition to many Jewish people, seeing a person's interconnectedness as a problem rather than helping them to use it as a strength. Another microaggression may be to rely on the Western association that music in a minor mode is sad. This convention does not apply to Jewish music (Rykov, 2001). Judging all Jewish music in a minor key as sad without examining context can in effect pathologize this music.

Debbie: *I led a* klezmer *band at a Jewish Day school. Most of the pieces we played were joyous, best suited for celebratory dancing, and in a minor key. The kids loved to push my tempos, playing the songs as fast as they could. The concert concluded with "Hatikva," the Israeli national anthem. I was asked by an audience member, "Why is all Jewish music so sad?" I was surprised at the question after such an upbeat, energetic concert. I responded that I hear "Hatikva" as stirring, yearning, and beautiful, and shared that the title literally translates to "the hope." "No," she said dismissively, failing to hear the hope that I had articulated. "It is like all Jewish music ... all just so sad and tragic."*

Whether deliberate or unintentional, endorsement of Jewish stereotypes is another form of microaggression (Nadal et al., 2010). Some stereotypes are clearly malevolent, such as those depicting Jews as pushy, insular, ill-mannered, cruel, dishonest, greedy, arrogant, or cheap. Other stereotypes masquerade as compliments but are no less damaging. These include those which depict Jews as financially successful, ambitious, intelligent, loyal, hardworking, or energetic (Nadal et al., 2010). Lightstone (2013) also identifies "philo-Semitism" (p. 38), an interest, fascination, or affection for Jewish people. Exoticization allows oneself to see people as a group rather than as individuals; thus it is another form of microaggression.

Debbie: *When I was 12 years old, my family went on vacation to San Francisco. While my Dad and I were in a trolley car, we spoke to another tourist. Making small talk, the man asked where we were from. "New Jersey." He asked, "New Jersey? Where is New Jersey?" "It is the state that is just south of New York," we explained. "Oooh! New York. Yeah, I can tell, you do look Jewish." Not only was I amazed that this man presumed that we are Jewish based on New Jersey's proximity to New York, but I was mystified by his assumption that everyone from New York is Jewish. Does my non-Jewish father "look Jewish"? What did the man mean when he said I "look*

Jewish"? In other contexts, I have been told that I do not look Jewish. Why does it matter?

The "assumption of religious homogeneity" (Nadal et al., 2010, p. 303) is the assumption that all Jews are the same. Any assumption of homogeneity dehumanizes individuals within a group, thus enabling genocide and perpetuating misconceptions into new generations. While there is some homogeneity among Jewish people, Jews certainly do not all have the same views—political, religious, or otherwise. Nevertheless, the assumption that all Jews have the same political agenda has had catastrophic results historically and continues to emerge in hateful rhetoric. This assumption incited the battle cry "death to all Jews" (Willsher, 2014, July 21) during an anti-Israel riot that flooded the media in 2014. The angry rioters used "Jewish" and "Israel" interchangeably, holding all Jews responsible for the actions of a handful of Israeli politicians (Jewish Federation of Greater Ann Arbor, personal communication, July 22, 2014). Because many Jews have felt the sting of assumed homogeneity and have witnessed its effects throughout history, Miller and Lovinger (2000) suggest that such rioting or other anti-*Zionist* or anti-*Semitic* actions could be terrifying to any Jew.

Becky: A client of mine came to a session after watching a news program and whispered, "It's like the Holocaust *all over again. Is it okay to sing Jewish songs today?"*

Debbie and Becky: We also find the news terrifying on some days. Nonetheless, while we have stood on the receiving end of personal microaggressions and oppression and we have bared witness to microaggressions to the Jewish people as a whole, we do not believe that they are major contributors to serious distress in our current lives. In a therapeutic setting, we might be surprised or even annoyed by a suggestion to examine them. Trust us, we have other pressing issues that would warrant prioritization in therapy! For some people, microaggressions and oppression do cause considerable stress and might be worth examining, depending, of course, upon the client.

Meaning of Medicine, Health, and Well-Being

Becky: Fall is my favorite season, hands down. I love all things autumnal: apple-picking, pumpkin-flavored coffee, the scent of fresh school supplies (even when I'm not in school — we're all lifelong learners, right?), and gathering with friends and family to observe the Jewish High Holidays. Rosh Hashanah and Sukkot lend themselves well to ushering in autumn, although I recall sweelteringly hot days sitting in synagogue longing for cooler fall breezes. Yom Kippur, the most solemn of the Jewish holidays, does not necessarily fit in thematically with my autumnal joy, despite taking breaks from the long services outside among the changing trees and piles of fallen leaves. Every year, almost without fail, the somber and serene atmosphere outside of services is interrupted by the wailing siren sounds of an ambulance rushing to the rescue of a congregant who attempted the ritual of fasting on Yom Kippur but probably should not have for health reasons.

While it is a Jewish law for Jewish adults to fast on Yom Kippur, the Jewish law of *pikuach nefesh,* which safeguards life above all else, excuses anyone from the fast if it would jeopardize their health. In fact, the preservation of life is held above all other commandments; any law (except those against adultery, murder, and idolatry) may be broken in order to save a life (Miller & Lovinger, 2000; Wigoder, 2002). Jewish laws and texts codify many specific issues relating to physical and mental health and well-being quite specifically (Levin & Prince, 2010). It is important for a music therapist to account for the relationship between *halakhah* (Jewish law) and ethics with regard to health care and decision-making (Levin & Prince, 2010), especially as technological advances in health care evolve and require new insight into Jewish law. As has been true since biblical times, one must interpret Jewish law in the face of modern medical and health issues (Rabinowitz, 2000; Vorspan & Saperstein, 1998). These decisions may vary based on many factors, including denomination, family history, the individual, and the situation.

Halakhah regarding the preservation of Jewish life pervades many areas of health that a music therapist may encounter with clients across multiple settings. According to Jewish law, it is expected that a Jewish person will accept medical treatment to preserve life (Meyerstein, 2004). If these means are deemed either heroic or artificial (e.g., feeding tubes, resuscitation, life support), they fall into a very gray area, and individual opinions will vary as to how to interpret the law (Vorspan & Saperstein, 1998). There is also *halakhah* to consider when deciding to start or stop treatment, especially if these decisions would result in prolonging life or accelerating death. These factors, while influencing patients' and their families' decisions, can become entangled with both understanding and misconception about medical treatment and hospice care.

Becky: As a music therapist in a medical setting or working with a hospice team, I have found it crucial to be aware of these factors in order to support my Jewish clients through their decision-making processes and to help my colleagues sort through the ramifications of clients' choices. I've witnessed decisions made by families against the medical team's best advice based on pikuach nefesh *and other* halakhah, *adding tension and stress to moments that were already incredibly difficult for all involved.*

The issue of organ donation challenges the Jewish custom of preservation of the body, yet is also considered a *mitzvah* (good deed) (Vorspan & Saperstein, 1998). Likewise, circumstances in which the donor's life would be at risk or shortened in order to prolong that of another constitute a gray area. Adult stem cell donation, embryonic stem cell research, and related issues are also subject to various religious interpretations.

Becky: I recall my younger sister grappling to interpret halakhah *when she needed a stem cell transplant from an unrelated matched donor as the next step of her cancer treatment. For my sister, a professional Jewish social justice advocate and aspiring Reform Jewish* rabbi, *choosing to pursue her stem cell transplant involved research of Jewish texts, consultation with* rabbis *and Jewish scholars, and her own inner process exploring opinions and beliefs.*

Another area of health that may be affected by interpretation of Jewish law is pregnancy and birth. According to *halakhah,* Jewish life begins once a baby has passed through the mother's birth canal (Goldman, 2000). Little is defined in *halakhah* with regard to donation of eggs, artificial insemination, in vitro fertilization, and surrogacy (Jotkowitz, 2011). Traditionally, using birth control is not in accordance with Jewish law unless it is being used for urgent health and well-being purposes (Miller & Lovinger, 2000; Rabinowitz, 2000). Today, the acceptability of various methods differs according to denomination and individual decision (Miller & Lovinger, 2000). All denominations agree that termination of a pregnancy is acceptable if it is necessary to protect the health of the mother; in other circumstances, other denominations are more accepting of abortion than the Orthodox (Miller & Lovinger, 2000). As with so many other issues, a combination of denomination and individual evaluation will factor into the decision. When confronting such issues, it may be advisable to consult with a Jewish chaplain or with a *rabbi* for support and insight. Traditionally, Jews have sought counsel from their *rabbis* when dealing with various issues, and following the *rabbi's* counsel is considered by some to be a religious obligation (Rabinowitz, 2000; Schnall, 2006).

When facing physical or mental health challenges, some Jews attribute causality to a divine test from *G-d* or to negative consequences for the violation of a Jewish law (Schnall, 2006). Viewing circumstances as part of a larger divine plan or seeking *G-d's* guidance during a difficult time can provide comfort or bolster one's personal relationship with religion. However, the viewpoint of divine intervention can also foster negativity toward one's religion if results are disappointing (Rosmarin, Paragament, Krumrei, & Flannelly, 2009). In general, since a person's belief in *G-d* can both support and hinder coping with health struggles, it is crucial to examine the degree to which a person understands *G-d* to be involved in health and well-being (Meyerstein, 2004; Rosmarin et al., 2009).

Throughout each era in Jewish history, free will and divine providence have been debated and interpreted in different ways. Jewish texts across time from the most notable Jewish philosophers of multiple denominations yield significantly varying viewpoints, making it hard to predict what an individual might believe. Modern secular knowledge, acceptance of science, and tragedies in Jewish history all pose challenges to more traditional concepts of a divine plan and locus of control (De Lange, 1997).

Although there are many individual differences, the commonalities across denominations and practices of Judaism include an interest in healing, the need to preserve life, the desire to make health care decisions informed by *halakhah,* and the connection between body and spirit (Levin

& Prince, 2010; Meyerstein, 2004). Maimonides, an important Jewish philosopher and scholar in the 12th century, recognized the impact of positive physical health on good mental health and encouraged those in need to seek help for both (Meyerstein, 2004). This connection is reflected in the powerful prayer "Mi Shebeirach," which asks for the renewal of body and spirit. Although it is part of prayer and *Torah* services, it is often recited or sung outside of the *synagogue* by those in need of support.

Becky: *To borrow from the blog my sister, Elissa Froman z"l* (may her memory be a blessing), *wrote while ill: "… this prayer is part of every service in which the* Torah *is read, including every* Shabbat *morning, and is a regular part of Jewish worship. It is also said by congregations and individuals at times when healing is needed. Debbie Friedman wrote a version of the 'Mi Shebeirach,' adding meaningful words and a beautiful melody that is now used in congregations across the country, including and far beyond Reform temples. There is a mystical, inexplicable healing power in the singing of Debbie Friedman's 'Mi Shebeirach' that is difficult to articulate with words alone … the energy that comes from having beloved friends … by your bedside is healing. The energy that comes from a person hundreds of miles away sending renewal through the mystically powerful words of Debbie Friedman's 'Mi Shebeirach' is healing."*

Meaning and Function of Music

Debbie: *As soon as I could read music, I played in my Grandmother's (Omi's)* klezmer *band. Traditionally, a* klezmer *band did not have written music, relied upon playing songs by ear, picked up new songs as the band traveled, and changed arrangements to accommodate new musicians as they joined. Omi's group harkened back to the roots of* klezmer, *and we played music from Russia, Greece, Romania, the United States, and many other places. Omi often said, "We played whatever was called for … happy, sad, serious, celebratory, patriotic." Especially when she first arrived in the United States, music was Omi's way of connecting to other people, and* klezmer *music was the common language.*

Despite years of not playing Jewish music and an inability to correctly pronounce many Hebrew *words, for me, all of the music felt like coming home when I began working with children and older adults at the Jewish Community Center (JCC) as a music therapist. The modes, not just the aeolian, but the freygish, Ukrainian, and modified mixolydian modes, felt like a balm to my soul. As I played and listened to more Jewish music, I became more connected to my Jewish roots, as if the music was telling me something that I had forgotten. Shortly after that, I joined my current congregation, largely because of the quality of the music. A sung prayer or blessing holds more power for me than one that is simply spoken. At the JCC, I connected to those familiar melodies and created new connections. The JCC serves families who are Orthodox, Conservative, Reform, Reconstructionist, Humanistic, and unaffiliated and born in the United States, Israel, Russia, South America, Europe, and other countries. Yet, we all know common songs and melodies for holidays, festivals, celebrations, and dancing. As each group offers new songs, melodies, and traditions, our community grows. Just as my grandmother did, we use music to create community.*

Liturgical Music

Daily and holiday-specific prayers share similarities across different denominations and congregations, as prayers and traditional liturgical music share sacred text sources (Shiloah, 1992). Melodies may be based on *Torah* tropes, which are small cantillations indicating a pattern of notes that have been passed down orally and can vary depending upon different individual and congregational traditions. Some prayer melodies transcend congregational differences, such as those that use traditional "from Sinai" melodies like the Yom Kippur prayer "Kol Nidré" (Wigoder, 2002). Rhythm often follows the text's meter and melodies are often modal (Rykov, 2001). The specific mode used for a prayer may vary depending on the time of year or day of the week. These liturgical modes are explained in Appendix E.

Although some Jews and specific *synagogues* use more of the vernacular language then others, the core prayers are in *Hebrew* (Froman, 2009; Goldman, 2000). Often found alongside the *rabbi* leading Jewish worship services, a *cantor* serves as the music leader of the congregation, as music plays such a large role in Jewish religious life (Wigoder, 2002). What differs in congregations is whether other instruments are used, whether the singing is restricted to chanted prayer or extended to other songs, and who is allowed to musically lead the congregation.

Types of Jewish Music

Most Jewish music can be classified as either religious or secular (Rykov, 2001). However, within these categories there is just as much diversity as there are practices and beliefs among those who consider themselves Jewish (Froman, 2009). Music plays many different roles and may be personally or spiritually meaningful for a variety of reasons in the lives of Jewish people. For some, Jewish music can transcend categorization. Music is used in the *synagogue* and in the home for purposes of ritual, dance, and entertainment (Summit, 2000). Various genres of music are considered "Jewish" because of their connection to Jewish tradition, religion, and/or culture (Froman, 2009).

Songs associated with a holiday might not carry a heavy sacred connotation or derive their text from liturgical sources. For example, most Hanukkah songs are not sacred in nature, such as "I Have a Little Dreydl," which refers to a game associated with the holiday and contains nothing about any religious aspects of the holiday. Other Jewish music may have a connection to the cultural or religious roots of Judaism, although it may not function as religious music (Kligman, 2000).

Another type of popular Jewish music exists which parallels closely the genre of Christian rock. This music sounds more "mainstream" and may incorporate aspects of Jewish traditional prayer or pertain to Jewish values or Jewish culture. American Jews may also listen to Israeli music, which ranges from "Top 40", to folk, to hip-hop.

Perhaps most well-known and recognizable to the non-Jewish American public is a type of secular Jewish music known as *klezmer*. Although *klezmer* music is occasionally mournful, most of it is joyous dance music. "Hava Nagila" may be the most familiar piece in this genre; it is ubiquitous at *Bar* and *Bat Mitzvah* celebrations and at Jewish weddings. *Klezmer* is often distinguished by improvisation, virtuosity, and the prominence of specific instruments such as the violin and clarinet (Wigoder, 2002). When *klezmer* was brought to the United States, it borrowed American jazz melodies and songs from the *Yiddish* theater repertoire; however, it evolved from the tradition of traveling musicians playing for Jewish celebrations. *Klezmer* songs had a wide range of influences, including eastern European folk songs, Middle Eastern songs and scales, and the modes used in liturgical music (Strom, 2006). Horowitz (2012) noted that although the modes of *klezmer* music resemble Western modes, each mode also includes a specific mood and melodic pattern. A description of four common modes is provided in Appendix E.

Klezmer bands were not the only venue for preserving folk songs; lullabies and other songs have also been passed down within families. Jewish folk songs reflect the wide range of geographic, ethnic, and cultural contexts in which Jewish people have lived and been acculturated. Therefore, the languages found in Jewish folk songs may include *Yiddish, Ladino, Judeo-Arabic,* Hebrew, English, and other languages associated with Jewish culture (Fonda, 2012). Whether they were written by people living in America, Europe, or the Middle East, these songs reflect the spiritual life and struggle of the people; they are "the tonal expression of Jewish life and development over a period of more than two thousand years" (Idelsohn, 1967, p. 24).

Niggunim (plural of *niggun*) are melodies that use syllables such as "bim bam" or "lai, lai, lai" instead of words. These wordless melodies were historically connected to Jewish mysticism; *rabbis* in the *Hasidic* movement believed that chanting *niggunim* could help a person prepare for prayer (Fonda, 2012; Rykov 2001). Today, *niggunim* are used as familiar chants in many congregations. A *niggun* is often easy to learn, might be familiar-sounding even if the melody is slightly different, and does not require mastery of languages associated with Judaism.

Debbie: A music therapy student of mine was working with a hospice patient who was Jewish and originally from Russia. The student did not speak Russian or Yiddish, but I suggested that she sing the folk song "Tumbalalaika" on the syllable "lai, lai, lai." The patient opened her eyes at the familiar song and quietly sang along with the folk song presented in the style of a niggun.

Jewish music has been described by musicologists as "music written by Jews, for Jews" (Bohlman, 2002). However, some works written independently of Jewish association may take on a Jewish religious or cultural connotation through interpretation, association, or use. For example, the theme to the Israeli national anthem, "Hatikva," was part of *Die Moldau* by Smetana, a classical music composition that borrows its main theme from a Czech folk song. Listeners of different backgrounds might attach different meanings to it given its multiple appearances in the repertoire. Likewise, just because a piece of music is written by someone who is Jewish doesn't mean that it should be considered "Jewish music" (Rykov, 2001). "White Christmas," for instance, was written by Irving Berlin, a Jewish-American composer, yet it does not fit Bohlman's criteria for having been written for Jews.

The line between sacred and secular is not always firm, and it can be difficult to classify Jewish music because much of it belongs under multiple categories (Froman, 2009). Liturgical texts and Jewish musical elements (e.g., folk melodies or certain scales) have been the basis of non-religious classical music (Kligman, 2000). Likewise, sacred texts have been set to non-traditional music and sung in religious worship services. Many songs from youth movements and summer camps, which are often based on popular music styles and intended to motivate and teach children and teenagers about Judaism, have found their way into the repertoire of music sung in the *synagogue* (Summit, 2000).

Rules About Using or Playing Music

It is true that the boundaries defined by genres of Jewish music are transcended at times. Yet, a music therapist should be aware that the genres of Jewish music do have specific functions and fixed places in Jewish religious practice and/or culture as a whole. Some clients will take offense at having secular music in a religious setting. Other Jewish clients will take offense at using prayers outside their intended context, as there are specific rules and circumstances regarding where and how these prayers should be chanted (Miller & Lovinger, 2000). For example, according to strict Jewish law, prayers such as the *"Mourner's Kaddish"* should be chanted only if there is a *minyan* of 10 Jewish adults.

Becky: *I am always aware of the function of the music I am using within the context of Judaism, as well as whether or not the words or melodies come from a sacred source. If I incorporate the liturgical "Mourner's Kaddish" during an individual session to facilitate coping with grief, I make sure that the client is comfortable chanting it outside of its traditional synagogue setting, and I am fully aware that some would say that what I do is wrong. Likewise, it is important to be thoughtful regarding using secular music in a sacred setting. During a Rosh Hashanah service at a retirement community, I witnessed a rabbi attempt to engage the sleepy congregation by leading them in selections from "Fiddler on the Roof." While some of the participants loved his rousing renditions of these songs, others considered the presence of Broadway music during the service to be sacrilege.*

Jewish laws indicate that work is not permitted on Jewish holidays, meaning that the work of playing an instrument is prohibited. Singing and the chanting of prayers is allowed, but one might be hard-pressed to find an Orthodox congregation using musical accompaniment at a service. However, just as Jewish law in other situations is impacted by personal choice and community custom, the use of instruments and music varies case by case.

Becky: *Something else I must consider as a music therapist is when the use of instruments might be distasteful. When I was filling in as a leader for a brief* Shabbat *service in a unit at a Jewish nursing home, I happened to have my guitar and a cart full of instruments with me as I was hurrying from a session to the service. One Orthodox woman exclaimed, "Don't you dare even think about playing! It isn't what you are supposed to do on* Shabbos!*" I assured her that I would not dream of it. Yet, if one were to walk into my parents'* Reform *synagogue on* Shabbat, *they would find a guitar strapped to the* rabbi *and a* djembe *in the* cantor's *lap. Using instruments and playing different types of music need to be purposeful decisions made with insight into the clients' perspectives and setting, as well as Jewish custom.*

Vocal music is more traditional and therefore seems like it could be universally called upon when working with Jewish clients. However, this is not the case. When I co-treat with physical therapists in the large therapy gym at a Jewish-affiliated facility, I ask if I am in the presence of Orthodox Jewish men who are not permitted to hear a woman sing (Rykov, 2001). Sometimes I have been assured of their comfort with me singing in their proximity, while at other times I have been asked to refrain. However, I always ask and use my best judgment, as I would rather ere on the side of caution.

Debbie: *Incorporation of holidays is another area to consider carefully. As a music therapist, I love holidays because they provide a meaningful session theme. At my son's public school, while there are no parties for "religious holidays" such as Christmas or Passover, costumes are worn on Halloween, cards are exchanged on Valentine's Day, and everyone wears green on St. Patrick's Day. These "American" holidays are considered to have minimal religious significance today even if the holidays trace their origins to a religion. When I worked with children at the Jewish Community Center, I could use patriotic repertoire in conjunction with the Fourth of July (American Independence Day) or incorporate Thanksgiving songs because these holidays celebrate American events. However, because Halloween, Valentine's Day, and St. Patrick's Day are not Jewish holidays and have non-Jewish religious roots, using them in sessions in this setting would have been frowned upon at the least. It should not be assumed that these holidays are universally observed; at some settings and with some Jewish clients, the inclusion of these holidays would not be appropriate.*

When making decisions about music, denomination gives some insight and setting may dictate policy, but ultimately choices about how to use music depend on the individual case (Froman, 2009). Start with more traditional arrangements of

Jewish music, making initial repertoire decisions based on background, and monitor client response. It is helpful to ask before taking liberties with traditional Jewish customs, such as using liturgical pieces out of the context of *synagogue*, using instruments on *Shabbat*, or exposing Orthodox men to a female singing voice.

Music as a Way of Forming and Affirming Identity

Debbie: *When I lead children's services or work with groups of Jewish children, I depend on the music as a tool to convey the meaning of the holidays, to teach* Hebrew *words, and to instill Jewish values. When I lead the kids'* klezmer *band, the music is a tool to connect to traditions. When I lead multigenerational services or lead children in performing for older adults, the music is the link that connects several generations, despite varying backgrounds.*

A Jewish person can go to a *synagogue* anywhere in the world and hear the universal and familiar texts of the prayers. If they do not understand the *Hebrew* words, then often the melody is the element with which they associate (Summit, 2000). Miller and Lovinger (2000) elaborate on this idea: "… Jewish prayer, usually sung or chanted, is learned very early in childhood. It is therefore not surprising that the familiar words and melody of traditional prayer can evoke a profound set of emotional and spiritual memories among adults. If prayer harkens in the psyche to a time prior to illness, it may exert an uplifting or organizing effect on the patient's psyche" (p. 274).

Becky: *I rely on this principle in working with clients of Jewish background, whether I am helping them to observe a holiday or ritual that is meaningful to them or helping them to connect to their sense of self. When I am called upon to adapt and conduct services for a memory care unit, I choose to skip the parts that do not lend themselves to successful participation for those with dementia, such as those that are heaviest on* Hebrew *reading or responsive readings in English. Instead, I go right for the music. For many of my clients with dementia, the melodies and songs are the most meaningful part of the holiday with which they can still connect and in which they can actively engage with others. It taps into their roots, their cores.*

Debbie: *My grandmother, Omi, was on hospice for several weeks before she died. I played music with her: folk songs, music from musicals, favorite piano pieces, but only an occasional "Jewish" piece. Although* klezmer *music had been her way of connecting to other Jewish immigrants, it was not her way of connecting to me, nor was it what she wanted to hear as she was nearing death. In her last weeks, her connection was strongest to the music she associated with her childhood in Germany and to the music she associated with family. The social worker repeatedly asked if Omi wanted to speak to a rabbi. "What do I want with a rabbi?" she asked. She had never felt a strong connection to the Jewish religion. Her connection to Judaism during her life had mostly been a cultural one, and it had been forged through music: Israeli folk songs,* songs with Jewish musical or cultural references, liturgical music, *Yiddish* songs, Ladino *songs, and* klezmer *music.*

Mazel Tov!

Mazel Tov! (Congratulations!) You now know a *mish mosh* (assortment) of *Judaica* (things relating to Judaism). With so many opinions, affiliations, backgrounds, questions, and circumstances, only this is certain: There is diversity within Jewish religious practice, culture, familial experience, and expression. Just because you have a Jewish client does not mean that he or she will know or want Jewish music or that the client will not know music of other religions. Jewish custom and religion might be incidental to the person or might be critically important. If one person answers the awkward question "What are you?" with "I am Jewish," it is likely to mean something different than it does for another individual and can even mean something different to one person throughout the course of their lifetime.

References

Abrams, M. S. (1999). Intergenerational transmission of trauma: Recent contributions from the literature of family systems approaches to treatment. *American Journal of Psychotherapy, 53*(2), 225–231.

Alpert, R. T., & Staub, J. J. (2000). *Exploring Judaism: A Reconstructionist approach.* Elkins Park, PA: The Reconstructionist Press.

Amir, D. (1997). Understanding the role of folk songs in Jewish-Israeli culture: Implications for music therapy. *The World of Music, 39*(1), 111–127.

Anti-Defamation League (2001). *Anti-Semitism.* Retrieved from http://archive.adl.org/hate-patrol/antisemitism.html#.U_qSxbxdU01

Baker, A. (1993). *The Jewish woman in contemporary society.* Washington Square, NY: New York University Press.

Baranowsky, A. B., Young, M., Johnson-Douglas, S., Williams-Keeler, L., & McCarrey, M. (1998). PTSD transmission: A review of secondary traumatization in Holocaust survivor families. *Canadian Psychology, 39*(4), 247–256.

Berger, A. L., & Berger, N. (Eds.). (2001). *Second-generation voices: Reflections by children of the Holocaust survivors and perpetrators.* Syracuse, NY: Syracuse University Press.

Bohlman, P. V. (2002). Music. In M. Goodman (Ed.), *The Oxford handbook of Jewish studies* (pp. 852–869). Oxford, UK: Oxford University Press.

Bronstein, L. (2014). *Reconstructionism on one foot.* Retrieved from http://www.jewishrecon.org/resource/reconstructionism-one-foot

Cardin, S. (2005). Community versus individualism. In M. Gerstenfeld (Ed.), *American Jewry's challenge: Conversations confronting the twenty-first century* (pp. 199–208). Lanham, MD: Rowman & Littlefield.

Chaitin, J. (2002). Issues and interpersonal values among three generations in families of Holocaust survivors. *Journal of Social and Personal Relationships, 19*(3), 379–402.

Cohen, A. B., Gorvine, B. J., & Gorvine, H. (2013). The religion, spirituality, and psychology of Jews. In K. Pargament (Ed.-in-Chief), J. Exline, & J. Jones (Assoc. Eds.), *APA handbooks in psychology: APA handbook of psychology, religion, and spirituality: Vol 1.* (pp. 665–679). Washington, DC: American Psychological Association.

Cohen, S. (2005). Non-denominational and postdenominational: Two tendencies in American Jewry. *Contact: The Journal of Jewish Life Network. 7*(4), 7–8. Retrieved from http://www.steinhardtfoundation.org/wp-install/wp-content/uploads/2013/10/summer_2005.pdf

Cohen, S., Landres, J. S., Kaunfer, E., & Shain, M. (2007). Emergent Jewish communities and their participants: Preliminary findings from the 2007 National Spiritual Communities Study. Retrieved from http://www.jewishemergent.org/survey/documents/NatSpirComStudyReport_S3K_Hadar.pdf

De Lange, N. (1997). Introduction. In N. de Lange (Ed.), *The illustrated history of the Jewish people* (pp. vii–xiv). Orlando, FL: Harcourt Brace & Company.

Dinnerstein, L. (1994). *Anti-Semitism in America.* New York, NY: Oxford University Press.

Fonda, B. (2012). Jewish musical heritage. *Jewish Folk songs.* Retrieved from http://www.jewishfolksongs.com/en/heritage#references

Foxman, A. (2005). The resuscitation of anti-Semitism. In M. Gerstenfeld (Ed.), *American Jewry's challenge: Conversations confronting the twenty-first century* (pp. 171–180). Lanham, MD: Rowman & Littlefield.

Froman, R. J. (2009). Music therapy practice with Jewish people in the United States of America. *Music Therapy Perspectives, 27*(1), 33–41.

Goldman, A. (2000). *Being Jewish: The spiritual and cultural practice of Judaism today.* New York, NY: Simon & Schuster.

Goldschmidt, H. (2006). *Race and religion among the chosen peoples of Crown Heights.* New Brunswick, NJ: Rutgers University Press.

Goldstein, E. L. (2006). *The price of whiteness: Jews, race, and American identity.* Princeton. NJ: Princeton University Press.

Hass, A. (1990). *In the shadow of the Holocaust: The second generation.* New York, NY: Cambridge University Press.

Heskes, I. (2009). *Cantors: American Jewish women.* Jewish women: A comprehensive historical encyclopedia. Jewish Women's Archive. http://jwa.org/encyclopedia/article/cantors-american-jewish-women

Idelsohn, A. Z. (1967). *Jewish music in its historical development.* New York, NY: Schocken Books.

Ingall, M. (2005). *Why are there so many Jewish feminists?* Retrieved from http://forward.com/articles/2305/why-are-there-so-many-jewish-feminists/

Jewish Orthodox Feminist Alliance. (n.d.). *Agunot and Jewish divorce overview.* Retrieved from http://www.jofa.org/Advocacy/Agunot_Overview

Jones, R. P., & Cox, D. (2012). *Chosen for what?: Jewish values in 2012.* Washington, DC: Public Research Institute Inc. Retrieved from http://publicreligion.org/site/wp-content/uploads/2012/04/Jewish-Values-Report.pdf

Jotkowitz, A. (2011). Surrogate motherhood revisited: Maternal identity from a Jewish perspective. *Journal of Religious Health, 50*(4), 835–840.

Khazzoom, L. (2016). Ancient Jewish history: Jews of the Middle East. Retrieved from http://www.jewishvirtuallibrary.org/jsource/Judaism/mejews.html

Keller, R. R. (2000). Religious diversity in North America. In P. S. Richards & A. E. Bergin (Eds.), *Handbook of psychotherapy and religious diversity* (pp. 27–55). Washington, DC: American Psychological Association.

Kligman, M. (2000). Music in Judaism. In J. Neusner (Ed.). *Encyclopedia of Judaism* (Vol. 2, pp. 905–926). New York, NY: The Continuum Publishing Company.

Kosmin, B. A. (1990). *The class of 1979: The 'acculturation' of Jewish immigrants from the Soviet Union.* New York, NY: North American Jewish Data Bank.

Kosmin, B. A., & Keysar, A. (2014). *National demographic survey of American Jewish college students 2014: Anti-Semitism report.* Retrieved from http://www.brandeiscenter.com/images/uploads/articleuploads/trinity-Anti-Semitism.pdf

Levitt, D. H., & Balkin, R. S. (2003). Religious diversity from a Jewish perspective. *Counseling and Values, 48*(1), 57–66.

Levin, J., & Prince, M. F. (2010). Judaism and health: Reflections on an emerging scholarly field. *Journal of Religion and Health, 50*(4), 765–777.

Limor, O. (1997). A rejected people. In N. de Lange (Ed.), *The illustrated history of the Jewish people* (pp. 87–139). Orlando, FL: Harcourt Brace & Company.

Lugo, L., Cooperman, A., & Smith, G. A. (2013). *Pew Research Center Survey of U.S. Jews: A Portrait of Jewish Americans.* Washington, DC: Pew Research Center. Retrieved from http://www.pewforum.org/2013/10/01/jewish-american-beliefs-attitudes-culture-survey/

Meyerstein, I. (2004). A Jewish spiritual perspective on psychopathology and psychotherapy: A clinician's view. *Journal of Religion and Health, 43*(4), 329–341.

Miller, L., & Lovinger, R. J. (2000). Psychotherapy with Conservative and Reform Jews. In P. S. Richards & A. E. Bergin (Eds.), *Handbook of psychotherapy and religious diversity* (pp. 259–286). Washington, DC: American Psychological Association.

Nadal, K. L., Issa, M., Griffin, K. E., Hamit, S., & Lyons, O. B. (2010). Religious microaggressions in the United States:

Mental health implications for religious minority groups. In D. W. Sue (Ed.), *Microaggressions and marginality: Manifestation, dynamics, and impact.* Hoboken, NJ: John Wiley & Sons.

Pasternak, V. (Ed.). (1997). *The Jewish fake book.* Owings Mills, MD: Tara Publications.

Prager, D., & Telushkin, J. (2003). *Why the Jews? The reason for anti-Semitism.* New York, NY: Simon & Schuster.

Rabinowitz, A. (2000). Psychotherapy with Orthodox Jews. In P. S. Richards & A. E. Bergin (Eds.), *Handbook of psychotherapy and religious diversity* (pp. 237–258). Washington, DC: American Psychological Association.

Reconstructionist Rabbinical College. (2014). *About Reconstructionist Judaism.* Retrieved from http://www.rrc.edu/node/1749

Robinson, G. (2001). *Essential Judaism: A complete guide to beliefs, customs, and rituals.* New York, NY: Simon & Schuster.

Rosmarin, D. H., Pargament, K. I., Krumrei, E. J., & Flannelly, K. J. (2009). Religious coping among Jews: Development and initial validation of the JCOPE. *Journal of Clinical Psychology, 65*(7), 670–683.

Rosten, L. (2001). *The new joys of Yiddish.* New York, NY: Three Rivers Press.

Russell, A., Plotkin D., & Heapy, N. (1985). Adaptive abilities in nonclinical second-generation Holocaust survivors and controls: A comparison. *American Journal of Psychotherapy, 39*(4), 564–579.

Rykov, M. H. (2001). Insights from a Jewish hospice experience. *Canadian Journal of Music Therapy, 8*(1), 64–74.

Saxe, L., & Tighe, E. (2013). Estimating and understanding the Jewish population in the United States: A program of research. *Contemporary Jewry, 33,* 43–62. doi:10.1007/s12397-013-9099-1

Schlossberger, E. S., & Hecker, L. L. (1998). Reflections on Jewishness and its implications for family therapy. *The American Journal of Family Therapy, 26*(2), 129–146.

Schnall, E. (2006). Multicultural counseling and the Orthodox Jew. *Journal of Counseling and Development, 84*(3), 276–282.

Schwartz, S. (1997). Beginnings. In N. de Lange (Ed.), *The illustrated history of the Jewish people* (pp. 3–51). Orlando, FL: Harcourt Brace & Company.

Sheskin, I. M. (2001). *How Jewish communities differ: Variations in the findings of local Jewish population studies.* Storrs, CT: The Mandell L. Berman Institute-North American Jewish Databank.

Shiloah, A. (1992). *Jewish musical traditions.* Detroit, MI: Wayne State University Press.

Sorkin, D. (1997). Into the Modern World. In N. de Lange (Ed.), *The illustrated history of the Jewish people* (pp. 199–253). Orlando, FL: Harcourt Brace & Company.

Steinsalz, A. (2005). *We Jews: Who are we and what should we do?* San Francisco, CA: Jossey-Bass.

Stone, A. (2013). *Orthodox women rabbis by any other name.* Retrieved from lilith.org/blog/2013/06/orthodox-women-rabbis-by-any-other-name.

Strom, Y. (2006). *The absolutely complete klezmer songbook.* Schaumburg, IL: Transcontinental Music.

Sue, D. W. (2010). *Microaggressions in everyday life: Race, gender, and sexual orientation.* Hoboken, NJ: John Wiley & Sons.

Summit, J. A. (2000). *The Lord's song in a strange land: Music and identity in contemporary Jewish worship.* New York, NY: Oxford University Press.

Takaki, R. (1993). *A different mirror: A history of multicultural America.* New York, NY: Back Bay Books.

Telushkin, J. (2008). *Jewish literacy revised ed: The most important things to know about the Jewish religion, its people, and its history.* New York, NY: William Morrow and Co.

Terry, M. (Ed.). (2000). *Reader's guide to Judaism.* Chicago, IL: Fitzroy Dearborn Publishers.

Union for Reform Judaism. (2011). *LGBT—Lesbian, gay, bisexual, and transgender inclusion.* Retrieved from www.urj.org/cong/membership/diversity/glbtq/

The United States Holocaust Museum. (n.d.). *Protocols of the Elders of Zion: Timeline.* Retrieved from https://www.ushmm.org/wlc/en/article.php?ModuleId=10007244

The United Synagogue of Conservative Judaism. (2012). *Jewish living.* Retrieved from http://www.uscj.org

Vorspan, A., & Saperstein, D. (1998). *Jewish dimensions of social justice: Tough moral choices of our time.* New York, NY: UAHC Press.

Wasserstein, B. (1997). The age of upheavals. In N. de Lange (Ed.), *The illustrated history of the Jewish people* (pp. 355–397). Orlando, FL: Harcourt Brace & Company.

Weinstein, L. (2003). Bereaved Orthodox Jewish families and their community: A cross-cultural perspective. *Journal of Community Health Nursing, 20*(4), 233–243.

Wigoder, G. (Ed.). (2002). *The new encyclopedia of Judaism* (2nd ed.). New York, NY: New York University Press.

Willsher, K. (2014, July 21). French officials decry rioters who target synagogue, Jewish shops. *Los Angeles Times.* Retrieved from http://www.latimes.com/world/europe/la-fg-france-rioters-synagogue-20140721-story.html

World Jewish Congress. (2014). *Communities.* Retrieved from http://www.worldjewishcongress.org/en/about/communities

Appendix A

Glossary

Throughout this chapter and in many of the appendices, we have used italics in the text, or plain font in the italicized sections, to identify Hebrew words, Yiddish words, or words that have a particular meaning in Jewish culture. If the italicized words are not defined in the context of the text, they can be found here. This glossary also includes words that a music therapist might find helpful in clinical practice.

A note on transliteration: The English spelling of a Hebrew or Yiddish word cannot be exact because the Hebrew alphabet is not the same as the English alphabet. Since Hebrew written in transliteration uses a phonetic version of Hebrew sounds, the English versions are inconsistent. For example, the correct way to spell Chanukah or Hanukkah is to spell it using Hebrew letters.

Aliyah—Hebrew: *going up*. Used to refer to moving to Israel, pilgrimage to Israel, or being called up to take part in reading the Torah (Wigoder, 2002).

Agunah—Hebrew: *chained*. A woman who has not been given a "get," or a document of permission from her husband to get a divorce, as is required in some forms of Orthodox Judaism (Jewish Orthodox Feminist Alliance, n.d.).

Anti-Semitism—Inimical views, actions, opposition, bigotry, or racism against Jews because they are Jews (Anti-Defamation League, 2001; Vorspan & Saperstein, 1998).

Ashkenazi (plural Ashkenazim)—From Hebrew: *German*. Jews with linage from Europe (Rykov, 2001), in particular from Germany, Italy, and France (Robinson, 2000; Wigoder, 2002), as well as many parts of eastern Europe.

Bar Mitzvah—Hebrew: *son of the commandment*. Ceremony when a 13-year-old boy reaches age of adulthood in Jewish law and is able/obligated to perform religious duties. The boy usually reads from the Torah and is given an aliyah. *Bar Mitzvah* may also be understood to include the celebration after the ceremony. It is not a confirmation (Rosten, 2001).

Bat (or Bas) Mitzvah—Hebrew: *daughter of the commandment*. Equivalent of a Bar Mitzvah for females (Rosten, 2001).

BCE/CE—Abbreviations that stand for "Before Common Era," which corresponds to the Gregorian time denotation of "BC" and "Common Era," which corresponds to the Gregorian time denotation of "AD" (Wigoder, 2002).

Blood Libel—Term used to describe false accusations made against Jews. Claims the use of blood or murder for ritual purposes (Dinnerstein, 1994; Wigoder, 2002).

Cantor/Hazzan—Leader of the prayer service in synagogues who is trained in liturgy and music. Teacher and music director of the congregation (Wigoder, 2002).

Chag Sameach—Hebrew: *happy holiday*. Used generically for Jewish holidays.

Diaspora—Dispersion of the Jews among the lands outside of Israel (Rosten, 2001).

Feh!—Rosten writes that this expletive should not be written without an explanation point. It is a Yiddish expression of disgust, "a crisp and exact delineation of distaste" (2001, p. 103).

Freygish Mode—(Phrygian dominant mode) The scale for this mode is composed of the root, minor 2nd, major 3rd, perfect 4th, perfect 5th, minor 6th, and minor 7th.

G-d—It is customary to avoid writing out G-d where it can be discarded or erased. Therefore, some Jewish people replace the "o" with a "-" (Wigoder, 2002). Some consider it blasphemy to write G-d with the vowel.

Gemara—From Aramaic: *that which is learned via tradition*. The Gemara consists of the rabbinical discussions and interpretations of the Mishna (Wigoder, 2002).

Gesundheit—Yiddish and German: *health*. Verbal response when someone sneezes (Rosten, 2001).

Get—Document of divorce written by the husband or by his representative, issued by a rabbinic expert, and given to the wife (Telushkin, 2008).

Ghetto—Overcrowded neighborhoods into which Jews were forcibly confined during the medieval period and later during Nazi control in Europe (Telushkin, 2008).

Goy/Goyim—A Gentile, or anyone who is not a Jew. Sometimes used in a pejorative sense (Rosten, 2001).

Gut Shabbos—Yiddish: *good Sabbath* (Rosten, 2001).

Hasidic/Hasidic Judaism—A type of Orthodox Judaism that emphasizes the intensity of prayer and aims to bring the mystical into daily practice (Sorkin, 1997).

Halakhah—Hebrew: *law*. Includes the laws/commandments and the part of the Talmud that interprets the laws (Rosten, 2001).

"Have an easy fast"—Phrase used during Yom Kippur, as it would be inappropriate to wish someone happiness during this holiday.

Hebrew—Language of the Jewish scriptures and liturgy, and the national language of Israel (Wigoder, 2002).

Holocaust—Systematic genocide of six million Jews and members of other groups, by the Nazi regime, between 1939 and 1945 in Europe (Takaki, 1993; Telushkin, 2008).

Judeo-Arabic—Language used by some Mizrahi Jews, which came from *Hebrew* and an Arabic dialect (Khazzoom, 2016).

Kabbalah—Mystical practice of Judaism, affiliated with, but not synonymous with Hasidism. Views liturgy as paramount, but stresses depth of intimate connection between G-d and the individual (Wigoder, 2002).

Kaddish/Mourner's Kaddish—A Jewish prayer that functions in different ways during worship services, including as a prayer for the deceased (Wigoder, 2002).

Ketubah—Marriage contract that traditionally spells out a husband's obligations to his wife (Telushkin, 2008).

Kippah/Kippot/Yarmulke/Skullcap—Kippah is the Hebrew word for the skullcap worn by some Jews, mostly males. Kippot is plural of kippah. Yarmulke (which rhymes with "bar culpa") is the Yiddish word for the same skullcap. Covering the head is a sign of respect before G-d (Goldman, 2000; Rosten, 2001).

Klezmer—First used to refer to eastern European Jewish instrumentalists, came to indicate the orally transmitted genre of Jewish music characterized by embellishments, virtuosity, and a certain timbre (Wigoder, 2002).

Kosher/Kashrut—The word kosher is a Hebrew term used to describe food and beverages deemed proper to eat according to kashrut, Jewish dietary laws according to the Bible as well as rabbinic texts (Wigoder, 2002).

Kristallnacht—German: *night of crystal.* Also referred to as the night of broken glass. Largest pogrom historically, which occurred in Germany on the night of November 9–10, 1938. Jewish synagogues, schools, businesses, health facilities, and homes were destroyed and burned; Jews were attacked and arrested (Dinnerstein, 1994).

L'Chaim—Hebrew: *to life!* A toast offered when one would say: "To your health" (Rosten, 2001).

L'Shanah Tovah/L'Shanah Tova Tikateyvu—Hebrew: *good new year/may you be inscribed for a good year.* Phrase used typically near Rosh Hashanah to greet or wish someone "happy new year" (Goldman, 2000).

Ladino—Language of Sephardic Jews in the Balkan countries and in Turkey, sometimes referred to as Judeo-Spanish (Wigoder, 2002).

Lulav and Etrog—The lulav is created from palm, willow, and myrtle branches; the etrog is a fruit from a citron tree. On Sukkot, it is the custom to hold and shake these items to the north, south, east, and west, and up and down. The custom is derived from a biblical ritual called "The Four Species," which includes these and other symbols found in nature (Wigoder, 2002).

Mazel Tov—Hebrew: *congratulations.* Although the phrase literally means "Good (Tov) Luck (Mazel), it is always used to mean "Congratulations" or "Thank G-d!" Rosten (2001, p. 222) writes, "Don't 'mazel tov' a man going into the hospital; say 'mazel tov!' when he comes out."

Menorah/Hanukkiyah—A menorah is a candelabra with seven branches; a symbol of Judiasm. A Hanukkiah is a candelabra with eight branches and a center candle called the "shamesh"; it is lit during the Hanukkah celebration (Wigoder, 2002). Hanukkiyahs are often called menorahs, but this is not accurate. "Menorah" may be a more generic term for any Jewish candelabra.

Messiah—Jewish tradition states that the Messiah will be a leader who will be a descendant of King David, gather Jews from the four corners of the world, restore them to full observance of Torah, and bring peace to the world. Jews do not consider Jesus to have been the Messiah. Today, Jews differ in their belief that a single leader will accomplish the work of the Messiah. Although some place great emphasis on the Messiah's arrival, others speak of the arrival of a Messianic age of peace (Telushkin, 2008).

Mezzuzah—Hebrew: *doorpost.* It is a commandment and a tradition to place a scroll of parchment with biblical passages on the right side of the entrance into a Jewish home. It is customary to touch it when entering and exiting. Some are worn as a necklace (Goldman, 2000).

Midrash—Hebrew: *commentary* or *interpretation.* Skilled analysis of biblical texts. This may refer to the method of inquiry or the classic books of compiled analysis (Rosten, 2001).

Minyan—10 adults, the minimum number necessary to form a quorum and say certain prayers, including the prayer for mourning. An adult was traditionally understood to be a post–Bar Mitzvah male (Telushkin, 2008).

Mish mosh—Yiddish: *hodgepodge* (Rosten, 2001).

Mishna—Hebrew: *to repeat one's learning.* Codified core of oral law consisting of analysis and interpretations; it is one of two basic parts of the Talmud (Rosten, 2001).

Mitzvah (plural Mitzvot)—Hebrew: *commandment.* Used to mean an act that is virtuous, kind, considerate, or ethical; an act that expresses G-d's will (Rosten, 2001).

Mizrahi (plural Mizrahim)—Hebrew: *Eastern* or *Oriental.* Jews of Middle Eastern ancestry, most notably from Babylonia and Persia (modern-day Iraq and Iran) (Khazzoom, 2016).

Niggun (plural niggunim)—Yiddish: *melody.* A wordless melody popularized by Hasidic mystics. The songs have made-up words such as "lai, lai" or "bim bam" instead of lyrics. These few words are sung over and over again for the duration of the song or dance (Strom, 2006).

Oy Vey!—From Slavic: *oy* meaning *oh!* Oy vey! means "Oh, pain!" but is used as an all-purpose exclamation "to express anything from trivial delight to abysmal woe" (Rosten, 2001, p. 275).

Pikuach nefesh—Hebrew term referring to consideration of human life. Jewish law that places preservation of life above adherence to all other laws except those against idolatry, sexual offenses, and murder (Wigoder, 2002).

Pogrom—Organized riots, brutal torture, pillage, and mass murder of a Jewish community. There were three waves of attacks in Russia (1881–1884, 1903–1906, and 1918–1920), as well as attacks in Spain (1492), Iraq (1941), and Poland (1946) (Telushkin, 2008).

Protocols of the Elders of Zion—Anti-Semetic propaganda that outlines a false plot for world domination by Jews. A Russian newspaper published a version in 1903, which was tied to stories written in the 1860s. Since then, other adaptations have been circulated around the world, making it impossible to pinpoint an exact citation (United States Holocaust Museum, n.d.).

Rabbi—Hebrew: *my teacher.* A rabbi is a teacher of the Torah who is responsible for teaching and overseeing religious instruction, counseling and advising congregants, interpreting tenets of Judaism, and performing ceremonies to mark birth, marriage, and death. A rabbi is not an intermediary between G-d and people and is not necessarily a spiritual arbiter; a rabbi does not have priestly privileges and does not necessarily lead services (Rosten, 2001).

Rabbinic Judaism—Since the destruction of the Temple in 70 CE, rabbis have been the authority in Judaism. All of today's denominations are shaped by teachings of the rabbis (Schwartz, 1997).

Seder—Hebrew: *order.* Rituals observed in the home during Passover that include retelling the story of the Jews' exodus from Egypt and eating a festive meal (Wigoder, 2002).

Sephardi/Sephardic/Sephardim—From Hebrew: *Spain*. Jews who trace their ancestry to medieval Spain or the Iberian Peninsula. May also include Jews who trace their ancestry to the Ottoman Empire (Wigoder, 2002).

Shalom—Hebrew: *whole*, *entire*, or *peace*. Used to mean peace, hello, or good-bye (Rosten, 2001).

Shalom Aléchem—Hebrew and Yiddish: *peace upon you*. Used as a greeting.

Shabbat/Shabbos/Sabbath—Weekly observance of a day of rest from sundown Friday until sundown Saturday. Rituals include lighting candles, reciting blessings over wine and bread, having a family meal, and attending synagogue. The Talmud dictates 39 types of work forbidden during Shabbat, and today's denominations apply this list to modern life in different ways (Goldman, 2000).

Shabbat Shalom—Hebrew: *peaceful Sabbath*. Traditional greeting on the Sabbath (Goldman, 2000).

Shikse/Shiksa—Yiddish term for a non-Jewish girl; considered offensive.

Shiva—From Hebrew: *seven*. Refers to the period immediately following a funeral where mourners return home or to the deceased's home. In traditional circles, for seven days regular routines are replaced by accepting visits from the community, introspection, and modesty. The term "sitting shiva" comes from the tradition of mourners sitting on low chairs (Goldman, 2000).

Shtetl—Yiddish word from the German word *stadt*, which means *town*. Small town or village in eastern Europe prior to the Holocaust in which most, or all, of the residents were Jewish. There were few amenities, and life was hard (Rosten, 2001).

Star of David/Magen David—Hebrew: *Shield of David*. Symbol that came to be associated with Judiasm (Wigoder, 2002).

Swartze/Svartze—Yiddish: *black*. Also used as a derogatory/offensive term for a person of African descent.

Synagogue/Shul—From Greek: synagogue means *assembly* or *congregation*. From Greek: shul comes from the Greek *schola*, meaning *to study*. Both terms are used to refer to a Jewish house of worship, where worshipers address G-d directly and individually, not through a priest or rabbi (Rosten, 2001).

Tallit/Tallis—Prayer shawl worn traditionally by men, today also worn by some women (Rosten, 2001).

Talmud—Hebrew: *to study*. A compendium of 63 books, including the Torah and the Mishna, as well as other commentaries on the Torah. Rather than dogma or catechism, it offers explanations of the Torah text (Rosten, 2001).

Temple/temple—The first Temple was built by Solomon in Jerusalem. It stood for over 400 years until it was destroyed in 586 BCE. The second Temple was built on the same site and stood until it was destroyed in 70 CE. The Temples were the center for Jewish worship. Temple (with a capital "t") usually refers to the first or second Temple. (Telushkin,

2008). Some Jews use this word (with a lowercase "t") interchangeably with the words "shul" and "synagogue."

Tikkun Olam—Hebrew: *repairing/healing the world*. The work of social justice and action (Meyerstein, 2004; Robinson, 2001).

Torah—Hebrew: *teaching* or *doctrine*. The Five Books of Moses: Genesis, Exodus, Leviticus, Numbers, and Deuteronomy, or the scroll on which they are written (Rosten, 2001).

Tzedakah—From Hebrew: *tzedek* meaning *righteousness*. The obligation to establish justice by helping others (Rosten, 2001).

Yahrzeit—From German: *jahrzeit*, meaning *year's time* or *anniversary*. This is the anniversary of someone's death (Rosten, 2001).

Yasher Koach—Hebrew: *straight strength*. Congratulatory phrase meaning "good job." Used in synagogue to acknowledge a person's participation in the service or to acknowledge a mitzvah.

Yiddish—Language used by Ashkenazi Jews, based on a combination of medieval German and Hebrew (Wigoder, 2002).

Yizkor—From Hebrew: *to remember*. Memorial service held four times each year to remember those who have died.

Yuntif—From Yiddish and Hebrew: *yom* meaning *day*, and *tov* meaning *good*. A holiday. "Good yuntif" is used to mean happy holiday.

Z"l —From Hebrew: *of blessed memory*. Abbreviation of the Hebrew honorific *may their memory be a blessing*.

Zion/Zionism—Early name used in reference to Jerusalem and the land that is currently the State of Israel, also used to refer to the Jewish people or the Jewish obligation and law to "return to Zion" for the arrival of the Messiah (Wigoder, 2002). Modern Zionism ranges from "philanthropic to political, from messianic to utopian, from religious to secular" (Wigoder, 2002, p. 749). Since the 1970s, also used in the context of anti-Semitism (Vorspan & Saperstein, 1998).

Appendix B

Holidays and the Jewish Calendar

The Jewish calendar is basically a lunar calendar, with each month starting on a new moon. The standard calendar in the United States (the Gregorian calendar) is a solar calendar. Therefore, the dates of the two calendars do not consistently match. In a true lunar calendar, the months do not coincide with the seasons. The Jewish calendar adds a 13th month (the month of Adar) seven times in 19 years so that the holidays occur in the same season each year, although not on the same date on the Gregorian calendar. Thus, Passover always occurs in the springtime; Hanukkah almost always occurs in December.

The Jewish Year is numbered as the years since Creation. For example, in the spring of 2016, it is the Jewish year 5776. The

Sabbath and all Jewish holidays begin at sundown on the night before the first day and end at sundown as well. Thus, Shabbat, the day of rest, begins on Friday at sunset and concludes on Saturday at sunset.

Please note that this table gives only a brief overview of the holidays. We have included a few songs for the more focal holidays. However, not all holidays have strong musical associations. Music therapists should take this as a starting point since observance of the holiday and familiarity with these songs will depend on background, denomination, and tradition of each individual client. In addition, the standard liturgical songs have multiple melodies, sometimes even within a single denomination.

Information on the Jewish Holidays

Holiday/ Observance in Order of Occurrence	Approximate Dates and Time of Year	Length in Days	Meaning	Basic Information for Music Therapists	Sample Songs
Shabbat	Friday sunset until Saturday sunset, weekly.	1	The weekly day of rest.	No "work", light candles, say blessing over wine and challah bread. May attend synagogue and/or have family meal.	Adon Olam (liturgical) Shabbat Shalom/ Bim Bam (traditional) Shalom Aléchem (liturgical) Ose Shalom (liturgical)
Rosh Hashanah	Early fall: 1st and 2nd of Tishrei, September or early October.	1 or 2	Jewish New Year; G-d inscribes one in the Book of Life. With Yom Kippur, considered the High Holy Days or Days of Awe.	Considered a "High Holy Day;" customary to attend synagogue and gather for festive meal with family.	L'shana Tova (traditional) Apples and Honey (traditional)
Yom Kippur	Early fall: 10th of Tishrei, 9 days after the first day Rosh Hashanah.	1	Day of Atonement; G-d seals the Book of Life. With Rosh Hashanah, considered the High Holy Days or Days of Awe.	A day of fasting and the most holy day of the Jewish calendar. Customary to attend synagogue and gather to "break the fast."	Avinu Malkénu (liturgical) Kol Nidré (liturgical)
Sukkot/ Sukkos	Early fall: 15th of Tishrei, 14 days after the first day Rosh Hashanah.	7 or 8	Feast of Booths (Tabernacles), a harvest holiday.	Families may build and have meals in a "tent" (sukkah), as a symbol of taking in the harvest. Symbolic waving of a lulav and etrog.	
Shemini Atzeret	Early fall: the 8th day of Sukkot.	1 or 2	Literally "The assembly of the 8th day."	End of the harvest. Prayers for rain and a bountiful year are recited.	

Simchat Torah	The day after Shemini Atzeret.	1	Literally "Rejoicing in the Torah."	Finish reading the end of the Torah and begin reading the Torah at the start. Customary to dance with the Torah.	
Chanukkah/ Hanukkah/ Chanukah	Winter: 25th of Kislev, usually in December.	8	Commemorating Jewish survival and the miracle of finding oil to light the ancient Menorah for 8 days.	Light candles and eat foods fried in oil, symbolic of the historical event. Dreydl (4-sided top game) is played. Traditionally, gifts of money or gelt (coins) are given. In modernity, gifts are exchanged, although not a universal tradition.	Ma'oz Tsur (secular) Oh Hanukkah (secular) I Have a Little Dreydl (secular) S'vivon (secular)
Tu B'Shevat	Winter: 15th of Shevat, late January or early February.	1	The new year for trees.	Customary to consume fruit and nuts grown on trees.	
Purim	Late winter or early spring: 14th Adar.	1	Holiday celebration commemorating Queen Esther helping to save the Jews from destruction in ancient Persia.	Megillah (Book of Esther) is read, children may dress in costumes, gifts of food are exchanged, charity is given. A festive meal may be held.	Chag Purim (secular) A Wicked Wicked Man (secular)
Pesach/ Passover	Spring: 15th of Nissan.	7 or 8	Holiday celebrating the Jews' exodus (led by Moses) from slavery in Egypt to freedom.	No leavening products can be consumed. Observed at home more than at synagogue with a special meal called a "seder." Seder typically occurs on the first and second nights of holiday.	Dayénu (traditional) Go Down Moses (American folk song) Chad Gadya (traditional) The Four Questions/ Ma Nishtana (liturgical)
Yom HaShoah	Spring: 1 week after Passover.	1	Day of Remembrance of the Holocaust.	Memorial services held and candles lit. Serves as an anniversary of the death of victims of the Holocaust who perished on an unknown date.	

Yom HaAtzmaut	Late spring: 5th of Iyyar, April or May. Approximately one week after Yom HaShoah.	1	Israeli Independence Day.	A day of celebration.
Lag B'Omer	Late spring: 18th of Iyar, 33 days after the second day of Passover.	1	Day commemorating the end of a plague that killed thousands of Jews. Also commemorates the Bar Kokhba revolt, a Jewish uprising against the Roman Empire.	Minor holiday celebrated with bonfires. In some traditions, a day for weddings.
Shavu'ot	Early summer: 6th of Sivan, 49 days after the second day of Passover.	1	Festival holiday celebrating the giving of the Torah. Confirmation may be celebrated.	Celebrates harvest of first fruits. Dairy foods are eaten.
Tisha B'Av	Summer: 9th of Av, July or August.	1	Commemorates destruction of first and second Temples, expulsion of Jews from Spain in 1492, from England in 1290, and other Jewish tragedies.	A day of fasting, solemn day of remembrance, reading/chanting of Eicha (Lamentations).

Appendix C

Range of Jewish Expression

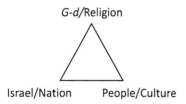

Kessler (2007) suggests that the factors in Jewish expression include the following:

G-d/Religion: This may represent the balance of secular and religious. How much does one observe? What importance does one place on religion?

Although the denominations may influence this factor because they may reflect how strictly a person interprets *Torah*, denomination is not the only influence here. A Conservative *rabbi* could be more religiously observant than a Modern Orthodox man who does not uphold all of the laws pertaining to the *Sabbath*. A Reform congregant could attend services or recite prayers more regularly than her Conservative counterpart.

People/Culture: To what extent does one follow *Torah* to the letter? To what extent does one's religious life reflect assimilation with the culture? What importance does a person place on traditional celebrations, language, and foods or on Jewish art, music, and literature?

A person may identify strongly as Jewish because of Jewish ancestry, or a person may identify strongly with Jewish culture or values, having been raised as Jewish with a background that includes both Jewish and non-Jewish ancestry. Someone who prepares all of the traditional foods and sings the traditional songs and prayers for a holiday might do so with a strong appreciation for both the religious and cultural aspects or might do so with no regard to the holiday's religious meaning. On the other hand, some groups of Orthodox Jews are not concerned at all with Jewish culture, or with Israel, as they are only concerned with religion.

Israel/Nation: What is the person's relationship to the Land of Israel? Does he or she feel a need to return to Israel? Does he or she believe that Jews have a right to live there?

A Jewish person might live in Israel or choose to live in another country. Those living outside of Israel may feel strong ties to Israel or might feel no tie to Israel at all. Some Jews living in Israel are secular and follow no religious practice, while other Israeli Jews are very observant.

Appendix D

Life Cycle Events and Customs

Birth

In the United States, babies may be given a secular name and a name in *Hebrew*. Full *Hebrew* names used primarily in religious contexts include the parents' names; for example, *Elesheva Tziporah bat Moshe v'Gitel,* translates to Elissa Sarah, daughter of Michael and Gloria. Names may or may not be direct *Hebrew* translations of vernacular names, and some parents choose not to bestow both. There is a tradition of naming Jewish babies in honor of relatives; *Ashkenazi* Jews may choose a name that connects to someone who is deceased, while *Sephardi* Jews may choose to name a baby after someone who is alive (Goldman, 2000).

Some Jewish parents may wait to announce a new baby's name until an official ceremony. For baby girls, this takes place in the *synagogue* the next time the *Torah* is scheduled to be read (Goldman, 2000*)*. For baby boys, the name is often revealed eight days after birth at the *brit milah* (abbreviated to *brit* or *bris*), the circumcision ceremony (Wigoder, 2002). Some Jews choose to utilize the services of a *mohel,* a professional trained in Jewish circumcision, while others may choose to have the circumcision done upon birth and not at the ceremony. Male converts into Judaism are expected to have a *brit/bris,* or if they were previously circumcised, to have a drop of blood drawn (Wigoder, 2002).

Bar/Bat (or Bas) Mitzvah

Goldman (2000) explains that the next significant milestone in the Jewish life cycle is the *Bar/Bat* (or *Bas) Mitzvah*. This signifies the entry into the covenant with Moses to follow the Jewish laws/commandments and marks the beginning of Jewish adulthood and responsibility for boys at the age of 13 and for girls at between 12 and 13. *Bar Mitzvah,* meaning Son of the Commandments, means that a boy can be counted toward a *minyan* (Goldman, 2000; Wigoder, 2002). Those who did not participate in this ritual at the age of 12 or 13 may have an adult *Bar/Bat* (or *Bas) Mitzvah* to honor the first time they are called to the *Torah* and to acknowledge their commitment to the responsibilities of Jewish adulthood (Goldman, 2000; Wigoder, 2002).

Judith Kaplan, whose father was Mordechai Kaplan, the founder of the Reconstructionist Movement, was the first young woman to celebrate a *Bat* (or *Bas) Mitzvah,* in 1922 (Alpert & Staub, 2000; Goldman, 2000). Today, a *Bat* (or *Bas) Mitzvah* may be celebrated in Reconstructionist, Reform, Conservative, and other denominations' *synagogues.* In Orthodox communities, girls are accepted as adult members of the congregation at age 12, but typically do not read from the *Torah* or lead others in prayer unless they do so during a special women's service (Goldman, 2000).

While the *Bar/Bat Mitzvah* service may differ for young men and women, it is common for both to have a celebratory meal to commemorate this rite of passage with the community. In some communities, these parties have grown large and can overshadow the religious event. However, recent trends have turned against these over-the-top parties in favor of a social action focus (Goldman, 2000).

Marriage/Weddings

The *Zohar,* a mystical Jewish text from the 13th century, explains that marriage reunites two parts of one soul (Goldman, 2000). Traditionally, the purpose of marriage is to create a Jewish home and a Jewish family and to further Jewish society (Wigoder, 2002). Although there will be variation according to individual choice, it may be helpful to be aware of a few key elements found in Jewish wedding ceremonies.

Before the ceremony begins, a *ketubah,* or marriage contract, is signed (Goldman, 2002). During the ceremony, the couple stands under a *chuppah,* or canopy, that is laden with symbolism: the hospitality of Abraham's tent, the couple's new home together, and fertility (Goldman, 2000). There are seven marriage blessings that are bestowed upon the couple, although some couples incorporate variations on these during their ceremonies (Goldman, 2000). The ceremony ends with a breaking of a glass, which some equate with various meanings, although for most this signals the beginning of the celebration (Goldman, 2000). Although Jewish traditions abound during the ceremony, many Jewish weddings also incorporate elements of their surrounding communities (Wigoder, 2002).

If one of the two people being married is not Jewish, they may have difficulty finding a *rabbi* of any denomination to conduct the ceremony (Goldman, 2000). It may be easier to find a Reform or Conservative *rabbi* to conduct a gay or lesbian commitment ceremony or wedding if both people in the couple are Jewish than it is to find a *rabbi* to conduct an intermarriage because intermarriages are less likely to result in a Jewish household than marriage between two Jews, gay or straight (Goldman, 2000).

Death/Mourning

According to Goldman (2000), "Judaism believes there is a world of the living and a spiritual realm of those who once lived. Death, the *Talmud* states in a lovely phrase, is where the two worlds kiss" (p. 87). Judaism does not offer a definitive explanation of what happens after death, nor does it view heaven as an ultimate goal or culmination. Some Jews do believe that the spirit endures and returns to *G-d*. The promise of resurrection for all at the "end of days," when combined with the biblical idea of people being created with clay and spirit, is interpreted to indicate a timeless and infinite existence (Goldman, 2000).

Jewish tradition lays out practices that are followed regarding death and mourning for the bereaved family and the larger community. Although individuals vary in their adherence to these customs, it is important to be aware that there are very specific rules that Jewish people may follow. Once a person has died, the eyes and mouth are closed, the face is immediately covered, and movement of the body is reserved only for purposes of dignity (Weinstein, 2003). A *shomer* (watcher) may stay with the body so that it is not alone from the time of death to the time of burial. Prayer is permitted in the room, but singing and music are traditionally avoided (Weinstein, 2003). *Taharah* (body preparation for burial) usually occurs at a funeral home or with a *chevra kadisha* (Jewish volunteer burial society; one can be found in many cities across the United States) and involves washing and purification of the body, followed by dressing the deceased in simple white shrouds of modest material (Weinstein, 2003; Wigoder, 2002). As mutilation of the body is forbidden in traditional Jewish law, bodies are not cremated or embalmed, and some families may choose to avoid autopsies. Burial occurs as quickly as possible (Vorspan & Saperstein, 1998) but cannot coincide with a Jewish holiday or *Shabbat*. Music is avoided in favor of reading psalms at Orthodox and Conservative funerals, although preferred or meaningful music may be included in services in other denominations (Goldman, 2000). It is considered a *mitzvah* at a Jewish funeral for all to shovel earth onto the coffin.

By Jewish law, mourners are considered to be a parent, sibling, child, or spouse of the deceased, although many may mourn the loss of the deceased (Goldman, 2000; Weinstein, 2003). After the funeral, there may be a *shiva,* a period for the community (Jews and non-Jews) to gather to visit and console the bereaved (Wigoder, 2002). It is appropriate to bring food (*kosher,* depending on the family) or simply offer company when *"making a shiva call"* (visit). It is not appropriate to bring flowers. During the *shiva,* there is a *minyan* to recite the *"Mourner's Kaddish"* (prayer for the deceased) (Goldman, 2000). A candle remains lit for the duration of the *shiva* (Weinstein, 2003).

After approximately a year has passed, a gravestone may be placed at the cemetery, known as a *dedication* or *unveiling*. Beginning the first year and every year after, the anniversary of the death is marked by observing *yahrzeit* (Weinstein, 2003). The bereaved may attend *synagogue* to recite the *"Mourner's Kaddish"* or may light a candle or choose other ways of commemorating the *yahrzeit*. They may also attend *yizkor* services, which are held four times a year on significant holidays to remember those who have died. There are other laws and traditions that Jewish mourners may follow. While Jews may or may not follow all of the traditions, some may adapt customs to create their own meaningful rituals.

Kosher/Kashrut

The word *kosher* is a *Hebrew* term used to describe food and beverages deemed proper to eat according to *kashrut,* Jewish dietary laws as prescribed in the Bible and *rabbinic* texts (Wigoder, 2002). According to Goldman (2000), *kashrut* intends to elevate the entire act of food preparation to a sacred level. Particular methods regarding meat and *rabbinic* oversight of other types of food are necessary to earn a *kosher* label (Wigoder, 2002). The term "keep *kosher*" refers to maintaining a *kosher* home as well as following rules about what foods cannot be eaten (e.g., shellfish, birds of prey) and what foods cannot be mixed together (e.g., milk and meat) (Goldman, 2000).

As with other Jewish laws, the degree to which people adhere to *kashrut* varies. For example, some Jews may be more lenient outside of their home than in their home (Goldman, 2000). The degree to which a Jewish person follows the laws cannot be ascertained simply by their denominational affiliation (Goldman, 2000).

The word *"kosher"* has taken on a slang connotation equated with being right, correct, and even ethical (Goldman, 2000). It is also used to describe cuisine that is associated with Jewish culture, but might not necessarily be *kosher,* for example, *"kosher*-style deli" (Wigoder, 2002).

Appendix E

Music Resources

Modes

The following modes are used frequently in Jewish liturgical, klezmer, and folk music. Most of the modes are variants of the Western Dorian and Phrygian modes (Strom, 2006). The modes were originally named according to a prayer that was sung in each mode, although today other melodies are used for the same prayers. The modes are presented here in their basic forms according to Strom (2006) and Horowitz (2012) so that a music therapist might understand the sound and construction of each.

- Ahavah Raba Mode/Freygish/Altered Phrygian Mode: E, F, G#, A, B, C, D, E
- Mi Shebeirach/Ukranian Mode: This mode is the natural minor scale with an augmented 4th and an interval of an augmented 2nd between the 6th and 7th steps of the scale: D, E, F G#, A, Bb, C#, D
- Adonoy Moloch/Mixolydian: C, D, E, F, G, A, Bb, C
- Natural Minor/Aeolian: D, E, F, G, A, Bb, C, D

Books

Eglash, J. N. (Ed.). (2001). *The complete shireinu.* New York: NY: Transcontinental Press.
  Fake book with 350 songs from Jewish tradition. Includes Hebrew texts, English translations, and transliterated lyrics. Includes chords for piano or for guitarists using capo. Liturgical pieces have multiple versions using traditional and contemporary liturgical melodies. Includes songs from liturgy; Jewish folk and rock; popular tunes from Jewish summer camps; Israeli, Ashkenazi, Hasidic, and Sephardic songs.

Pasternak, V. (Compiler & Arranger). (1997). *The Jewish fake book*. Owings Mills, MD: Tara Publications. Available at: http://www.jewishmusic.com/
Fake book with 212 songs and dance melodies from Jewish tradition. Includes lyrics written as transliterations for Yiddish and Hebrew songs or written in English. Includes chords and melody. Has the most traditional melody or melodies for songs. Includes songs from liturgy; klezmer and dance music; Israeli, Ashkenazi, Hasidic, Sephardic, and Yiddish songs.

Richards, S. (Ed.). (2002). *Complete Jewish Songbook for Children Volume I: The Manginot*. New York: NY: Transcontinental Press.
A collection of Jewish children's songs for various times of the year, including songs about holidays, festivals, and Jewish values. Includes English songs and Hebrew songs.

Websites

Hebrew Songs: www.hebrewsongs.com
A database of Israeli songs and lyrics with translation.
Jewish Guitar Chords: http://jewishguitarchords.com/
A website of free chords for some Conservative and Orthodox Jewish artists' songs.
Jewish Rock Radio: www.jewishrockradio.com,
Live streaming radio of American and Israeli Jewish rock and contemporary music, as well as links to artists.
OySongs: www.oysongs.com
Jewish music and sheet music downloads and a Jewish-only version of iTunes.
Tara Music: http://www.jewishmusic.com/
Publisher of songbooks and e-books of Jewish music.
TotShabbat.com: http://www.totshabbat.com/
Free sheet music and resources for Tot Shabbat (children's Shabbat services).
Transcontinental Music:
http://www.transcontinentalmusic.com/
The music-publishing branch of the URJ (Union for Reform Judaism).

Musicians' Web Pages

Peter & Ellen Allard, http://peterandellen.com/
Specializing in Jewish children's music.
Debbie Friedman, http://www.debbiefriedman.com/
Highly influential songwriter whose songs have been used in many Reform, Conservative, and Reconstructionist synagogues as well as in some Orthodox synagogues.
Noam Katz, http://www.noamkatz.com/Noam Katz/ Music.html
Jeff Klepper, http: //www.jeffklepper.com
Josh Nelson, http://joshnelsongroject.com
Dan Nichols, http://www.jewishrock.com/resources.asp
Rick Recht, http://www.rickrecht.com
Peri Smilow, http://www.perismilow.com
Craig Taubman, http://www.craignco.com

Joey Weisenberg, http://joeyweisnberg.com
Shir Yaakov, http://www.shiryaakov.com

Musicians/Artists/Bands of Note

Shlomo Carlebach
Composer, Rabbi, and singer; wrote many widely used liturgical melodies.
Klezmer bands:
Klezmatics
Maxwell St. Klezmer
Boston Klezmer Conservatory Band
Velvel Pasternak: Jewish musicologist, arranger, and compiler of Ashkenazi, Yiddish, klezmer, Israeli, Hasidic, Sephardic, and other Jewish melodies.
Itzhak Perlman: Classical violinist who also plays Israeli and Yiddish songs.
Richard Tucker: Cantor

Nonholiday Song Repertoire*

Song	Type of Jewish Music	Meaning
Am Yisraél Chai	Traditional	"The People of Israel live."
David Melech Yisraél	Traditional	"David King of Israel."
Music from Fiddler on the Roof	Jewish art music, Broadway musical	Songs connect to Jewish religious and cultural life.
Hatikva	Israeli National Anthem	"The hope."
Hava Nagila	Secular song	Celebratory dance song.
Hiné Ma Tov	Traditional	"How good it is for us to be sitting together."
Ose Shalom	Liturgical	Prayer for peace.
Mi Shebeirach	Liturgical	Prayer for health and healing.
Shalom Chaveirim	Israeli folk song	"Hello/good-bye friends."
Tumbalalaika	Yiddish folk song	Love song.
Zum Gali Gali	Israeli folk song	"Zum Gali Gali" are nonsense symbols. Verses tell story of settling in Israel.

* These are suggestions of the authors, based on Froman (2009) and their clinical experience.

Chapter 13

THE CULTURES OF THE LESBIAN, GAY, BISEXUAL, TRANSGENDER, AND QUESTIONING COMMUNITIES

Spencer Hardy & Annette Whitehead-Pleaux

Annette: *As I reflect upon my earliest memories, I think I have always been queer. I did not know the language to describe the difference I felt, but I knew I was different, and it was not something I felt safe sharing with my family or others in my life at that time. As I grew up, I started to hear the terms "gay," "faggot," and "lesbian" as derogatory terms. These words were frequently flung at me with hate during my adolescence. Hearing these insults and hateful words reinforced the feeling of being different and not belonging. Through junior high and high school, I had crushes on classmates, much like my peers, but these crushes were on females, not males. Again, I was reminded of how very different I was and knew I could not share these feelings with my friends or anyone in the small town where I lived. Through television shows, I finally saw gay and lesbian people. While I was relieved to not be the only one, it was unnerving to me because these television characters (who were often portrayed as very unstable, unhappy, and unhealthy) led very different lives than that for which I hoped. I became worried that my life would not follow the path to becoming a professional music therapist but instead would be as I saw portrayed on television.*

When I got to college, my life changed dramatically. I was fortunate to room with a friend my sophomore year who was in the process of coming out. Watching her come out and hear how her lesbianism was not going to affect her career goal—to become an occupational therapist—I finally saw a way to be all aspects of myself and not sacrifice my career or my happiness. Together, with a gay male friend who lived in our dorm, we learned to navigate the gay scene by going to LGBTQ+ dances, meetings at the campus GLB center, and, finally, clubs and bars. I made friends at the college, in the music therapy program, and in the gay community. It was good to be able to openly be who I was.

Throughout my life, I have experienced many unpleasant experiences related to being a lesbian. I have been to several therapists (including a music therapist) who believed that my lesbianism was a transient phase out of which I could grow. When in music therapy school, I was told that my lesbianism and activism could hinder my music therapy career. I have experienced verbal abuse and threats because I am a lesbian. I was denied health insurance benefits for my wife by an employer for 10 years. And, finally, many of my family members have had a very difficult time accepting my lesbianism, not attending my wedding and not talking to me for over a decade. However, the stress I felt when I was struggling to come to terms with who I am was far greater than the stress I felt facing the discrimination directed at me. Despite the jarring effects of the discrimination and rejection, the love and support I have found in my friends and community have brought comfort and healing to me.

I am in a place in my life where it is safe for me to be open with my lesbianism. Yet, I am well aware that there are many who are not in safe circumstances. Their jobs, housing, relationships, and physical safety could be jeopardized by being out. Knowing that my peers do not have the safety I have has driven me to step up and make positive changes for my community. I don't want another music therapy client who is LGBTQI+ to hear that their sexual orientation or gender identity is a phase. I don't want a LGBTQI+ music therapy student to worry that their career is jeopardized by their sexual orientation or gender identity. I don't want another LGBTQI+ music therapist to be discriminated against in their work place. I don't want another LGBTQI+ client to feel unsupported, discounted, and/or discriminated against by their music therapist. It is in this spirit that together with Spencer I share what I know about the LGBTQI+ communities with regard to music, cultures, and health. I come to you as a community member, not as an expert in queer studies. I speak from my experiences, what I have learned from others, and what I have read. And I share this to help each of us to become stronger music therapists.

Spencer: *Feeling different is never easy, and growing up, every kid feels different at some point in his or her childhood. But feeling different without the language or the tools to communicate that difference can be stifling. I was blessed as a child with a loving family and a loving community, but knowing I was different from a young age kept me quiet and, quite honestly, confused for most of my youth. It wasn't until I was 18 that I was able to say out loud that I was attracted to women, having been raised a woman myself. It did not feel freeing to me just yet, I was still confused. It wasn't until two years later when I came out as transgender that I finally felt like my authentic self.*

Now I still wonder why I felt so trapped and unable to share my feelings as a youth, not coming out until young adulthood. I had a supportive family, I had friends and family members who were gay, and I had probably somewhere heard of transgender people before. But the truth is that I had never met a transgender person, I had never seen one on TV, I had never heard one's music on the radio. The feelings I had were foreign. I could not find a place for them in my world. I could not find the words or the language to express those feelings or to understand them myself.

I began my coming out process and transition while at Berklee College of Music in Boston, studying in the music therapy department. I could not have asked for a better place to embrace and support me during that difficult process. I experienced a wealth of love and support from professors, supervisors, friends, classmates, and coworkers. I was able to transition smoothly while living in the dorms and working as an RA. I came out to my family, who embraced me with open arms. Finding the LGBTQI+ community and finding the transgender community was a very freeing experience for me. I found a place where I fit, where I was a part of something, and where I could truly be myself.

I share all this because I am lucky and blessed to have had all this support. I share my story as a transgender person because I know that too many transgender voices in this country and across the world are still silenced. Too many people are still discriminated against in places that are supposed to be safe, in their schools, by their doctors or therapists, by their own families. Too many transgender people struggle with finding the resources and support they need to come out or to start transitioning. I often feel that I am the exception. Not everyone's journey is as supported as mine was. But it should be. We should be able to create a space for our youth to come out and transition, free of the fears or shame that so many have. Free of the discrimination, violence, fear of losing their families, losing their homes, losing their jobs, or losing their lives.

Like Annette, I agree that as music therapists we need to actively create spaces where LGBTQI+ students, clients, coworkers, and employees feel safe from discrimination. We need to play an active role in improving the health care and mental health systems to include gay, lesbian, bisexual and transgender people. I too am not an expert in this field, but I am here to share my experiences, my knowledge, and my activism, knowing that we all continue to grow as we learn about and embrace other cultures.

Worldview

The lesbian, gay, bisexual, transgender, and questioning (LGBTQ) community is one with an expansive worldview, pulling from the diversity of its many subcultures, as well as the diversity of its members—coming from all different cultural backgrounds and upbringings themselves. Unlike other cultural groups, LGBTQ persons are not born into this community; therefore, their individual worldviews have already been molded and developed by their own unique upbringings. However, this is not to say that one's worldview does not change as a member of this complex community. In addition, despite our reference to the LGBTQ community, it is actually an amalgam of many communities and subcommunities, bound together by gender, sexual orientation, and gender expression variance from the societally dictated heterosexual norms. Many LGBTQ people find subcommunities within the greater LGBTQ communities where they have a network with similar social,

political, and cultural perspectives.

As a cultural group here in the United States, the LGBTQ community is one that has grown out of the Civil Rights Movement of the 20th and now 21st centuries. The LGBTQ culture has a history of activism; the present-day LGBTQ community continues to fight an equal rights battle in this country. While many strides have been made during this civil rights movement's history, as well as in recent years, many in our country continue to battle with discrimination, fear, and hatred toward this community. These factors contribute greatly to a worldview in which activism and equal rights are high priorities. Unfortunately, this worldview is also one where a fear of discrimination and physical harm is still a reality to many of its members. A recent example of this reality is the mass murder of 50 people and wounding of 53 at the Pulse Nightclub, a gay bar in Orlando, FL (Chappell, 2016).

When broken down into its subcategories, the acronym LGBTQ stands for lesbian, gay, bisexual, transgender, and questioning and also sometimes the word "queer." What do these groups have in common? Lesbian, gay, and bisexual people all have a sexual orientation that is outside of the norms of society. "Transgender" and "intersex" are terms related not to sexual orientation, but instead to gender identity. For a transgender person, their gender identity is what differs from the norms of society and does not align with the sex they were assigned at birth. People with the gay, lesbian, and bisexual identities are also defying our society's gender norms, therefore tying in transgender, intersex, and genderqueer identities with these other communities. The Q in this acronym also includes questioning, a person who is still exploring and understanding their own sexual orientation and/or gender identity. Especially when providing LGBTQ support services for youth, questioning is an important identity to include for those young persons still coming to terms with or trying to understand their identity. The term "queer" comes from a history of being a derogatory term toward the LGBTQ community. However, many within the community have reclaimed this term and turned it around in a positive way. Those LGBTQ people who don't feel that the terms listed above can accurately work to fit their personal identities instead prefer an "umbrella term" or inclusive term for the community and movement as a whole. The word "queer" has come to be that inclusive umbrella term for a group outside of the sexual orientation and gender norms of our society. The term "transgender" has also been accepted as an umbrella term, encompassing not just those individuals who transition from one gender to another, but those who live outside the traditional "male" and "female" identities, such as those with a "genderqueer" or "gender fluid" identity. The LGBTQ acronym is often expanded to include other identities as well. You will sometime see LGBTQA, with the A standing for "ally," a straight person who identifies as a supporter of the LGBTQ community. At other times, the A may stand for "asexual," a person who "does not experience sexual attraction" (Asexual Visibility and Education Network, 2012). In yet other instancs, the acronym will include I, for "intersex." The Intersex Society of North

America defines intersex as "a general term used for a variety of conditions in which a person is born with a reproductive or sexual anatomy that does not seem to fit the typical definitions of female or male" (Intersex Society of North America, 2008). Although not all intersex people identify as a part of the LGBTQ community, many do, and it is important to acknowledge their presence as a part of the diversity within the LGBTQ community.

Throughout this chapter, we will use the acronym LGBTQ as an umbrella term to represent the diverse identities of this community. It is important to acknowledge that like the terms "queer" and "transgender," the LGBTQ acronym can also be considered an overarching term that, although limited, is meant to be inclusive of varying sexual orientations and gender identities, not just those listed above. (For a complete list of LGBTQ-inclusive definitions and to better understand them, go to http://community.pflag.org/glossary.)

Historical Realities Versus Popular Myths

As with most minority groups, there exist a variety of popular myths about LGBTQ populations. It is important to compare these to the historic realities of the population and its many subpopulations. These myths are based on generalizations, opinions, and misconceptions and are often based in homophobia, biphobia, and transphobia and perpetuated by people in power, peers, and the media. Although there are many stereotypes, we have chosen to focus on some of the most prevalent and destructive.

Myth 1: LGBTQ People Choose to Be Gay/Lesbian/Bisexual/Transgender

This is one of the most common popular myths, that sexual identity, gender identity, and gender expression are choices one makes. But we ask readers: When did you choose to be straight (if you are straight) or choose to be cisgender (having the sex you were assigned at birth align with your gender identity)? The research about sexual orientation and gender identity does not show a clear causal relationship but instead indicates a complex interplay between factors that are nature and nurture (APA, 2015a, 2015b; Royal College of Psychiatrists, n.d.).

Myth 2: "It Is a Phase. You Will Grow Out of It."

As with the previously discussed myth, many believe that sexual orientation and gender identity are only a phase of adolescent or young adulthood. With time and experience, the individual will "grow out" of being LGBTQ. The research about sexual identity and gender identity indicates that neither is truly a phase. The way people express and cope with their sexual and gender identity may differ, giving the appearance of a phase, when it is truly differing ways of coping. In fact, over the past few years, several research studies have been conducted looking at sexual orientation, sexual orientation identity, and fluidity of

sexuality (Diamond, 2015; Katz-Wise & Hyde, 2015; Schwartz, Luyckx, & Vignoles, 2011). Some research indicates that parts of "sexual identity, such as relationships, emotions, behaviors, values, group affiliations, and norms, appear to be relatively fluid," while sexual orientation appears to be stable for many individuals for their lifetime (Schwartz, Luyckx, & Vignoles, 2011, p. 652). Differing from this, Katz-Wise and Hyde (2015) surveyed 188 young adults on several items, including sexual fluidity of attractions and sexual orientation identity. They found that 63% of females and 50% of males reported fluidity in their sexual attractions (being attracted to all genders). In addition, they found within the groups of people reporting fluidity in attraction that 48% of the females and 34% of the males expressed a fluidity in sexual orientation identity. Interestingly, more females than males endorsed sexual fluidity. Whether sexual orientation is fixed or fluid is still not fully determined. The research indicates that there are some for which it is fixed, while for others, it is fluid. Or, the research indicates that attraction to more than one gender is much more common than attraction to only one gender.

Related to the myth that sexual orientation can change is reparative and conversion therapies, also known as sexual orientation change efforts. These forms of therapy believe that same-sex attraction is "symptomatic of developmental defects or spiritual and moral failings" (Anton, 2010, p. 464). The treatment, often including psychotherapy, works to change attractions and desires for people of the same sex. The American Psychological Association, American Psychiatric Association, American Academy of Pediatrics, American Medical Association, American Counseling Association, and National Association of Social Workers oppose the use of sexual orientation change efforts. Stating that there is "insufficient evidence to support the use of psychological interventions to change sexual orientation," the American Psychological Association suggests that therapists use affirming, multicultural, ethical, client-centered approaches that incorporate the understanding of the effects of minority stress on individuals with same-sex attractions (Anton, 2010, p. 465).

Myth 3: LGBTQ People Are Child Molesters

There continue to be no credible scientific studies that support this myth (APA, 2008). However, this myth has been perpetuated by a number of antigay activists and psychologists who continue to promote this misinformation in order to facilitate anti-LGBTQ legislation. This was started in 1977 when Anita Bryant made a public campaign against an equal rights ordinance which included the myth that gay men molest children (Schlatter & Steinback, 2011).

Myth 4: LGBTQ Culture Is One of Partying, Drugs, and Alcohol

This myth may have been generated from the historic reality that before the modern gay rights movement, the main place to meet other LGBTQ individuals was at the local bar (Davis & Heilbroner, 2011). Bars were and in some places still are the centers of the community. This developed from the persecution that LGBTQ individuals faced prior to the Stonewall rebellion. Bars and clubs were the few places where LGBTQ individuals could somewhat safely congregate and find community (Davis & Heilbroner, 2011). The LGBTQ cultures then and now are much richer than this oversimplified assumption based on the few semisafe gathering places LGBTQ individuals had at the time.

Myth 5: LGBTQ People Are White, Middle-Class, Able-Bodied Young Adults

This is a myth perpetuated by the media despite the fact that LGBTQ individuals are characterized by all races, all socioeconomic classes, all abilities, all ages, and all religions. Please read the following section for further information about diversity within the LGBTQ community.

One way this myth is perpetuated is through the portrayal of LGBTQ people in movies and on TV. GLAAD (formerly the Gay & Lesbian Alliance Against Defamation) is an organization that watches the media for LGBTQ concerns as well as analyzes the presence of LGBTQ characters in the media. An analysis of motion pictures released in 2015 found that 17.5% of major studio movies had LGB characters and, of the 28 characters, 68% were males and 32% were females. Of the 28 characters in the movies, 68% were males and 32% were females. Further analysis of the 28 characters shows the majority, 68% (19 characters) were White, while 11% (3 characters) were African-American, 14% (4 characters) were Asian/Island Pacifiers, and 7% (2 characters) were Latino (GLAAD, 2016a). According to GLAAD, there were no Arabic or Native American/First Peoples characters who were LGB in 2015.

In a similar analysis of television for the 2015-16 season, GLAAD looked at the broadcast networks, cable networks, and streaming programs. When looking at the prevalence of LGBT characters on broadcast networks, GLAAD found 69% to be White, while 19% were Black, 7% were Latino/a, and 6% Asian/Pacific Islander. The breakdown of the race of LGBT characters on cable networks differed slightly, with 71% of the characters being White, 11% Black, 8% Latino, 4% Asian/Pacific Islander, and 5% other racial identity. The breakdown of the race of LGBT characters on streaming programs was 73% White, 12% Black, 12% Latino/a, 2% Asian/Pacific Islander, and 2% other. The disparity between the portrayal of White LGBT characters in film and television continues to promote this myth. Unfortunately, there were no statistics on the age or ability/disability of LGBTQ characters in the media, but from our personal experience, we would anticipate that the data would indicate that most characters are young adults who are able-bodied.

Myth 6: LGBTQ People Are Going Against God's Will

This is a common myth from some Christian denominations and other religions. The discrimination and persecution of

LGBTQ individuals by faith-based organizations can have very damaging effects upon LGBTQ individuals as they come out, define their identity, and attain different milestones in their adult lives. In order to protect themselves from discrimination and ostracism from their faith-based communities, many individuals have to turn away from the religion which was a cornerstone of their early development and identity.

Myth 7: All Gay Men Are Promiscuous

This myth developed out of the repression of gay male relationships and sexuality by society. Prior to the Stonewall riots, gay males faced such oppression and discrimination that the outlets for their sexuality and needs for relationship were often limited to semipublic arenas (bathrooms, storage containers, bars) (Davis & Heilbroner, 2011). Given the semipublic nature of these areas, men were easily persecuted by law enforcement and others for engaging in male-on-male sexual acts.

Myth 8: All Lesbians Are Either Ugly and Cannot Get a Man or Are a Male Heterosexual Fantasy-Type Woman

Similar to the Madonna or whore dichotomy for women, lesbians are often stereotyped as either too ugly to get a man or seen as beautiful women who fit a male heterosexual fantasy. The reality is that these myths of women who have sex with other women are based in the heterosexual male viewpoint, that women who do not want him are either undesirable by all males or an item of his pleasure, engaging in a fantasy version of his desire to have multiple partners (Elledge, 2010).

Myth 9: Bisexuals Are Promiscuous and Unable to Be Faithful

Many individuals have learned the myth about bisexual individuals, that they are promiscuous and unable to be faithful to one partner. People even say that promiscuity is part of the definition of a bisexual individual. However, this is not what it means to be bisexual. Bisexuality means simply lthat the person is attracted to individuals of both male and female genders. Related to bisexuality is pansexuality, the attraction to all gender expressions and gender identities. Finally, there are individuals who find either term too limiting and choose to not identify other than to say that they are attracted to more than one gender.

As stated before, there is research indicating that many men and women report that they have fluidity in their sexuality (Katz-Wise & Hyde, 2015), which could indicate that there are more people who are attracted to multiple genders. Interestingly, Diamond (2008) found that most women in her study who identify as nonheterosexual were in monogamous relationships. The myth of bisexual nonmonogamous behavior and promiscuity, along with beliefs both in the straight and queer communities that bisexuals are just getting the best of both worlds, creates tremendous stress and isolation for those who are bisexual/pansexual/attracted to more than one gender. Members of both communities openly express distrust of bisexuals/pansexuals/people attracted to more than one gender and perpetuate this myth.

Myth 10: Transgender Individuals Are Mentally Ill

In recent years, *DSM-V* marked a change from diagnosing transgender individuals as having a disorder (gender identity disorder) to having gender dysphoria (Bockting, 2015). This change is significant, as it changes from the view that to be transgender is to have a disorder to a diagnosis that focuses only on the presence of significant distress in some of the community of transgender individuals (APA, 2013). Many, but not all, transgender individuals experience distress and dysphoria associated with the process of coming to terms with ones transgender identity, as well as with the medical, psychological, and social issues associated with transitioning to living as a person of a different gender. This dysphoria is normal. If the transition is causing extreme amounts of distress or dysphoria, then the person would fit the criteria for gender dysphoria.

Myth 11: Transgender Individuals Are Hermaphrodites

"Hermaphrodite" is an outdated term used for individuals born with both male and female reproductive organs. In more recent years, this term has become derogatory, as it is negative and inaccurate; the correct term is "intersex," which is just one term for varying congenital disorders in which a person's reproductive anatomy does not fit into a male or female category. A transgender individual is someone with a gender identity that differs from that of their biological sex.

Myth 12: Transgender Individuals Are Gay/Lesbian

Transgender identities are linked only to gender identity, not to sexual orientation. As stated before, if transgender, one's gender identity does not align with the sex assigned at birth. Transgender individuals may be gay, straight, lesbian, bisexual, pansexual, queer, or any other orientation. In the 2012 study, Grant et al. measured how transgender individuals identify their sexual orientation: 25% self-identified as bisexual; 23%, straight; 23%, gay/lesbian/same gender-loving; 23%, queer; 4%, asexual; and 2%, trans-attracted.

Myth 13: AIDS Is a Gay Disease

In the early days of AIDS in the United States, the main populations that were affected by AIDS were gay men, Haitians, and drug users. An early name for AIDS was GRID (Gay-Related Immune Deficiency) (Shilts, 1987). Over the years, as more has been understood about this pandemic, the medical community has acknowledged that AIDS does not target only gay men.

Throughout our world, there are locations where AIDS is mainly spread through heterosexual contact and is causing the destruction of vast portions of communities (e.g., in Washington, DC, 17% of African-American males are HIV-positive [Frontline, 2012]). Clearly, AIDS is neither a gay disease nor an illness that affects only the gay and bisexual male communities. However, the stigma related to our culture's history of negatively associating AIDS with gay communities continues to persist today.

Even though there are many more popular myths about LGBTQ individuals, these give the reader an indication of the depth of these myths and the historic sources for the myths. Now that these myths are debunked, let us explore the LGBTQ culture from a variety of points of view. We will look at the diversity within gender differences, generational differences, acculturation/assimilation, oppression, meaning of wellness/health, and locus of support within the culture.

Diversity Within the LGBTQ Culture

The LGBTQ community is as diverse as the world we live in. Although there may be the cultural misconception that most LGBTQ-identified people are young, White, and middle-class, this is only a misconception based on the lack of visibility of the diversity that is the LGBTQ community. LGBTQ people span all ages, races, ethnicities, classes, genders, gender identities, religions, and abilities.

To begin with, over the past 50 years in the United States, the visibility of LGBTQ-identified people has changed drastically. Although visibility has changed in a way that makes it more possible for youth and young people to be living openly about their sexuality, gender expression, and gender identity, this is not to say that all LGBTQ people are young or that there has been an increase in LGBTQ identity. Many older adults are also coming out and living more open lives, which they were not able to do when they were younger. However, because of the homophobia in our society and the heteronormative assumptions often made about others' identities, it has been found that older and elderly LGBTQ-identified people often choose, or are forced, to go back into hiding their sexual orientation. This arises when in a situation with caretakers or nursing homes where they do not feel comfortable or safe disclosing their identities. Other issues that come up for LGBTQ elders are an inability to successfully access health care, inability for partners or spouses to receive benefits as a widow or widower through Social Security, inability to access affordable housing, tax law discrimination against same-sex couples, lack of support from family members, and, as they age, isolation from the LGBTQ community itself (National Gay and Lesbian Task Force Foundation, 2012).

Youth and young adults also experience a unique set of challenges within the LGBTQ community. Many youths are struggling with coming out and seeking safe spaces and support where they feel able to be open and honest about themselves and their identity. Both LGBTQ- and straight-identified youth are battling with the present-day issue of bullying and the terrible impact it can have on their lives. In a report by the National Coalition of Anti-Violence Programs on the 2014 status of LGBTQ hate-related violence, it is stated that youth and young adults up to the age of 24 were "2.5 times more likely to be injured due to hate violence" and "2.2 times more likely to experience police violence" (Ahmed & Jindasurat, 2015, p. 39). Homelessness is also an issue for young people in the LGBTQ community, with the fact that 20% to 40% of homeless youth are LGBTQ versus only 10% of the general youth population identifying as LGBTQ (Quintana, Rosenthal, & Krehely, 2010).

LGBTQ-identified people come from all different racial and ethnic groups. Although in the mainstream media we are more likely to see the LGBTQ community represented as a White community, the LGBTQ community has a strong movement of LGBTQ people of color, who are confronted by both the presence of homophobia and transphobia and racism in our culture. Many LGBTQ people of color come from strong cultural and/or religious backgrounds where LGBTQ acceptance is lacking, creating an additional barrier or challenge for these individuals in bringing together their various identities. Other challenges faced by LGBTQ people include that "Black and Latino LGBT people are more likely to be in poor health than both their heterosexual and nontransgender counterparts within communities of color and their White counterparts within the LGBT community" (National Coalition of LGBT Health, p. 1). According to a 2015 report by the National Coalition of Anti-Violence Programs on the 2014 status of LGBTQ hate-related violence, "LGBTQ people of color were 2.2 times as likely to experience physical violence compared to White LGBTQ" individuals and "[t]ransgender people of color were 3.1 times more likely to experience any form of police violence." Also, 80% of the 20 documented hate violence homicides in 2014 were LGBTQ people of color (Ahmed & Jindasurat, 2015).

LGBTQ people come from all different socioeconomic statuses. However, "evidence indicates that individuals who identify as lesbian, gay, bisexual, or transgender (LGBT) are especially susceptible to being placed at a socioeconomic disadvantage" (American Psychological Association, p. 1). Job discrimination in the LGBTQ community is a large factor in creating this issue. It is important for us to note that at the time of publication, termination of an employee based on sexual orientation is prohibited in only 22 of our 50 states, while termination based on gender identity is prohibited in 20. Termination of a public employee based on gender identity is prohibited in an additional 7 states; termination of a public employee based on sexual orientation, in an additional 12 states (Human Rights Campaign, 2016b). This leaves 16 states in which there are currently no protections against employment discrimination for LGBTQ individuals. Studies also report that "[g]ay men earn up to 32% less than similarly qualified heterosexual men" (American Psychological Association, p. 1).

LGBTQ people come from all different religious groups and upbringings. The movement against LGBTQ equal rights in the United States and across the world has come strongly from a mix of religious groups. However, many LGBTQ people identify with their own personal spirituality and/or religion. It is also important to recognize that LGBTQ people do not just come from or identify with Christianity. LGBTQ people exist throughout the world and in all cultures and religions. Despite the prominence of many anti-LGBTQ religious groups in this country, there are many religious groups, denominations from various religions as well as individual congregations across the country, that have come out as LGBTQ-affirming. Within the LGBTQ community there are also many religious support organizations of various faiths.

LGBTQ people come with many varying abilities. There are many subcommunities within the greater LGBTQ community, including communities for those who are queer and deaf, communities for those who are queer and blind, and communities for those who are queer with physical handicaps. Like LGBTQ people of color, LGBTQ people with a disability are also at the disadvantage of experiencing discrimination as a person in multiple minority groups.

Individuals within the LGBTQ community identify with many different genders. We call this "gender identity." It is important for us to remember that gender identity is different from sexual orientation. While sexual orientation is about to whom a person is attracted, gender identity is what a person internally identifies with as their own gender. For most people, gender aligns with the sex they were assigned at birth, but this is not the case for all people. Some people identify as transgender, meaning that their gender identity does not align with their assigned gender at birth. Some transgender people identify specifically with the opposite gender (e.g., biologically male at birth but identifies as female), while others do not. As we described early in this chapter, the term "transgender" has become an umbrella term inclusive of all those people with varying gender identities outside of the norms of male and female. Although transition from one gender to another is the necessary path for some, others are more comfortable staying somewhere more in the middle, and some will call themselves genderqueer, gender fluid, androgynous, cross dressers, drag performers, or transvestites.

Transgender people are not the only ones within the LGBTQ community whose gender identity lies outside of the societal norms. Many gay and lesbian people defy the basic male and female gender stereotypes, not just by having same-sex relationships, but also by identifying their own personal gender as more masculine or feminine. All men and women, regardless of their biological sex or sexual orientation, have a right to express their gender in a way that is congruent with their internal gender identity as well as their life experiences.

Some of the unique challenges that are faced by the transgender community are the issues of discrimination and hate crimes. Although this is a problem for all of the LGBTQ community, transgender people face an even higher rate of discrimination, homelessness, and joblessness (Grant, Mottet, Tanis, Harrison, Herman, & Kesling, 2011). A 2015 report by the National Coalition of Anti Violence Programs on the 2014 status of LGBTQ hate-related violence revealed that transgender women made up 55% of the 20 reported hate murders in 2014 and "[t]ransgender people were 4.6 times more likely to experience police violence compared to cisgender survivors and victims" (Ahmed & Jindasurat, 2015).

Just as gender roles are diverse and wide-ranging in the general "straight" population, they are also diverse and wide-ranging in LGBTQ cultures. What is different for the LGBTQ community is that as "queer" people, without necessarily intending to, they defy the "gender norms" that have been created in our society just by the way they identify. Just by living as himself, and loving his partner, a gay man is going against the typical gender roles that are ingrained in our society. Within their personal identities as well as relationships, there is often a question of whether same-sex partners fall into gender-specific roles. This concept reflects a perspective of both the heteronormativity and gender norms that are engrained from the dominant culture. However, this topic is one that the LGBTQ community often observes and discusses, one that would most likely have answers as unique and diverse as the varying gender identities and personalities within this great community. Do transgender men and women fall into stereotypical gender roles within their own personal identities? Again, the answer is unique to each individual. However, many transgender individuals do have the unique experience of having been raised and socialized in the beginning of their life as one gender and then having transitioned and lived with the identity and social norms of another.

There are many—not just in the transgender community, but also in the LGB communities—who defy the stereotypes and expectations of basic male/female gender identities through the way in which they present themselves in dress, behavior, and language and through whom they choose to love. Many within the LGBTQ community would describe this concept as a gender spectrum. In reality, not only does this gender spectrum define those in the LGBTQ community, but also it is relative for all human beings, crossing all cultures and identities. Gender is not just one or the other, the way our society has perpetuated it to be, but instead it is a whole range and spectrum of behaviors and presentations. If we put the very feminine identity at one end of that spectrum and the very masculine at the other end, we have the basic gender stereotypes or expected roles. But any person, straight- or LGBTQ-identified, can walk up to that spectrum on any day and place their finger on the line between those two to identify where their personal gender identity lies. Many within the LGBTQ community identify with this spectrum of gender where they can have the freedom to go against the basic cultural roles of male and female and live within a gender identity that matches not what is expected of them, but where they truly feel themselves to be.

Gender norms and differences also occur within the LGBTQ community as manifested in its subcommunities. There are a number of subcommunities: lesbian women, gay men, bisexual men and women, transgender men, transgender women, genderqueer communities, and others. All of these communities are made up of individuals who are seeking others with their common identities, relating to one another, and finding support. These subcommunities all have various ways of defining and identifying with gender roles, often creating their own terms and language for how these roles play out in the community.

Just as there is great diversity within the LGBTQ communities in terms of gender norms and identities, the LGBTQ communities have cultural changes from generation to generation that differ from many of the other cultures discussed in this book. Except for a very few, LGBTQ individuals are not raised in a household with LGBTQ parents. Because of this, the history and cultural norms are not learned from an early age, but are learned when one joins the LGBTQ community, usually sometime between the late teenage years and later adulthood. Each "generation" of LGBTQ individuals has norms and cultures that develop from the current history and move forward. Unless an individual seeks to learn what the generations before have experienced either by talking with elders or through researching LGBTQ history, a connection to the historic events of the LGBTQ communities is not always present.

An example of generational difference within the LGBTQ communities is outness. With those who realized they were LGBTQ prior to the beginnings of the modern gay rights movement, these individuals are more likely to not be out due to persecution by the police, medical and mental health professionals, families, churches, armed services, and society in general. At the time, to be out placed the individual's entire life in jeopardy, opening the individual up to potential physical violence, emotional abuse, loss of job/housing/public accommodation, removal from the church, loss of family/ friends/significant relationships, and so forth. Being out is not a quality that is valued by all members of this community. However, when examining the cultures of the queer youth of today, there are significant differences in the level of comfort with being out. The youth of today have grown up in a society (especially in large urban areas) that is more accepting, seeing some positive laws expanding LGBTQ people's rights (however, there were more than 100 new anti-LGBT bills introduced in 2015), as equal marriage and transgender rights spread across the land. The changes in society have allowed these youths to come out fully at earlier ages, sometimes in elementary or middle school. The assistance and community provided by organizations like PFLAG, GLSEN, and school- or community-based gay straight alliances across the country have given these youths the support and role models necessary to learn how to live a life that is out and proud.

Acculturation and Assimilation

Similarly, the issues of acculturation and assimilation within the LGBTQ cultures differ greatly from those in other cultures. LGBTQ people often need to give up aspects of the dominant culture(s) in their lives as they learn to embrace who they are within their sexual orientation, gender expression, and/or gender identity. Some of the dominant cultures (race, ethnicity, religion, etc.) are embracing or permissive of the LGBTQ cultures, while some are not. For those who are able to maintain their ties to their dominant cultures, the process of coming out and changing one's self-identity can be less difficult as compared to those who do not have that support.

The process of "coming out," making public one's sexual orientation and/or gender identity, can be one with many challenges for the individual. LGBTQ persons are often born and raised into predominantly heteronormative cultures, meaning cultural environments where they are assumed to be straight and cisgender. Heteronormative refers to the concept or worldview in which heterosexuality is considered the norm and/or preferred identity. The LGBTQ individual socialized in these cultures may struggle with exploring and coming to terms with their own identity as well as with their own internalized homophobia and transphobia. Because of this, coming out often first involves a process of internal exploration and self-discovery.

Transgender individuals also face the additional step of "transitioning," which refers to "the process—social, legal, or medical—one goes through to discover and/or affirm one's gender identity." Each transgender individual will choose for themselves how and when they transition, but it "may, but does not always, include taking hormones; having surgeries; and changing names, pronouns, identification documents, and more" (Parents, Families, Friends, and Allies United with LGBTQ People, 2016).

By coming out and transitioning, an LGBTQ individual may become subject to discrimination and harassment. A 2012 survey by the Human Rights Campaign reports that 42% of youth surveyed stated that the community in which they live is not accepting of LGBTQ people and 26% of LGBTQ-identified youth surveyed reported their biggest concern was a lack of acceptance from their families (Human Rights Campaign, 2012). However, we also see changes in the coming out process over generational differences. As our predominant culture(s) begins to shift more toward acceptance of the LGBTQ community, we see that more and more young people are coming out and doing so at younger ages. Although coming out is often associated with youth, an individual can come out at any point in their lifetime.

Coming out is an important choice, and one that is unique for each individual. While some choose to be out on a very public level, other individuals make a very conscious choice not to come out. Each individual must decide for themselves how and when to come out to their families, friends, and dominant culture(s). "Outing" or revealing an individual's sexual orientation or gender identity without their consent, can be dangerous, as individuals who are outed or come out themselves, even now, have been rejected by family, friends, communities, church, school, an armed service, and/or other members of their community when they have come out. These losses can be substantial and difficult to heal from. Maintaining an identity as a member of the LGBTQ community while

maintaining the identity of a member of an unaccepting culture is challenging.

Luckily, there are many LGBTQ-friendly organizations based on race, ethnicity, religion, and other interests that help individuals to bridge the gap between the cultures in which they grew up and the LGBTQ cultures. There are organizations for LGBTQ individuals to find community with others of the same ethnic or racial background. These organizations can be national or international and include but are not limited to Gay Asian & Pacific Alliance, Gay & Lesbian Arab Society, National Latino/a Lesbian & Gay Organization, and National Black Lesbian & Gay Leadership Forum. Other organizations may be region- or city-based and can be located through Internet searches, the local LGBTQ newspaper, local community centers, or the local Pink Pages directory.

Within religious cultures, there are a variety of options for LGBTQ individuals to continue their connection to the religious culture of their upbringing if they so desire. First, religious organizations like Dignity USA (Roman Catholic), Al-Fatiha Foundation (Islam), Affirmation (LDS/Mormon), and Integrity (Episcopalian) have developed to provide community and support for LGBTQ individuals within that specific faith. These organizations allow the LGBTQ individual who continues her/his identity to include the specific religious culture to be a part of the community with other LGBTQ individuals and allies. Another response to religious rejection has been to create new churches with open and affirming messages. One prime example of this is the Metropolitan Community Church. Finally, many pre-existing religious cultures either already had an open and affirming message or have developed it over the years. Some examples of these religious organizations include the United Church of Christ, Unitarian Universalists, Centers for Spiritual Living, and Masjid An-Nural Isslaah. It is important to note that these organizations, despite being national organizations, may not be located in all communities across the country. LGBTQ-friendly religious organizations in a specific area can be found using similar methods to race and ethnic groups as well as through the local Freedom to Marry chapter.

Many communities, especially in larger metropolitan cities, have groups that focus on similar interests, identities, and affiliations with the local LGBTQ community. These can range from groups that focus on political action to recreational activities, to health needs. Groups can focus on small subcultures within a specific city/region. Some examples of these types of groups in the Massachusetts/Boston area are Women Outdoors (a lesbian and bisexual women's group that engages in outdoor recreational activities), Gay Fathers of Boston, Mad Femme Pride, and Mass Bay Bears. Within these community groups, members of the LGBTQ culture find community, kinship, and belonging.

Minority Stress

Despite the various supportive organizations and individuals in our lives, the LGBTQ communities suffer from oppression, which causes minority stress. The forms of discrimination that LGBTQ individuals face include institutional, interpersonal, and internal. The effects of minority stress on LGBTQ individuals has been studied over the past two decades. The outcomes of the studies have indicated that LGBTQ individuals suffer a variety of physical and mental health problems related to the discrimination they endure. One significant mental health problem is an increased suicidal ideation in adults and youth (Clements-Golle, Marx, & Katz, 2006; Rotheram-Borus, Hunter, & Rosario, 1994; Savin-Williams, 1994). Youth report large numbers of suicidal ideations and attempts which are related to environmental stressors rather than being LGBTQ (Reynolds, 2011). Lesbian, gay, and bisexual youth have been found to be four times more likely to attempt suicide than heterosexual youth (Massachusetts Department of Elementary and Secondary Education, 2008). Additionally, half of transgender youth have suicidal ideations and a quarter report attempting suicide (Grossman & D'Augelli, 2008). Even questioning youth have higher rates of suicidal thoughts than straight or out lesbian, gay, and bisexual youth (Potreat, Aragon, Espelage, & Koenig, 2009). Clearly, LGBTQ individuals, especially youth, experience suicidal thoughts as a direct response to minority stress.

In addition to suicidal ideations and attempts, LGBTQ individuals experience other mental health effects of minority stress. In youth studies, there has been found to be a link between bullying based on sexual orientation and gender expression and mental health issues (Bontempo & D'Augelli, 2002; D'Augelli, Grossman, & Starks, 2006; Epstein & Spirito, 2009; Poteat & Espelage, 2007; Swearer, Turner, Givens, & Pollack, 2008; Williams, Connolly, Pepler, & Craig, 2005). In youth and adults, studies have found that LGBTQ individuals also suffer from high-risk behavior (Heck, Flentje, & Cochran, 2011; Savin-Williams, 1994); mental health problems, including substance abuse (Cochran, Sullivan, & Mays, 2003; D'Augelli, 2002; Heck, Flentje, & Cochran, 2011; Lewis, Derlega, Clarke, McElligott, Jacobs, & Kuang, 2004; Meyer, 2003; Savin-Williams, 1994); and compromised physical health (DiPlacido ,1998; Lewis, Derlega, Clarke, McElligott, Jacobs, & Kuang, 2004; Ryan, Huebner, Diaz, & Sanchez, 2007) due to minority stress. In the workplace, LGB individuals have been found to be twice as likely to be fired from jobs as heterosexuals (Mays & Cochran, 2001). And, in a 2011 survey of transgender individuals, "44% of survey respondents reported they did not get a job they applied for because of being transgender or gender nonconforming" (Grant, Mottet, Tanis, Harrison, Herman, & Kesling, 2011).

Hate messages come not only from outside the LGBTQ communities. These messages can come from within the community (member against member) and within oneself. Internalized homophobia and internalized transphobia occur when members of the LGBTQ communities "internalize significant aspects of the prejudice experienced within a heterosexist society" (Williamson, 2000, p. 99) and turn that prejudice upon themselves. Meyers (1995) theorizes that this internalized discrimination is one aspect of minority stress. A

review of literature has linked homophobia to a variety of psychological issues (Williamson, 2000), health issues (Williams, 2000), and relationship difficulties (Frost & Meyer, 2009). Very little research has been conducted on the effects of internalized transphobia.

Within groups that experience minority stress, it is not uncommon to see different subcultures within the culture exhibit discrimination among themselves. The LGBTQ community is no different. There are subcultures of gay men who are misogynistic. Some lesbians practice separatism (the removal of one gender from the greater culture). Many lesbians and gay men are biphobic. Transgender individuals often find themselves segregated from the greater queer community. Racism, ageism, Protestantism, and ableism exist within the LGBTQ community. One of the subcultures to receive the most internal discrimination has been the transgender group. However, with time and education, many have become more accepting.

The good news is that resilience and positive support from peers and adults has been shown to decrease the effects of minority stress in LGBTQ individuals. It is important for music therapists to realize that individual resilience and coping is not enough to deal effectively with minority stress (Meyer, 2003). To effectively cope with minority stress, one needs a group that can help to change or replace the prejudicial norms and values placed on LGBTQ individuals by the heterosexist society, provide positive role models, and provide social support (Crocker & Major, 1989). Studies on youth have found family acceptance to have a positive impact on mental and physical health outcomes (Ryan, Huebner, Diaz, & Sanchez, 2007). Similarly, if an LGBTQ youth has one adult to talk to about being LGBTQ he or she is one-third as likely to be injured or threatened or to attempt suicide (Goodenow, Szalacha, & Westheimer, 2002). Third, youth who participated in Gay–Straight alliances had better school outcomes and decreased mental health issues (Heck, Flentje, & Cochran, 2011; Fetner & Kush, 2008). With this, a positive relationship with health care workers has been shown to increase lesbians' physical and mental health (Bjorkman & Malterud, 2012). Clearly, positive, nonheterosexist interactions with others increase positive outcomes in LGBTQ individuals.

Meaning of Medicine and Well-Being

Health and well-being is an extremely important aspect of the LGBTQ community. Across the country, many different programs exist specifically to help LGBTQ people get access to the health care and mental health services that they need. Many of these programs also include HIV prevention and safe-sex education programs for the LGBTQ community. Suicide prevention is another important movement within the LGBTQ community that many organizations have taken on to provide support and alternative options to LGBTQ individuals. Many of these programs are nonprofits and grassroots organizations often started by LGBTQ people themselves seeing a need for it within their community.

As mentioned earlier in this chapter, factors such as job discrimination and socioeconomic status impact the ability of persons in the LGBTQ community to have access to health insurance. In a study by the Center for American Progress, it was reported that while 82% of heterosexual adults have health insurance, only 77% of LGB adults and 57% of transgender adults report having health insurance (Krehely, 2009). This report also explains that …

> due to factors like low rates of health insurance coverage, high rates of stress due to systematic harassment and discrimination, and a lack of cultural competency in the health care system, LGBT people are at a higher risk for cancer, mental illnesses, and other diseases and are more likely to smoke, drink alcohol, use drugs, and engage in other risky behaviors. (Krehely, 2009, p. 1)

Because of the lack of knowledge around LGBTQ issues, many in the community are hesitant about seeking health care or choose not to be out with their health care provider. In a survey by the National Center for Transgender Equality, it was reported that 50% of transgender people report having to educate their health care provider around transgender health care. Other issues include refusal of care, 19%, and postponing medical care due to discrimination, 28% (Grant, Mottet, Tanis, Harrison, Herman, & Kesling, 2011). In a 2010 study by Lambda Legal, 7.7% of LGB people, 26.7% of transgender people, and 19% of people living with HIV reported having been refused needed health care outright (Lambda Legal, 2010). Of the following scenarios—being refused needed care, health care professionals refusing to touch them or using excessive precautions, health care professionals using harsh or abusive language, being blamed for their health status, or health care professionals being physically rough or abusive—56% of LGB, 70% of transgender, and 63% of people living with HIV responded that they had experienced at least one (Lambda Legal, 2010).

Another important aspect of health care with LGBTQ individuals is the history of abuses perpetrated on LGBTQ individuals by mental and physical health professionals. During the first half of the 20th century, sexual orientations beyond those of heterosexual and gender identity that did not conform to the heteronormative gender roles were seen as mental illnesses. A variety of techniques were used to "cure" LGBTQ individuals, including lobotomies, electroconvulsive therapy, aversion therapy with electrical shock, a variety of psychopharmacological interventions, and castration. Many of these techniques are no longer used, yet some psychologically damaging psychotherapy techniques still remain, mainly reparative and conversion therapy. At the time of the writing of this chapter, California, Illinois, New Jersey, Oregon, Vermont, and the District of Columbia have laws preventing the practice of conversion/reparative therapy on minors. In addition, over 20 states have similar legislation in the works (Human Rights Campaign, 2016a). The laws in New Jersey and California have held up under appeal to higher courts. Further legislation and legal actions continue to stop the practice of conversion/reparative therapy (Human Rights Campaign, 2016a). It is important to keep these current and historical abuses in mind as one works with elders, as well as youth and adults, in the LGBTQ community.

In the larger metropolitan areas, there often exist health care organizations that focus on the needs of the LGBTQ communities or portions thereof. However, in small towns in the United States, these types of service centers do not exist, and the LGBTQ individual must find compassionate care through friends, calling insurance networks, asking for an LGBTQ-friendly physician, or luck. It is clear that while within the community itself there is a lot of continuous support and education around LGBTQ health and important issues specifically affecting the LGBTQ community, the general population is in great need of education. Extensive education is needed for our health care professionals around the needs specific to the LGBTQ community, as well as comprehensive programs for transgender health care.

Meaning of Music

We, as music therapists, are part of the health care system that serves LGBTQ people. To effectively conduct our sessions with LGBTQ people, we must discuss the music of the LGBTQ cultures. Given that LGBTQ individuals come from a variety of cultures, there are a myriad of meanings for music. However, one nearly universal meaning and function of music within the LGBTQ cultures is that music is a way to bring the community together. In the 20th and now 21st centuries, there have been a variety of venues and ways that music has brought LGBTQ people together. Musical theatre, opera, concerts, song circles, choirs, drum circles, dances, music groups, and bars are just a few ways in which music has served to bring LGBTQ people together for socialization, support, dating, and recreation. The music in clubs and bars has played a large part in creating an environment and activity through which LGBTQ individuals could interact.

The LGBTQ community is heterogeneous and influenced by many other cultures, including the dominant culture, in regard to music. This is easily noted in bars and clubs. Throughout the history of LGBTQ bars, one will often have heard popular music from one of the more dominant cultures. The genre of music played is often dictated by the subculture that frequents the establishment; different generations of specific subcultures within the greater LGBTQ culture have genres of music associated with that subculture. Each bar or club usually specializes in a specific subculture of the LGBTQ community, either entirely or on specific days of the week. Throughout much of this century, there have existed bars that featured cabaret, drag performances, piano, country and western, and popular music from the dominant cultures. As different genres of popular music filtered into bars and clubs, different generations of LGBTQ subcultures developed associations with those genres of music. From these associations, different songs that had significant meaning became anthems.

In the 1970s, one of the popular genres of music in the LGBTQ club culture was disco. Artists and bands that were popular in the clubs and bars were ABBA, Donna Summer, the Bee Gees, David Bowie, and the Village People. Very few musicians on the popular scene were "out" during this decade. There were inquiries into the sexual orientation of artists like David Bowie and Freddie Mercury from Queen. Other bands were out within the gay community and sang about LGBTQ themes, but the mainstream community remained somewhat unaware of their sexual orientation. One example of this was the Village People. Some anthems from the LGBTQ communities during that decade included Gloria Gaynor's "I Will Survive"; "YMCA" by the Village People; "You Make Me Feel (Mighty Real)" by Sylvester; and "We Are Family" by Sister Sledge.

In the 1980s, various genres of music, including New Wave, punk, and metal, were heard in bars. LGBTQ-identified artists and bands were coming out and could be heard in the clubs. These groups and artists included Erasure, Culture Club, Lou Reed, Joan Jett, the Smiths, Dead or Alive, Bronski Beat, Yaz, and George Michael. Other club favorites who crossed over to the LGBTQ club culture included bands and artists like Madonna, the Eurythmics, and Diana Ross. Some of the anthems of that decade included "It's Raining Men" by The Weather Girls; "I Am What I Am" from La Cage au Folies; "Sisters Are Doing It for Themselves" by Aretha Franklin and the Eurythmics; and "True Colors" by Cyndi Lauper.

The 1990s saw the rise of music genres that included grunge, hip-hop, urban, industrial, and alternative rock. The LGBTQ bars and clubs reflected these changes in the dominant music culture as had happened in previous years. LGBTQ artists and bands continued to be present in the LGBTQ club music scene as well as in the mainstream music cultures. Some of the popular musicians who were LGBTQ-identified included k. d. lang, the Pet Shop Boys, RuPaul, Ani DeFranco, the Indigo Girls, Melissa Etheridge, and Jill Sobule. Some of the anthems from that decade included "Go West" by the Pet Shop Boys; "Finally" by Ce Ce Peniston ; "Yes, I Am" by Melissa Etheridge; and "Free" by Ultra Nate.

With the new century has come increased acceptance and visibility of LGBTQ musicians. High-profile artists like Lady Gaga, Adam Lambert, Rufus Wainwright, Frank Ocean, Clay Aiken, and Luther Vandross have been successful in the dominant popular music culture and even had significant hits with songs based on LGBTQ-related themes. Some of the club anthems from this decade-plus have included "Single Ladies" by Beyoncé; "We Are Who We Are" by Ke$ha; and "Born This Way" by Lady Gaga.

The music cultures of the LGBTQ bars and clubs is only one aspect of how music has been associated with community and bringing people together. Throughout the last portion of the past century, there were many instances of LGBTQ music subgenres and movements being created out of a desire for community within a genre of music. These genres of music grew out of the existing music scenes and became associated with specific generational subcultures of the LGBTQ community. One great example of this is the women's music genre that started in the '70s and continues today. The women's music genre grew out of the second wave of feminism and was a response to the male-dominated popular music scene. Women desired music that was by women and about women's interests. This genre of music is not exclusive to lesbians, but many lesbians of that subculture and generation are fond of this music genre. Some of the popular artists within this genre of music include Holly Near, Chris Williamson, Margie Adams, Meg Christian, and Bernice Johnson Reagon. From this genre of music developed a variety of independent record labels and women's music festivals that are still in existence today. The largest of these festivals was Michigan Womyn's Music Festival, which celebrated its 40th anniversary and final festival in the summer of 2016.

Similar to the women's music genre, the riot grrl music genre developed in the early to mid-1990s in response to the male-dominated punk rock scene. Like woman's music, this genre of music was not exclusively for lesbians or bisexual women, but many of the band members and audiences were lesbian or bisexual. Some of the bands to come from this movement include Bikini Kill and Bratmobile. The riot grrl genre focuses strongly on issues affecting women, including empowerment, violence against women, sexuality, and discrimination. It was strongly influenced by the third wave of feminism.

A third way that music has played a role in the LGBTQ communities to bring people together is through music groups. In many large cities across the United States, there exist LGBT choirs, bands, and orchestras. Recordings of the larger and more successful choirs are available at many online music outlets, while many Pride parades feature the local LGBT marching band. National organizations have formed for these different groups, which include the Gay and Lesbian Association of Choruses (GALA Choruses) and the Lesbian and Gay Band Association (LGBA).

One interesting point to consider is that to be out as a musician or to sing about issues within the LGBTQ communities is often seen as a political act by the mainstream culture. Whether a musician wants to be political or just wants to express her/his experiences, these themes are often seen by the mainstream culture as militant, part of the gay agenda, or political in nature. The mainstream community often misinterpreted these lyrics to be about experiences other than those of being gay, lesbian, bisexual, or transgender. Other musicians have written songs that were clearly political statements. It is important as music therapists to become aware of the historical times in which a song was written and the meanings within the song if it is not clear. It is important, as with all cultures, for music therapists to avoid assumptions and to talk with the client about her/his preferred music and genres.

Conclusion

Looking toward the future for the LGBTQ community, it is clear that there is a continued need for support and growth on many differing levels. Mental health services are needed for those struggling with everything from bullying to suicidal thoughts, to support needed during coming out and/or transitioning processes, to coping with the effects of minority stress, in addition to the physical and mental health challenges that all people face. Comprehensive health coverage is needed that includes issues unique to the LGBTQ community. Inclusive, open, and affirming programs are a continuous need for youth and young adults, as well as programs to address homelessness and other important issues that exist within the LGBTQ community, such as domestic violence, substance abuse, safe-sex programs, and HIV and AIDS prevention.

As mentioned earlier, there are many nonprofit and grassroots organizations, as well as more large-scale and national organizations, that have been created to support the LGBTQ community. Some important ones with which to familiarize yourself are:

AIDS Action
Bisexual Resource Center
COLAGE—Children of Lesbians and Gays Everywhere
Family Equality Council
GLSEN—Gay Lesbian Straight Education Network
Lambda Legal
National Black Justice Coalition
National Center for Transgender Equality
National Coalition for LGBT Health
National Gay and Lesbian Cancer Network
National Gay and Lesbian Task Force
National Resource Center on LGBT Aging
PFLAG—Parents Families and Friends of Lesbians and Gays
Safe Schools Coalition
The Trevor Project
Transgender Law Center

With the help of supportive organizations like those listed above and the continued advocacy and support from the community itself, the LGBTQ community will continue to grow and progress. With recent strides in the civil rights movement, including the 2015 Supreme Court ruling on same-sex marriage, the inclusion of LGBTQ persons in nondiscrimination policies in some states, the removal of the Don't Ask, Don't Tell policy from our military, and the recent ruling to allow transgender individuals to serve openly in the military, it is clear that strides are being made and many persons, both LGBTQ and allies, are working hard toward progress.

It is clear that although progress is being made for this community, there are large discrepancies in areas such as health care and mental health. As music therapists, it is our responsibility to educate ourselves and become more competent providers. By learning more about the LGBTQ community, what their specific needs are, and how to respectfully work with and address those needs within our field and our practice, we can be a part of changing these health care discrepancies and work toward eliminating some of the startling statistics coming out of the LGBTQ community.

In conclusion, the LGBTQ community itself has in many ways banded together to enable health and well-being while creating a locus of support within its own community. However, the greater community as a whole is needed to reduce the stigma and cultural misconceptions that lead to discrimination against the community and minority stress within the community. Competent care and professionals are needed in the areas of health care and mental health care. Along with this, continued support is needed for inclusive spaces and programs that create safe spaces for LGBTQ people of all diverse backgrounds.

References

Ahmed, O., & Jindasurat, C. (2015). Lesbian, gay, bisexual, transgender, queer and HIV-affected hate violence in 2014. *A report from the National Coalition of Anti Violence Programs*. Retrieved from http://www.avp.org/storage/documents/Reports/2014_HV_Report-Final.pdf

American Psychological Association. (n.d.). Understanding Child Sexual Abuse: Education, Prevention, and Recovery. Retrieved from http://www.apa.org/pubs/info/brochures/sex-abuse.aspx

American Psychological Association. (2013). *Gender dysphoria*. Retrieved from http://www.dsm5.org/documents/gender%20dysphoria%20fact%20sheet.pdf

American Psychological Association. (2015a). *Answers to your questions for a better understanding of sexual orientation and homosexuality*. Retrieved from https://www.apa.org/topics/lgbt/orientation.pdf

American Psychological Association. (2015b). *Answers to your questions about transgender people, gender identity, and gender expression*. Retrieved from http://www.apa.org/topics/lgbt/transgender.aspxAnton, B. S. (2010). Proceedings of the American Psychological Association for the legislative year 2009: Minutes of the annual meeting of the Council of Representatives and minutes of the meetings of the Board of Directors. *American Psychologist, 65*, 385–475. doi:10.1037/a0019553

Bjorkman, M., & Malterud, K. (2012). Lesbian women coping with challenges of minority stress: A qualitative study. *Scandinavian Journal of Public Health, 40*, 239–245.

Bockting, W. (2015). *The psychology of transgender.* Retrieved from http://www.apa.org/news/press/releases/2015/11/psychology-transgender.aspx

Bontempo, D. E., & D'Augelli, A. R. (2002). Effects of at-school victimization and sexual orientation on lesbian, gay, or bisexual youths' health risk behavior. *Journal of Adolescent Health, 30*(5), 364–374.

Chappell, B. (2016). Orlando sees worst mass shooting on U.S. soil: What we know Monday. Retrieved from http://www.npr.org/sections/thetwo-way/2016/06/13/481835963/worst-mass-shooting-on-u-s-soil-what-we-know-monday

Cochran, S. D., Sullivan, J. G., & Mays, V. M. (2003). Prevalence of mental disorders, psychological distress, and mental health service use among lesbian, gay, and bisexual adults in the United States. *Journal of Consulting and Clinical Psychology, 71,* 53–61.

Crocker, J., & Major, B. (1989). Social stigma and self-esteem: The self-protective properties of stigma. *Psychological Review, 96*(4), 608–630.

Davis, K., & Heilbroner, D. & Samels, M. (Producers). Davis, K., & Heilbroner, D. (Directors). (2011). *Stonewall uprising* (Motion picture on DVD). USA: American Experience, Public Broadcast System.

D'Augelli, A. R. (2002). Mental health problems among lesbian, gay, and bisexual youths ages 14 to 21. *Clinical Child Psychology and Psychiatry, 7,* 439–462.

D'Augelli, A. R., Grossman, A. H., & Starks, M. T. (2006). Childhood gender atypicality, victimization, and PTSD among lesbian, gay, and bisexual youth. *Journal of Interpersonal Violence, 21*(11), 1462–1482.

Diamond, L. M. (2015). Sexual fluidity. *The international encyclopedia of human sexuality,* 1115–1354.

DiPlacido, J. (1998). Minority stress among lesbians, gay men, and bisexuals: A consequence of heterosexism, homophobia, and stigmatization. In G. M. Herek (Ed.), *Stigma and sexual orientation* (pp. 138–159). Thousand Oaks, CA: SAGE.

Elledge, J. (2010). *Queers in American popular culture.* Santa Barbara, CA: Praeger.

Epstein, J., & Spirito, A. (2009). Risk factors for suicidality among a nationally representative sample of high school students. *Suicide and Life-Threatening Behavior, 39*(3), 241–251.

Fetner, T., & Kush, K. (2008). Gay-Straight alliances in high schools: Social predictors of early adoption. *Youth Society, 40,* 114–130.

Frontline. (2012). *Endgame: AIDS in Black America.* Retrieved from http://video.pbs.org/video/2254967747/

Frost, D. M., & Meyer, I. H. (2009). Internalized homophobia and relationship quality among lesbians, gay men, and bisexuals. *Journal of Counseling Psychology, 56*(1), 97–109.

GLAAD. (2016a). *2015 studio responsibility index.* Retrieved from http://www.glaad.org/files/2015_SRI.pdf

GLAAD. (2016b). 2015–2016: where we are on TV. Retrieved from http://www.glaad.org/files/GLAAD-2015-WWAT.pdf

Goodenow, C., Szalacha, L., & Westheimer, K. (2006). School support groups, other school factors, and the safety of sexual minority adolescents. *Psychology in the Schools, 43*(5), 573–589.

Grant, J. M., Mottet, L. A., Tanis, J. D., Harrison, J., Herman, J. L., & Kesling, M. (2011). Injustice at every turn: A report of the national transgender discriminationsurvey. *National Center for Transgender Equality and National Gay and Lesbian Task Force.* Retrieved from http://www.thetaskforce.org/downloads/reports/reports/ntds_full.pdf

Grossman, A. H., & D'Augelli, A. R. (2007). Transgender youth and life-threatening behaviors. *Suicide and Life-Threatening Behavior, 37*(5), 527–537.

Groth, A. N., & Birnbaum, H. J. (1978). Adult sexual orientation and attraction to underage persons. *Archives of Sexual Behavior, 7*(3), 175–181.

Heck, N. C., Flentje, A., & Cochran, B. N. (2011). Offsetting risks: High school gay-straight alliances and lesbian, gay, bisexual, and transgender (LGBT) youth. *School Psychology Quarterly, 26*(2), 161–174.

Human Rights Campaign. (2012). *Growing up LGBT in America.* Retrieved from http://www.hrc.org/youth-report

Human Rights Campaign. (2016a). *The lies and dangers of efforts to change sexual orientation or gender identity.* Retrieved from http://www.hrc.org/resources/the-lies-and-dangers-of-reparative-therapy

Human Rights Campaign. (2016b). *Maps of state laws & policies.* Retrieved from http://www.hrc.org/state_maps

Intersex Society of North America. (2008). What is intersex? Retrieved from http://www.isna.org/faq/what_is_intersex

Kosciw, J. G., Greytak, E. A., & Diaz, E. M. (2009). Who, what, where, when, why: Demographic and ecological factors contributing to hostile school climate for lesbian, gay, bisexual, and transgender youth. *Journal of Youth and Adolescence, 38*(7), 976–988.

Kosciw, J. G., Greytak, E. A., & Diaz, E. M. (2010). *2009 National School Climate Survey: The experiences of lesbian, gay, bisexual and transgender youth in our nation's schools.* New York, NY: Gay, Lesbian and Straight Education Network. Retrieved from http://www.glsen.org/cgi-bin/iowa/all/library/record/2624.html

Krehely, Jeff. (2009). How to close the LGBT health disparities gap. *Centers for American Progress.* Retrieved from http://www.americanprogress.org/issues/2009/12/lgbt_health_disparities.html

Lambda Legal. (2010). *When health care isn't caring: Lambda Legal's survey of discrimination against LGBT people and people with HIV.* Retrieved from http://www.lambdalegal.org/health-care-report

Lewis, R. J., Derlega, V. J., Clarke, E. G., McElligott, M. D., Jacobs, A. M., & Kuang, J. (2004). Stigma consciousness, social constraints, and lesbian well-being. Poster session presented at the 112th Annual Convention of the American Psychological Association, Honolulu, HI.

Martin, K. A., Huston, D. J., Kazyak, E., & Scherrer, K. S. (2010). Advice when children come out: The cultural "tool kits" of parents. *Journal of Family Issues, 31,* 960–991.

Massachusetts Department of Elementary and Secondary Education. (2008). *Health and risk behavior of Massachusetts youth, 2007: The report.* Malden, MA:

Author. Retrieved from http://www.doe.mass.edu/cnp/hprograms/ yrbs/2007YRBS.pdf

Mays, V. M., & Cochran, S. D. (2001). Mental health correlates of perceived discrimination among lesbian, gay, and bisexual adults in the United States. *American Journal of Public Health, 91,* 1869–1876.

Meyer, I. (1995). Minority stress and mental health in gay men. *The Journal of Health and Social Behavior, 36,* 38–56.

Meyer, I. H. (2003). Prejudice, social stress, and mental health in lesbian, gay, and bisexual populations: Conceptual issues and research evidence. *Psychological Bulletin, 129*(5), 674–697.

National Coalition for LGBT Health. (n.d.). *All of the above: LGBT people of color.* Retrieved from http://lgbthealth.webolutionary.com/sites/default/files/LGBT%20POC.pdf

National Gay and Lesbian Task Force Foundation. (2012). *Challenges facing LGBT elders.* Retrieved from http://www.thetaskforce.org/issues/aging/challenges

Parents, Families, Friends, and Allies United with LGBTQ People. (2016). *The PFLAG National Glossary of Terms.* Retrieved from http://community.pflag.org/glossary

Poteat, V. P., Aragon, S. R., Espelage, D. L., & Koenig, B. W. (2009). Psychosocial concerns of sexual minority youth: Complexity and caution in group differences. *Journal of Consulting and Clinical Psychology, 77*(1), 196–201.

Poteat, V. P., & Espelage, D. L. (2007). Predicting psychosocial consequences of homophobic victimization in middle school students. *Journal of Early Adolescence, 27*(2), 175–191.

Quintana, N. S., Rosenthal, J., & Krehely, J. (2010). On the streets: The federal response to gay and transgender homeless youth. *Center for American Progress.* Retrieved from http://www.americanprogress.org/issues/2010/06/pdf/lgbtyouthhomelessness.pdf

Reynolds, D. V. (2011). Preventing bullycides: The school nurse's role in breaking the link between victimization of sexual minority youth and suicide. *NASN School Nurse, 26,* 30–34.

Royal College of Psychiatrists. (n.d.). Royal College of Psychiatrists' position statement on sexual orientation. Retrieved from http://www.rcpsych.ac.uk/pdf/rcpsychposstatementsexorientation.pdf

Ryan, C., Huebner, D., Diaz, R., & Sanchez, J. (2007). Family rejection as a predictor of negative health outcomes in White and Latino lesbian, gay, and bisexual young adults. *Pediatrics, 123*(1), 346–352.

Savin-Williams, R. C. (1994). Verbal and physical abuse as stressors in the lives of lesbian, gay male, and bisexual youths: Associations with school problems, running away, substance abuse, prostitution, and suicide. *Journal of Consulting and Clinical Psychology, 62,* 261– 269.

Schlatter, E., & Steinback, R. (2011). 10 anti-gay myths debunked. Retrieved from http://www.splcenter.org/get-informed/intelligence-report/browse-all-issues/2010/winter/10-myths

Schwartz, S. J., Luyckx, K., & Vignoles, V. L. (2011). *Handbook of identity theory and research.* New York, NY: Springer Science & Business Media.

Shilts, R. (1987). *And the band played on.* New York, NY: St. Martin Press.

Swearer, S. M., Turner, R. K., Givens, J. E., & Pollack, W. S. (2008). "You're so gay!" Do different forms of bullying matter for adolescent males? *School Psychology Review, 37*(2), 160–173.

The Asexual Visability and Education Network. (2012). *Definitions and FAQ.* Retrieved from http://www.asexuality.org/home/general.html#def

Williams, I. (2000). Internalized homophobia and health issues affecting lesbians and gay men. *Health Education Research, 15*(1), 97–107.

Williams, T., Connolly, J., Pepler, D., & Craig, W. (2005). Peer victimization, social support, and psychosocial adjustment of sexual minority adolescents. *Journal of Youth and Adolescence, 34*(5), 471–482.

Chapter 14

INTERSECTIONS OF GENDER AND CULTURE

Sandra L. Curtis

The truth will set you free. But first it will piss you off.
—Gloria Steinem

When I was first approached to write this chapter on gender and culture, I wondered, Can I do this? Can any one individual? In learning that other chapters would also include a focus on gender, I realized I would be in good company. I gained confidence that, working together, the diverse voices of women could be heard. On my part, I draw from my experiences in gender issues and in working with diverse women. I do, however, see the world from my own perspective, one which is constructed from my own experiences and social locations. Given this, I will start by outlining those first.

My social locations, along with my personal and professional experiences, reflect instances of both privilege and marginalization, of being at times the "default," while at other times the "other." I am a White woman who is single, child-free, able-bodied, middle-class (for the most part, with occasional exceptions during my career path), heterosexual, and born in 1955. I am a bilingual anglophone Canadian (English being my mother tongue; French, my second language), who has lived substantial time in both Canada and the United States.

I have had the experience of being marginalized as a woman growing up and living in a patriarchal culture. Patriarchies are "social systems in which attributes associated with maleness are privileged and those attributed to women are denigrated" (Brown, 2008a, p. 277). In such cultures, male is pervasively the default, with woman the other, often times to such an extent that she becomes invisible. This is seen in something as fundamental, and I would say as powerfully influential, as our very language, where, despite some change, popular use persists of male-based generics such as man and mankind, where all men are created equal, and women's rights and human rights are often spoken of as separate and distinct. The exclusion and the sexism of patriarchies can be intentional or nonintentional, overt or covert, and conscious or unconscious. My own experiences have included all. Specific instances have included profound awareness of being the other and of dissatisfaction with traditional gender roles. They have also involved issues surrounding woman as body in a culture where women are objects of the male gaze and women's worth is often measured in terms of physical beauty, with this beauty being increasingly defined in terms of thinness and youth. I have also experienced male violence against women, from its more subtle forms of catcalls and fear of walking alone at night to more overt forms. As a single woman in a decidedly "couple-ist" culture, I have experienced no significant disadvantages; the same can be said for my experience as a Canadian living in the United States. In both experiences, however, I was in the position of other, and this provided me opportunities for reflection on the meaning of being insider and outsider.

My experiences of marginalization have, however, been tempered by the intersection of other social locations. As a White woman, my experiences of patriarchy are considerably modified by White privilege in a racist culture. Similarly, as a heterosexual woman, I am accorded many privileges not granted others in a homophobic culture. I took for granted things others could not—something as simple as being able to talk freely about my romantic interests without fear of public scrutiny. It was when I began working in the deaf community that I began to explore more deeply my social locations of privilege. I learned that I was a member of a default group of which I had no knowledge—the hearing community. Until then, my default status and privilege as a hearing person were so pervasive that they were invisible to me. This profound eye-opener caused me to re-evaluate all my other social locations. In what other ways was I privileged and to such an extent that it was invisible to me?

An outline of my personal context would not be complete without touching upon the identities and work that developed for me out of my understanding of privilege and marginalization. I am a feminist and a feminist music therapist, and I am active in social justice work. My identity as a feminist developed as an adolescent through my personal experiences and self-directed reading. Only much later did I engage in academic feminist literature and discourse. My identity as a feminist music therapist developed later in my professional life as I learned not only that I could combine my feminist self and my music therapist self, but also that combining them was a moral imperative to ensure best practices for my clients. My work in social justice began long before my feminist music therapy practice evolved. It seemed so essential, so obvious. This became more explicitly a part of my music therapist self in developing a feminist music therapy practice, a practice which stresses the importance of the sociopolitical understanding of women's and men's lives, of our clients' lives, and of our own lives. This understanding makes clear the importance of both personal and social change, inside and outside therapy. It dictates that therapists are responsible for bringing about personal and social change in their clients' lives and in their own lives as well.

Introduction

Until all of us have made it, none of us have made it.
—Rosemary Brown, officer of the Order of Canada; lifelong activist, feminist, opponent of racism, and champion of human rights

Originally coined in 1989 by legal scholar Kimberly Crenshaw, "intersectionality" evolved out of a critique of the singular focus of both feminism and antiracism discourse (Nash, 2008). Intersectionality acknowledges the complex, multifaceted, and dynamic ways in which systems of inequality impact people differently, based on such social locations or identity markers as gender, ethnocultural identity, socioeconomic status, sexual orientation, age, and ability. In the words of Madam Justice L'Heureux-Dubé:

> Categories of discrimination may overlap and … individuals may suffer historical exclusion on the basis of both race and gender, age, physical handicap, or some combination. The situation of individuals who confront multiple grounds of disadvantages is particularly complex. Categorizing such discrimination as primarily racially oriented or primarily gender-oriented misconceives the reality of the discrimination as it is experienced by individuals. (Ontario Human Rights Commission, 2001, p. 5)

The intersections of identity markers are irrevocably intertwined and in changing ways over time, in terms of both marginalization and privilege. As such, any examination of multicultural intersections would be incomplete without addressing dimensions of gender. Gender intersects with every other identity marker. Its impact is so pervasive and starts at such an early point in our formative years that it can become almost unquestioned for some, like the color of the inside of our eyelids.

In a "postfeminist" world, however, some argue that gender is no longer an issue, that gender discrimination has been eliminated, that patriarchy and sexism are dead, and that anyone who believes otherwise should just stop whining. Yet at the time of writing this chapter, I was struck by three separate events that hit the news media headlines within the span of a single week: the Ray Rice/National Football League (NFL) scandal, the celebrity star photo-hacking incident, and the Kirsten Gillibrand U.S. Senate story.

The Rice/NFL scandal revolved around not only an incident of male violence against women but also the response of the judicial system and the collusion of the NFL to minimize the story and maintain a good NFL public image. In this incident, Rice was arrested and charged with assault on his then fiancée (later, wife), Janay Palmer, having knocked her out with a punch to the face that was captured on video. Charges were dropped in return for Rice's participation in a first-time offenders' pretrial intervention program (a program granted for less than 1% of domestic violence cases). The NFL suspended Rice for a mere two games, with Rice's lawyer referring to it as a minor altercation. Rice and his fiancée made a *joint* apology in the media for both of their roles. Only months later, after a video of the incident was released to the news media with great public outcry, did the NFL revise its domestic violence policy and consider more serious sanctions for Rice. This video

provided incontestable documentation of the severity and nature of the violence; rather than a minor, mutual spat between a couple, it was a one-sided affair with Rice violently punching Palmer in the face and then dragging her unconscious body out of the elevator and dumping it in the hallway. It was this video that resulted in public outcry and that made clear the undeniable nature of the violence. Yet throughout it all, most news media referred to the incident as domestic violence—a term that has been criticized for masking the dimensions of gender and for minimalizing the degree and severity of the violence. Without the support of video evidence and public outcry, other women victims of domestic violence have not been believed, have been blamed for the violence, and have had their experiences minimalized and trivialized.

In the photo-hacking incident, nude photos of hundreds of women celebrities were posted online by someone who had illegally hacked into their personal iCloud accounts. These photos were then further widely circulated by third parties around the Web. The telling part of this incident was the initial response of the news media and the public, a response of blaming the women celebrities themselves—for taking the photos, for not taking precautions to safeguard their privacy, and for deserving what they got. Only later was the media called on this victim-blaming, as some of the celebrity women spoke out, identifying this as a crime—a sex crime—with the hacker, not the women, as the responsible culprit.

The Gillibrand/U.S. Senate story that hit the news the same week highlighted the focus for women on their physical appearance and the demand to adhere to incredibly narrow beauty standards of thinness. In her book *Off the Sidelines*, U.S. Senator Gillibrand (2014) described responses from fellow male senate members that focused on her looks rather than her work. These included such comments as: "Good thing you are working out, because you wouldn't want to get porky" and "You know, Kirsten, you are pretty even when you're fat." Another senate member squeezed her stomach, saying "Don't lose too much weight now; I like my *girls* [my italics] chubby." Gillibrand had been pregnant at the time—one of only six women to give birth while in the U.S. Congress. Again, the public response was one of victim-blaming—Gillibrand was blamed for complaining, blamed for taking it too seriously (some indicated that these were *just* catcalls, while others indicated that they were compliments), and blamed for not naming names. In response, Gillibrand indicated that she wanted the focus to be on the challenges all women face in their career paths and the sexism which underlies these, commenting that "women's voices need to be heard" (Lauer, 2014).

These three news media events are just a few of many. They reflect an underlying sexism which is pervasive, yet at times not always recognized by all. The sexism is reflected not only in the actions of the main participants, but also in the response of the public at large. This perhaps speaks to its covert nature more than previously. For many in North America, it may be tempting to see sexism elsewhere in the world and think that nothing remains here. However, while we have indeed come a long way here, much still remains to be done. This chapter looks at the situation as it exists currently. It is restricted to the North American context (in particular, the United States and Canada) because of my own particular frame of reference and because a need exists to make clear the role that gender plays in our lives and in our sociopolitical environment—even here, or perhaps even more so here because of its more covert nature. To remedy a situation, it is essential first to identify it and understand it. Many of the population at large remain unaware of the tremendous impact of gender and its sociocultural implications; music therapists are not so very different. A recent survey (Curtis, 2013c) indicated that only 67% of music therapists felt that sexism had an impact in people's lives in general (down from 90% in 1990), rating it as "not a problem" in their own personal lives. For music therapists to provide music therapy best practices, an understanding is critical of the impact of gender in our clients' lives, in our own lives, and in our sociopolitical environment.

Prior to delving further into the gender impact, some clarification might be helpful concerning the concepts of sex, gender, and the gender spectrum. Typically, sex is defined as "a descriptive and biologically based variable that is used to distinguish two categories of individuals: females or males" (Worell & Remer, 2002, Chapter 1, Sex or Gender, para. 1). Gender, on the other hand, is seen as a social construct (Brown, 2008a; Curtis, 2000) and refers to "culturally constructed beliefs and attitudes about the traits and behaviors of females and males" (Worell & Remer, 2002, Chapter 1, Gender, para. 1). Gender is assigned different meanings in different cultures. Women's and men's experiences diverge dramatically from the onset, in that:

> Humans are born into bodies that are sexed, and that, in Western cultures, are forced into two sexes. … Gender, a set of socially constructed roles and ways of relating, is conveyed to infants based on the sex to which they are assigned. Gender is commonly the first identity that people experience, coming before other identity markers such as culture, ethnicity, or social class because gender, as a sex-derived social construct, is frequently the variable of greatest importance to the human world into which a child is born: Is it a boy or a girl? (Brown, 2008a, p. 285)

As a result, it becomes impossible to separate the complexly interwoven threads of sex and gender (Curtis, 2000). While looking at sex and gender, it is important to be aware that current understanding of gender views it as a spectrum, rather than the traditionally static binary concept of male and female. This spectrum reflects the reality of human variability in terms of anatomy, gender identity, gender expression, sexual orientation, and gender fluidity (Gender Spectrum, 2014).

Despite this latest understanding, most Western cultures, and all patriarchal societies, persist in strong adherence to a dichotomous division of the world into two categories—male and female—with differential treatment of individuals in these two categories, valuing male over female (Brown, 2008a). The ramifications of this dichotomous gender view and treatment are outlined next, including areas of popular conceptions/ misconceptions, and the realities of their impact in the lives of women and men in the United States and Canada.

Myths, Stereotypes, Double Standards, and Realities

From the boardroom to the bedroom, women are still getting the short end of the stick.
—Jessica Valenti, feminist blogger

Having exposed one of the main myths—that feminism has accomplished all that is necessary, with no further change needed—this section examines the myriad remaining myths, stereotypes, and double standards challenging men and women alike. Given the pervasive nature of the impact of gender and its intersection with sexism, it would be impossible to cover this topic in its entirety within the scope of a single chapter. I have chosen, therefore, eight areas which I believe to be the most significant: work, education, leadership, male privilege, gender role socialization, body politics, human rights, and violence against women.

There are also some myths specific to music therapists. These include: (1) Since the majority of music therapists are women, no gender problems exist; (2) Since I'm a female music therapist, no gender problems exist; (3) My music therapy work is personal, not political; and (4) Since I'm a male music therapist in a female-dominated profession, I am the one experiencing discrimination (Curtis, 2013c). These will be examined once those areas impacting women and men in general are addressed. In reviewing all of these, it is important to be mindful of their impact in our lives and those of our clients, as well as of their complex interplay within our client–therapist interactions.

Work

The Gender Wage Gap. Despite the firmly entrenched myth to the contrary, the gender wage gap is still very much in existence in both the United States and Canada (American Association of University Women, 2014; Statistics Canada, 2006, 2010). Women still earn significantly less than their male counterparts in every occupation (Corbett & Hill, 2012). When compared internationally, both Canada and the United States earned grades of C, ranking 11th and 12th respectively among their 17 peer countries, with Canada having a 19% gender pay gap (Statistics Canada, 2010) and the United States having one of 23% (American Association for University Women, 2014). While the American Association for University Women (AAUW) indicates that some of the gap may be a result of women's choices (e.g., education, work area, parenting, etc.), these choices are themselves influenced by gender role socialization.

Ultimately, the AAUW notes that 12% of the gap has no other explanation than discrimination (AAUW, 2014). This wage gap is even more pronounced for women of color and aboriginal women (Heyninck, 2014). While the gap has improved to some extent over time since the 1970s, it has remained static in recent years and clearly remains large enough to dramatically disadvantage women. The Royal Bank of Canada notes that if the gap were eliminated, women would have an additional $168 billion in disposable income (Heyninck, 2014). Music therapists find themselves in similar circumstances, with women earning significantly less than their male counterparts, yet the women were not significantly more concerned about their salaries than the men (Curtis, 2013c).

It is interesting to note that at the time of the writing of this chapter, yet another event hit the mainstream news media. Microsoft CEO Satya Nadella made the headlines for his address to the Grace Hopper Celebration of Women in Computing, in which he commented that women in computing should not ask for raises:

> It's not really about asking for a raise, but knowing and having faith that the system will give you the right raise. That, I think, might be one of the additional superpowers that, quite frankly, women who don't ask for a raise have. Because that's good karma. It'll come back because somebody's going to know that's the kind of person that I want to trust. That's the kind of person that I want to really give more responsibility to. (Clawson, 2014)

While Nadella later apologized for his comments, recent research indicates that his views are not uncommon. In asking for raises, men are rewarded financially (getting the raise), while women are penalized financially (denied the raise) and socially, with both men and women finding them undesirable to hire or work with (Bowles, Babcock, & Lai, 2007; Tinsley, Cheldelin, Schneider, & Amanatullah, 2009).

The Glass Ceiling. While women are increasingly present in the workforce, comprising 50% (Banaji & Greenwald, 2013), they are not equally represented in leadership roles there (Gillibrand, 2014; Heyninck, 2014). In Canada, women comprise only 16% of corporate board membership (Heyninck, 2014); the situation is similar in the United States, with proportionately minimal numbers of women in managerial positions and other higher positions such as law partner, professor, and judge (Gillibrand, 2014; Valenti, 2009). "The stories in pop culture tell of women's advances leaving men in the dust … research presents an alternative sobering view: Gender inequality persists" (Harnois, 2013, pp. 9–10). This may be a direct reflection of the persistent gendered view of ambitiousness being a good quality for men, but not for women (Gillibrand, 2014). "Being powerful and being feminine … just aren't compatible" (Valenti, 2009, Chapter 19, para. 6).

Gender Division of the Workforce. Substantial division of the workforce along gender lines still persists today and contributes further to the gender wage gap. Despite inroads made, women still are very poorly represented in the traditional male occupational areas such as science, technology, engineering, and math. These traditionally male fields typically provide more lucrative salaries than female-dominated fields. In the United States, only 17% of Google's engineers and 10% of Twitter's engineers are women (Blakely, 2014). Furthermore, many women have found the male-dominated fields to be unwelcoming. Of the small number of women in the technology industry, they are leaving it at twice the rate of their male counterparts, in no small part due to "a lewd brand of *brogrammer* chauvinism [that] underpins the tech industry culture" (Blakely, 2014, p. 76). Music therapy represents the flip side of the workforce gender division, as a female-dominated profession with approximately 90% women music therapists in both Canada and the United States (Curtis, 2013c). Typical of many female-dominated fields, music therapy salaries are quite low—although, as noted earlier, they are significantly lower for women. Furthermore, there is a significantly greater number of men (38% men, 11% women) in academic music therapy positions, positions which typically pay better (Curtis, 2013c).

Costly Living. While women are earning less, they are paying more for everything from haircuts, dry cleaning, and cars to mortgages and health care (Valenti, 2009). American women pay 20% more for haircuts and 25% more for dry cleaning and are 32% more likely to have higher mortgage interest rates. White women pay $150 more for car purchases, while African-American women pay $800 more than White men and $400 more than African-American men. Gender-biased pricing practices cost American women almost $15 billion annually (Valenti, 2009). American women are disadvantaged even further in the area of health care. With men considered the default, many of their health care needs are covered as standard while many for women is not (e.g., Pap smear exams, mammograms, etc.). American women typically pay more in deductibles than men. "High deductible plans punish women for having breasts and uteruses and having babies" (Valenti, 2009, Chapter 42, para. 11).

Work–Family Responsibilities. While some progress has been made in the division of labor within the family, women are still doing the majority of domestic work in the home. In 2010, 39.1% of men and 33.7% of women still believed that it is most desirable for the man to work outside the home and the woman to remain at home taking care of the family (Harnois, 2013), yet the reality is that women's work outside the home is an economic necessity for most families (Gillibrand, 2014). As a result, more women are working outside the home but still taking primary responsibility for the family at home. American women are now doing approximately 27 hours per week caring for their children at home, with 16 hours per week for the men (Valenti, 2009). Not only does this result in significantly less leisure time for women, but also it means greater work–family conflicts for women. As the primary caregiver for the family, women bear the brunt of the responsibilities for negotiating time off for sick children, maternity leave, family sick leave, and so forth. Furthermore, women's and men's contributions within the family continue to be compared in relation to the traditional model of mothers doing it all and husbands doing nothing. As a result, women are often judged inadequate in comparison to the idealized motherhood, while small contributions from the men are lauded (Gillibrand, 2014; Valenti, 2009). This is reflected further in the discourse around whether women can or should "have it all." Gillibrand (2014) argues that the concept of women having it all is based on faulty premises arising from traditional gender role stereotypes. This concept falsely assumes that women are being greedy in asking for more than their fair share—an assumption not made with men. Additionally, this discourse ignores the reality that increasing numbers of women find themselves in single-parent households with the double burden of serving as both the primary caregiver and sole breadwinner (Vespa, Lewis, & Kreider, 2013). Gillibrand contends that for the sake of women, men, and families, the workplace is long overdue for a restructuring to support both men and women in balancing work and family responsibilities, along with providing better maternity and paternity leave, a better minimum wage, and equal pay for all.

With women earning less for a variety of gendered reasons, taking on more responsibilities for the family, and experiencing the very real effects of the feminization of poverty, what does this mean for our clients in music therapy? It can have an impact in a myriad of ways, and as music therapists we are well advised to be open to exploring these and to be careful to avoid any false assumptions. How can we help empower our clients effectively if we focus only on personal work in therapy and ignore their need for genuine interpersonal and political empowerment? An abused woman may be unable to seek help and escape her abuser as a result of a very real fear of losing her children because of an inability to live up to a false ideal of motherhood which ignores the reality of the lives of women living in poverty.

While working at a women's shelter in Georgia, I met a courageous woman, a survivor of male violence and mother of a young boy. During the course of her time in music therapy with me, she came to me with the exciting news that the shelter had arranged for some housing for her and her son so that she could escape her abuser. Not long after, she returned devastated, having discovered that the housing was in the neighborhood projects with drug dealers everywhere and great danger for her son. She made the choice that no one should have to, choosing her son's safety over hers, and returned to her abuser. At the time, the system considered her a failure for returning. In music therapy, we began focusing not only on her personal empowerment, but also on developing the confidence and skills to identify and negotiate a solution that worked for her, given her financial circumstances; we worked toward building an understanding on her part and on those of the professionals working with her that the failure lay with the system and not with her.

Education

In terms of education, girls and women have made considerable progress over the past 100 years. Yet, recent AAUW research indicates that substantial gender differences and biases still exist; these are further exacerbated along lines of ethnicity and socioeconomic status (Corbett & Hill, 2008; Gates & Clinton Foundations, 2015; Hill, 2010; Hill & Silva, 2005). This is particularly evident for women in the traditionally male fields of science, technology, engineering, and math (STEM). Negative stereotypes about girls and women impact their interest and achievement in college, as well as their later career choices and success (Hill, 2010). In 2010, women in the STEM fields were much less satisfied with their academic environment and much more likely to leave prematurely than their male counterparts. Furthermore, women who did persist in STEM careers were seen as less competent than men—even by those explicitly rejecting gender stereotypes. Those women who demonstrated undeniable competence in male jobs were perceived as less likable—a catch-22 for women. "Bias, often unconscious, limits women's progress" (Hill, 2010, p. 3). Additionally, the majority of women in all academic areas in college experienced sexual harassment at some point in their studies significant enough to result in life changes (Hill & Silva, 2005).

Politics

Women's political leadership and participation at all levels around the world is significantly limited.

> Women in every part of the world continue to be largely marginalized from the political sphere, often as a result of discriminatory laws, practices, attitudes, and gender stereotypes, low levels of education, lack of access to health care, and the disproportionate effect of poverty on women. (United Nations General Assembly, 2011, p. 2)

The average representation of women within parliament was 20% worldwide, with 25.2% in the Americas (United Nations, 2014). In the United States, women account for only 16% of the seats in Congress and, of that small percentage, women of color account for only 24%; only four women have served on the U.S. Supreme Court. Valenti (2009) notes wryly that these statistics represent an all-time best for the United States. U.S. Sen. Gillibrand (2014) observes that this underrepresentation of women is not surprising given underlying gender role socialization and recent research findings that both men and women are uncomfortable with "ambitious" or "power-seeking" women. Some may argue that this has little impact on our lives or those of our clients. Yet, our work often involves empowering our clients—and empowerment, to be complete, entails personal, interpersonal, and political power. The outcomes of political decisions impact

211

our daily lives in myriad ways. And without representation of women in those political decisions, women's voices risk being unheard and disregarded. In the United States in 2013, over 700 bills were proposed to regulate a woman's body, and the political entities making these decisions were over 80% male (Strasser, 2013). The well-known feminist catchphrase—"the personal is political"—still holds true today, but equally meaningful is its flip side: The political is personal.

Male Privilege

Having looked at the impact of gender in some of the more visible areas in the public sphere, attention is now directed to areas that are more covert, underlying both private and public spheres. Male privilege is one of these. Male privilege refers to:

> a set of privileges that are given to men as a class due to their institutional power in relation to women as a class. While every man experiences privilege differently due to his own individual position in the social hierarchy, every man, by virtue of being read as male by society, benefits from male privilege. (Finally, a Feminism 101, 2007)

The myth exists that there is no male privilege, along with its alternate that it exists but so too does female privilege. The reality is that it exists, is pervasive—even in the North American context—and is reflected in many overt and covert ways (Brown, 2008a; McIntosh, 2008). Gillam (n.d.) comments:

> Male privilege [is] … so ubiquitous that it's invisible. It is so pervasive as to be normalized, and so normalized as to be visible only in its absence. The vast, vast, vast majority of institutions, spaces, and subcultures privilege male interest, but because male is the default in this culture, such interests are very often considered ungendered. As a result, we only *really* notice when something privileges female interests. (para. 14)

Brown (2008a) contends that it is a moral imperative for therapists to examine and understand the impact of male privilege, and its interaction with such others as White privilege, in therapy work with clients: "Privilege unexamined increases power, and privilege unspoken of operates in an oppressive manner" (Brown, 2008a, p. 295).

The need for work around male privilege is no less true for music therapists. An understanding of male privilege and its impact in our clients' lives as well as our own is critical. Therapeutic relationships will be enhanced dramatically if men music therapists understand what they represent to their women clients, if White men and women music therapists understand what they represent to their clients of color.

I often recommend that men music therapists work with women survivors of violence only if they are partnered with a woman music therapist. In that way, rather than serving as the sole male expert and running the risk of re-enacting traditional male privilege and entitlement, they are able to model a healthy, mutually benefiting working relationship that exemplifies an egalitarian sharing of power between men and women.

Gender Roles, Stereotypes, and Socialization

Gender roles are "patterns of culturally approved behaviors that are regarded as more desirable for either males or females in a particular culture" (Worell & Remer, 2002, Chapter 1, Gender Roles, para. 1). These derive from socially constructed meanings of gender that in our culture, as noted earlier, typically value male/masculine and devalue female/feminine. Our understanding of ourselves is informed by this social construction of gender from our earliest experiences. "We are born into a symbolic and material world that is already gendered in every possible way; it is impossible to overstate its effects on mind and culture" (Weingarten, 2013, Boys Will Be Men: A Response, para. 5). Weingarten (2013) notes that in the process, each sex is asked to diminish itself by half, with girls inhibiting their assertive agency and boys inhibiting their relational and affective selves. The process is harmful for boys and girls, for men and women. Through this gender role socialization, we learn early and well what it means to be a man or a woman, what roles are appropriate for each, and what beliefs/stereotypes belong to each. They play out in myriad ways—overt and covert, explicit and implicit.

In *Blind Spot*, Banaji and Greenwald (2013) indicate that much of our bias (including gender bias) exists at an automatic level of which we are unaware—in our blind spot. Through development of the *Implicit Association Test* (IAT), they were able to identify those automatic stereotypes that individuals hold without conscious awareness. These automatic stereotypes impact attitudes, thoughts, and behaviors and can have long-lasting effects on educational and career paths and success, and ultimately on life satisfaction. Results from some of the IAT research among men *and* women showed, despite verbal indications to the contrary: (1) preferences for male bosses, even if it entailed lower pay (Caruso, Rahnev, & Banaji, 2009), and (2) strong associations of men with careers and women with the home (Banaji & Greenwald, 2013). Furthermore, women who showed a stronger hidden and unconscious bias against women in math and science were less likely to choose either as a college major and were more likely to perform poorly (Banaji & Greenwald, 2013; Nosek, Banaji, & Greenwald, 2002). Additionally, hidden bias against a particular group was associated with withholding of help from that group.

> Blind spots hide both discriminations and privileges, so neither the discriminators nor the

targets of discrimination, neither those who do the privilege nor the privileged, are aware. No small wonder that any attempt to consciously level the playing field meets with such resistance. (Banaji & Greenwald, 2013, Chapter 7, final paragraph)

Some more overt instances of gender stereotypes can be seen in language, in emotional expression, and in ideas surrounding masculinity and femininity. Worell and Remer (2002) note that language reflects gender bias—first, in its exclusion of the female: A single person over the course of a lifetime will hear the generic *"he"* more than 10 million times. In similar fashion, common language use often reserves a subordinate position for women (e.g., men and women, boys and girls) and makes use of diminutives (e.g., bachelor and bachelorette), belittlement (e.g., girls), and dehumanization (e.g., chicks). Valenti (2009) uses the term "femiphobia" in describing the fear of being feminine that is part of boys' and men's gender role socialization. It is reflected in the use of the term "girl" as a powerful insult against boys: "Don't be a girl," "You throw like a girl," and so forth. To be seen as female, whether through choice of toys, clothes, or activities, is anathema. It serves not only as an insult, but as a way to control. It carries through to adulthood with the importance of being manly, which often translates as not being feminine—or even run the risk of being perceived as feminine. It is not uncommon to see grown men on sports teams insult each other with "Don't be a bunch of girls." Similarly, women should not be seen as "manly." In terms of emotional expression, anger is typically permissible for men, but not for women. If they express anger, girls run the risk of being seen as bossy and women, as bitches. Women's anger is trivialized or pathologized—seen as just PMS, crazy, or strident. "Women, it seems, aren't allowed to be just pissed off" (Valenti, 2013, Chapter 14, para. 4).

It is important in examining traditional gender role socialization to understand its negative impact on both men and women (Bograd, 2014; Gooding, Gilbert, & Scher, 1990). Even though men may benefit from male privilege within this culture, the constraints of the social construction of masculinity can be as powerful as those of femininity. Their impact in daily experiences, in mental health, and in happiness should not be underestimated.

It is also important, therefore, that those working with men and women in therapy understand and be competent to address these cultural constraints of gender as they play out in their lives (Bograd, 2014; Weingarten, 2013; Worell & Remer, 2002). Weingarten (2013) argues that

Cultural resistance [to these gender constraints] then, must also take place daily in the way we live our lives with others. … Practicing cultural resistance [is] an activity that I strongly believe deserves a place in every therapist's repertoire. …

Peeling off layers from what is commonplace to reveal the oppression of the usual. (Introduction, para. 11–14)

It is clear that this applies equally to music therapists in their practice. Work is needed on the part of both men and women music therapists for a self-reflection that examines their own understanding of gender roles and stereotypes. This work is not easy, since it involves attitudes which are learned early, are deeply internalized, and are not easily recognized. The work is critical in music therapy because it impacts our perceptions of our clients, identification of their needs, determination of appropriate goals, selection of therapeutic interventions, and evaluation of therapy outcomes. It also integrally impacts our therapeutic relationship and the involvement of our clients in the therapeutic process.

Body Politics

I wish I looked like Cindy Crawford.
—Cindy Crawford, internationally successful American model

The Male Gaze, Beauty, and Aging. Pervasively across many components of Western cultures, women are reduced to their physical bodies, objects of the male gaze, rather than as individuals with their own personality, desires, and agency; they are objectified and commodified (Gillibrand, 2014; Valenti, 2009). At the same time, the beauty standards for women as body are increasingly restrictive in terms of thinness and youth—to a point past being realistically achievable. Even models, with overreliance on cosmetic surgery and severely restricted diets, cannot achieve this without additional computer image editing—as wryly alluded to by Cindy Crawford in her wish to look like Cindy Crawford. In 1990, Naomi Wolf first discussed this in *The Beauty Myth:*

The more legal and material hindrances women have broken through, the more strictly and heavily and cruelly images of female beauty have come to weigh upon us … during the past decade, women breached the power structure; meanwhile, eating disorders rose exponentially and cosmetic surgery became the fastest-growing specialty … and 33,000 American women told researchers that they would rather lose 10 to 15 pounds than achieve any other goal. … More women have more money and power and scope and legal recognition than we have ever had before; but in terms of how we feel about ourselves physically, we may actually be worse off than our unliberated grandmothers. (Wolf, 1990, p. 10)

Armstrong (2013) comments: "[R]evisiting [The Beauty Myth] now, 20 years later, evokes an all-too common feeling I get when reading old feminist texts: Holy shit, nothing has changed" (para. 1). In reality, things may have changed—for the worse. In the media, where there are still men of all sizes, women must be thin, but not too thin; women in the media are under more scrutiny than ever before—increasingly criticized for being too heavy or accused of being anorexic if they appear too thin (Valenti, 2009). Either way, women cannot win. This beauty double standard is now frequently disguised with myths of empowerment and liberation. With financial success, women are told they have the power to create the bodies they want through cosmetic surgery. And more and more of a woman's body is being targeted for improvement, with the increasing popularity of such procedures as labiaplasty and vaginal rejuvenation (Valenti, 2009).

Age is a part of the beauty double standard for women, but it has its own twist. Women's age is under scrutiny not only on its own, but also in its comparison to the age of their significant others. Older men are seen as distinguished; older women as undesirable. Older men with younger women are seen as virulent; older women with younger men are seen as cougars (Valenti, 2009). Furthermore, in their older years, men can expect more financial success. The average income for men over 65 years of age is $14,000 more than for their female counterparts. In fact, older women comprise the "poorest of the poor" in the United States (Valenti, 2009, Chapter 15, para. 10).

Sex, Sexy, or Sexualized. While women are to be sexy, it is for the male gaze. Women are not to be sexual with their own sexual desires and lives. Valenti (2009) describes this as a double standard in which with more sexual partners men are congratulated for being "players," while women are shamed for being "sluts." This negative view of women's sexuality is reflected in language practices with terms for female sexual body parts used as insults and with a preponderance of slurs against sexually promiscuous women—220 for women, 20 for men (Finally, A Feminism 101, 2007). Social constraints strictly police women with regard to "acceptable sexuality" for women. This underpins discourse in the media and in legal situations concerning "rape-able" or "sexually harassable" women. Was the women's dress and behavior socially acceptable such that an act could be considered rape or harassment, or did they ask for it? A 2005 Amnesty International study found that:

> One in three people believes that women who behave flirtatiously are at least partially responsible if they are raped. ... A similar number think that women are partially or wholly responsible for being raped if they are drunk, and more than a quarter believe women are responsible if they wear sexy or revealing clothing. (Fickling, 2005, para. 1)

Valenti (2009) contends that this double standard for women serves to control women through shame.

Body in the Media and Politics. In the media, focus is also on woman as body, with limited representation of women except for those who are young and beautiful. And in

Hollywood, the definition of young is increasingly narrow. The lessons learned about men and women from mainstream movies can be powerful. In 2011, only 11 of the 100 top movies had female protagonists. In response to pronounced gender bias in movies, the *Bechdel Test for Women in Movies* was developed, with three simple criteria to evaluate movies: (1) Are there at least two women in it? (2) Do they talk to each other? and (3) Do they talk about something other than a man? (Hickley, 2014). Of 1,794 movies released between 1970 and 2013, only 50% met the Bechdel criteria (Hickley, 2014). Hickley notes that while progress is being made, perhaps as a result of younger audiences with more equitable gender views, there is still considerable room for improvement.

In politics, women are also experiencing the double standard of a heightened focus on their appearance that their male counterparts do not face (Gillibrand, 2014). U.S. Sen. Gillibrand describes how women are judged often on their looks rather than on their work. She adds that regardless of being judged beautiful or ugly, the end result is to trivialize their work and to damage voters' impressions.

Given the documented impact of the reduction of women to body and the gendered message about that body, what does this mean for music therapists? First and foremost, it plays out very critically in the music we use. For those music therapists who use pop music in their practice, an understanding will be essential of the powerful role that it plays in reflecting, shaping, and perpetuating this reduction of women to body. This will be explored further in the section on the Meaning and Function of Music. Beyond our music, the reduction of woman to body may directly impact our clients in how they perceive themselves and in their experiences. It may also impact music therapists in our own lives. A careful self-reflection on the impact of the gendered dimensions of this and how it may play out in our therapeutic interactions could serve to enhance our therapeutic effectiveness.

Women's Rights Versus Human Rights

It may seem self-evident to some that women's rights are human rights; this is not the case in reality, as women's rights have often been framed as those of a special interest group. The United Nations (UN) identified a need to address this as late as 1993:

> Forty-five years after the Universal Declaration of Human Rights was adopted, and eight years after CEDAW entered into force, the UN World Conference on Human Rights in Vienna confirmed that women's rights were human rights. That this statement was even necessary is striking— women's status as human beings entitled to rights should have never been in doubt. And yet this was a step forward in recognizing the rightful claims of one-half of humanity, in identifying neglect of women's rights as a human rights violation and in

drawing attention to the relationship between gender and human rights violations. (UN Population Fund, 2014)

Despite this UN adoption, this perception persists and continues to be seen in popular discourse and activity. Shirinian (2010) argues that while there are benefits to viewing women's rights as human rights, there are also problems. Noted legal expert Catherine McKinnon remarks that:

> Human rights principles are based on experience, but the experiences have not been those of women. What most often happens to women escapes the human rights net. Whether in peacetime or in war, at home or abroad, in private or in public, by our side or by the other side, man's inhumanity to women is ignored. (WomenAid International, 2012)

As a result, in 2014, women continued to be denied basic human rights around the world and in our own backyard (Gates & Clinton Foundations, 2015; UN Population Fund, 2014).

Violence Against Women

Violence against women is perhaps the most shameful human rights' violation, and it is perhaps the most pervasive. It knows no boundaries of geography, culture, or wealth. As long as it continues, we cannot claim to be making real progress toward equality, development, and peace.
—Kofi Annan, former UN Secretary-General

Violence against women is an entirely gendered phenomenon in terms of the targets of violence, the perpetrators, and the underlying causes. Women's and men's experiences of violence are entirely different, with overwhelming numbers of women experiencing violence at the hands of male abusers (Curtis, 2013b; Gates & Clinton Foundations, 2015). In domestic violence, women account for 96% to 98% of the victims; of the 2% to 4% that involve male victims, a portion are the result of response by women to their abusers (Curtis, 2000). The impact for the small remaining portion should not be ignored; however, the larger scope and the remarkable severity of male violence against women make it a phenomenon that must be addressed. It is a phenomenon which has a long history of societal acceptance and support—first explicit, then later more covert. It is rooted in a culture of gender inequality (Curtis, 2013b). It can be understood only with attention given to the dimensions of gender and power, with their sociopolitical underpinnings.

The term "rape culture" has been coined to describe those countries with a high prevalence of such violence (Buchwald, Fletcher, & Roth, 2005); these include the United States and Canada. Rape cultures comprise gendered beliefs which permit

and condone male violence against women; they frequently conflate sexuality with violence. Rape is used as a weapon, with rape of some women serving to control all women through fear. In rape cultures, women victims of male violence are held responsible for the violence itself and for failing to prevent it. It is important, however, to understand the connection of all forms of male violence against women. From catcalls and sexual harassment to sexual assault and violence within intimate relationships, all are supported by the sociopolitical underpinnings of gender inequality (Curtis, 2000).

Rather than a rape culture, the United States and Canada represent more broadly a culture of violence against women (Curtis, 2013b; Harnois, 2013). Within this culture, women experience male violence in many forms, although their experiences differ as a result of the complex intersections of gender and race, along with such other social markers such as socioeconomic status, ability, and age (Weingarten, 2013). Some may be tempted to rank the harm done to women from different locations, the harm done by sexual harassment versus sexual assault. But that would be nonproductive and would ultimately value one woman's experience at the cost of another's. Each woman's experience is unique, and the meaning she gives it is unique.

What is the cost of such violence? Staggering, given its pervasive nature (Curtis, 2013b). One in two women in Canada will experience male violence at some point in her lifetime (Curtis, 2000). In the United States, one in four will be abused in their intimate relationships; one in five will be raped; and 12% to 38% will be abused as children (Black et al., 2011; Curtis, 2013b; Kanani, 2012; Schacter, Stalker, Teram, Lasiuk, & Danilkewich, 2009). Because of a culture which blames and shames victims of male violence, these numbers do not reflect all instances.

While not measured officially, catcalls or street harassment is something almost every woman in Canada and the United States has experienced. One woman, wearing a simple black t-shirt and jeans and walking Manhattan streets, experienced more than 100 instances of street harassment over a 10-hour period; this did not include whistles or gestures. While discounted by many as inconsequential or as complimentary, the video makes clear, much as the Rice/NFL video did, that it is anything but. What is the cumulative effect of 100 over 10 hours? Of exponentially more over a lifetime? (ihollaback.org, October 27, 2014). Just days after the release of the video, the organization issued a PSA noting that the subject of the video had received an "onslaught of rape and death threats" (ihollaback.org, October 30, 2014, para. 6). The connection between *inconsequential* street harassment and other forms of male violence is made clear: "When women are visible in online or offline spaces, they experience harassment. When women demand change, they meet violent demands for their silence" (ihollaback.org, October 30, 2014, para. 6).

While the costs of uncounted and unreported violence against women cannot be assessed, the costs alone of those that can be are substantial. The costs are both short-term and long-term, both personal and societal (Curtis, 2013b). The U.S. Surgeon General identified violence as the single greatest health risk to American women (Carmona, 2003). It is also considered one of the most pressing health care issues in Canada, with domestic violence in 2012 accounting for an estimated $4.8 billion (CAD) in costs to victims and society in terms of health, criminal justice, social services, and lost productivity (Sinha, 2013). Annual costs in the United States are similarly in the billions of dollars (Teague, Hahna, & McKinney, 2006).

Given the numbers of women experiencing male violence, and given its impact in their lives and in society at large, the need is great for music therapists to have a firm understanding of the phenomenon and its gendered sociopolitical underpinnings. Regardles of whether they are working directly with identified women survivors, music therapists can expect to see some—perhaps many—in their practice (York & Curtis, 2015). Without an understanding of the gendered dimensions of violence against women, music therapists will be less likely to recognize it among their clients and less effective in assisting their clients in overcoming the harm of such violence.

A review of some of the myths, stereotypes, double standards, and realities facing women and men shows a number of challenges facing them as a result of the social construction of gender in the United States and Canada. If male violence against women were the only challenge facing women, there would still be a need for change, given its documented impact. If only a single woman experienced male violence, there would still be a need for change. But many women experience male violence, and women and men in the United States and Canada face significant challenges in a number of areas as a result of the intersections of gender and culture.

Music Therapist Myths

These intersections of gender and culture cannot help but have an impact on music therapists as well. They result in some myths that are particular to the practice of music therapy. As noted earlier, these include beliefs held by some music therapists that: (1) Since the majority of music therapists are women, no gender problems exist; (2) Since I'm a female music therapist, no gender problems exist; (3) My music therapy work is personal, not political; and (4) Since I am a male music therapist in a female-dominated profession, I am the one experiencing discrimination (Curtis, 2013c). While the majority of music therapists are indeed women, this does not preclude them from being subject to the influences of gender in a sexist culture. Whether music therapists are women or men, whether our clients are women or men, we all grow up in a gendered world. To deny its existence does not make it any less real; it simply eliminates any opportunity to examine it consciously and thoughtfully, to incorporate an informed understanding of its meaning into our thoughts, our actions, and our practice.

The denial is in a vein similar to that of those who profess to be *"color-blind"* (Holoien & Shelton, 2011; Williams, 2011). Their thinking is reflected in phrases such as "I don't see color" or "We are all just humans." This thinking "creates a society [for people of color] that denies their negative racial experiences, rejects their cultural heritage, and invalidates their unique perspectives" (Williams, 2011, para. 3). It does not eliminate racism; it simply eliminates the opportunity to discuss it and perhaps do something about it.

The results are the same with *gender blindness*. It does not eliminate sexism or a gendered world; it simply eliminates the opportunity to discuss it and do something about it. In this light, the first two music therapy myths are debunked. Neither being a female music therapist nor being in a female-dominated profession eliminates gender issues. Instead, a committed willingness is needed to examine and work toward an understanding of the challenges presented by the intersections of gender and culture; this is critical for music therapists if we are to best meet our clients' needs.

Gender work, however, will take us beyond the therapy room. It is a myth that music therapy work can ever be personal and not also political:

> Our work is political. We may meet our clients in therapy, but we bring with us our experiences and social locations of the outer world; we also, clients and therapists alike, return to that outer world (Curtis, 2013a, p. 371).

Enhanced understanding of the intersections of gender and culture requires a look at their impact for the client in the private sphere and the public sphere. It also requires a look at their impact on the client-therapist interactions and the therapeutic relationship. Feminist music therapy, which has contributed substantially to a discourse within music therapy about the importance of gender (Curtis, 2000, 2006; Hadley, 2006), extends the scope of political work even further:

> Critical feminist understanding of gender contends that not only is our work as therapists political, our responsibility as therapists is to be political activists for social change in the community at large. We are held accountable to work to change lives in therapy and to work to change the world. (Curtis, 2013a, p. 371)

A final music therapist myth, although held by a smaller number, has recently emerged in music therapy discourse and debate (Curtis, 2013c; Hadley, 2008): Since I am a male music therapist in a female-dominated profession, I am the one experiencing discrimination. This myth can be debunked on two fronts: within the profession and within the therapy room. Within the profession, male music therapists do represent a minority; however, the experiences of token men in a female-dominated profession differ dramatically from token women in a male-dominated profession (Budig, 2002; Simpson, 2004; Williams, 1992). Rather than facing discrimination, "men benefit from their minority status through assumptions of enhanced leadership (the assumed authority effect), by being given differential treatment (the special consideration effect), and by being associated with a more careerist attitude to work (the career effect)" (Simpson, 2004, p. 349). While token women face a glass ceiling, token men are presented with a *glass escalator* (Budig, 2002; Williams, 1992). In general, research shows that "men are advantaged, net of controls, in both pay levels and wage growth in all jobs, regardless of gender composition" (Budig, 2002, p. 258). This is in keeping with previously noted findings that male music therapists earn significantly more than their female counterparts (Curtis, 2013c). Ultimately, whether as the dominant or minority gender, men bring with them a male privilege that is accorded them in patriarchal cultures. This holds as true in the profession as in the music therapy room. Music therapists will need to bring with them into the therapy room an understanding of male privilege and its meaning for clients in conjunction with other dynamics such as White privilege.

Having debunked the music therapist myths, it becomes clear that gender work is important for all music therapists, regardless of their own particular circumstances or those of their clients. The impact of gender should not be underestimated, nor the myriad ways it unfolds in our clients' lives, our lives, and our therapeutic relationships.

Diversities Within Gender

As highlighted in the title and tone of this chapter, gender does not stand alone; it intersects with culture in myriad and complex ways. As a result, while there is a discourse about the commonalities of our experiences of gender, it is counterbalanced by an understanding of the diversity of our experiences as well. This diversity is rooted in such differences of social locations or identity markers as ethnicity, socioeconomic status, sexual orientation, gender identity, age, and ability.

Because other chapters in this book so carefully and ably examine the intersections of gender and culture with those from diverse backgrounds, this chapter's section focuses on some overarching challenges that arise with multiple intersections. The most important of these include: (1) the challenge of identification; (2) the challenge of conflicting allegiances/oppressions; and (3) the challenge of gender lacking a sense of community.

The challenge of identification refers to the difficulties individuals face in identifying which of multiple oppressions is in play at any given time (Ontario Human Rights Commission, 2001). Is it racism? Is it sexism? Is it heterosexism? Is it some other "ism"? Additionally, in the case of multiple oppressions, individuals may be forced into the impossible task of ranking them. Which one is the worst?

The challenge of conflicting allegiances/oppressions also arises in the instance of multiple oppressions and can involve considerations of the individuals themselves as well as of their significant others. For example, a woman of color abused by her husband faces a dilemma: Should she report the violence and run the risk of exposing her husband to a racist response from the criminal justice system? Should she remain silent and continue to be abused and perhaps also run the risk of her children being taken from her by social services for putting them at risk? Her status as a woman, a woman of color, a poor woman, and a mother complicates the issue with multiple dilemmas over identity, allegiances, and responsibilities.

The challenge of gender lacking a sense of community lies in the very nature of gender itself. While gender is one of our first identities experienced, it does not generally bring with it a sense of community; allegiances to other social identities typically come first. Women do not vote as a group, nor do they have a common set of beliefs and practices. Gender can be a powerful but oftentimes invisible identity.

Internalization

Given the importance of gender but its unique nature in comparison to other cultures, what does this mean in terms of internalization? The very early onset of gender identity formation contributes to the powerful and insidious effect of internalization for women in our gendered world. Internalized sexism involves taking in and believing messages of gender bias and discrimination, and it is typically involuntary, unconscious, and unavoidable. Banaji and Greenwald's research (2013) points to its deeply hidden nature for both women and men. Banaji and Greenwald contend that internalization serves to perpetuate the dominant systems of inequity. Internalization can be powerfully undermining and affects individuals differently, depending on their other individual social locations. Its self-defeating outcomes can be seen in women who come to believe themselves unsuited for positions of power and subsequently do not apply for them; it can be seen in men who come to believe themselves unsuited for child care and subsequently avoid it (Banaji & Greenwald, 2013). Internalization is reflected in the sustaining power of gendered myths, stereotypes, and double standards and the support of these by both women and men. It is also reflected in the strength of those myths identified as specific to music therapists. While unavoidable, internalization can be counteracted, but only through increased awareness and acceptance. For music therapists, this also includes taking responsibility for this work on the part of themselves and their clients.

Meaning of Health and Well-Being

The social construction of gender has an incredibly powerful impact in all dimensions of health and well-being. It impacts women's and men's health, their experiences of it, the very definition of health, men's and women's differential responses to gender role socialization, and the differential in help-seeking, diagnosis, goal-setting, and treatment for women and men (Brown, 2008b; Curtis, 2000; Worell & Remer, 2002). Traditional medicine and therapy has been criticized for its pathologization of women. It set the male as the default in its definition of mental health. If women adhered to the expected standards of femininity, they could not meet the standards for mental health; if women adhered to the standards of this male model of mental health, they breached standards of femininity and thus were deemed mentally ill—another catch-22 for women. Intervention for both women and men focused typically on conforming to traditional gender roles and other cultural norms at all costs (Curtis, 2000; Worell & Remer, 2002). While progress has been made over the years, health care continues by and large to ignore the impact of the sociocultural and political in women's and men's lives. It also continues to re-enact in far too many areas the abusive dimensions of power and gender within the client-therapist and the patient-doctor relationship. While existing to a much lesser extent today than previously, sexual abuse of women by their therapists continues to occur far too frequently. Much still needs to be learned about the differential experiences of women and men. Women are diagnosed with depression in far greater numbers than men. Is this a result of the different responses of women or the differential expectations on the part of therapists? Shelters for alcoholic and homeless men far exceed those for women. Is this a result of a greater incidence among men or differential expectations for women? Men are far more likely to receive referrals for talking therapies, and women more likely to receive prescriptions for medication. Does this reflect differential needs or societal expectations (Brown, 2008a; Curtis, 2000; Worell & Remer, 2002)?

Feminist therapy, arising in response to the failure of traditional therapy to meet the needs of women, continues today to provide an alternative approach to better meet the needs of both women and men, with an understanding of the impact of gender and such other dimensions as ethnicity, sexual orientation, socioeconomic status, age, and ability (Brown, 2008a; Worell & Remer, 2002). So too does feminist music therapy (Curtis, 2006; Hadley, 2006). Feminist therapists contribute in the struggle to improve diagnosis and treatment so that they include an understanding of the sociopolitical nature of men's and women's lives and health. This has contributed to some improvements in the Diagnostic and Statistical Manual 5 (American Psychiatric Association, 2013). The struggle around labeling and pathologizing, however, continues. For example, issues still surround use of the diagnosis of posttraumatic stress disorder (PTSD) for women survivors of male violence:

> PTSD is a grab bag of contextless symptoms, divorced from the complexities of people's lives and the social structures that give rise to them. As such, this diagnosis individualizes social problems and pathologizes traumatized people. (Burstow, 2003, p. 1296)

Still, there has been some considerable headway made in better meeting the needs of women and girls in therapy. Brown (2008a) notes the widespread acceptance of feminist contributions with the adoption by the APA in 2007 of Guidelines for Psychotherapy with Girls and Women. Furthermore, health care professions are increasingly aware of the importance of incorporating an understanding of intersections of gender and culture in their practice. While entering the game a little later than some of the other health care professionals, music therapists are also now coming to understand this (Curtis, 2013a).

Meaning and Function of Music

As noted earlier, gender is unique among many of the other cultural identity markers. As a result, there is no single, homogenous body of music or singular meaning or function of music for women as a group; nor is there for men. How this plays out in the intersection of gender with other particular cultures can be found in the other chapters of this book. That being said, there does exist a body of music under the category of women's music. This comprises music that is by women and about women. It is as diverse as women themselves. In working with women in therapy, this women's music may be appropriate, but so too might be the vast array of other available music, depending on the interests of the individuals involved.

Whichever music is used, it should be chosen with careful thought and attention by the music therapist, with an understanding of the powerful messages about and to women included in such music—messages which are both overt and covert. Much of pop music today continues to portray women in a very negative light (Coy, 2014; Jones, 2006; Warner, 2013). This portrayal can have a powerful effect as it reflects, shapes, and perpetuates traditional gendered views of men and women, including gendered violence against women. Pop music and music videos, along with other pop culture, consistently and persistently present women as eye candy, reduced to body parts, to be objects of the male look and male possession, and to be sexually available (Coy, 2014; Warner, 2013). There is an accompanying message of male entitlement. There is also an underlying misogyny, which conflates sexuality with sexual violence. Research indicates the pervasive nature of this misogyny and its underpinning sexism and racism (Coy, 2014; Dagbovie-Mullins, 2013). Despite advances made in other areas for women, this misogyny seems to be increasing and to be increasingly unapologetic; in discussing his 2013 hit Blurred Lines, Robin Thicke commented "What a pleasure to degrade a woman. I've never gotten to do that before. I've always respected women" (Warner, 2013, para. 6). Thicke's hit certainly was not singular; it was just one of many (Coy, 2014; Jones, 2006; Warner, 2013). While more of the research has focused on rap music, Coy (2014) contends that we should not ignore the broader view of the impact of misogyny in all of pop music. We must also not ignore the broader view of all forms of sexism, looking not just at violence against women but at all the myriad messages of sexism told in the stories presented about women's and men's roles in love, in life, at home, and in the world. Making song choices can be a critical responsibility of each music therapist; an understanding of gender issues is an essential part of the process. Music which portrays women negatively can be used; in the hands of a skilled and informed music therapist, such music can be effectively used to challenge gender role stereotypes and debunk myths (Curtis, 2000; Jones, 2006). The importance of also including music which is nonsexist or pro-woman, however, should not be underestimated (Curtis, 2000; Jones, 2006). "The very process of critical reflection about our song choices has the effect of empowering ourselves and, in turn, our clients" (Jones, 2006, p. 339).

Whether working specifically with women, with men or women on gender-related issues, or simply with any client with an eye toward providing a gender-/culturally sensitive practice, music therapists might be well advised to learn more about feminist music therapy practices (Curtis, 2013b; Hadley, 2006). Feminist influences in music therapy, along with specific feminist music therapy practices, represent a relatively new and considerably diverse phenomenon (Edwards & Hadley, 2007; Hadley, 2006; Hadley & Edwards, 2004; Rolvsjord & Halstead, 2013; York & Curtis, 2015). The practice of feminist music therapy incorporates the tenets of feminism and, for some, those of feminist therapy.

In outlining a theory for this practice, Curtis (2006) identifies its hallmark technique as a feminist analysis of power, gender, and culture, with the goal of increasing understanding of the sociopolitical underpinnings of women's and men's lives and experiences. This can be accomplished through adaptation of a number of traditional music therapy techniques, including, but not limited to, lyric analysis, songwriting, recording, and performance. The themes addressed are broad-ranging and the music styles diverse. Specific music suggestions are available for general music therapy work (Curtis, 2000; Jones, 2006) and for work with women survivors of violence (Curtis, 2013b).

For the most part, the music used involves songs written and performed by women. This can provide a powerful connection, particularly for our women clients. Jones (2006) notes that it can effectively counter the powerful but unspoken message in much pop culture where the male voice or narrative so dominates that the "only voice worthy of being heard is that of a man" (p. 339). In music therapy work with women survivors of violence, use of songs written and performed by women can be even more important. The experience of the abused woman is often one of loss of voice and of social isolation (Curtis, 2000, 2006, 2013b). In listening to songs of other women surviving violence, they can hear their voices in the narratives of the others and can come to learn that they are not alone and that it is not their fault (Curtis, 2013b; York & Curtis, 2015).

At one point in my career working with women survivors of violence, I noticed that Eminem's '97 Bonnie & Clyde was a big hit—not only on the radio, but also with my own teenage

nephews and nieces. Everyone was enjoying it and singing along, apparently oblivious to the horrific content of the lyrics—a man talking to his young daughter while the mother (who he has just killed) lies dead in the trunk of the car. While shocked at the time by the disregard for the lyrics' violence on the part of the song's fans, I realize that this reflects the way violence against women has taken on an everyday nature because of its pervasiveness in pop culture. Shortly thereafter, Tori Amos released a cover of '97 Bonnie & Clyde, turning the aggressive song into a chilling version which gave voice to the dead woman and made clear the horrific nature of violence against women (Van Horne, 2001). Amos later discussed her cover of the song:

> Music is always a reflection of what's going on in the hearts and minds of the culture. If you're singing songs that are about cutting women up, usually these guys are tapping into an unconscious male rage that is real, that's existing—they're just able to harness it. So to shut them up isn't the answer. They're a gauge; they're showing you what's really happening in the psyche of a lot of people. (Van Horne, 2001, para. 5)

In this way, the power of music can be seen not only in its perpetuation of misogyny but also in its ability to challenge that misogyny, to challenge the status quo. I was able to bring into my music therapy sessions both versions of '97 Bonnie & Clyde for a powerful opportunity to explore and challenge societal views on violence against women, as well as the underpinning gender issues that impact the lives of women and men. It is a thoughtful and informed approach to the complex issues surrounding gender that can best guide music therapists' work with all of their clients.

Conclusion

This chapter has examined the impact of gender and its intersections with culture in the lives of women and men in the United States and Canada. The powerfully gendered nature of their lives has been identified, along with how this continues to play out in terms of persistent myths, stereotypes, and double standards. Gender bias and discrimination have been shown to have a pervasive impact in diverse ways, although much of the underpinnings are increasingly covert in nature, making it sometimes difficult to recognize—particularly when accompanied by internalization.

In light of this, music therapists are learning of our responsibility to ensure a gender- and culturally sensitive practice for all of our clients. This may appear simple at first, when seen as a clear written statement included in our *Professional Competencies* (American Music Therapy Association, 2013). It can, however, be quite complex. It requires change that involves both actions and attitudes. It involves a commitment to increasing our awareness, examining our personal beliefs and attitudes, and gaining an understanding of the complex and diverse interplay of gender and culture in our lives and in our clients' lives, both within therapy and in the public sphere. It is challenging work involving a lifelong journey for each music therapist, but it is critical to ensuring best practices for our clients.

References

American Association for University Women. (2014). *The simple truth about the gender pay gap*. Washington, DC: American Association for University Women.

American Music Therapy Association. (2013). *AMTA professional competencies*. Silver Spring, MD: American Music Therapy Association.

American Psychiatric Association. (2013). *Diagnostic and statistical manual of mental disorders* (5th ed.). Arlington, VA: American Psychiatric Association.

Armstrong, Jennifer (2013). *Revisiting "The Beauty Myth."* Retrieved from http://www.huffingtonpost.com/jennifer-armstrong/revisiting-the-beauty-myth_b_3063414.html

Banaji, M., & Greenwald, A. (2013). *Blind spot: Hidden biases of good people*. New York, NY: Dellacorte Press.

Black, M. C., Basile, K. C., Breiding, M. J., Smith, S. G., Walters, M. L., Merrick, M. T.,

Chen, J., & Stevens, M. R. (2011). *The national intimate partner and sexual violence Survey (NISVS): 2012 Summary Report*. Atlanta, GA: National Center for Injury Prevention and Control, Centers for Disease Control and Prevention.

Blakely, R. (2014, October). Silicon Valley, we have a problem. *Marie Claire Australia, 73–77*.

Bograd, M. (Ed.). (2014). *Feminist approaches for men in family therapy* (2nd ed.). New York, NY: Routledge.

Bowles, H., Babcock, L., & Lai, L. (2007). Social incentives for gender differences in the propensity to initiate negotiations: Sometimes it does hurt to ask. *Organizational Behavior and Human Decision Processes, 103*, 84–103.

Brown, L. S. (2008a). Feminist therapy. In J. L. Lebow (Ed.), *Twenty-first century psychotherapies: Contemporary approaches to theory and practice* (pp. 277–306). New York, NY: Wiley.

Brown, L. S. (2008b). *Cultural competence in trauma therapy: Beyond the flashback*. Washington, DC: American Psychological Association.

Buchwald, E., Fletcher, P., & Roth, M. (Eds.). (2005). *Transforming a rape culture* (2nd ed.). Minneapolis, MN: Milkweed Editions.

Budig, M. J. (2002). Male advantage and the gender composition of jobs: Who rides the glass escalator? *Social Problems, 49*(2), 258–277.

Burstow, B. (2003). Toward a radical understanding of trauma and trauma work. *Violence Against Women, 9*, 1293–1317. doi:10.1177/1077801203255555

Carmona, R. (2003). Family violence as a public health issue. *Symposium on Family Violence: The Impact of Child, Intimate Partner, and Elder Abuse*. Retrieved from http://www.surgeongeneral.gov/news/speeches/violence08062003.html

Caruso, E., Rahnev, D., & Banaji, M. (2009). Using conjoint analysis to detect discrimination: Revealing covert preferences from over choices. *Social Cognition, 27,* 128–137.

Clawson, L. (2014). *Microsoft CEO admits he was "completely wrong" to tell women not to ask for raises*. Daily Kos Labor. Retrieved from http://www.dailykos.com/story/2014/10/10/1335684/-Microsoft-CEO-admits-he-was-completely-wrong-to-tell-women-not-to-ask-for-raises#

Corbett, C., & Hill, C. (2008). *Where the girls are: The facts about gender equity in education*. Washington, DC: American Association of University Women.

Corbett, C., & Hill, C. (2012). *Graduating to a pay gap: The earnings of women and men one year after college graduation*. Washington, DC: American Association of University Women.

Coy, M. (2014). *"Pornographic performances": A review of research on sexualisation and racism in music videos*. London, UK: End Violence Against Women.

Curtis, S. L. (2000). *Singing subversion, singing soul: Women's voices in feminist music therapy* (Doctoral dissertation, Concordia University, 1997). *Dissertation Abstracts International, 60*(12-A), 4240.

Curtis, S. L. (2006). Feminist music therapy: Transforming theory, transforming lives. In

S. Hadley (Ed.), *Feminist perspectives in music therapy* (pp. 227–244). Gilsum, NH: Barcelona Publishers.

Curtis, S. L. (2013a). On gender and the creative arts therapies. *Journal of Arts in Psychotherapy, 40*(3), 371–372. doi:10.1016/j.aip.2013.05.014

Curtis, S. L. (2013b). Women survivors of abuse and developmental trauma. In L. Eyre (Ed.), *Guidelines for music therapy practice: Mental health* (pp. 263–268). Philadelphia, PA: Barcelona Publishers.

Curtis. S. L. (2013c). Women's issues and music therapists: A look forward. *Journal of Arts in Psychotherapy, 40*(3), 386–393. doi:10.1016/j.aip.2013.05.016

Dagbovie-Mullins, S. (2013). Pigtails, ponytails, and getting tail: The infantilzation and hypersexualization of African-American females in popular culture. *The Journal of Popular Culture, 46*(4), 745–771.

Edwards, J., & Hadley, S. (2007). Expanding music therapy practice: Incorporating the feminist frame. *The Arts in Psychotherapy, 34*(3), 199–207.

Fickling, D. (2005). *One in three blames women for being raped*. London, UK: The Guardian. Retrieved from http://www.theguardian.com/uk/2005/nov/21/ukcrime.prisonsandprobation

Finally, a Feminism 101 (Blog). (2007). *FAQ: What is male privilege?* Retrieved from http://finallyfeminism101.wordpress.com/2007/03/11/faq-what-is-male-privilege/

Gates & Clinton Foundations (*2015). The full participation report*. The full participation project: no ceilings. Retrieved from http://noceilings.org/about/

Gender Spectrum. (2014). *Understanding gender*. Retrieved from www.genderspectrum.org

Gillam, L. (n.d). *When worlds collide: Fandom and male privilege*. Retrieved from http://www.trickster.org/symposium/symp181.htm

Gillibrand, K. (2014). *Off the sidelines: Raise your voice and change the world* (E-reader version). New York, NY: Random House.

Gooding, G. E., Gilbert, L. A., & Scher, M. (1990). Gender aware therapy: A synthesis of feminist therapy and knowledge about gender. *Journal of Counseling & Development, 68,* 376–380.

Hadley, S. (Ed.). (2006). *Feminist perspectives in music therapy*. Gilsum, NH: Barcelona Publishers.

Hadley, S. (2008). Debate: Feminism and music therapy. A response to "Feminist perspectives in music therapy: An essay response by Anthony Meadows." *British Journal of Music Therapy, 22*(1), 45–49.

Hadley, S., & Edwards, J. (2004). Sorry for the silence: A contribution from feminist theory to the discourse(s) within music therapy. *Voices: A World Forum for Music Therapy, 4*(2). Retrieved from https://normt.uib.no/index.php/voices/article/view/177/136

Harnois, C. (2013). *Feminist measures in survey research*. Washington, DC: SAGE.

Heyninck, E. (2014, March 8). Women's day in Canada: Much to celebrate, much more work to do. An update from the Commissioner of the Pay Equity Commission of Ontario. *Globe & Mail*. Retrieved from http://www.theglobeandmail.com/globe-debate/womens-day-in-canada-much-to-celebrate-much-more-work-to-do/article17370856/

Hickley, W. (2014). The dollars-and-cents case against Hollywood's exclusion of women. *Five Thirty Eight Life*. Retrieved from http://fivethirtyeight.com /features/the-dollar-and-cents-case-against-hollywoods-exclusion-of-women/

Hill, C. (2010). *Why so few? Women in science, technology, engineering, and mathematics*. Washington, DC: American Association of University Women.

Hill, C., & Silva, E. (2005). *Drawing the line: Sexual harassment on campus*. Washington, DC: American Association of University Women. Retrieved from http://history.aauw.org/files/2013/01/DTLFinal.pdf

Holoien, D. S., & Shelton, J. N. (2011, October). You deplete me: The cognitive costs of color-blindness on ethnic minorities. *Journal of Experimental Social Psychology, 48*(2), 562-565. doi:10.1016/j.jesp.2011.09.010

ihollaback.org. (2014, October 27). *You won't believe how many times this woman gets harassed in 10 hours*. Retrieved from www.ihollaback.org

ihollaback.org. (2014, October 30). *Statement about recent street harassment PSA*. Retrieved from www.ihollaback.org

Jones, L. (2006). Critical reflections on song selection for women's empowerment in music therapy. In S. Hadley (Ed.), *Feminist perspectives in music therapy* (pp. 329–354). Gilsum, NH: Barcelona Publishers.

Kanani, R. (2012). *DOJ director on violence against women in the United States*. Retrieved from http://www.forbes.com/sites/rahimkanani/2012/03/08/doj-director-on-violence-against-women-in-the-united-states/

Lauer, M. (2014, September 8). Senator Kirsten Gillibrand on sexism, the Senate: Women's voices need to be heard (Television broadcast). In *Today Show*. NBC News.

McIntosh, P. (2008). White privilege and male privilege: A personal account. In M. McGoldrick & V. Hardy (Eds.), *Revisioning family therapy: Race, culture, and gender in clinical practice* (2nd ed., pp. 238–249). New York, NY: Guilford Press.

Nash, J. C. (2008). Rethinking intersectionality. *Feminist Review, 89,* 1–15.

Nosek, B., Banaji, M, & Greenwald, A. (2002). Math = male, me = female, therefore math [1] me. *Journal of Personality & Social Psychology, 83,* 44–59.

Ontario Human Rights Commission. (2001). *An intersectional approach to discrimination: Addressing multiple grounds in human rights claims*. Retrieved from http://www.ohrc.on.ca

Rolvsjord, R., & Halstead, J. (2013). A woman's voice: The politics of gender identity in music therapy and everyday life. *The Arts in Psychotherapy, 40*(4), 420–427.

Schacter, C., Stalker, C., Teram, E., Lasiuk, G. C., & Danilkewich, A. (2009). *Handbook on sensitive practice for health professionals: Lessons learned from women survivors of childhood sexual abuse*. Retrieved from http://www.phac-aspc.gc.ca/ncfv-cnivf/pdfs/nfntsx-handbook_e.pdf

Shirinian, S. (2010). *Women's rights as human rights*. United Human Rights Council. Retrieved from http://www.unitedhumanrights.org/2010/12/womens-rights-as-human-rights

Simpson, R. (2004). Masculinity at work the experiences of men in female-dominated occupations. *Work, Employment & Society, 18*(2), 349–368.

Sinha, M. (Ed.). (2013). *Measuring violence against women: Statistical trends 2013*. Commissioned by the federal/provincial/territorial ministries responsible for the status of women. Ottawa, ON: Statistics Canada.

Statistics Canada. (2006). *Earnings and incomes of Canadians over the past quarter century, 2006 Census: Earnings*. Ottawa, ON: Statistics Canada.

Statistics Canada. (2010). *Income in Canada 2010*. Ottawa, ON: Statistics Canada.

Strasser, A. R., (2013). Republicans push 700 new laws to regulate women's bodies. *Alternet*. Retrieved from http://www.alternet.org/republicans-push-700-new-laws-regulate-womens-bodies

Teague, A. K., Hahna, N. D., & McKinney, C. H. (2006). Group music therapy with women who have experienced intimate partner violence. *Music Therapy Perspectives, 24*(2), 80–86.

Tinsley, C., Cheldelin, S., Schneider, A., & Amanatullah, E. (2009). Women at the bargaining table: Pitfalls and prospects. *Marquette University Law School Negotiation Journal, 233*. Retrieved from http://ssrn.com/abstract=1397699

United Nations. (1999). *Press release: Violence against women most shameful, pervasive human rights violation*. New York, NY: United Nations.

United Nations. (2014). *Women's leadership and political participation*. Retrieved from http://www.unwomen.org/en/what-we-do/leadership-and-political-participation/facts-and-figures

United Nations General Assembly. (2011). *Resolution on women's political participation*. New York, NY: United Nations. Retrieved from http://www.unwomen.org/en/what-we-do/leadership-and-political-participation

United Nations Population Fund. (2014). *The human rights of women*. Retrieved from http://www.unfpa.org/rights/women.htm

Valenti, J. (2009). *He's a stud, she's a slut, and 49 other double standards every woman should know* (E-reader version). Berkeley, CA: Seal Press.

Van Horne, T. (2001). Tori Amos Says Eminem's Fictional Dead Wife Spoke to Her: Rapper's "'97 Bonnie & Clyde" is one of a dozen songs given new sound, new perspective on Strange Little Girls. *MTV News*. Retrieved from http://www.mtv.com/news/1449422/tori-amos-says-eminems-fictional-dead-wife-spoke-to-her/

Vespa, J., Lewis, J. M., & Kreider, R. M. (2013). America's families and living arrangements: 2012. *Current Population Reports*, P20-570. Washington, DC: U.S. Census Bureau. Retrieved from http://www.census.gov/prod/2013pubs/p20-570.pdf

Warner, A. (2013). *Misogyny makes a comeback: Kanye, Robin Thicke, and degrading women*. Toronto, ON: CBC Music Online. Retrieved from http://music.cbc.ca/#!/blogs/2013/6/Misogyny-makes-a-comeback-Kanye-Robin-Thicke-and-degrading-women

Weingarten, K. (Ed.). (2013). *Cultural resistance: Challenging beliefs about men, women, and therapy*. New York, NY: Routledge.

Williams, C. L. (1992). The glass escalator: Hidden advantages for men in the "female" professions. *Social problems, 39*(3), 253–267.

Williams, M. (2011). Color-blind ideology is a form of racism. Culturally speaking: challenging assumptions about culture, race, and mental health. *Psychology Today*. Retrieved from http://www.psychologytoday.com/blog/colorblind/201112/colorblind-ideology-is-form-racism

Wolf, N. (1990). *The beauty myth*. New York, NY: William Morrow & Company.

WomenAid International. (2012). *Women's rights are human rights*. Retrieved from http://www.womenaid.org/press/info/humanrights/hum.html

Worell, J., & Remer, P. (2002). *Feminist perspectives in therapy: Empowering diverse women* (2nd ed.) (E-reader version). New York, NY: John Wiley & Sons.

York, E., & Curtis, S. (2015). Music therapy with women survivors of domestic violence. In B. Wheeler (Ed.), *Trends in Music Therapy* (pp. 379–389). New York, NY: Guilford Press.

Chapter 15
SURVIVOR CULTURE

Dawn McDougal Miller, Deforia Lane, & Annette Whitehead-Pleaux

---

Annette: There are several ways in which I am connected to cultures of survivors. My career has brought me in contact with a several types of survivors, including survivors of sexual abuse/violence, survivors of child abuse, survivors of intimate partner violence, and survivors of burns. In addition, my life has been touched by trauma, and these personal experiences have helped to shape who I am today, as a person and as a music therapist.

In my work, I have seen people with like experiences coming together to form groups. I have seen this in small groups (as in music therapy groups of survivors of sexual violence in psychiatric units) and in organizations (as in feminist organizations serving survivors of intimate partner violence). Over the years, I have seen these groups of survivors and the cultures within these groups, as well as similarities between these cultures in beliefs and outlooks on life. I have often wondered about this phenomenon and why there were similarities in these populations, who are quite different except for the fact that a traumatic event has touched their lives.

Over the past 15 years, my career has focused on working with survivors of burn injuries at Shriners Hospitals for Children—Boston. Trauma paints with a broad brush, affecting so many, so survivors in this field include not just the individual who was physically injured but also the family/loved ones of that individual. I had the honor to deepen my work with burn survivors by becoming a coordinator for SOAR, the burn survivor peer support network through the Phoenix Society. I saw again these similar phenomena of a specific burn survivor culture in so many of the burn survivors I have met through this organization and my work at the hospital, and I was curious as to what was going on with survivors of traumatic events that created these similar cultures.

As Xueli and I discussed the chapters to be contained in this book, we discussed the idea of survivor cultures. Xueli has experience in working with burn survivors as well as survivors of cancer. We discussed the phenomena that we both had witnessed and decided that this broad category of culture needed to be included. We, the music therapists who work with survivors—whether of cancer, natural disaster, sexual violence, childhood abuse, intimate partner violence, school shootings, burns, war, heart attacks, criminal action, illnesses, traumatic accidents, or whatever—need to be aware of these cultures and the fact that not all survivors of traumatic events or debilitating illnesses will subscribe to these cultures. With eyes wide open and awareness of these cultures, why they form, and their influence, we can better serve each individual we encounter.

Authors' note: As you read this chapter, you will find the personal experiences of Dawn and Deforia interspersed

throughout. Additionally, in the medical model culture of cancer care, the word "patient" is commonly used when describing a person with cancer who is receiving treatment or therapy. Thus, we have chosen to use the terms "patient," "person with cancer," and "cancer survivor" interchangeably throughout this chapter, as a reflection of the culture in which they live and work.

Introduction

What is culture? Daher (2012) summarized culture in the following two statements:

> Culture is defined as a set of shared and socially transmitted ideas about the world that are passed down from generation to generation. Culture, as a socially transmitted phenomenon, carries with it the idea that people who interact on a regular basis know the same unwritten rules and criteria for social life that confer status as a member of the group. (p. 66)

As we examine cultures throughout this book, we see some fit into the first sentence (cultures of heritage and religion), while others fit into the second sentence (cultures of gender, sexual orientation, and gender identity). Survivor cultures fit into the second sentence. But, what is a survivor? Arthur Frank (1991), sociologist and survivor of cancer and a heart attack, reflected that a common theme of being a survivor is:

> the experience of being taken to the threshold of life, from which you can see where your life could end. From that vantage point, you are both forced and allowed to think in new ways about the value of your life. (It) takes away part of your life, but in doing so it gives you the opportunity to choose the life you will lead, as opposed to living out the one you have simply accumulated over the years. (p. 1)

No matter the cause of the traumatic event, whether illness or man-made or natural disaster/accident, there are universalities among each type of trauma. The survivor cultures are cross-cultural. Although there are some general themes that apply to all survivors, each type of survivor culture has its own challenges. A survivor of the Holocaust may experience different challenges than a survivor of a traumatic automobile accident, yet there are universalities that exist in both types of survivors, as a whole.

Etymology of the Term "Survivor"

Bell and Ristovski-Slijepcevic (2013) reviewed the history of the use of the term "survivor." They posed that the term "survivor" may have been first used in literature in 1594 by Shakespeare in his poem, "Rape of Lucrece." In this poem, Shakespeare referred to a survivor as a person who is still alive after someone has died. Bell and Ristovski-Slijepcevic (2013) also posited that in the late 1880s, the social Darwinism movement emphasized the survival of the fittest, and the term "survival" became associated with evolution, through which maladaptive traits would die out over generations.

In the book *Massive Psychic Trauma,* Krystal and Niederland (1968) first described "survivor syndrome" as a recognizable clinical mental health syndrome occurring in survivors of the Holocaust concentration camps. After reviewing mental health treatment charts of 149 Holocaust survivors, Krystal and Niederland (1968) described common clinical symptoms in survivors, including depression, anxiety, physical and psychosomatic symptoms, disruptions in faith, and the concept of survivor guilt. Krystal and Niederland (1968) posed that the "survivor syndrome" also included people who had survived other types of trauma, such as victims of natural disasters, poverty, incarceration, rape, and war.

As we look to understand why there are similarities among the different survivor cultures, the study of posttraumatic growth brings some clarity to our quest. Posttraumatic growth is the "positive psychological change experienced as a result of the struggle with a highly challenging life circumstance" (Tedeschi & Calhoun, 2004, p. 1). Within the field of posttraumatic growth, a traumatic event is an event that challenges our assumptive world, the world of "everything we know or think we know" (Parkes, 1971, p. 103). An event happens in our life that shakes us to the core, leaving in shambles all that we thought we knew and understood about life and leaving us questioning things we had once trusted, like the "benevolence, predictability, and controllability of the world around us" (Tedeschi & Calhoun, 2004). The growth does not take place because of the event, but happens as we struggle to come to terms with this new reality, one where the safety of our world no longer exists (Tedeschi & Calhoun, 2004). It is in this time of rebuilding that posttraumatic growth may occur, for not all individuals who experience a traumatic event will experience posttraumatic growth. There are five dimensions where posttraumatic growth occurs within individuals: Relating to Other, New Possibilities, Personal Strength, Spiritual Change, and Appreciation of Life. Lindstrom, Cann, Calhoun, and Tedeschi (2013) have found a connection between sociocultural elements and posttraumatic growth within the individual. The presence of a supportive environment (culture) with individuals to whom the survivor can connect about the experiences of going through a traumatic event can enhance growth in these five dimensions of posttraumatic growth.

Seeing the connection between sociocultural elements and posttraumatic growth, it is no wonder that organizations like LIVESTRONG, Rape Crisis Centers, Mothers Against Drunk Driving, and the Phoenix Society exist. Other survivors who have experienced posttraumatic growth often are members of these organizations; they provide the support and understanding that only another survivor can give. As music therapists, we know the value and power in creating groups with people who have had similar experiences (e.g., cancer survivors group, parents of burn survivors, groups for survivors of childhood abuse). These five dimensions of posttraumatic growth happen with people who have experienced a variety of traumas and are the universality among the cultures of survivors.

Although there are many types of survivors, this chapter will focus on cancer survivors in order to speak from the authors' areas of expertise and personal experience. Mukherjee (2010) wrote in his book *The Emperor of All Maladies, A Biography of Cancer,* "Cancer is not a concentration camp, but it shares the quality of annihilation: it negates the possibility of life outside and beyond itself; it subsumes all living" (p. 398).

Cancer Survivorship

Dr. Fitzhugh Mullan (1985), one of the first people to write about cancer survivorship, proposed:

> Survival, in fact, begins at the point of diagnosis, because that is the time when patients are forced to confront their own mortality and begin to make adjustments that will be part of their immediate and, to some extent, long-term future. (p. 271)

One of the unique challenges which cancer survivors have that many other types of survivors do not is that although the possibility of recurrence may diminish over time, it never fully disappears (Deimling, Kahana, & Schumacher, 1997).

Deforia: *I did not expect it. When the doctor handed me a piece of paper with the test results of the biopsy, the words on the page were in doctoreze—a medical mash of terms and numbers. "Carcinoma," however, was clear and struck me like a white-hot dagger. It blinded my eyes to what followed. Although I searched the page for more, at the sight of that word, a fog began to blur each typed line that followed. This began my first step of survival. It was to take many phases and faces. That day, I became a statistic—one of 90k women diagnosed with breast cancer. In disbelief, I joined the ranks of an army—unenlisted. I don't remember the word "survivor" coming to mind, but rather the feeling of disruption and intrusion in my life. I had no room for that, no time to be invaded by this intruder. Stop. Wait. Not me. Not now. I am marching to the tune of a different drummer, and this is not in the score. The troops I'm marching with are on the move—advancing forward—I need to keep in step. My job is to keep going—the Parent-Teacher meeting tonight at the developmental center, the laundry waiting at home, my son's baseball practice tomorrow, my husband's dinner tonight, my church choir rehearsal, my mind is racing. My body is still and my hand is still holding the paper. The doctor is looking at me. I shift my eyes to meet his, and the words empty out across my tongue, "Where do we go from here?" A part of me had slipped into a new gear—out of "drive," no longer on automatic pilot. "Reverse" was not an option. Cancer was here. I had to slow down. This was a detour, a delay. Looking back, I see that this moment marked a mind-set of survival. I was already moving on. Staying the course.*

Dawn: *I remember the exact details of the moment when I was told "you have cancer" and suddenly became a "cancer survivor." I can still hear the concern in my doctor's voice on the phone as she explained the results of my biopsy. I was sitting at my dining room table, aware of the stark contrast of this unwelcome news of cancer with the backdrop of sounds of everyday life from my two young children and husband in the next room. I can still feel the tears streaming down my face and the unexpected shock of hearing this news.*

In those early weeks, I rode an erratic roller coaster of emotions. I would lie awake at night, grappling with fears and existential questions. I experienced a "dark night of the soul," as I faced my greatest fear that I might die and would not be able to have the gifts of raising my young children and living out my life, hopes, and dreams. I think that the poet Jason Shinder described it well when he wrote, "Cancer is a tremendous opportunity to have your face pressed right up against the glass of your mortality" (as cited in Mukherjee, 2010, p. 398).

After I was diagnosed, I would long for those ordinary days of life, before I was dealt the cancer card. I remember waking up, and just for a few fleeting moments, I would forget that I had cancer and would feel a sense of relief. But then that black cloud would descend on my consciousness: "Ooh yeah, I have cancer."

Surbone et al. (2010) reported that "the experience of chronic illness is inseparable from the family life history and is embedded within cultural, religious, and historical contexts that shape families' appraisal and value orientations toward cancer" (p. 258). Spirituality is also related to culture and religion, and it "must be addressed with utmost respect for individual and cultural differences" (p. 258).

Mullan (1985) made several statements in his landmark article which provided support to the idea that a cancer survivor culture exists: "[T]he person who has come through a cancer experience is indelibly affected by it" and people who have been cured of cancer have a "kinship and continuum with the previous seasons of survival" (p. 272). "Patients with cancer, whether recently diagnosed and being treated or previously diagnosed and relatively stable, have more in common with one another than they do with people who have not experienced cancer" (p. 271). "For better *and* for worse, physically and emotionally, the experience leaves an impression. No matter how long we live, cancer patients are survivors" (p. 272).

Dr. Kenneth Miller (2010) noted that cancer survivors share some common experiences of survivorship and that, surprisingly, for some cancer survivors, many of these benefits are positive. These include personal growth, compassion, enhanced relationships, appreciation for life and each day, deepened sense of meaning and/or spirituality, development of intentional strategies to cope with their mortality threat and illness demands, and adoption of healthier lifestyles.

Stanton (2010) presented thorough reviews of studies that support the positive benefits of a cancer survivorship, but noted that positive benefits from an experience are not the same as positive thinking. Stanton described a common belief in the lay culture that if a cancer survivor focuses on positive thinking and suppresses negative thoughts and feelings, then that cancer survivor will have a more positive adjustment to cancer and improved disease outcome. Stanton pointed out that this belief is not supported in the research literature and posed that healing may be a much more complex process which involves exploring and expressing all of the emotions related to cancer.

Cancer survivor Natalie Davis Spingarn (1999) described a new generation of cancer survivors in her book *The New Cancer Survivors: Living with Grace, Fighting with Spirit.* Spingarn suggested that this new culture of cancer survivors is seeking a partnership role in health care decisions and expecting to be treated as a whole person, not as a diagnosis.

The National Coalition for Cancer Survivorship (NCCS) recognized the survivorship experience as "living with, through, and beyond a cancer diagnosis." Their definition also included the patient's family and support network: "[A]n individual is considered a cancer survivor from the time of diagnosis, through the balance of his or her life. Family members, friends, and caregivers are also impacted by the survivorship experience and are therefore included in this definition" (National Coalition for Cancer Survivorship, 2014).

The National Cancer Institute (NCI) also included family members in the definition of "cancer survivors" to recognize that cancer impacts the entire family, not just the person with cancer (Strada & Sourkes, 2010). Some family members become caregivers for their family member with cancer, often assuming the caregiving role with without any training or consideration to their prior knowledge, skills, or resources for caregiving (Northouse, Williams, Given, & McCorkle, 2012). In 2009, there were 4.6 million American households providing care in their home for a family member with cancer (National Alliance for Caregiving, 2009).

Cancer Survivor Terminology

"Cancer survivor" is a relatively new term, first proposed in 1985 in the landmark article by Dr. Fitzhugh Mullan to replace the term "cancer victim" or "cancer patient." Dr. Mullan was a physician who had been diagnosed with cancer at the age of 32. His dual status as a cancer survivor and a physician provided more acceptance and validity for this term and definition (Bell & Ristovski-Slijepcevic, 2013). In this same article, Dr. Mullan also described the qualitative components of cancer survivorship and helped the medical field move beyond focusing only on quantitative statistics regarding years of cancer survival (Leigh, 2007).

In 1986, Dr. Mullan, along with two dozen other cancer survivors, cancer health care providers, and advocates were invited by Catherine Logan Carrillo, the founder of (People) Living Through Cancer, to come together for a groundbreaking meeting (Leigh, 2007). They created the National Coalition for Cancer Survivorship (NCCS) and proposed national guidelines for replacing the words "cancer victim" with "cancer survivor." They suggested that the definition of a cancer survivor begins at the point of diagnosis (National Coalition for Cancer Survivorship, 2014). The term "cancer survivor" was meant to be a motivating psychosocial term to promote advocacy and awareness (Khan, Harrison, Rose, Ward, & Evans, 2012; Khan, Rose, & Evans, 2012; Twombly, 2004).

History of Terminology

Prior to the development of modern multimodal cancer treatments in the 1950s, there were very few people who survived cancer. Cancer was often viewed as a death sentence (Bell & Ristovski-Slijepcevic, 2013; Holland & Weiss, 2010). Thus, the terms "cancer patient" andr "cancer victim" were commonly used, whereas the term "cancer survivor" was reserved to refer to the loved ones of people who had died from cancer.

Although the term "cancer survivor" is commonly used in North American culture, other terms which have been used are "cancer patient," "cancer ex-patient," "cancer veteran," "cancer victor," "cancer hero," "cancer-recovered," person who is "living past cancer," "in remission," "cancer-free," person who has "survived cancer" or has "had cancer," patient with "acute cancer," patient with "cured cancer," and patient with "chronic cancer" (Khan, Harrison, Rose, Ward, & Evans, 2012; Khan, Rose, & Evans, 2012; Miller, 2010; Tralongo, Annunziata, Santoro, Tirelli, & Surbone, 2013). The term "cancer survivor" has replaced an older and more offensive term: "cancer victim." The term "cancer thriver" or "cancer thrivor," although not in common usage, may be the most positive term which has been suggested to empower people who are now *thriving* after cancer treatment. "One hopes that the cancer diagnosis will ... be transformed ... from surviving to genuine flourishing, from 'survivorship' perhaps to 'thrivorship'" (Astrow, 2012, p. 1640).

Differing Views of Terminology

The definition and usage of the term "cancer survivor" varies, depending on the person or organization using it, the country in which it is being used, the time frame in history, and whether it is being used to describe research, advocacy, or government policy. The term has been impacted by historical, social, cultural, and political factors (Bell & Ristovski-Slijepcevic, 2013). Some people living with cancer or who have had a history of cancer embrace the term "cancer survivor," while others do not.

Within the cancer survivor culture, the term "cancer survivor" is a controversial term. Some people with cancer do not embrace the term because it can be associated with war, violence, or battlefield analogies. Amy Dockser Marcus (2004) wrote in her *Wall Street Journal* article that some people with cancer do not like the word "survivor" because it is "so closely associated with the Holocaust or victims of violent crime such as rape" (p. 2). Marcus (2004) noted that people who have had heart attacks are not commonly identified as heart attack survivors.

The term "cancer survivor" is commonly used in the United States, but is not commonly used or accepted in all countries. In some cultures, the translation for the term "cancer survivor" has negative connotations. In European countries, the term "cancer survivor" is not used as commonly as in the United States, and their focus of cancer survivorship research is primarily on cancer patients who have remained tumor-free for at least five years after their diagnosis. A qualitative study by Khan, Harrison, Rose, Ward, and Evans (2012) examined the attitudes and interpretations of people living in the United Kingdom who were at least five years post diagnosis. The researchers found that a majority of participants did not identify with the term "cancer survivor." They recommended the following more acceptable terms: "people living with cancer," "people living past cancer," "people who have survived cancer," or more specific operational definitions, such as "people who are six years post diagnosis of cancer or post primary treatment and not receiving end-of-life care" (Khan, Rose, & Evans, 2012, p. 35). Khan, Harrison, Rose, Ward, and Evans (2012) found that a majority of people with cancer in their study in the United Kingdom rejected the concept of being labeled a cancer survivor and did not gain a new personal identity through having cancer.

Like their European counterparts, people with cancer in the United States vary in their use of the term "cancer survivor." Kaiser (2008) interviewed 39 women in the United States with a history of breast cancer and found that approximately 50% of them also rejected the label of "cancer survivor." In her qualitative study, Kaiser (2008) examined the following two questions: (1) Do women embrace the survivor identity as a way to make sense of their lives following cancer? and (2) To what extent do women craft new meanings for their experiences? Common themes for rejecting the term "cancer survivor" were that the term alienated many groups of women who had experienced breast cancer, including those who were concerned about the possibility of recurrence, those who felt that their cancer experience was not severe enough, those who were still in the trenches and had not finished cancer treatments, and those who preferred to experience their cancer as an individual experience and private disease rather than joining the sisterhood of breast cancer survivors. All of these authors suggested that a more palatable term is "someone who has survived cancer" instead of "cancer survivor."

Interestingly, some research studies have shown that cancer

survivors who have adopted a survivor orientation have improved outcomes, including increases in healthy lifestyles, which may reduce the odds of recurrence; compliance with symptom monitoring; and improved mental health outcomes, including personal growth, self-esteem, self-transformation, identity reformulation, and overall well-being (Deimling, Bowman, & Wagner, 2007). As with any member of a culture, it is important for the music therapist to ask the individual what language and terms they prefer to use in relation to themselves and their experiences with cancer. A term one person prefers may be an offensive term to another.

Dawn: *Do I embrace the label of "cancer survivor"? I have been reflecting on that question as I've been delving into the cancer survivor literature. I have resonated with many of the statements made by people with cancer in the publications that I have reviewed. Was my cancer "bad enough" to define myself as a cancer survivor? Thankfully, I didn't need to go through radiation or chemotherapy or have disfiguring side effects. I had a very curable cancer and I am filled with gratitude that I am healthy. I didn't "battle" cancer like many people that I have known. I also did not resonate with the violent "battle" language that some cancer survivors use. My journey was one of healing from cancer. I also know many people who were not cured of their cancer; does this mean that they didn't battle hard enough or heal well enough? No, I can't buy that!*

Yes, I am a person who has survived cancer. This process of surviving cancer has caused me to grieve, stretch, grow, and learn. Facing cancer and my own mortality has helped me to become the person that I am today. But being a cancer survivor is not my only identity. I am so much more than just a cancer survivor. I choose not to share the news of the cancer chapter of my life journey with everyone I meet. And I am intentional in my work in cancer care to meet each patient as a person, not a "lung cancer diagnosis in Room 492."

Seasons of Cancer Survivorship

Mullan (1985), the originator of the term "cancer survivor," divided cancer survivorship into three distinct "seasons of survival:"

(1) acute survival—the time of diagnosis and active treatment
(2) extended survival—when the person is in remission or active treatment is complete
(3) permanent survival—people who have been cured of cancer

Other authors have expanded on Mullan's proposed initial stages. Miller (2010) proposed a modified model that included cancer survivorship research and information over the past two decades since Mullan originally proposed his "seasons of survival" model. Miller (2010) divided survivorship into the following categories:

(1) acute survivorship
(2) transitional survivorship—the time when treatment ends
(3) extended survivorship

Miller (2010) separated the latter category into three more subcategories:

(1) people who are living with cancer without treatment
(2) people who are living with cancer which is maintained or kept in remission with ongoing treatments for the remainder of their lives
(3) permanent survivors—people who are cured of cancer

Miller (2010) noted that although some people may be *cancer-free*, they may not be *free of cancer* due to long-term side effects of cancer treatment that may impact their health, career, finances, insurance, fertility, or sexuality.

Deforia: *Moving forward is a process of steps—small, medium, and large. Each step of living with and through cancer has a life and an end point all its own. There is a beginning, middle, and end to each event, and yet the impact of each step becomes a permanent part intimately woven into the fabric of who we are. Hearing and digesting the diagnosis of cancer was almost blinding. That constituted a large step of facing the unknown. Yet that moment gives way to the next and the next, until the initial shock is past and I look back and see that I moved past or through it.*

Deciding how to proceed proved more of medium step. It was daunting and at times paralyzing, yet I was propelled into action by those around me, that is, doctors, tests, family, coworkers, and the unrelenting tick of the clock that would not stop. Time would not wait for me.

A small step of survival for me was taking the tamoxifen pill each day. There were no side effects that I could see. Applying cream to tender skin turned a deeper shade of brown from radiation seemed a small, doable step. I compare these small, medium, and large steps to a mother who gives birth. The birth itself can be rightfully labeled as the large step, but once that process is over, the task of caring for the baby begins. Once my cancer diagnosis was birthed, then came the task of caring for my body, mind, and spirit. It felt natural and necessary. This baby, my body, needed and demanded my attention.

While the term "cancer survivor" applies to an individual who has been diagnosed with cancer, the term "cancer survivorship" describes a process that happens to a person. There is not as much controversy in the literature about the use of the term "cancer survivorship phase." In clinical cancer care, the cancer survivorship phase is often recognized as the time period that begins after a person has completed an active cancer treatment regime of surgery, chemotherapy, and/or radiation therapy.

In 2015, the American College of Surgeons Commission on Cancer (COC) began to require cancer survivorship care plans (American College of Surgeons Commission on Cancer, 2012). Why are cancer survivorship care plans needed? People with cancer often receive medical care from multiple specialists in many departments and move throughout various inpatient and outpatient settings. When the medical care of cancer survivors is transferred from an oncologist to a primary care physician, which often occurs after active treatment, and several years of monitoring have been completed, specific cancer survivorship care issues may get lost in the transition (Ganz & Hahn, 2008).

Myths About the Culture

Although it is common in the United States for celebrities with cancer to publicly share their stories of cancer diagnosis, treatment, and survivorship, this is not always consistent in other areas of the world. Cancer-related myths and stigmas about cancer diagnoses and treatments are prevalent in Middle Eastern countries (Daher, 2012). These myths and stigmas may prevent people from sharing stories about their cancer. There are also more stigmas about cancer in some European countries. This has led to limited public discourse about cancer and fewer political policies and less government funding for cancer research in these countries (Rowland et al., 2013).

Throughout history and in various cultures, there have been many other myths about cancer. In some cultures today, some of these beliefs are still prevalent (Bell & Ristovski-Slijepcevic, 2013; Die-Trill, 1998; McDougal Miller & O'Callaghan, 2010; Mukherjee, 2010; Rowland, 2007). These myths (with their truths) include the following:

Cancer is contagious. Cancer is not contagious.

Cancer is an automatic death sentence. There are many types of cancer. Not all forms of cancer mark one's impending death. Many have treatments which can abate the cancerous growth.

Cancer is a punishment for bad behavior, sins, or transgressions. Cancer is an illness on the cellular level. It is not a punishment.

Radiation therapy causes a person to become radioactive. Radiation therapy does not cause a person to become radioactive. Radiation therapy utilizes high-energy ionizing radiation doses to target cancer cells in a specific anatomical area.

People receiving chemotherapy are experimental "guinea pig" subjects. Chemotherapy, like other medications, has been tested and approved by the government for use with patients. However, as with many other illnesses and conditions, there is active ongoing clinical research that explores new treatment options. Some people who are being treated for cancer may opt for these experimental treatments, but that is only a small portion of the entire population of people being treated for cancer.

Thinking positive and focusing on positive emotions will cure cancer. While there are studies that find links between positive thought and prayer and healing, the connection between these has not been found to be powerful enough to cure cancer.

Battle language must be used in order to fight and beat cancer. Language and images are unique for every individual with cancer. For some individuals, cancer is a battle; for others, cancer is a journey or a healing process. What is most important is that the language is meaningful to each individual with cancer. As music therapists working with people whose lives have been touched by cancer, one of our first tasks when we conduct our initial assessment is to ask how the individual refers to herself/himself/zerself and how they would like us to refer to them. And given that identity development is a continuous process that changes with experiences and time, we need to continue to be cognizant of the changes in our client's identity and how she/he/ze chooses to identify.

Diversity Within the Culture

The cancer survivor culture is diverse and has no cultural boundaries. Unfortunately, no one is immune to cancer. People from all ethnic backgrounds, walks of life, countries, ages, genders, sexual orientations, religions, socioeconomic levels, educational backgrounds, and lifestyles are diagnosed with cancer. Rowland summarized it well: "[C]ancer is an incredible equalizer, touching the lives of all kinds of people representing all manner of backgrounds, races, ethnicities, beliefs, ages, and resources" (as cited in Lock, 2013, p. 3). Nevertheless, it is important to highlight the diversities within this culture.

In the United States, survival rates for all racial and ethnic groups improved from 1988 to 1997 (Clegg, Li, Hankey, Chu, & Edwards, 2002). However, the incidence of cancer diagnoses and mortality rates from cancer in the United States is still higher for people of some ethnic backgrounds, including African-American, American Indian, and Alaskan and Hawaiian Native, and lower for people from Asian and Pacific Islander backgrounds (American Cancer Society, 2013). American Indians and Alaskan Natives have the highest cancer death rates.

Even though both men and women are diagnosed with cancer, there are several differences within these groups. Although 25% more men are diagnosed with cancer than women, there are more women who are long-term cancer survivors than men, with breast cancer survivors making up the largest group (Miller, 2010). Rates of cancer incidence in men are highest in Australia and New Zealand and lowest in Western Africa; for women, they are highest in North America and lowest in Central Asia (Ferlay et al., 2013).

Cancer itself is considered to be a collection of different diseases, characterized by uncontrolled growth of cells, rather than one disease (Mukherjee, 2010). Cancer occurs in various forms, such as breast cancer, prostate cancer, lung cancer, lymphoma, and leukemia. Each of these types of cancer has different treatment protocols, prognoses, and research focuses, and the cultural norms may vary from one type of cancer survivor to another.

Children or young people with cancer are often either cured of cancer or have cancers recur quickly. The long-term effects of cancer treatment on children could impact their future life decisions, including their personal identity and career and whether they are able to bear children (Astrow, 2012). These early health care experiences may also influence their willingness to engage in medical and mental health care. On the other end of the life spectrum, elderly people with cancer may decide not to receive aggressive treatment and thus live the rest of their lives with a slow-growing or chronic cancer.

Daher (2012) proposed a cultural model of disease which influences peoples' perceptions about the meaning of an illness and the types of treatment that are acceptable. Daher (2012) pointed out that cultural beliefs and values are important to consider because they impact cancer prevention and psychological and behavioral outcomes following cancer diagnosis and treatment.

There are major differences in how information about cancer is presented to patients in different parts of the world: In Eastern countries, the focus is on the family, whereas in Western countries, the focus is on the individual, respecting patient autonomy, decision-making. and informed consent. These differences may bring about misunderstandings when someone with cancer from an Eastern culture is being treated with a Western medical model, and vice versa. In addition, in some cultures, it is considered inhumane or harmful to provide information about a cancer diagnosis or prognosis to the person with cancer, and this information is often withheld from anyone outside of the immediate family. These cultural beliefs about cancer can be found in Latin America, Africa, southern Europe, China, Japan, India, Pakistan, Bangladesh, Nepal, and Sri Lanka (Die-Trill, 1998; McDougal Miller & O'Callaghan, 2010).

Global/Geographical Differences

Pandey et al. (2000) reported that there were more women in India with advanced breast cancer and posited that this was due to lack of active breast cancer screening programs. A study from Israel by Baider et al. (2000) found that second-generation Holocaust survivors reacted with extreme psychological distress to the trauma of a breast cancer diagnosis, when compared to a group of women who also received breast cancer diagnoses but whose parents were not Holocaust survivors. The authors of this study proposed that a family history of one type of trauma may impact generations of families when another major stressor or trauma emerges (Baider et al., 2000).

There is a global misperception that cancer is only a major health problem in wealthy nations because of the use of tobacco and prevalence of fatty diets and sedentary lifestyles (López-Gómez, Malmierca, de Górgolas, & Casado, 2013). Historically, cancers that may be caused by infections, such as cervical, liver, and stomach cancers, have been more prevalent in economically disadvantaged countries. However, as economically disadvantaged countries have adopted Western habits, the incidence of other cancers such as lung cancer and

breast cancer has increased dramatically.

There is a large variance in regions and countries around the world of cancer incidence and mortality (Coleman, 2014). Some of the theories regarding this include differences in genetics, exposure to environmental factors, obesity, smoking, access to health care, and poverty (Holland & Weiss, 2010). At this time, there is no one unifying theory that explains these variances.

Cancer is an enormous global burden, and there is a huge disparity in access to health care resources, qualified personnel, and funding throughout the world (Coleman, 2014). In many economically disadvantaged counties, the survival rate is less than 50% and there are fewer long-term cancer survivors. Survival rates for many cancers are almost double in more developed countries (López-Gómez et al., 2013). Rowland posited that in low-income countries, where resources are limited, resources may be "better spent trying to improve access to earlier detection and delivery of effective cancer therapies, along with providing outstanding palliative care, than working on a survivorship program" (Lock, 2013, p. 4).

Treatment Paradigm Differences

There are many treatment paradigms for people with cancer, which may vary depending on where the person lies on the cancer treatment continuum. The main treatment paradigms are: curative, which, if successful, leads to long-term survivorship; maintenance; palliative; or hospice. Each of these treatment paradigms has very different goals and approaches for treatment. A person going through cancer treatment may experience one or all of these treatment paradigms, and the culture within each of these treatment paradigms may differ. Even within one health care system, there are different cultures between inpatient oncology, cancer center, rehabilitation, palliative care, inpatient hospice, and home care hospice settings.

Many people with cancer are treated with a *curative* paradigm, where the goal is for the patient to be in remission or cured of cancer. Treatments focused on curing cancer may be more aggressive, creating more acute and challenging side effects during the period of active treatment.

The *long-term survivorship phase* begins at the end of active treatment. In addition to the more acute posttreatment period of emotions, cancer survivors may also continue to experience challenges in physical, emotional, psychosocial, spiritual, existential, and practical areas of their lives.

With advances in the effectiveness of cancer treatment, more people are living with cancer as a chronic disease (Bell & Ristovski-Slijepcevic, 2013; McCorkle et al., 2011). People in this *maintenance* treatment paradigm may receive regular treatments for many years or for the rest of their life, in order to prevent the growth or spread of cancer and to optimize their quality of life.

A *palliative* treatment paradigm may be utilized for people with more advanced cancer, when the cancer adversely impacts their daily life or predictably reduces their life expectancy

(National Hospice and Palliative Care Organization, 2014). Palliative care emphasizes patient- and family-centered care that optimizes quality of life.

A *hospice* treatment paradigm is often appropriate for people with terminal cancer who have a limited life expectancy. In the United States, this is defined as statistically having six months or less to live. Hospice is focused on caring, not curing, and decisions are made with the goal of optimizing comfort (National Hospice and Palliative Care Organization, 2014).

Counternarratives

Ehrenreich (2001), a breast cancer survivor and author, reported a negative interpretation of her experience of the breast cancer culture. Ehrenreich (2001) described the breast cancer world as a "cult." She wrote "in the mainstream of breast-cancer culture, one finds very little anger … the overall tone, almost universally upbeat. … So pervasive is the perkiness of the breast-cancer world that unhappiness requires a kind of apology" (p. 48). Ehrenreich (2001) continued:

> In the seamless world of breast-cancer culture, where one website links to another—from the personal narratives and grassroots endeavors to the glitzy level of corporate sponsors and celebrity spokespeople—cheerfulness is more or less mandatory, dissent a kind of treason. (p. 50)

Ehrenreich (2001) discussed the overcommercialism of breast cancer products as "seen through pink-tinted lenses, the entire breast-cancer enterprise—from grassroots support groups and websites to the corporate providers of therapies and sponsors of races" (p. 51) and noted the over abundance of breast cancer advocacy products such as teddy bears, pink-ribbon brooches, bedazzled pink-ribbon shirts, pink socks worn by football and soccer teams, and numerous other breast cancer–pink products.

Sulik (2011) completed in-depth interviews with 60 women with breast cancer in order to understand the norms surrounding breast cancer survivor culture. The women that Sulik (2011) interviewed identified some of the unwritten rules of breast cancer culture as the notions that breast cancer survivors must not whine or feel sorry for themselves and breast cancer survivors should not express negative emotions or fears of death. Instead, breast cancer survivors should cheerfully join the breast cancer sisterhood, adopt an optimistic attitude, and "embody the 'she-ro' who will 'smile thru the tears' and 'kick cancer's butt!'" (Sulik, 2011, p. 240). Sulik (2011) posed that normative "pink ribbon" expectations thrive in breast cancer culture, and the breast cancer culture emphasizes "traditional feminine" attributes. Sulik (2011) pointed out that women are often raised to be the nurturing caregivers of their families and that guilt often arises for women who choose to focus on their own needs in order to survive the rigors of cancer treatment.

Kaiser (2008) wrote:

> In constructing a positive, cure-oriented definition of survivorship, the breast cancer culture has left many women searching for representations which acknowledge their fears and the *ongoing* presence of cancer in their lives. Moreover, women's responses to breast cancer are varied. Thus, a better model of life after cancer would acknowledge the variety of responses to the disease and the ongoing significance of the disease in women's lives. (p. 12)

Many of the these authors also noted that there is an emphasis within the cancer survivor culture for survivors to connect with each other for the purpose of organizing or participating in cancer advocacy and large public fund-raising events, rather than to connect with each other for the purpose of emotional support.

Deforia: *Consciously, I was not focused on being a survivor. I did not like that term. It signified being other than normal. It brought attention to the question "survivor of what?," and I wanted to be acknowledged for where I was going rather than from whence I had come. I know now that they (the past and the future) are inseparable. Whatever normalcy is, this was not it. However, I was surviving/functioning one day, sometimes one minute, at a time. Getting beyond the nagging "what-ifs" was major. In this phase of survival, I was concentrating on not being defined by my diagnosis. Yet I could not divorce myself from my diagnosis. I am a product/composite of every experience I've had, and whatever name I called it, I was grateful to say, "I'm still here."*

Meaning and Functions of Music

Cancer has touched the lives of musicians, and music has touched the lives of people who have cancer. In exploring the music that has meaning and function within this culture, several generalized areas were noted. These include music that describes the cancer experience, music that advocates for survivorship, and music that is healing/expressive/inspirational. These three areas will be explored here.

Music That Describes the Cancer Experience

People going through cancer have been the subject of a number of songs in the popular, rock, and contemporary Christian genres and with an even higher prevalence in country music. In addition, there are many songs which have themes that may inspire or provide support to people going through the emotions of cancer. Some people with cancer have described the experience of listening to these songs as one that is similar to going to a cancer support group. They reported that if a songwriter has written a song which expressed a struggle, emotion, or experience which was similar to their own, then they felt supported and not so alone in their own experiences of the emotions of cancer. The song might be one that moves a listener to tears or one that provides hope or inspiration because the listener can personally relate to the emotions or sentiments expressed in the music. At times, people with cancer have reported listening to one song many times each day to help them get through the challenges of cancer treatment, and the song becomes like a comforting blanket or transitional object.

Examples of songs about cancer:

Artists Stand Up to Cancer (a group of famous pop, rhythm and blues, rock, and country artists who came together to perform a live version of the song): *Just Stand Up!*
Craig Morgan: *Tough*
David Roth, Anne Hills: *Manuel Garcia*
Eels: *Dead of Winter*
Joe Jackson: *Cancer*
Lupe Fiasco: *Mission*
Martina McBride: *I'm Gonna Love You Through It*
My Chemical Romance: *Cancer*
Rascal Flatts: *Skin (Sarabeth)*

Music Advocating for Survivorship

Music is an important part of cancer survivorship events, including the Relay for Life, sponsored by the American Cancer Society, and the Race for the Cure, sponsored by the Susan G. Komen Breast Cancer Foundation. These events recognize and celebrate cancer survivors and their caregivers. They also serve as fund-raisers and advocacy events. Live music is often performed by well-known artists, and recorded music is specifically programmed for events.

The American Cancer Society's Relay for Life signature fund-raising program was begun in 1985 by Gordon "Gordy" Klatt, MD, and has grown to four million participants in 5,200 communities and 20 countries. The American Cancer Society's (2007) manual for organizing Relay for Life events recommends that music and poetry selections be chosen to support the three themes—Celebrate, Remember, and Fight Back—for these 12- to 24-hour overnight events. The music is selected intentionally to change the mood for each part of the event.

Some of the recommendations for music are:

Celebrate: Upbeat, energetic music, such as *Celebration* by Kool and the Gang, plays loudly as cancer survivors dance and celebrate their way around the track.
Fight Back: Upbeat music selections, such as *Eye of the Tiger* by Survivor, are used during the Fight Back Ceremony to motivate people to take action.
Remember: People who have died from cancer are remembered with luminaria while a song like *I Will Remember You* by Sarah McLachlan is played.

Music That Is Healing, Expressive, and Inspirational

Examples of songs that have been inspiring to some people with cancer:

Gloria Gaynor, Aretha Franklin: *I Will Survive*
Jason Mraz: *The Remedy (I Won't Worry)*
Mandisa: *Overcomer*
Martina McBride: *Ride*
Melissa Etheridge: *Message to Myself*
Tim McGraw: *Live Like You Were Dying*

Lucanne Magill (2010), a pioneering music therapist in the oncology field, wrote:

Music takes on deeper significance during times of transition, loss, and grief. Music therapists strive to assist patients, families, and staff in finding ways to integrate the medium of music to ameliorate grief and suffering, as well as to relieve stress, anxiety, depression, and isolation. (p. 425)

Magill (2010) acknowledges David Aldridge's book, *Music Therapy in Palliative Care* (1999), in summarizing how music speaks to existential and spiritual questions: "[M]usic therapy naturally provides the means to sustain these quests, as music has innate associations with nature, infinity, and humanity across borders and throughout history" (Magill, 2010, p. 426).

There are many ways in which music therapists encourage cancer survivors to use music in their healing process through music therapy sessions. Some of these include (1) the use of music for emotional support or expression, comfort, and hope; (2) the use of music for relaxation, guided imagery, focus on healing, or supportive images; (3) the use of music for decreasing anxiety and fear, creation of a healing environment, procedural support, enhancement of the patient's treatment experience, or focus on healing; and (4) the use of music after active treatment has ended, during the cancer survivorship phase, to reflect on the cancer journey, explore existential and spiritual questions, develop music-assisted relaxation and meditation practices within daily routines for stress management, and manage anxiety related to tests and monitoring.

For a more complete list of the uses of music and music therapy interventions for cancer survivors, please refer to *Music Therapy in Adult Cancer Care: Across the Cancer Continuum* (McDougal Miller, 2010).

Dawn: *I survived my crisis of cancer by accepting the support of friends, family, colleagues, and other professionals with cancer and by becoming a client in counseling, massage therapy, reflexology, and music therapy—specifically, the Bonny Method of Guided Imagery and Music. My experiences as a client were key in my own process of healing. I had to pull out all the stops in my own symphony of self-care. I incorporated many tools that I had learned in my music therapy education and the Bonny Method of Guided Imagery and Music trainings. Ah … music! Music was at the center of my most profound, supportive, and healing experiences. Music was my "go to" for expressing emotions and fears, dealing with side effects, finding comfort and hope, and facilitating healing imagery.*

One of the most important nuggets of wisdom that helped me get through those early days of cancer survivorship was shared with me by my supervisor, who was also a cancer survivor. She said, "Stay in the moment. Stay with what you know. Remember that right here, right now, you are OK. You only have to handle what is in front of you today. Fear is exacerbated by jumping to an unknown future which may never come true."

The Therapist's Own Emotions

There are many definitions of countertransference, including "the collection of feelings and emotional reactions evoked in the therapist during the course of the therapeutic relationship" (Strada & Sourkes, 2010, p. 400). Bruscia (1998) defined countertransference as occurring "whenever a therapist interacts with a client in ways that resemble relationship patterns in either the therapist's life or the client's life" (p. 52). Often people with cancer are wrestling with losses, anticipatory grief, fear of death, and/or intense emotions, and the therapist working in cancer care is "vicariously forced to become more in touch with his or her own feelings about mortality and past or current losses" (Strada & Sourkes, 2010, p. 400).

Dawn: *To self-disclose or not to self-disclose? That is a tricky question. Before I disclose that I am a cancer survivor to a patient with whom I am working, I ask myself, "What is my intention and purpose for disclosing this information? Will it directly benefit this patient and enhance the therapeutic relationship? How might this person react?" My answers to these questions often guide me* not *to disclose that I am a cancer survivor. If I make the intentional choice to disclose this information, the patient often responds by moving more deeply into the therapeutic process and may state, "Oh, you really do understand what it is like to have cancer." Even though every person's experience of the cancer journey is unique, somehow, there is a kinship that is felt with other cancer survivors.*

If cancer progresses, the therapist must be able to be comfortable and fully present with the person with cancer who may want to express emotions related to the possibility of death. When working with people with advanced cancer, sessions may end abruptly due to death or sudden changes in the person's condition. Some therapists consider every session with a person with advanced cancer to be a potential final good-bye.

"At times, the personal reality of the therapist may mirror the patient's experience; the therapist may lose a loved one to cancer or the therapist may be diagnosed with a threatening illness" (Strada & Sourkes, 2010, p. 400). For a therapist in this difficult situation, there are tools and interventions available, including support, the therapist's own personal therapy work,

consultation with colleagues, intentional decisions as to if and when to disclose information (and how much), and a consideration of the reactions of the patient.

Deforia: *My work as a music therapist prior to diagnosis had been with 4- to 18-year-olds with severe and profound developmental delay. I had had no exposure to oncology patients as I have had now for the past 31 years at the University Hospitals Seidman Cancer Center in Cleveland. I began volunteering there a year and a half after my initial diagnosis and an unexpected recurrence. I did so as a means to give back. I knew the simple yet profound way that music had helped me and wanted to extend that to others who were just like me—surprised, on guard, and scared. I admit to feeling a kinship with anyone with a cancer diagnosis. Seeing patients was neither frightening nor a reminder of what might be my future plight. Instead, I sensed that I could provide a listening ear, a supportive presence, a unique kind of sensitivity. I wanted to learn from others who were navigating this road. Perhaps we could be of help to each other. This turned out to be truer than I could have imagined.*

Armed with an omnichord and music books, I knocked on one door at a time in the adult bone marrow transplant unit. I seemed to put patients at ease and to build rapport without pretense when first meeting them. This often opened wide the door to patients sharing their most intimate thoughts, fears, hopes, dreams, and inquiries. Most of the time, I never mentioned to patients that I had had cancer. I sometimes saved this disclosure as my trump card for the hard-nosed, what-is-music-supposed-to-do-for-me skeptics.

Dawn: *Sometimes I have been asked, "Do you have to be a cancer survivor in order to provide excellent care and support to people with cancer?" My answer is always a resounding, "No!" There is no need to be dealt the cancer card to be an effective and compassionate therapist in cancer care. However, the experiences of facing my own mortality, living with uncertainty, waking up at 2:00 a.m. with a "dark night of the soul" existential crisis, losing the myth of good health, and worrying about whether I would be healthy enough to raise my family and work and have cancer—these became familiar parts of my life experience. My own experiences of navigating the foreign land of cancer survivorship have allowed me to understand others' cancer journeys at a deeper level than in life B.C. (before cancer).*

After my diagnosis, there was a period of time when I found it extremely difficult to provide music therapy for some patients who resembled my age, type of cancer, or life situation. Fortunately, my supervisor, also a cancer survivor, supported me, recommended consultation, and gave me permission not to see these patients until I felt ready. She and I knew that I couldn't effectively provide support for others going through the challenging emotions of their cancer journey when I was in the midst of my own turbulent emotions.

When I am leading a cancer survivors group and am introduced as a cancer survivor, it automatically gives me credibility. Hearts are open. The connection is greater. The group members understand that I too have been dealt the cancer card, I have survived, and I "get it." "Oh, you are one of us." Yet, because I can relate personally, it is imperative for me to have an awareness of my own feelings and reactions, receive consultation, and adhere to boundaries within the therapeutic relationship.

Conclusion

Deforia: *This chapter has attempted to look into the world of "survivorship" from a global/general and personal perspective. A review of the literature, cogent definitions, statistics, and some state-of-the-art resources are listed to provide scope and insight. There is tremendous value in navigating life's challenges and coming out on the other side. Abuse, violence, trauma, and disease can be life-changing. These events can enter and exit our lives unpredictably, with varying intensity or with seeming regularity. How we survive can take as many forms as the reasons that require that we do. The key is moving "through" them, moving forward, moving beyond.*

The truth is that these unwelcomed visitors (of disease and trauma) can stop us in our tracks, but in doing so create in us areas of growth and development that provoke us to rethink, regroup, and revise our lives. Surviving compels us to respond and insists (or imposes) on our attention. It is not always our choice nor do we feel prepared to handle it. Similarly, as music therapists, we are partners/participants in the survival of our clients—sometimes feeling underequipped and ill-prepared.

I am finding that survivorship, whatever its precipitating source—abuse, disease, personal or professional loss—is not formulaic. Guiding principles, however, point to the need for acquiring reliable information and seeking group and/or one-on-one support and counsel. Patience, tenacity, persistence, and, yes, surrender have their place. The issue of timing varies for everyone— time to hurt, time for help, time to heal. It may take days, months, or years to move into action or to experience resolve. For others, the circumstances dictate an immediate response (to a heart attack, a home lost to fire,) or the decision is made for us (a court mandate, emergency surgery, abandonment). How we respond in any of these circumstances is not as black and white as we might desire or imagine. What we tend to miss is how our traumas and failures equip and shape us for purposes yet to be realized.

As music therapists, we are in the business of assessing and addressing the needs of our clients. We vary in our styles and approaches based on our education, intuition, opportunities , and life experience. We approach a grieving patient differently if we have been personally acquainted with grief. There is some truth to that adage, "It takes a worried man to sing a worried song." Although we don't have to "experience" every trauma and emotion to empathize and be effective with our clients, there is a different kind of "knowing" and "being" that survivorship affords us—an earned mantle of awareness, and this impact can rise to the surface with power and sensitivity when we least expect it. It has been my experience that

patients listen with different ears when they know that I have walked a mile in their shoes. However, even if I choose not to disclose my cancer survivorship or other life-altering experiences, surviving them has changed me, altered my physical and emotional DNA. Are my ears and perceptions more sensitive to their questions? Am I still emerging and learning and able to grow along with my patient? In short, all that happens to us and around us, how we move in and through it, shapes who we are and can potentially equip us to be of practical and profound benefit to others.

Whether spoken, in song, or shared in silence, the rewards of survivorship are transforming.

References

Aldridge, D. (1999). *Music therapy in palliative care: New voices.* London, UK: Jessica Kingsley.

American Cancer Society. (2007). *Celebrate. Remember. Fight back. Relay for Life resource book.* Atlanta, GA: American Cancer Society.

American Cancer Society. (2013). *Cancer Facts & Figures 2013.* Atlanta, GA: American Cancer Society. Retrieved from http://www.cancer.org/acs/groups/content/@epidemiologysurveilance/documents/document/acspc-036845.pdf

American College of Surgeons Commission on Cancer. (2012). Cancer Program Standards 2012: Ensuring Patient-Centered Care. *Survivorship Care Plan* (p. 78). Retrieved from https://www.facs.org/~/media/files/qualityprograms/cancer/coc/programstandards2012.ashx

Astrow, A. B. (2012). Cancer survivorship and beyond. *JAMA: The Journal of the American Medical Association, 308*(16), 1639–1640. doi:10.1001/jama.2012.13258

Baider, L., Peretz, T., Hadani, P. E., Perry, S., Avramov, R., & De-Nour, A. K. (2000). Transmission of response to trauma? Second-generation Holocaust survivors' reaction to cancer. *American Journal of Psychiatry, 157,* 904–910.

Bell, K., & Ristovski-Slijepcevic, S. (2013). Cancer survivorship: Why labels matter. *Journal of Clinical Oncology, 31*(4), 409–411. doi:10.1200/JCO.2012.43.5891

Bruscia, K. E. (1998). Understanding countertransference. In K. E. Bruscia (Ed.), *The dynamics of music psychotherapy* (pp. 51–70). Gilsum, NH: Barcelona Publishers.

Clegg, L. X., Li, F. P., Hankey, B. F., Chu, K., & Edwards, B. K. (2002). Cancer survival among U.S. Whites and minorities: A SEER (Surveillance, Epidemiology, and End Results) Program Population-Based Study, *Archives of Internal Medicine, 162*(17), 1985–1993. doi:10.1001/archinte.162.17.1985

Coleman, M. P. (2014). Cancer survival: Global surveillance will stimulate health policy and improve equity. *The Lancet, 383*(9916), 564–573. doi:10.1016/S0140-6736(13)62225-4

Daher, M. (2012). Cultural beliefs and values in cancer patients. *Annals of Oncology,23*(Suppl. 3), 66–69. doi:10.1093/annonc/mds091

Deimling, G. T., Bowman, K. F., & Wagner, L. J. (2007). Cancer survivorship and identity among long-term survivors. *Cancer Investigation, 25*(8), 758–765. doi:10.1080/07357900600896323

Deimling, G. T., Kahana, B., & Schumacher, J. (1997). Life-threatening illness and identity: The transition from victim to survivor. *Journal of Aging and Identity, 2*(3), 165–186.

Die-Trill, M. (1998). The patient from a different culture. In J. C. Holland (Ed.), *Psycho-oncology* (pp. 857–866). New York, NY: Oxford University Press.

Ehrenreich, B. (2001, November). Welcome to cancerland. A mammogram leads to a cult of pink kitsch. *Harper's Magazine,* 43–53.

Ferlay, J., Soerjomataram, I., Ervik, M., Dikshit, R., Eser, S., Mathers, C., … & Bray, F. (2013). GLOBOCAN 2012 v1.0, *Cancer Incidence and Mortality Worldwide: IARC Cancer Base No. 11.* Lyon, France: International Agency for Research on Cancer. Retrieved from http://globocan.iarc.fr

Frank, A. (1991). *At the will of the body.* Boston, MA: Houghton Mifflin.

Ganz, P. A., & Hahn, E. E. (2008). Implementing a survivorship care plan for patients with breast cancer. *Journal of Clinical Oncology, 26,* 759–767. doi:10.1200/JCO.2007.14.2851

Holland, J. C., & Weiss, T. R. (2010). History of psycho-oncology. In J. C. Holland, W. S. Breitbart, P. B. Jacobsen, M. S. Lederberg, M. J. Loscalzo, & R. McCorkle (Eds.), *Psycho-oncology* (2nd ed., pp. 3–12). New York, NY: Oxford University Press.

Kaiser, K. (2008). The meaning of the survivor identity for women with breast cancer. *Social Science & Medicine, 67*(1), 79–87.

Khan, N. F., Harrison, S. E., Rose, P. W., Ward, A., & Evans, J. (2012). Interpretation and acceptance of the term "cancer survivor": A United Kingdom–based qualitative study. *European Journal of Cancer Care, 21*(2), 177–186. doi:10.1111/j.1365–2354.2011.01277.x

Khan, N. F., Rose, P. W., & Evans, J. (2012). Defining cancer survivorship: A more transparent approach is needed. *Journal of Cancer Survivorship, 6*(1), 33–36. doi:10.1007/s11764-011-0194-6

Krystal, H., & Niederland, W. G. (1968). Clinical observations on the survivor syndrome. In H. Krystal (Ed.), *Massive psychic trauma* (pp. 327–348). New York, NY: International Universities Press.

Leigh, S. (2007). Cancer survivorship: A nursing perspective. In P. Ganz (Ed.), *Cancer survivorship today and tomorrow* (pp. 8–13). New York, NY: Springer.

Lindstrom, C. M., Cann, A., Calhoun, L. G., & Tedeschi, R. G. (2013). The relationship of core belief challenge, rumination, disclosure, and sociocultural elements to posttraumatic growth. *Psychological Trauma Theory, Research, Practice, and Policy, 5*(1), 50–53.

Lock, J. (2013, November 2). Dr. Julia Rowland—Cancer survivorship research in Europe and the United States. *Global Oncology,* 1–7.

López-Gómez, M., Malmierca, E., de Górgolas, M., & Casado, E. (2013). Cancer in developing countries: The next most preventable pandemic. The global problem of cancer. *Critical Reviews in Oncology/Hematology, 88*(1), 117–122. doi:10.1016/j.critrevonc.2013.03.011

Magill, L. (2010). Music therapy. In J. C. Holland, W. S. Breitbart, P. B. Jacobsen, M. S. Lederberg, M. J. Loscalzo, & R. McCorkle (Eds.), *Psycho-oncology,* (2nd ed., pp. 425–428). New York, NY: Oxford University Press.

Marcus, A. D. (2004, March 24). Debate heats up on defining a cancer survivor. *Wall Street Journal, Eastern edition,* p. D4.

McCorkle, R., Ercolano, E., Lazenby, M., Schulman-Green, D., Schilling, L. S., Lorig, K., & Wagner, E. H. (2011). Self-management: Enabling and empowering patients living with cancer as a chronic illness. *CA: A Cancer Journal for Clinicians, 61*(1), 50–62.

McDougal Miller, D. (2010). Music therapy in adult cancer care: Across the cancer continuum. In D. Hanson-Abromeit & C. Colwell (Eds.), *Medical music therapy for adults in hospital settings* (pp. 284–306). Silver Spring, MD: American Music Therapy Association.

McDougal Miller, D., & O'Callaghan, C. (2010). Cancer care. In D. Hanson-Abromeit & C. Colwell (Eds.), *Medical music therapy for adults in hospital settings* (pp. 217–283). Silver Spring, MD: American Music Therapy Association.

Miller, K. D. (2010). *Medical and psychosocial care of the cancer survivor.* Sudbury, MA: Jones and Bartlett.

Mukherjee, S. (2010). *The emperor of all maladies: A biography of cancer.* New York, NY: Scribner.

Mullan, F. (1985). Seasons of survival: Reflections of a physician with cancer. *New England Journal of Medicine, 313*(4), 270–273.

National Alliance for Caregiving. (2009). *Caregiving in the U.S.* Retrieved from http://www.caregiving.org/data/Caregiving_in_the_US_2009_full_report.pdf

National Coalition for Cancer Survivorship. (2014). *NCCS Mission.* Retrieved from http://www.canceradvocacy.org/about-us/our-mission/

National Hospice and Palliative Care Organization. (2014.) *How does hospice care work?* Retrieved from http://www.nhpco.org/about/hospice-care

Northouse, L., Williams, A., Given, B., & McCorkle, R. (2012). Psychosocial care for family caregivers of patients with cancer. *Journal of Clinical Oncology, 30*(11), 1227–1234. doi:10.1200/JCO.2011.39.5798

Pandey, M., Singh, S. P., Behere, P. B., Roy, S. K., Singh, S., & Shukla, V. K. (2000). Quality of life in patients with early and advanced carcinoma of the breast. *European Journal of Surgical Oncology, 26,* 20–24.

Parkes, C. M. (1971). Psycho-social transitions: A field for study. *Social Science and Medicine, 5,* 101–115.

Rowland, J. H. (2007). Survivorship research: Past, present, and future. In P. Ganz (Ed.), *Cancer survivorship today and tomorrow* (pp. 28–42). New York, NY: Springer.

Rowland, J. H., Kent, E. E., Forsythe, L. P., Loge, J. H., Hjorth, L., Glaser, A., ... & Fosså, S. D. (2013). Cancer survivorship research in Europe and the United States: Where have we been, where are we going, and what can we learn from each other? *Cancer, 119*(Suppl. 11), 2094–2108. doi:10.1002/cncr.28060

Spingarn, N. D. (1999). *The new cancer survivors: Living with grace, fighting with spirit.* Baltimore, MD: Johns Hopkins University Press.

Stanton, A. L. (2010). Positive consequences of the experience of cancer: Perceptions of growth and meaning. In J. C. Holland, W. S. Breitbart, P. B. Jacobsen, M. S. Lederberg, M. J. Loscalzo, & R. McCorkle (Eds.), *Psycho-oncology,* (2nd ed., pp. 547–550). New York, NY: Oxford University Press.

Strada, E. A., & Sourkes, B. M. (2010). Principles of psychotherapy. In J. C. Holland, W. S. Breitbart, P. B. Jacobsen, M. S. Lederberg, M. J. Loscalzo, & R. McCorkle (Eds.), *Psycho-oncology,* (2nd ed., pp. 397–401). New York, NY: Oxford University Press.

Sulik, G. A. (2011). *Pink ribbon blues: How breast cancer culture undermines women's health.* New York, NY: Oxford University Press.

Surbone, A., Baider, L., Weitzman, T. S., Brames, M. J., Rittenberg, C. N., & Johnson, J. (2010). Psychosocial care for patients and their families is integral to supportive care in cancer: MASCC position statement. *Supportive Care in Cancer, 18*(2), 255–263. doi:10.1007/s00520-009-0693-4

Tedeschi, R. G., & Calhoun, L. G. (2004). Posttraumatic growth: Conceptual foundations and empirical evidence. *Psychological Inquiry, 15*(1), 1–8.

Tralongo, P., Annunziata, M. A., Santoro, A., Tirelli, U., & Surbone, A. (2013). Beyond semantics: The need to better categorize patients with cancer. *Journal of Clinical Oncology, 31*(20), 2637–2638. doi:10.1200/JCO.2013.50.0850

Twombly, R. (2004). What's in a name: Who is a cancer survivor? *Journal of the National Cancer Institute, 96*(19), 1414–1415. doi:10.1093/jnci/96.19.1414

Chapter 16
THE CULTURE OF DISABILITY

Marcia Humpal

Introduction

Looking back, I do not remember having any friends who had disabilities. In fact, there were no children with disabilities in my school. The only child with a "difference" was an extremely bright boy who had a cleft lip and palate. He would later have surgery to correct this, but I'm afraid he endured many stares and hurtful comments prior to that surgery. No one talked about disabilities in those days before laws made education a right. In fact, education was not even an option. In high school, I volunteered at a swimming program one summer, helping teenagers from a nearby "school for special children" change into swimwear prior to entering the pool. That was my very first personal encounter with anyone with intellectual limitations. I don't recall being shocked or saddened by this experience. Perhaps this was an early indication that I would find my life's passion by working with people with disabilities.

I left my small hometown in Ohio and went on to college at a conservatory of music near a large city. I received my music education degree and took a job as an elementary general music teacher in a nearby suburb. My classes were typical of the times (this was back in 1970): 35 children per room; few behavior problems; students who were interested in various activities, anxious to please, and, all in all, very similar to each other in all ways. However, I also was expected to teach two "special classes," the EMRs and the NHs. I had no idea what those letters stood for and even less of an idea of what the children were like, for I never saw them in the halls or anywhere in the school, for that matter. Those classes even ate lunch alone in their classrooms. I later learned the letter stood for Educable Mentally Retarded, and Neurologically Handicapped. These classes were not yet required by law, and, actually, this school district was somewhat ahead of the times for making them available. I had no experience teaching music to children with disabilities (or "handicaps," as they were called in those days). I just jumped in and learned by trial and error. We made music together, and it was joyful. Over the years, these classes became some of my favorite assignments. After five years, I stepped down from teaching and started a family.

Thoughts of those "special" children were never far from my mind, however. When my alma mater established a new equivalency program in music therapy, I decided to explore this relatively new field. I have said several times that this was the best career decision of my life. I went to classes on weekends, taking one course at a time. When my youngest child entered first grade, my course requirements were finished and it was time for me to intern. I luckily ended up in a developmental center for toddlers through age 21. I learned so much from the

amazing interdisciplinary teams and of course from my internship director. Fast-forward ahead, through a job as a music therapist at a group home for adults, and then as a consultant at a city school district with adolescent boys with behavior challenges. I then received a call that another school like the one where I interned was hiring. Thus began almost 30 years as a music therapist, working with individuals with disabilities.

Through those years, I have witnessed many changes. Service delivery changed from direct service to consultation, from individual to group, and then to community-based instruction. The focus changed from pre-academic to functional curriculum, and on to embracing the doctrine of self-determination for our older students. Terminology changed, as did definitions. Special education focused on where service was delivered. As times changed, so did the public's perception of our students. I proudly took my handbell choirs into the community; the students performed to rave reviews. Our Sing and Sign Choir traveled to local public schools for shared experiences with their choirs. Gradually, mainstreaming, then inclusion, became the norm. Developmental centers closed and the public schools educated all students in the same buildings. The focus of my agency switched to early childhood, and my new passion became early intervention and using music with children of all abilities, working along with their families.

It has been an amazing experience being part of all the changes that have evolved for those with disabilities. My experiences are but a fraction of what is the Culture of Disability. I hope that the information that follows can give a brief overview that illuminates the background and complex issues of this unique culture.

General Overview

The term "disability" has been defined in numerous ways and from a wide variety of perspectives. Often official definitions reflect policies and organizational requirements of governments, institutions, and professionals who provide services to those with disabilities (Goodley, 2011). The *2008 Amendments to the Americans with Disabilities Act (ADA)* defines and describes terminology surrounding the word in great detail, initially stating, "The term 'disability' means, with respect to an individual ... a physical or mental impairment that substantially limits one or more major life activities of such individual ..." (U.S. Equal Employment Opportunity Commission, 2008).

Disabilities can manifest prior to or at birth, through accidents or elements in the environment, or as a product of illness or aging. Disabilities can affect anyone and may occur at any point throughout our lives. Disabilities may be described by what aspect of the individual is affected (e.g., hearing, vision, movement, thinking, remembering, learning, communicating, mental health, socialization) or by ways that hinder full participation in society (e.g., health, body structure, body function, limitations, restrictions) (Centers for Disease Control and Prevention, 2012).

At some point in our lives, each of us may be temporarily or permanently disabled, for disability actually is part of the human condition. Unless we die suddenly, we will eventually cease to be "able-bodied" in some way (Goodley, 2011; Taormina-Weiss, 2011; Wendell, 2008).

The World Health Organization (WHO) and the World Bank estimated that as of 2011, there are now over one billion people with disabilities in the world, making this subgroup the largest minority group on earth. The numbers continue to grow, especially in nations where adequate food, transportation, health care, rehabilitation services, communication technology, and access to basic information do not exist and where stigma impacts the level of discrimination (Goodley, 2011; Taormina-Weis, 2011). In the United States, there is a steady growth in the number of people with disabilities due in part to increased the incidence of autism spectrum disorder and attention deficit disorder, as well as lifestyle factors that lead to specific debilitating conditions (e.g., obesity, diabetes, heart disease, and cancer). Unfortunately, military action across the globe, paired with improved medical interventions, have yielded many more cases of survivors with catastrophic physical injuries (e.g., traumatic brain injury, loss of body parts, and spinal cord injury) as well as related mental health concerns (e.g., posttraumatic stress and substance addictions) (G. Corey, Schneider-Corey, C. Corey, & Callanan, 2015).

The ways in which one may be disabled vary by specific type as well as by level of severity. In fact, some disabilities may be hidden or difficult to recognize or understand. The lives of those with disabilities are indelibly entwined with and influenced by those others who offer support and provide care and services that are critical to their survival and quality of life; the institutions, agencies, and governments, plus the social, cultural, and political positions of these "others," also hold much influence (Goodley, 2011; Johnson, 2008; Lovern, 2008). Are those with disabilities actually part of a specific culture? If so, for the above reasons, the Culture of Disability is quite unique. Furthermore, this specific disability culture would be highly influenced by, and would overlap with, other cultures to which its members belong.

The attitudes, core values, strengths, and skills of the persons with disabilities must be central to this discussion. Psychologist Carol Gill (2009) suggests that there is reason to believe that a distinct Disability Culture does exist, noting that very many individuals with disabilities share a similar unified worldview that has at its core an acceptance of human differences; an orientation toward interdependence and acceptance of helping as part of life; a tolerance of living with the unknown and less-than-ideal outcomes; the ability to laugh at oneself (i.e., "disability humor"); the skill to manage several

layers of problems, systems, people, and technology; a sophisticated view of the future, recognizing various aspects and obstacles that will influence planning and outcomes; the ability to sort through contradictory and implied social messages; and a creative, flexible, and adaptive approach to tasks (based on the necessity of dealing with limited resources and driven by untraditional modes of operating within society).

Worldview

Those with disabilities are viewed differently in different areas of the world, and factors pertaining to such aspects as governments, economy, health care, and the availability of education opportunities influence what worldviews various cultures hold. In many parts of the world, countries are simply unable to respond to the many needs of people with disabilities. Resources are few. Therefore, those who are less able experience higher rates of poverty, lower educational achievements, poorer health, and fewer economic opportunities. The WHO's report in 2011 also notes that in low-income nations, people with disabilities are 50% more likely to experience catastrophic health expenditures yet have only half the rate of employment opportunities of their peers without disabilities (Goodley, 2011; Taormina-Weiss, 2011).

Including multiple worldviews is necessary for studying the Culture of Disability. Those with disabilities are a culture within a culture; they are products of the influences that are embedded in the worldviews of those who surround them (Lovern, 2008).

Various dominant perspectives color worldviews of disabilities. A disability may be viewed as an impairment that is a defect caused by moral lapse or sin, resulting in shame for the family as well as for the individual with the disability. The person may be seen as less than human and may serve as a constant reminder of a previous sin or lapse. This perspective of a disability as a moral condition is the oldest of all disability models and remains the most prevalent worldwide. Finding meaning and purpose in "affliction" may result in a sense of spiritual intervention and acceptance.

Disputing the idea of "moral condition," the perspective of disability as a medical condition almost merges individuals with their medical problem (e.g., "Down Syndrome child"), describing them clinically and offering labels as explanations. Thus the person may be viewed as a defective product that must conform to the norms of society to be accepted. This worldview is prevalent in wealthier countries. It endorses obtaining services from trained professionals who will work for a cure, rehabilitation, or adjustment. It may heavily involve outsiders rather than the person with the disability, resulting in paternalism and the promotion of benevolence (Goodley, 2011).

A universal view of disability is yet another perspective often acknowledged. This view stresses that levels of ability fall on a continuum; society should endorse policies and procedures that are universally compatible with the variations therein, assuring a great amount of flexibility to ensure that those at the lower end of the continuum will not be marginalized or excluded. This progressive approach stresses acceptance and equal access and focuses less on normalization, thereby indicating that each person is valued as created (Guzman & Balcazar, 2010; Staeger-Wilson, 2010).

Studies surrounding the topic of disability often go beyond looking at causal themes and instead address various theoretical models and perspectives that are products of national contexts and historical times. These models often represent sociopolitical, structural, and economic discrimination against those with disabilities and came about as a product of the Disabled People's Movement.

The *Social Barriers Approach* (prominent in Great Britain) examines how socially constructed barriers have added limitations or actually hindered people due to a perception that they were disabled. It offfers a distinction between social barriers (which can be changed) and impairment (which cannot be changed).

The *Minority Model* (influenced by civil rights movements of various minorities in the United States) is grounded in the positive acceptance of one's disabled self and views those with disabilities as a distinct minority group that has been devalued and offered only limited societal opportunities. It is activist in nature and works toward systematic change, accessibility, and so forth.

In the *Cultural Model* (most often seen in the United States and Canada), disabilities are seen as a distinct part of societal culture and often are analyzed in books, films, and so on and used as metaphors for reflecting on deeper issues. It is a product of the humanities and social sciences.

The *Relational Model* (predominant in Nordic countries) lauds the positive influences of professionals and services in the lives of those with disabilities. It is influenced by ideas of normalization, welfare, self-advocacy, and participation in the community as a whole (Goodley, 2011).

In other countries as well as in minority cultures, a more eclectic approach to disability studies and the establishment of a culture of disability have become more and more obvious. The World Health Organization (2001) has noted that models cannot stand alone; some aspects of a person's disability are internal yet some are external—therefore, a *biopsychosocial* model might better synthesize the integration of each. Environmental, socioeconomic, sociocultural, and historical factors highly influence attitudes and policies toward and within the specific Culture of Disability (Goodley, 2011; Johnson, 2008). Expanded dialogue and examination of multiple worldviews are opening avenues for discussions that apply to social construction in general (Lovern, 2008) and increasingly focus on an *affirmative* model that validates lives and experiences (Rickson, 2014).

So many factors and opinions surround and influence the Culture of Disability that it is easy to become bogged down by philosophy or to resort to a "quick fix" mentality. We must not forget the voices of those with disabilities, however. Whereas a *biomedical* model might address mainly the

disability per se, a *health and wellness model* (i.e., one that is more holistic and comes from a psychosocial approach) would first look to the client's unique abilities as well as how he or she perceives the disability to hinder functioning in daily life (G. Corey et al., 2015).

Cultures also are multifaceted and unique to each individual. Nevertheless, it must be noted that studies implemented in and relevant to highly industrialized parts of the world may have limited value on the other parts of the globe (Goodley, 2011; Wendell, 1996).

Historical Information

Background

The Culture of Disability in the United States has evolved through several stages and continues to emerge as a culture unto itself. Its history has been greatly influenced by countless individuals and agencies, as well as by forces within the governmental structure of our country. While exact information varies according to the sources gathering data and the defining aspects of the term, the U.S. Census Bureau reported that in 2010 over 56.7 million people in the United States had at least one disability; this represents around 18.7% of the total population (Brault, 2012).

Popular Myths

Throughout history, society's views on those with disabilities have been quite varied. Often these individuals were kept hidden, considered a source of shame, viewed with disgust, or ridiculed. Those with disabilities have been pitied as well as ignored, considered less than human and without value. Disability awareness campaigns and more open attitudes toward differences have helped to dissolve many of the popular myths surrounding disability.

More and more people are aware of person-first language, stressing the person rather than a category. Others feel strongly that this approach negates focusing on an inherent part of the individual's identity. Regardless of semantic and philosophical differences, society in general has begun to recognize and laud the accomplishments of those who have succeeded both within the culture of disability and in the mainstream (think of more frequent use of sign interpreters, paraplegic athletes who take part in marathons, or the phenomenal accomplishments of Stephen Hawking, a physicist with motor neuron disease spotlighted in the award-winning movie *The Theory of Everything*).

Still, discrimination and erroneous suppositions continue to exist. To this day, derogatory labels pepper our casual vocabulary and are used not necessarily to taunt but to insult those we wish to denigrate (e.g., "You're acting like a *retard!*"). While some hide behind the anonymity of social media to bully and jokingly insult via the use of this derogatory term, Special Olympics 2008 opted to utilize online messages and tweets to launch its *Spread the Word to End the Word* campaign. As of April, 2015, over 560,000 people had pledged support. Yet those who are disabled by age or conditions that may not be visible are often considered less valued citizens, held at a distance, totally ignored, or judged only by outward appearances. We have come a long way, but we also have a long way to go.

U.S. Historical Milestones

Throughout the history of the United States, people have advocated for the rights of those with disabilities. In fact, at our country's very inception, Stephen Hopkins, a man with cerebral palsy who was one of the signers of the Declaration of Independence, noted that "my hands may tremble, my heart does not."

The first school for children with disabilities in the Western Hemisphere was The American School for the Deaf (also known as The American Asylum for the Education and Instruction of the Deaf and Dumb), founded by Thomas Gallaudet in 1817 in Hartford, Connecticut. In 1818, the first patient was admitted to the Charlestown branch of the Massachusetts General Hospital, later named the McLean Asylum for the Insane. While The Perkins School for the Blind was established in 1832 in Boston, educational opportunities for individuals with other disabilities were extremely limited during this time period. Expanding into the area of employment, the Perkins institution developed the first "sheltered workshop" for the blind in 1849.

In 1841, Dorothea Dix began working with people with disabilities who were incarcerated or living in poor houses. In 1848, the first residential institution for people with mental retardation was established in Boston. For over a century, this type of facility would house hundreds of thousands of children and adults with developmental disabilities, often for their entire lifetimes.

Dr. Simon Pollak introduced the use of Braille at the Missouri School for the Blind in 1860. In that same year, the *Gallaudet Guide and Deaf-Mutes' Companion* was first published; it was the first publication in America for readers who had disabilities. In 1869, the first wheelchair patent was registered.

A dark chapter in the disability rights movement began in England in 1883 with the onset of the eugenics movement, a pseudoscience aimed at "improving the stock" of humanity by preventing "undesirables" (e.g., those with disabilities, members of targeted religions, or races) from having children. The movement spread to the United States, where laws were passed which led to forced sterilization and prevention of immigration for those with disabilities. As late as 1979, some states allowed sterilization against a person's will.

The U.S. Army formed its Veterans Reserve Corps in 1862; its members later joined the Freedman's Bureau and provided assistance to recently emancipated slaves. At the urging of progressive activists, the government again became involved in medically disabling issues during the years 1890–1920 by creating Worker's Compensation programs. In 1918, the

Veterans Vocational Rehabilitation Act ushered in programs for soldiers, and in 1920, the Fess-Smith Civilian Vocational Rehabilitation Act created a similar program for civilians.

Rights for those with mental illness were nonexistent in the 1800s. In the early 1900s, Clifford Beers was institutionalized for mental illness. He learned firsthand of the deficiencies in care as well as the cruel and inhumane treatment people with mental illnesses received, witnessing and experiencing horrific abuse at the hands of his caretakers. Once, he was strait-jacketed. for 21 days. Upon his release, Beers published his autobiography, *A Mind That Found Itself*, in 1908. In 1909, Beers, philosopher William James, and psychiatrist Adolf Meyer created the National Committee for Mental Hygiene, later the National Mental Health Association and what is now Mental Health America. Not until 1946 did the National Mental Health Act, which created the National Institute of Mental Health, pass into law.

The American Foundation for the Blind was founded in 1921, and one of its principle advocates and fund-raisers was Helen Keller, whose life story became the subject of much positive publicity and inspiration. In 1927, the Warm Springs Foundation was established in part by Franklin Roosevelt. It became a model rehabilitation and peer-counseling program for polio survivors.

The Social Security Act was passed in 1935. This opened the door for federal benefits and state grants for the elderly and children with disabilities. Also in this year, 300 members of the League for the Physically Handicapped staged a nine-day sit-in at the Home Relief Bureau of New York City, protesting that their requests for employment with the Works Progress Administration (WPA) had been stamped "PH" (physically handicapped). They ultimately helped secure several thousand jobs across the country. The League of the Physically Handicapped was recognized as the first organization of people with disabilities established by people with disabilities.

In 1943, the Vocational Rehabilitation Amendments added physical rehabilitation to the list of approved health care services. By 1944, rehabilitation medicine had become a new medical specialty. Increased advocacy efforts came to the foreground with the establishment of the Cerebral Palsy Society of New York and the National Mental Health Foundation in 1946. The latter organization led the movement to expose deplorable conditions in mental institutions.

The 1950s were years of change. Parents of children with disabilities joined forces and established several focus agencies to advocate for the rights of their children. The U.S. Supreme Court ruled that separate schools are unconstitutional, ushering in the Civil Rights Movement. The initial Social Security Disability Insurance program came into being.

Organized sporting opportunities were limited until 1949; at that time, the first Wheelchair Basketball Tournament was held in Illinois. In 1960, the first international Paralympic Games took place. In 1968, the first International Special Olympics were inaugurated at Soldier Field in Chicago, Illinois.

In 1963, President Kennedy called for a massive reduction

of residential institutions and stressed the need for individuals therein to be returned to the community with an emphasis on rehabilitation. Shortly thereafter, Congress passed the Community Mental Health Centers Act, authorizing construction grants for community mental health centers. Inclusion of mandated mental health services in Medicare became law in 1966.

The Autism Society of America was founded in 1965. President Johnson, in 1966, established the President's Committee on Mental Retardation. In 1967, the National Theatre of the Deaf was founded. The Architectural Barriers Act was passed in 1968, ensuring accessibility to those with physical disabilities. This act is considered to be the first piece of federal disability rights legislation.

While public schools had been in existence since the early 1900s, educational opportunities for children with special needs were extremely limited until the 1970s. Prior to this time, the majority of such children were educated in asylums or residential or separate settings and had little or no contact with children in general education settings. Parents and families fought long and hard for public education for their children. By 1975, approximately half of all children with disabilities were receiving free, appropriate education. This changed with the passage of P.L. 94-142, the *Education for All Handicapped Children Act*. By the 1980s, very young children who were at risk for developmental delay were being recognized as being in need of intervention, and they were included in federal mandates. Throughout the 1990s and into the early years of the next century, terms such as *least restrictive environment, mainstreaming, integration, full inclusion, related services, Adaptive Learning Environments, Regular Education Initiatives,* and *Due Process* became part of the common language in regular and special education circles. Isolation was no longer acceptable; the rights of all children to be educated and take part in experiences within the community were becoming ingrained.

Residential options for those with disabilities also were extremely rare prior to the 1970s. Upon the birth of a baby with obvious disabilities, parents were strongly urged to consider institutionalizing the child. Many struggled with the heartbreak and helplessness of not being able to care for their children or felt the stigma of abandonment. Even if families opted to initially raise their child at home, as the child grew and his or her needs became more significant, often no option other than asylums or institutional settings were available. Furthermore, these families were often cut off from friends and other family members if they decided to keep their children at home.

The 1960s set forth the disability rights movement , which led to the independent living movement (i.e., individuals themselves are the best experts on their own needs). In 1978, Staten Island's Willowbrook State School, an institution notorious for horrible conditions, finally closed after an eight-year battle by advocates and parents. Patients were moved to community-based settings, forever changing ideas about care for people with developmental disabilities. In the years that followed, various government and private agencies began opening group residential facilities that were located within the community. In 1989, Mental Health America released its *Report of the Invisible Children Project*, which revealed the gross neglect and over-institutionalization of children with emotional disorders in the United States.

The Fair Housing Amendments Act of 1988 expanded the Civil Rights Act of 1968 to require that a certain number of accessible housing units be created in all new multifamily housing. The act covers both public and private homes and not only those in receipt of federal funding. In 1999, the U.S. Supreme Court ruled that that unnecessary institutionalization of people with disabilities constitutes discrimination and violates the Americans with Disabilities Act, that individuals have a right to receive benefits in the "most integrated setting appropriate to their needs," and that failure to find community-based placements for qualifying people with disabilities is illegal discrimination. In addition to advances in residential matters, more community-based employment opportunities became available during this time period, offering specially trained job coaches for teaching essential skills, giving support, and monitoring job performance.

Numerous other landmark events, laws, and movements played major roles in shaping the Culture of Disability. In 1987, the U.S. Supreme Court established that people with infectious diseases cannot be fired from their jobs (a landmark precedent for those with HIV, etc.). Signed into law in 1990, the *Americans with Disabilities Act* required reasonable accommodations within businesses and modifications to ensure public access for persons with disabilities; access to public transportation was mandated. In 1990, the *Education for All Handicapped Children Act* was amended and renamed the *Individuals with Disabilities Education Act* (IDEA).

Today. people with disabilities are afforded better conditions and treatment, as well as a visible and viable place within their community. However, for those with significant needs or low-incidence diagnoses, few options exist. Long waiting lists for group home placement, not enough staff to provide adequate personal care, lack of funding, and aging or infirm caregivers (or no caregivers) are but a few of the road blocks that heavily influence the quality of life for those within the Culture of Disability.

For families and loved ones, these dilemmas become lifelong burdens that offer no concrete answers or assurances for good future outcomes. Residential placement issues and policy changes may even create more problems than solutions for the very people they are intended to protect and for whom they supposedly advocate. Such challenges are succinctly summarized in an open social media post by a guardian of an elderly brother with disabilities:

> Over fifty years ago, my mother and father fought
> for services for my brother and finally they found a
> place that met his needs. They are both deceased
> now and here I am, their daughter, again fighting for

appropriate services for him. Look at this picture of him smiling on a picnic bench at his residential facility. The state wants to shut it and says he can move to a group home … "when there is an opening." He has lived in his current place almost all his life, and all his friends are there. Who will explain to him why his life will be torn asunder and that he will never see them or the caregivers who understand him? Who can help me care for him until he gets placed? Who will really advocate for his needs when I am gone?

(Information for the above section was taken from Adamek & Darrow, 2010; Disabled World News, 2012; Mental Health America, 2015; National Consortium on Leadership and Disability for Youth, 2007; University of California, Berkeley, 2004a, 2004b; Wilson, 2002.)

Diversity Within the Culture

Not only are there extensive variations in the types and levels of the severity of disabilities, but also there are numerous diverse cultures to which those with disabilities belong. The World Health Organization (2001) attempted to provide language for the international community that would look beyond a purely medical or biological viewpoint and would also consider other critical aspects of disability. By organizing descriptions in such a way, the impact of the environment and other contextual factors on the functioning of an individual or a population may be considered, analyzed, and recorded. The *International Classification of Functioning, Disability, and Health (ICF)* was endorsed by all 191 WHO member states in the 54th World Health Assembly and evolved into the international standard to describe and measure health and disability, thereby providing a universally applicable framework and language to advance the development of policies and services to meet the needs of people with disabilities.

The *ICF* is organized into two lists of classifications. The first classification area is *functioning* (referring to body functions, activities, and participation). The second classification describes *disability,* an umbrella term for impairments, activity limitations, and restrictions that limit participation. Environmental factors that limit health and access and possibly create barriers that limit individuals from full participation in society are covered in both lists. The *ICF* recognizes that all may experience some degree of disability in their life through a change in health or environment; therefore, disability is a universal human experience and is not restricted to a small segment of the population.

Statistics continue to evolve regarding the various aspects and descriptors of individuals who have disabilities as well as of the disabilities themselves. Readers may check out the *Disability Statistics Compendium* (Houtenville & Ruiz, 2011), an extensive resource that gives a comprehensive view of disability statistics and trends, by accessing the following link: http://www.aapd.com/resources/publications/disability-compendium-2011.pdf.

Gender Differences

Each gender has unique characteristics, the most specific being different a chromosomal makeup. Direct differences result from the workings of the Y-chromosome (e.g., reproduction), while indirect differences are generally those that vary across individuals as quantified by empirical data and statistical analysis and tend to follow a range of normal distribution (e.g., men are usually stronger than women). However, indirect differences are indicative only of a mean, and it is not unusual for individual cases to fall outside of the mean (e.g., the average man is taller than the average woman, but some women are taller than some men). The terms *sex* and *gender,* when referring to differences, may take on a multilayered meaning. In many circles, sex differences are seen as those being mainly biological, whereas gender differences are those that mainly are caused by social conditions, cultural and religious beliefs, and norms regarding men and women (Buvinić, Medici, Fernández, & Torres, 2006). Some forms of disease and disabilities appear to be more gender-based. Duchene muscular dystrophy is most often seen in males. Recent studies indicate that boys are more prone to develop learning disabilities than girls. Researchers are discovering that the location of specific genes on X-chromosomes may be a major contributing factor (Wellcome Trust, 2009).

It appears that in most cultures worldwide, women with disabilities experience more discrimination than males who are disabled. Meekosha (2005) reports that in the Western industrial world, gendered studies of disability indicate that there are more women than men living with disabilities. Partly because of the differences in XX- and XY-chromosomes, female babies tend to be stronger and thus survive a chromosomal deficiency more often than males. In addition, the number may reflect the longer life span that is typical of women; as we age, more disabling conditions appear. Women with disabilities are more likely to live in poverty, attain lower educational opportunities, and earn less than their male counterparts. In their private lives, women with disabilities are more likely to be divorced and less likely to marry and may experience a higher rate of sexual violence. In the developing world, women with disabilities are struck more deeply by poverty due to patriarchal property ownership structures. They receive less access to aid and education and lack support when sexually abused or if their disabilities are the result of war or atrocities.

Those whose appearances differ from society's norms also face discrimination due to the overemphasis on beauty and youth; this is especially true for females. Films and television portray ever-present examples of the "perfect" body; stereotypes abound. Women with physical disabilities reportedly react in one of two ways to society's expectations of the ideal female body: via either emotional responses or stigma management (Taub, Fanflik, & McLorg, 2003). For males, a cultural obsession with achievement and winning can present additional barriers for those with disabilities. Anything less is considered weak and indicates failure. For both men and women, especially for those who have no control over their physical limitations, development of a positive self-concept may be a huge undertaking and adds yet another obstacle to their well-being.

Acculturation and Assimilation

Throughout history and across countries and cultures, the issue of how to assimilate those with disabilities into the mainstream culture has been the subject of much debate and speculation. As mentioned previously, there are major philosophical differences surrounding this question; worldviews, theoretical models, and perspectives have been examined in previous parts of this chapter.

Late in the last century, the Disability Studies movement began, challenging the view of disability as a deficit or defect to be addressed by service providers. While recognizing that medical research and intervention can be useful, Disability Studies focus mainly on social, political, cultural, and economic factors that define disability. Disability Studies encourage individuals to determine personal and collective responses to differences and work to remove the stigma of disease or impairment (Society for Disabilities Studies, 2015). Indeed, individuals within specific, identified subcultures of the Culture of Disability actually prefer remaining apart from society at large. Such is the case of those in the Deaf culture, who espouse and take pride in the values of their culture identity, use American Sign Language, and describe themselves as Deaf (with an uppercase D). Conversely, those who feel part of the hearing world tend to refer to themselves as deaf (with a lowercase d) or hard-of-hearing (Darrow, 2006). Likewise, those adhering to the neurodiversity model refer to themselves as Autistic, feeling that the descriptor is part of their innate identity; others want to be referred to as a person first (i.e., a person with ASD) and not by their disability. Silberman, author of the book *NeuroTribes* (2015), supports the neurodiversity movement and contends that those who self-identify as Autistic are part of a group that exhibits naturally occurring forms of cognitive differences. He advocates for a broader model for acceptance, understanding, and full participation in society for people who think differently.

Hadley (2014) elaborates that the advent of Disability Studies puts great importance on reclaiming language. Self-advocates refer to themselves not as people *with* a disability but rather include the disability category as an integral part of who they are or representative of a certain group that has set social and political experiences. Disability may be viewed not as a problem within an individual, but as an issue within our collective societal understanding of deviation from norms and lack of acceptance of any kind of human diversity. Regardless of defining terminology, the voices and preferences of those with whom we work must be listened to and respected.

In the United States, much progress has been made toward incorporating those with disabilities into mainstream society. The passage of laws such as the Americans with Disabilities Act and numerous provisions of laws pertaining to education protect their rights and have opened doors in employment and promoted greater access to the community. While higher education opportunities are now available, many of these institutions rely on the medical model of normalizing or accommodating the needs of the individual rather than making the environment more universally accessible. Some disability studies even postulate that we actually add to the stigma of disability by not approaching issues in a progressive and more universal perspective (Staeger-Wilson, 2010).

Recognizing that moving from late adolescence into adulthood is often a time of turmoil, significant change and limited options, the educational system has worked to ensure that this transitional process runs as smoothly as possible for those with special needs. Some colleges and universities are expanding their offerings to include training programs and avenues for community social and recreational experiences for those with disabilities. It is not unusual for these new options to be met with a sense of ambivalence by those for whom they have been cultivated. By layering in extra supports, these opportunities may address isolation and self-esteem issues which may develop when people age out of public school and are faced with unfamiliar settings and unknown expectations (Rickson, 2014). However, ultimately there comes a time when fewer external supports and services are available; then, ongoing family or caregiver support remains of prime importance in facilitating self-determination (Wehmeyer, 2014).

Laws and changing attitudes have improved the outlook for employment for those with disabilities, although workforce assimilation and challenges continue to exist. The Bureau of Labor Statistics (2014) reported that in 2013, 64% of those without a disability were employed, compared to 17.6% of those with disabilities. At all levels of education, persons with a disability were much less likely to be employed than their counterparts with no disability. Workers with a disability were more likely to be employed in production, transportation, and material-moving jobs and less likely to be in management positions or professional occupations. The jobless rate for those with a disability remained relatively stable, while the rate for the general populace declined. Employed persons with a disability were more likely to be self-employed.

Assimilation into the workforce is not always a realistic goal, especially for those with significantly challenging conditions. Budget concerns often guide policy, and many times those with the greatest needs are the ones who are left behind. The very regulations that push states to pull people out of institutions may also eliminate day workshops which may lose federal dollars if they are not community focused. When such settings or opportunities are not available or appropriate, what are the options for those whose needs are most definitely not being met?

Although international examples of projects that enable access to infrastructure, services, and jobs are encouraging, people with disabilities continue to be ostracized and discriminated against by many of the societies in which they live (Taormina-Weiss, 2011). Therefore, the United Nations directed the World Health Organization and the World Bank to develop a report that would provide a comprehensive description of issues pertaining to disability. This document is based on analysis of the best available scientific information and makes recommendations for action at both national and international levels. Published in 2011, the recommendations of the report are expected to remain in place until 2021 (World Health Organization, 2011). The full report may be viewed at http://whqlibdoc.who.int/publications/2011/9789240685215_eng.pdf.

Microaggression and Oppression

Disability Rights Movement

Within the Culture of Disability, the disability rights movement has been a vital force for recognition and acceptance of individuals within its ranks. The movement historically asserts that people with disabilities are first and foremost individuals with inalienable rights and that these rights must be secured through collective political action.

The negative connotation of words can usher in highly charged debate. Labels are constantly changing; what was once common usage may eventually become offensive. Such is the case with adequately defining terms that relate to individuals and upon which funding for services is often tied. Various organizations and also funding agencies over the years have attempted to succinctly and adequately describe and define the terms *disability* and *impairment*. The World Health Organization (2011) considers *impairment* to be a body function or structure problem, whereas *disability* refers to an umbrella term, one that covers impairments, activity limitations, and participation restrictions. Therefore, *disability* is a complex terms that requires interventions to remove both environmental and social barriers, reflecting the interaction between the features of one's body and the society in which one lives. The Social Security Administration's (2015) definition of *disability* is "… the inability to engage in any substantial gainful activity by reason of any medically determinable physical or mental impairment(s) which can be expected to result in death or which has lasted or can be expected to last for a continuous period of not less than 12 months" and furthermore describes *impairment* as a condition that "… results from anatomical, physiological, or psychological abnormalities which can be shown by medically acceptable clinical and laboratory diagnostic techniques."

The Disabled People's International (DPI) contends that beyond the stated descriptions, there is a major philosophical difference between the use of the terms "disability" and "impairment." They acknowledge *impairment* as a type of difference (e.g., biological, cognitive, sensory, or psycho-

logical) that is referenced within a medical context. *Disability* takes on a different context, one that is actually a social construct that implies a negative reaction to those differences and subsequently often yields social barriers (Goodley, 2011). The following vignettes (World Health Organization, 2011, Chapter 1, p. 2) may help to personalize these philosophical differences in terminology and give insight into the social barriers that prohibit many from the rights that should be basic for all:

Can you imagine that you're getting up in the morning with pain so severe that it disables you from even moving out from your bed? Can you imagine yourself having a pain which requires you to get assistance to do even very simple day-to-day activities? Can you imagine yourself being fired from your job because you are unable to perform simple job requirements? And finally, can you imagine that your little child is crying for a hug and you are unable to hug him due to the pain in your bones and joints? —*Nael*

My life revolves around my two beautiful children. They see me as "Mummy," not a person in a wheelchair, and do not judge me or our life. This is now changing as my efforts to be part of their life are limited by the physical access of schools, parks, and shops; the attitudes of other parents; and the reality of needing 8 hours of support a day with my personal care. … I cannot get into the houses of my children's friends and must wait outside for them to finish playing. I cannot get to all the classrooms at school, so I have not met many other parents. I can't get close to the playground in the middle of the park or help out at the sporting events my children want to be part of. Other parents see me as different, and I have had one parent not want my son to play with her son because I could not help with supervision in her inaccessible house. —*Samantha*

Near the start of the bus route, I climb on. I am one of the first passengers. People continue to embark on the bus. They look for a seat, gaze at my hearing aids, turn their glance quickly, and continue walking by. Only when people with disabilities will really be part of the society, will be educated in every kindergarten and any school with personal assistance, will live in the community and not in different institutions, will work in all places and in any position with accessible means, and will have full accessibility to the public sphere, only then will people feel comfortable to sit next to us on the bus. —*Ahiya*

Overlapping Cultures: The Additive Model of Oppression

Regardless of semantics or philosophical stances, those who are part of the Culture of Disability are also part of other cultures to which they belong, and often how they are treated depends on views held by the dominant culture. If persons with disabilities are part of an additional minority culture, they may be subjected to additional layers of discrimination or neglect, especially if diversity in worldview is not honored (Lovern, 2008). It is interesting to note that in our own country, cross-disability rights activism emerged in the 1960s, urged on by the African-American Civil Rights and Women's Rights movements (University of California, Berkeley, 2004a).

Others directly associated with persons with disabilities may even add to their feelings of inadequacy or being "less able." For instance, parents and families may be more protective than with their other children or may shy away from discussing certain topics with the person with disabilities. Parents may have less time for siblings who are developing typically or may expect them to take on responsibilities at too early an age, causing resentment or jealousy. On the other hand, siblings may become extremely caring, sensitive advocates whose own lives and careers are shaped by recognizing the struggles that accompany dealing with disabling conditions. Family attitudes and actions fall on a spectrum ranging from those who isolate their child to those who treat their children equally, totally accepting everyone as they are. Having a family member with a disability is not a one-dimensional issue; in fact, it is life-changing for everyone and affects all aspects of family life and interactions with friends, coworkers, and society in general (Humpal, 2012). No prototypical model exists for disability within the family unit; family structure seems to be widely variable and often depends on various stressors and demographics (e.g., economic hardship, single parent households, lack of respite care, or multiple members with a disability) (Fujiura, 2014). Stress, as well as resilience, characterizes these families (Farrell & Krahn, 2014).

Paid professions may be perceived as being friendly only because they are paid to be. Being warm and understanding with our clients is a natural trait of music therapists. We may accompany clients into the community for recreational events, take part in sharing music within the family setting, or, through musical experiences, be privy to our clients' deepest thoughts, loves, fears, and dreams. Ethically, our relationships are those of therapist/client, but are we also friends? If we put ourselves in our client's place, what would we expect? This dilemma presents a blurred line that is difficult to navigate, for there are distinct attitudinal differences between those with and without disabilities. The ways we view and therefore provide treatment for those with disabilities are influenced by such factors as our sociocultural conditioning, our childhood influences, and our possible anxiety and aversion to hidden as well as visible variations

from that which is considered "normal." As therapists, we must know ourselves and develop a sensitivity to the differences in our backgrounds and experiences. Advocating for and empowering our clients to achieve a higher level of independence may cultivate a healthy collaborative relationship, although some in the disability community contend that assuming an advocate role can lead to increased dependence upon the therapist (Corey et al., 2015).

> The random assignment of therapists to clients may take away a basic part of decision-making. The client selected her own self-care aides; they considered it an honor to work with her. She demanded respect, noting that without this, treatment could become humiliating. Retaining her dignity was paramount to our working relationship, and she taught us all that we were extensions of those with whom we work. This was not just a "job, but an intimate partnership of mutual giving, learning, and growth." (Hadley, 2014, p. 2)

Legal requirements designed to make the lives of people with disabilities easier may sometimes add to a feeling of oppression; those in the mainstream of society may be resentful of required accommodations or perceived unfair special treatment afforded to those with disabilities. Teachers who are not prepared or trained to make modifications to their curriculum or physical space or who have overcrowded classes may resent the student with special needs because he or she represents additional work. A letter to the editor in the local paper is written by a disgruntled father who resents more money being allocated to those with intellectual disabilities while his children have to pay to play sports because of limited tax dollars. The tired mother who must take four children with her after a long day of work grumbles about having to park far away from the grocery store entrance when a handicap parking space sits empty.

The law may be the law, but it may not be able to be implemented in the way that was intended. The following anecdote illustrates a parent's frustration with this dilemma:

> A parent of a child who was part of a small music therapy group lamented the following concerns to other parents, "By law, my son is entitled to special services and modifications as listed on his IEP. The inclusion classroom he's in doesn't meet his needs; he is falling further and further behind in reading, but is three grade levels ahead of his classmates in math. The special ed class only has children who are nonverbal and are working on functional goals. These are my only two choices for my child. Neither meets his needs, but we live in a rural area and it is very difficult to get teachers here … let alone those who have specializations in diverse learning styles."

Meaning of Medicine and Well-Being

Medical approaches to disabilities are very prevalent, especially in Western culture. In recent years, much progress has been made in the prevention of, treatments for, and ability to live with certain disabilities. The medical community continues to be extremely involved and proactive in these areas. Likewise, early intervention has helped countless very young children avoid future problems and issues and has saved society much money by eliminating the need for ongoing services and support.

Medical diagnoses may be needed for health reasons, educational placement, treatment, and modifications to improve the quality of life of persons with disabilities. For these reasons, music therapy services are often aligned with a medical model to justify funding for service delivery.

However, increasing numbers of people are looking to complementary therapies and wellness programs to add a sense of well-being and self-determination to their lives. Music therapy is one avenue that has a long history of providing these types of opportunities and services to those with disabilities. For example, a community music therapy approach strives to build a community around making music as a collective whole. Philosophically, it supports social justice and self-advocacy for individuals, recognizing the abilities that are innate parts of the person's makeup rather than focusing on treatment or fitting into societal norms (Shiloh & LaGasse, 2014).

Meaning and Function of Music

Throughout time, music has been interwoven into most cultures. Those who have disabilities are enveloped by the music of their family's larger culture. It appears that music therapists recognize the importance of providing culturally appropriate music experiences to their clients and feel comfortable in doing so. However, many feel that an additional emphasis on multiculturalism in their undergraduate studies would have added to their competency in this area (Chase, 2003; Darrow & Molloy, 1998; Shapiro, 2005). Taking part in the musical experiences of others' cultures or encouraging them to share their music may help establish a stronger therapeutic relationship (Shapiro, 2005). Furthermore, cross-cultural training may help to develop cross-cultural empathy, helpful for delivering effective culturally sensitive and appropriate music therapy services (Valentino, 2006).

The very nature of music therapy is inherently linked to the Culture of Disability. Our training, competencies, and standards of practice ensure that each of us will be capable of delivering effective music experiences for this culture. Our profession was founded based on the successful blend of music and therapist skills that led to a better quality of life for veterans who had various physical and emotional disabilities. Throughout time, music therapy has been influential and involved in service delivery to those with all categories, types, and levels of disabilities (Adamek & Darrow, 2010). We have led the way in

educational settings, often serving as consultants to train our music education colleagues on how to use and modify music and techniques to make the music available and applicable to all students, but remaining vigilant in our recognition that the individual and not the disability should be the prime focus of our expertise (Farnan, 2007; Wilson, 2002). Music therapists and their clients have joined forces, forming bands, choirs, drum circles, and musical revues in community settings that encourage involvement by any interested party. Music has soothed our infirm, helped heal our injured, nurtured and strengthened our littlest babies, provided expressive avenues for those haunted by memories or fractured thoughts, motivated and inspired others to unimagined accomplishments, and given opportunities for enrichment, enjoyment, and a sense of community.

Music therapy stands in support of rights for those with disabilities and stands with the individuals who are part of the culture. Music therapy may offer a distinct contribution to disability studies because it opens up arenas of social participation in culture (Metell, 2014). We all should be proud of the advocacy efforts taken by the American Music Therapy Association (AMTA) and the Certification Board for Music Therapists (CBMT). Not only have these organizations advocated for the profession of its members, but also they have been actively involved in government hearings and events that have had major implications for those with disabilities. By doing so, they (and we) demonstrate that it is a right of people of all abilities to have access to the joys and benefits of music.

Empowering Health and Well-Being

Music therapists have numerous avenues for supporting the health and well-being of members of the Culture of Disability. The very nature of our profession is geared toward these goals. Music groups can become a locus of support and source of empowerment for their members. Moreover, music therapists also can take the lead and become advocates for accepting differences and disabilities.

Music therapists have recognized that all people may not feel welcome or connected to all community-based musical events because of their unusual social behaviors or the lack of accommodations for their needs. For example, Sensory Friendly Concerts* were developed and are facilitated by music therapists to address these concerns. Audience members are not expected to sit quietly, but are encouraged to demonstrate their enjoyment and move freely to the music. Lights are kept low and the volume kept at a level that respects those who have heightened sensitivity to their environment. In some cases, members of the audience perform beside the musicians on stage or may even showcase their own talents by soloing. While these concerts are open to the public, they are mainly for those with autism spectrum disorder. These community music therapy events strive to make musical experiences enjoyable for the collective whole, as well as support social justice and celebrate neurodiversity and self-advocacy (Shiloh & LaGasse, 2014).

Over the years, those with disabilities have become more involved in the communities in which they live, work, and play. Self-determination and empowerment are oft-addressed themes. Employment and recreational options have become more available and accessible. Informal as well as formal support exists for those with disabilities and their families. Support groups within local communities bring people together, offer information, and provide social avenues for families. Online search engines list sites for numerous organizations across a variety of categories (e.g., information, advocacy, wish-giving, or by specific disability). For individuals, Internet blogs offer opportunities to share and learn.

Society has made many advances in the acceptance and understanding of disabilities. Allow me to share how music therapy helped me be a part of this journey.

Early in the 1990s, I worked in a county school for students from toddlerhood to young adulthood. All had some form of developmental disabilities. Very few opportunities existed for these students to interact with typical peers. I was fortunate to work for a principal who saw the value of music therapy and believed that it helped "level the playing field," as he put it. In other words, when making music, every child could be involved and successful in some way. The principal had contact with several other school administrators in the surrounding areas and called upon one of them whose school had a preschool class in one of her buildings. I went to her school and presented a detailed plan for a once-weekly music mainstreaming program between our school and hers. This was an unusual request at that time. There were still misconceptions about children with disabilities; we anticipated that parents would be worried that these children would frighten their children and that the typical children might pick up bad behaviors from the children with disabilities.

To counter these attitudes, my proposal included plans for disability awareness training across several layers: parents, staff, and the children themselves. Written material was distributed, and time for questions and open discussion were a part of each presentation. Good, factual information (presented at a level of understanding appropriate for each particular audience), plus some group-building music experiences, sold the program. We explained that there were benefits for all the children—children with disabilities would gain access to typically developing peers and would learn from them; children without special needs would learn acceptance and an understanding of differences. We bused a small group of our preschool children and two staff members to the neighboring school once weekly throughout the school year. Music experiences were tailored to encourage interaction and successful music-making. To say that the program was a success is a massive understatement. Parents clamored to have their children be a part of the program the next year. The program was the subject of journal articles, newspaper coverage, and TV commentaries on local stations. The curriculum that evolved from the pilot year was replicated throughout the country, in South America, and in Japan. Music therapy had expanded the locus of support for those with disabilities (Humpal, 1991).

Jumping ahead by over 20 years, one of the offshoots of that pilot program still exists. In fact, when I retired, the YMCA where I had established a community version of the program picked up my contract, and I continued to conduct classes there. As a sign of the times, the class is listed as being for young children "of all abilities"; no longer are children segregated by the nature of their disabilities. In addition, no disability awareness training is necessary. If questions arise about differences, they are answered forthrightly and factually, without judgment or fear. Open dialogue and sharing takes place among the families. Answers to the questions are met with casual acceptance, and often more shared experiences and fewer differences are discovered.

I like to use books in my sessions with young children. Many stress that we are all alike, yet we are all different. Many of the books automatically encourage the addition of music. Those that also teach a message bring an added bonus to the experience. *Giraffes Can't Dance* (Andreae & Parker-Rees, 2001) is such a resource. It offers a gentle reminder that not everyone is good at everything, but that we all have abilities … some just need to find a way to let these abilities emerge and, as the giraffe discovers, *"We all can dance … when we find music that we love."*

It takes every color in the spectrum to make the world so bright … we're not so different.
—from the music of Cassandra Kubinski, 2013

References

Adamek, M., & Darrow, A. (2010). *Music in special education* (2nd ed.). Silver Spring, MD: AMTA.

Andreae, G., & Parker-Rees, G. (2012). *Giraffes can't dance.* Special Edition for *Kohl's Cares*®. New York, NY: Cartwheel Books.

Brault, M. W. (2012). *Americans with disabilities: 2010, current population reports.* Washington, DC: U.S. Census Bureau.

Bureau of Labor Statistics. (2014). *Persons with a Disability: Labor Force Characteristics 2013*, USDL-14-1076. Washington, DC: Bureau of Labor Statistics, U.S. Department of Labor.

Buvinić, M., Medici, A., Fernández, E., & Torres, C. (2006). Gender differentials in health. In D. T. Jamison, J. G. Breman, A. R. Measham, G. Alleyne, M. Claeson, D. B. Evans, P. Jha, A. Mills, & P. Musgrove (Eds.), *Disease control priorities in developing countries* (2nd ed.; pp. 195–210). Washington, DC: The International Bank for Reconstruction and Development/The World Bank.

Centers for Disease Control and Prevention. (2012). *Types of Disabilities.* Retrieved from http://cdc.gov/ncbdd/disabilityandhealth/types.html

Chase, K. (2003). Multicultural music therapy: A review of the literature. *Music Therapy Perspectives 21*(2), 84–88.

Corey, G., Schneider-Corey, M., Corey, C., & Callanan, P. (2015). *Issues and ethics in the helping professions* (9th ed.). Belmont, CA: Brooks Cole.

Darrow, A. (2006). The role of music in Deaf culture: Deaf students' perception of emotion in music. *Journal of Music Therapy, 43*(1), 2–15.

Darrow, A., & Molloy, D. (1998). Multicultural perspectives in music therapy: An examinationof the literature, educational curricula, and clinical practices in culturally diverse cities of the United States. *Music Therapy Perspectives, 16,* 27–32.

Disabled World News. (2011, July 26). *Figures, facts and statistics relating to disability in America today.* Washington, DC: U.S. Census Bureau. Retrieved from http://www.disabled-world.com/disability/statistics/census-figures.php#ixzz24tosYrrK

Farnan, L. (2007). Music therapy and developmental disabilities: A glance back and a look forward. *Music Therapy Perspectives, 25*(2), 80–85.

Farrell, A., & Krahn, G. (Guest Eds.). (2014). Family life goes on: Disability in contemporary families. *Family Relations: Interdisciplinary Journal of Applied Family Studies, 63*(1), 16.

Fujiura, G. (2014). The political arithmetic of disability and the American family: A demographic perspective. *Interdisciplinary Journal of Applied Family Study, 63*(1), 7–19.

Gill, C. J. (2009). A psychological view of disability culture. In R. M. Baird, S. E. Rosenbaum, & S. K. Toombs (Eds.), *Disability: The social, political, and ethical debate* (pp. 163–170). Amherst, NY: Prometheus Books.

Goodley, D. (2011). Introduction: Global disability studies (Chapter 1). *Disability studies: An interdisciplinary introduction.* London, UK: SAGE.

Gutzman, A., & Balcazar, F. (2010). Disability services' standards and the worldviews guiding their implementation. *Journal of Postsecondary Education and Disability, 23*(1), 48–61.

Hadley, S. (2014). Shifting frames: Are we really embracing human diversity? *Voices: A World Forum for Music Therapy, 14*(3).

Houtenville, A. J., & Ruiz, T. (2011). *Annual disability statistics compendium: 2011.* Durham, NH: University of New Hampshire, Institute on Disability.

Humpal, M. (1991). The effects of an integrated early childhood music program on social interaction among children with handicaps and their typical peers. *Journal of Music Therapy, 28*(3), 161–177.

Humpal, M. (2012). Parents of children with Autism Spectrum Disorders. In P. Kern & M. Humpal (Eds.), *Early childhood music therapy and Autism Spectrum Disorders—Developing potential in young children and their families* (pp. 245–261). London, UK, & Philadelphia, PA: Jessica Kingsley Publishers.

Jamison, D. T., Breman, J. G., Measham, A. R., Alleyne, G., Claeson, M., Evans, D. B., … & Musgrove, P. (Eds.). (2006). *Disease control priorities in developing countries* (2nd ed.). Washington, DC: The International Bank for Reconstruction and Development/The World Bank.

Johnson, K. L. (2008, January 22). Views on disability around the world. *The ASHA Leader, 13*(24). doi:10.1044/leader.WB.13012008.24

Kubinski, C. (2013). Not so different. (Recorded by C. Kubinski). On *Not so different* (MP3). Atlanta, GA: Sunchild Entertainment.

Lovern, L. (2008). Native American worldview and the discourse on disability. *Essays in Philosophy, 9*(1), Article 14. Retrieved from http://commons.pacificu.edu/cgi/viewcontent.cgi?article=1300&context=eip

Meekosha, H. (2005). Gender, International. *Encyclopedia of disability, 2,* 764–769.

Mental Health America. (2015). *Mental health America: Our history.* Retrieved from http://www.mentalhealthamerica.net/our-history

Metell, M. (2014). Dis/Abling Musicking: Reflections on a disability studies perspective in music therapy. *Voices: A World Forum for Music Therapy, 14*(3).

National Consortium on Leadership and Disability for Youth. (2007). *Disability history timeline: Resource and discussion guide.* Washington, DC: Author.

Rickson, D. (2014). The relevance of disability perspectives in music therapy practice with children and young people who have intellectual disabilities. *Voices: A World Forum for Music Therapy, 14*(3).

Shapiro, N. (2005). Sounds in the world: Multicultural influences in music therapy in clinical practice and training. *Music Therapy Perspectives, 23,* 29–35.

Shiloh, C. J., & LaGasse, A. B. (2014). Sensory Friendly Concerts*: A community music therapy initiative to promote neurodiversity. *International Journal of Community Music, 7*(1), 113–128.

Silberman, S. (2015). *NeuroTribes: The legacy of Autism and the future of neurodiversity.* NewYork, NY: Avery.

Social Security Administration. (2015). *The faces and facts of disability.* Retrieved from http://www.ssa.gov/disabilityfacts/

Society for Disability Studies. (2015). *What is Disability Studies?* Retrieved from http://disstudies.org/about/

Special Olympics. (2008). *Spread the Word to End the Word.* Retrieved from http://www.r-word.org

Staeger-Wilson, K. (2010). Professional perspective. *Journal of Postsecondary Education and Disability, 23*(1), 62.

Taormina-Weiss, W. (2011, June 13). The World Health Organization and the World Bank present a new global estimate concerning the numbers of people with disabilities in the world. *Disabled World News.* Retrieved from http://www.disabled-world.com/disability/statistics/who-disability.php#ixzz2596IBlmE

Taub, D., Fanflik, P., & McLorg, P. (2003). Body image among women with physical disabilities: Internalization of norms and reactions to nonconformity. *Sociological Focus, 36*(2), 159–176.

University of California, Berkeley. (2004a). Introduction. *The Disability Rights and Independent Living Movement.* Recordings produced by the Regional Oral History Office of the Bancroft Library. Retrieved from http://bancroft.berkeley.edu/collections/drilm/introduction.html

University of California, Berkeley (2004b). Timeline. *The Disability Rights and Independent Living Movement.* Recordings produced by the Regional Oral History Office of the Bancroft Library. Retrieved from http://bancroft.berkeley.edu/collections/drilm/resources/timeline.html

U.S. Equal Employment Opportunity Commission. (2008). *ADA Amendments Act of 2008.* Retrieved from http://www.eeoc.gov/laws/statutes/adaaa.cfm

Valentino, R. (2006). Attitudes towards cross-cultural empathy in music therapy. *Music Therapy Perspectives, 24*(2), 108–115.

Wehmeyer, M. (2014). Self-determination: A family affair. *Interdisciplinary Journal of Applied Family Studies, 63*(1), 178–184.

Wellcome Trust Sanger Institute. (2009, April 20). Learning disabilities in males: Nine new X-chromosome genes linked to learning disabilities. *Science Daily.* Retrieved from http://www.sciencedaily.com/releases/2009/04/090419133841.htm

Wendell, S. (1996). *The rejected body: Feminist philosophical reflections on disability.* New York, NY: Routledge.

Wilson, B. (2002). Changing times: The evolution of special education. In B. Wilson (Ed.), *Models of music therapy interventions in school settings* (2nd ed.). Silver Spring, MD: American Music Therapy Association.

World Health Organization. (2001). *International classification of functioning, disability, and health.* Geneva, Switzerland: WHO Press. Retrieved from http://www.disabilitaincifre.it/documenti/ICF_18.pdf

World Health Organization. (2011). *World report on disabilities.* Geneva, Switzerland: WHO Press. Retrieved from http://whqlibdoc.who.int/publications/2011/9789240685215_eng.pdf

Chapter 17

MINORITY EDUCATORS

Xueli Tan

I teach a course called Examining Power, Privilege, and Oppression in Clinical Practice. In the middle of the semester, a student posed an offhanded question to the class: "Are most of the professors teaching this course people of color?" This student went on to name all the professors listed under the various sections of this course. Indeed, there were a handful of professors who were of Asian descent or who identified with the Latinx culture. (Note: Past literature being cited in this chapter generally uses the word "Hispanic," but I will use the gender-neutral term "Latinx" to move beyond gender binaries and be inclusive of all intersecting identities.)

Although I do have many intersecting minority identities, I choose not to subscribe to the thought of an implied "oppressed" stamp imprinted on my resume whenever I apply for a job. Least of all, that I "do diversity" or "be the diversity." From the students' perspective, does being a person of color make me a more "legitimate" professor of such courses? I hope not. Does my position as the professor tip the scale of power differentials? I do not have an answer. Because there were moments when I was acutely aware that the person standing in front of the class was the only person of color in the room. Why does it matter? Why focus on differences when, as therapists, shouldn't we be color-blind to all? Color-blindness runs the "risk of flattening difference" (Luft, 2010, p. 145). When I stand in front of my students and they say, "I don't see color," then either one of two things happens. First of all, I disappear; I cease to exist. Color-blindness robs away at identities that define a person's unique humanness. Second, I become like everybody else. I become the default; the norms, habits, preferences, likes and dislikes of the majority become synonymous with mine. So, during the first day of class, I dispel the myth that color-blindness equates equity.

Introduction

College and university faculty members take on multiple roles as lecturers, instructors, advisors, mentors, and role models for students in higher education. There are approximately 1.5 million faculty members in degree-granting postsecondary institutions in the United States, and about half of them hold full-time positions. This figure incorporates a 69% increase in the total number of faculty within the past 20 years (U.S. Department of Education, 2015). Despite the growth in overall faculty membership, minority faculty representation continues to trail way behind the ever-increasing numbers of minority students who are filling college and university classrooms (Zambrana, Ray, Espino, Castro, Cohen, & Eliason, 2015). This chapter will explore the current demographic landscape of our university classrooms, as well as take a precursory peek into future classrooms based on projections from current demographics in grade schools and immigration patterns. In addition, we will look to unravel some popular myths and assumptions made in regard to the perception and experiences of minority faculty. Last, this chapter will conclude by offering strategies for retaining and mentoring minority faculty members based on empirical research and positive case studies.

Current and Projected Landscapes

Student enrollment in degree-granting postsecondary institutions continues to increase by approximately 20% every 10 years (U.S. Department of Education, 2016). Although the increase in the number of male students (22%) was greater than the increase in female students (19%), the majority of students in 2013 were female (56%). From 1976 to 2013, the percentage of White students in American colleges fell from 84% to 59%. During that same period, the percentage of Latinx students rose from 4% to 16%; Asian/Pacific Islander students, from 2% to 6%; Black/African-American students, from 10% to 15%; and American Indian/Alaska Native students, from 0.7% to 0.8% (U.S. Department of Education, 2016). While it was predicted that 53% of the U.S. population would be composed of individuals from minority groups by 2050, this trend is already a reality in the education arena (Passel & Cohn, 2008; Williams, 2014). Williams (2014) reported that in August 2014, for the first time, the total number of minority students, that is, Latinx, Black/African-Americans, Asians/Pacific Islanders, and Native Americans combined, was greater than the number of White students in public grade school classrooms. It does not take much calculation to foresee what the racial demographic in university classrooms might look like in the 10 years, when these grade schoolers are ready to enroll in higher education.

The influx of international students into American colleges and universities in recent years complements the diverse demographic landscape in higher education classrooms. On November 16, 2015, the Bureau of Educational and Cultural Affairs at the U.S. Department of State released the document *Open Doors 2015,* which provides comprehensive statistics on the number of international students in the United States and an analysis of trends over time (Farrugia, 2015). The most significant finding from their report was that in 2015, the United States witnessed the highest rate of growth in the number of international students in 35 years. With a 10% increase last year, the figures culminated at 974, 926 international students in the 2014-2015 academic year. Students from China, India, and Brazil accounted for the largest increase on U.S. campuses, with China and India together accounting for 67% of the increase (Farrugia, 2015).

With the continual influx of international students at a 10% rate of increase each year and the current demographics in American grade school classrooms, it should not take long for university classrooms to be composed majorities with minority identity markers. Is the growth rate in minority faculty comparable? Minority faculty representation fails to catch up with the cumulative growth of minority students (Thompson, 2008; Zambrana et al., 2015). Among all full-time faculty members in degree-granting postsecondary institutions in 2013, close to 80% were White, followed by Asian/Pacific Islander at 10%, Black/African-American at 6%, Latinx at 5%, and American Indian/Alaska Native and mixed race both at less than 1% (National Center for Education Statistics, 2015). This imbalance in representation is not a present-day phenomenon. In a systematic review of literature from the past 20 years, researchers found that more than 300 authors had addressed the status and experience of faculty of color (Turner, Gonzales, & Wood, 2008). Of significance was their finding that from 1988 to 2007 there had been a sustained increase in publications addressing the concern about the low representation of faculty of color (Turner et al., 2008).

This amount of attention and effort geared toward unraveling minority faculty's experiences in institutions of higher learning is not yet evident in the music therapy profession. When addressing minority issues in education, researchers in our field leaned toward exploring the experiences of international students. For example, two recent publications highlighted international students' re-entry and reverse culture shock experiences when they returned back to their home countries after graduating from a music therapy program in the United States or Australia (Hsiao, 2011; Leung, Wilson, Roth, & Smith, 2014). There are currently no explorations of international students who, instead of returning to their home countries, chose to remain in the United States to practice as clinicians or take on the role of educators in universities or colleges. Thus, in this initial conversation about minority educators, I will borrow literature from the fields of higher education, social psychology, social teaching, cultural diversity psychology, and ethnic psychology. In order to contain this chapter within the space limit of this book and to carry on the dialogue started in previous chapters, the focus will be placed on the intersecting cultures of race, ethnicity, and gender.

Bringing Forward the Invisible

Jean Moule, professor emeritus at the College of Education, Oregon State University, extracted this passage from her personal journal:

It is as if we are all on a river that flows quietly and gently along. Most of my friends, students, and colleagues float on this river in a strong, sturdy boat of their majority status—a boat I cannot get into because I am not White. The river, our societal mainstream, is accepted and hardly noticed. I manage to swim or float alongside the boat as I am learning how to navigate this mainstream. Every once in a while, someone in the boat notices my struggle and tosses out an inner tube or briefly holds my hand. And then sometimes someone reaches out and pushes my head under with, "Just get over this race thing, Jean." I sputter, resurface, and continue on. In the long run, I figure that it makes sense to construct a raft for myself. So while I talk to those in the boat and we run difficult rapids together, at the same time I must lash together whatever supportive materials I can find. The response? "Hey, how come Jean gets a raft?" When I say, "Because I can't get in the boat with you and I'm getting tired of staying afloat without more support," some say, "What boat?" (Moule, 2005, p. 23)

Indeed, the invisibility of privilege becomes the norm. It was only within the past 10 years that the academic world brought forth the microscope lens to scrutinize the invisible burden that minority faculty carried. This is evident in a systematic review of literature concerning faculty of color, where Turner et al. (2008) identified emerging issues such as "scholarly contributions, teaching and pedagogy, job satisfaction, resiliency, mentorship, STEM fields, health fields, service, lack of diversity, recruitment and retention, isms, tokenism, bias in hiring, isolation/marginalization, tenure and promotion, affirmative action/legal issues" (p. 158).

Bringing this invisibility to the surface takes concerted efforts and time. Stanley (2006) acknowledged that it took 15 years of classroom observations, consultations, and conversations and literature analysis before it became apparent to her that faculty of color were experiencing the classroom experience in dissimilar ways from their majority counterparts. Stanley (2006) went on to write, edit, and publish prolifically the stories and experiences of faculty of color, noting that "for many, their narratives have been made to feel silenced for far too long" (p. 702).

For women faculty of color, the added layer of invisibility heaps onto the experience of multiple marginality. Turner (2002) cited one of her interviewees, who reported, "... Many [White] females in the college complain about the fact that up until recently ... we had never had a full professor in [department name]. It's changing, but it's not changing fast. And then you add to that being the Black female who has to the superwoman" (p. 80). She used the phrase "ambiguous empowerment" (Turner, 2002, p. 75) to portray the lived contradictions experienced by women faculty of color. On one hand, they do possess and exercise their power as professionals with academic accomplishments. On the other hand, they cannot ignore the various forms of gender and race inequality that scaffold the profession (Turner, 2002). When women faculty of color experience episodes of microaggression, they are often left to decipher whether it is attributed to their gender, ethnicity, or an intersection of both (Patton & Haynes, 2014).

Taxes and Tokens

Cultural Taxation

Amado Padilla, professor of developmental and psychological sciences in education at Stanford University, coined the term "cultural taxation" in 1994 (Padilla, 1994, p. 26) and stated:

> This "taxation" poses a significant dilemma for ethnic scholars because we frequently find ourselves having to respond to situations that are imposed on us by the administration, which assumes that we are best suited for specific tasks because of our race/ethnicity or our presumed knowledge of cultural differences. (p. 26)

These sentiments about being called upon to handle minority affairs and to be the expert on matters of diversity and inclusion are well documented (Dancy & Jean-Marie, 2014; Harley, 2008; Harris, 2012; Hirshfield & Joseph, 2012; Kelly & McCann, 2013; Laden & Hagedorn, 2000; Padilla, 1994; Reybold, 2014; Turner, 2002). Padilla (1994) also described being requested repeatedly to educate the majority group about diversity, even though it is not part of his job description and no authority or recognition is offered with the responsibility. Ahmed (2012) sums up the repercussion of cultural taxation by stating, "[T]he body that causes their discomfort (by not fulfilling an expectation of whiteness) is the one who must work hard to make others comfortable" (p. 41).

Tokenism

In the seminal book *Men and Women of the Corporation*, Kanter (1977) first described women who inhabit the position of *token* within a peer group of men. To further clarify the position of tokenism, Kanter (1977/1980) explained that if the proportion of individuals from a particular culture in an organization is less than 20%, then tokenism is likely to occur. Tokenism creates three damaging effects, namely: (1) being the only woman among a group of men or the only faculty of color among a predominantly White faculty heightens their visibility, thereby subjecting them to be pressured to overachieve or to limit their exposure; (2) feelings of isolation become apparent as the majority emphasize their commonality while highlighting the token minority's difference; and (3) stereotypical beliefs about the social characteristics of *tokens* pigeonholes them into specific yet limited roles (Kanter, 1977; Lewis & Simpson, 2012). Kanter (1977) not only expounded on the social situations of tokenism, but also further suggested that those who differ from

the norm face a cycle of cumulative disadvantage, while those who fit the norm encounter a cycle of cumulative advantage. More recently, researchers tested Kanter's (1977) hypothesis by studying the mentoring opportunities and professional development communications of 30 tenure-track junior faculty (Hyers, Syphan, Cochran, & Brown, 2012). They found that those faculty whose gender and ethnicity were not underrepresented in their departments reported having more interactions and more communications with higher-status colleagues, and more of these on topics related to faculty retention (Hyers et al., 2012).

Presumed (In)Competence

Women faculty of color often find themselves presumed to be incompetent scholars, teachers, intellects, and participants in academic governance (Comer, Medina, Negroni, & Thomas, 2016; Ford, 2011; Gutiérrez y Muhs, Niemann, González, & Harris, 2012; Moody, 2004; Wallace, Moore, Wilson, & Hart, 2012). Moody (2004) highlighted that the phrase "well-qualified White man" (p. 15) does not exist because there is already a notion of presumed competence and implicit deserved authority. Comments such as "people of color are always granted tenure" (Comer et al., 2016, para. 3) serve only to perpetuate the myth that faculty of color are hired and promoted because of their race rather than their capabilities as scholars, researchers, and teachers. The cascading consequence of microaggressions falls onto the shoulders of Latinx, Blacks/African-Americans, and women, burdening them to prove themselves twice as accomplished and just as intelligent (Moody, 2004). Asian-American faculty members' experiences, on the other hand, are in a quandary because while they are a marginalized group, they are stereotyped as the model minority (Beasley & Fischer, 2012). Research has showed that Asian-Americans continue to subscribe to the myth of the model minority (Li, 2005; Taylor, Landreth, & Bang, 2005). This subscription adds an extra burden on Asian-American faculty members, who feel like they have to constantly check themselves, lest they "underachieve" in their role as the "model minority." Nevertheless, women faculty of color find it harder to gain credibility and often feel more pressure to conform and make fewer mistakes (Turner, 2002). In a survey of the psychological climate on a university campus in the Midwest, researchers found that women and minority professors' experiences had been laden with discrimination and scrutiny and that they had been undervalued as intellectuals. The majority faculty, in contrast, expressed satisfaction with the academic climate in their departments and the collaborative interactions with peers (Smith, Turner, Osei-Kofi, & Richards, 2004).

Embodying invisibility gives us the vocabulary to call it out into our social consciousness. Breaking silence lets out the myriad whispers, culminating in a voice calling for a safe, welcoming, and inclusive environment.

Strategies to Promote a
Welcoming Environment

Mentorship

Healthy mentorship practices can significantly address many need areas, including professional development, research and scholarships, emotional support, intellectual community, safe space, access to opportunities, constructive feedback, and role models. This form of support is particularly essential for the professional development of women and minority faculty (Hanover Research, 2014; Padilla, 1994; Thompson, 2008). Mentorship programs can improve the retention rates of underrepresented minority faculty, reinforce a respectful and positive work environment, and combat social isolation in the academic environment (Guenter-Schlesinger & Ojikutu, 2009; Stanley, 2006). The following summarizes several mentorship models and best practices garnered from the School of Medicine at Wake Forest University and Aguirre (2000).

One-to-One Mentoring. This is the most traditional form of mentorship, where one mentor meets with one mentee at a time. The mentee gets individualized attention, and the rapport and relationships built between them often last for many years. This format is highly beneficial for minority faculty members who have unique experiences and challenges that are not shared by the majority.

Group Mentoring. In this setting, one mentor meets with multiple mentees at the same time. Usually, mentees have similar goals and rely on group synergy to tap into collective knowledge.

Team Mentoring. In direct contrast to group mentoring, team mentoring occurs when multiple mentors work with one mentee. This form of mentoring is usually goal-oriented, where the mentee consults with several mentors in order to move toward set goals. Minority faculty members may find team mentoring helpful, as they would have the opportunity to consult with multiple mentors who can address their intersecting identities.

Peer Mentoring. Faculty members provide guidance, feedback, and support for each other. This type of mentoring is usually informally structured and is effective for sharing similar challenges, experiences, and insights.

E-Mentoring. Similar to one-to-one mentoring, but instead of meeting in person, mentor and mentee meet via the Internet. This type of mentoring might be especially useful for minority faculty members who feel isolated in their institutions to seek out suitable mentors in other locations.

Informal Mentoring. The mentee self-selects the mentor, based either on informal conversations or having identified the mentor as a role model. The relationships develop naturally without any formal agreement or structure.

Reverse Mentoring. A junior faculty mentors the senior faculty member. This occurs because the junior faculty has more experience or knowledge in a particular area, for example, new technology that the senior faculty wants to learn.

This form of mentoring can increase cross-generational understanding, although to be successful, it is essential to remove barriers of status and position in order to create a safe and open environment.

Cross-Mentoring. Minority faculty members are mentored by nonminority faculty. This is probably the most common type of mentoring because of the skewed ratio of nonminority faculty to minority faculty in institutions of higher education in the United States. Aguirre (2000) cautioned that additional support and inclusive efforts are needed for cross-mentoring. Creating an appreciation for mentoring minority faculty sends a message that they are vital to professional socialization.

Awareness, Communication, and Collaboration

Seeking support through healthy mentorship greatly impacts the ways and means in which minority faculty navigate the climate of the institution. Collaborative relationships, whether formal or informal, could decrease feelings of isolation and increase the chances for faculty retention and scholarly productivity.

According to a number of researchers (Hernandez, Ngunjiri, & Chang, 2015; Kanter, 1977; Stanley, 2006; Turner, 2002; Zambrana et al., 2015), strategies to foster inclusivity can include conversations about the experiences of minorities in order to make necessary structural and climate changes and to add voices to ongoing narratives of lived experiences; discussions on race, ethnicity, or gender in the academy to validate the perceptions and observations of minority faculty; creating communities focused on professional and psychosocial support; advancing scholarship through collaborative research and publication; effecting change by heightening awareness about social justice and equity issues; being willing and able to discuss the unwritten rules of navigating through majority structures and spaces; building meaningful, inspirational, and reciprocal relationships that offer active support; strengthening social and institutional ties without demanding assimilation; increasing the representation of minority groups across the campus (i.e., students, administrators, and faculty); and starting the process of healthy mentoring early, including through mentoring minority graduate students to establish a solid foundation of trust and support even before they step into a faculty role.

Conclusion

Minority faculty representations in institutions of higher education are not on a par with the rapid proliferation of minority students in the classrooms. This reality will become apparent in the near future due to the annual 10% increase in the number of international students enrolling in U.S. universities and colleges. Furthermore, the minority-majority ethnic scale in grade schools had already tipped over in 2014. It won't be long before these students enter university gates, scouting for role models with similar backgrounds, cultures, and heritages toward which they can aspire. Being aware that minority faculty do encounter unique challenges and obstacles rooted in historical circumstances, false assumptions, and assigned stereotypes represents our first stride toward the commitment to embrace diversity and inclusion. What is the difference between diversity and inclusion? Vernã Myers (2011) aptly explained, "Diversity is being invited to the party; inclusion is being asked to dance" (p. 5). Minorities have lined up along the walls and inhabited the halls of assimilation for too long. "To inhabit Whiteness as a non-White body can be uncomfortable; you might even fail the comfort test. It can be the simple act of walking into the room that causes discomfort" (Ahmed, 2012, p. 40). Each of us brings multiple layers of historical circumstances and cultural backgrounds in our interactions with each other. Within the context of an academic landscape, it takes two to tango, three to jive, and a boatload of people to ensure that everybody has a good time.

References

Aguirre, A. (2000). *Women and minority faculty in the academic workplace: Recruitment and retention, and academies culture.* San Francisco, CA: Jossey-Bass.

Ahmed, S. (2012). *On being included: Racism and diversity in institutional life.* Durham, NC: Duke University Press.

Beasley, M. A., & Fischer, M. J. (2012). Why they leave: The impact of stereotype threat on the attrition of women and minorities from science, math, and engineering majors. *Social Psychology Education, 15,* 427–448. doi:10.1007/s11218-9185-3

Comer, E. W., Medina, C. K., Negroni, L. K., & Thomas, R. L. (2016). Women faculty of color in a predominantly white institution: A natural support group. *Social Work with Groups.* doi:10.1080/1609513.2015.1077641

Dancy, T. E., & Jean-Marie, G. (2014). Faculty of color in higher education: Exploring the intersections of identity, impostership, and internalized racism. *Mentoring & Tutoring: Partnership in Learning, 22*(4), 354–372.

Farrugia, C. A. (2015). *Open Doors 2015: Report on International Educational Exchange.* Institute of International Education. Retrieved from http://www.iie.org/Research-and-Publications/Open-Doors#.V5alvY6NvhP

Ford, K. A. (2011). Race, gender, and bodily (misrecognitions: Women of color faculty experiences with white students in the college classroom). *The Journal of Higher Education, 82*(4), 444–478.

Guenter-Schlesinger, S., & Ojikutu, K. (2009). *Best Practices: Recruiting & Retaining Faculty and Staff of Color.* Retrieved from http://www.wwu.edu/eoo/docs/Best%20Practices_Recruiting%20and%20Retaining%20Staff%20of%20Color.pdf

Gutiérrez y Muhs, G., Niemann, Y. F., González, C. G., & Harris, A. P. (2012). *Presumed incompetent: The intersections of race and class for women in academia.* Logan, UT: Utah State University Press.

Hanover Research. (2014). *Faculty Mentoring Models and Effective Practices.* Washington, DC: Author. Retrieved from http://www.hanoverresearch.com/media/Faculty-Mentoring-Models-and-Effectives-Practices-Hanover-Research.pdf

Harley, D. A. (2008). Maids of academe: African-American women faculty at predominantly white institutions. *Journal of African-American Studies, 12*(1), 19–36.

Harris, G. L. A. (2012). Multiple marginality: How the disproportionate assignment of women and minorities to manage diversity programs reinforces and multiplies their marginality. *Administration & Society, 45*(7), 775–808.

Hernandez, K-A. C., Ngunjiri, F. W., & Chang, H. (2015). Exploring the margins in higher education: A collaborative autoethnography of three foreign-born female faculty of color. *International Journal of Qualitative Studies in Education, 28*(5), 533–551. doi:10.1080/09518398.2014.933910

Hirshfield, L. E., & Joseph, T. D. (2012). "We need a woman, we need a black woman": Gender, race, and identity taxation in the academy. *Gender and Education, 24*(2), 213–227.

Hsiao, F. (2011). From the Ideal to the Real World: A phenomenological inquiry into student sojourners' reentry adaptation. *Journal of Music Therapy, 48*(4), 420–439.

Hyers, L., Syphan, J., Cochran, K., & Brown, T. (2012). Disparities in the professional development interactions of university faculty as a function of gender and ethnic underrepresentation. *The Journal of Faculty Development, 26*(1), 18–28.

Kanter, R. (1977). *Men and women of the corporation.* New York, NY: Basic Books.

Kanter, R. (1980). *A tale of "O": On being different in an organization.* New York, NY: Harper.

Kelly, B. T., & McCann, K. (2013). Women faculty of color: Success stories from the margins. *Journal of the International Association for the Study of the Global Achievement Gap,* Book 10. Retrieved from http://digitalcommons.georgiasouthern.edu/cgi/viewcontent.cgi?article=1005&context=jiasgag

Laden, B. V., & Hagedorn, L. S. (2000). Job satisfaction among faculty of color in academe: Individual survivors or institutional transformers? *New Directions for Institutional Research, 105,* 57–66.

Leung, H. Y. A., Wilson, B. L., Roth, E. A., & Smith, D. S. (2014). The re-entry experiences of international music therapy professionals from the Asia Pacific Rim area. *Australian Journal of Music Therapy, 25,* 45–64.

Lewis, P., & Simpson, R. (2012). Kanter revisited: Gender, power and (in)visibility. *International Journal of Management Reviews, 14,* 141–158.

Li, G. (2005). Other people's success: Impact of the "model minority" myth on underachieving Asian students in North America. *KEDI Journal of Educational Policy, 2*(1), 69–86.

Luft, R. E. (2010). Intersectionality and the risk of flattening difference: Gender and race logics, and the strategic use of antiracist singularity. In M. T. Berger & K. Guidroz (Eds.), *Intersectional approach: Transforming the academy through race, class, and gender* (pp. 145–179). Chapel Hill, NC: The University of North Carolina Press.

Moody, J. (2004). *Faculty diversity: Problems and solutions.* New York, NY: Taylor and Francis Books.

Moule, J. (2005). Implementing a social justice perspective in teacher education: Invisible burden for faculty of color. *Teacher Education Quarterly, 32*(4), 23–42. Retrieved from http://www.jstor.org/stable/23478744

Myers, V. (2011). *Moving diversity forward: How to go from well-meaning to well-doing.* Chicago, IL: ABA Books.

Padilla, A. M. (1994). Ethnic minority scholars, research, and mentoring: Current and future issues. *Educational Researcher, 23*(4), 24–27.

Passel, J. S., & Cohn, D. (2008, February 11). U.S. population projections: 2005–2050. *Pew Research Center: Hispanic Trends.* Retrieved from http://www.pewhispanic.org/2008/02/11/us-population-projections-2005-2050/

Patton, L. D., & Haynes, C. M. (2014). Using critical interpretive lenses to examine glass ceiling effects through qualitative research. *New Directions for Institutional Research, 159*, 25–35.

Reybold, L. E. (2014). The irony of ethics: (De)coding the lived experience of women and minority faculty. *International Journal of Higher Education, 3*(2), 92–105.

Smith, D. G., Turner, C. S. V., Osei-Kofi, N., & Richards, S. (2004). Interrupting the usual: Successful strategies for hiring diverse faculty. *The Journal of Higher Education, 75*(2), 133–160.

Stanley, C. A. (2006). Summary and key recommendations for the recruitment and retention of faculty of color. In C. A. Stanley (Ed.), *Faculty of color: Teaching in predominantly white colleges and universities.* Bolton, MA: Anker.

Taylor, C. R., Landreth, S., & Bang, H. K. (2005). Asian-Americans in magazine advertising: Portrayals of the "model minority." *Journal of Macromarketing, 25*(2), 163–174.

Thompson, C. Q. (2008). Recruitment, retention, and mentoring faculty of color: The chronicle continues. *New directions for higher education, 2008*(143), 47–54.

Turner, C. S. V. (2002). Women of color in academe: Living with multiple marginality. *The Journal of Higher Education, 73*(1), 74–93.

Turner, C. S. V., González, J. C., & Wood, J. L. (2008). Faculty of color in academe: What 20 years of literature tells us. *Journal of Diversity in Higher Education, 1*(3), 139–168.

U.S. Department of Education, National Center for Education Statistics. (2015). *The Condition of Education, 2016* (NCES 2016-144). Retrieved from https://nces.ed.gov/fastfacts/display.asp?id=61

U.S. Department of Education, National Center for Education Statistics. (2016). *Digest of Education Statistics, 2014* (NCES 2016-006), Chapter 3. Retrieved from http://nces.ed.gov/fastfacts/display.asp?id=98

Wallace, S. L., Moore, S. E., Wilson, L. L., & Hart, B. G. (2012). *African-American women in the academy: Quelling the myth of presumed incompetence.* Logan, UT: Utah State University Press.

Williams, J. P. (2014, September 22). College of tomorrow: The changing demographics of the student body. *U.S. News.* Retrieved from http://www.usnews.com/news/college-of-tomorrow/articles/2014/09/22/college-of-tomorrow-the-changing-demographics-of-the-student-body

Zambrana, R. E., Ray, R., Espino, M. M., Castro, C., Cohen, B. D., & Eliason, J. (2015). "Don't leave us behind": The importance of mentoring for underrepresented minority faculty. *American Educational Research Journal, 52*(1), 40–72. doi:10.3102/0002831214563063

Chapter 18

ALLIES FOR SOCIAL JUSTICE

Leah Oswanski & Amy Donnenwerth

Leah: *"Why can't anyone understand meeeeeee!!!!"* I whined to my grandmother as a six-year-old child in Tokyo, Japan. I had, yet again, grown tired of people staring at me, the strange cultures, the crowds, and the difficulty in communicating with those in my environment. *"Leah, please remember that we are guests in this country … don't let your frustration turn you in to an* Ugly American.*"*

Ugly American.

What exactly does this mean?

The phrase can be interpreted quite differently depending on your background, but what it meant to me as a child was a reminder that I wasn't in the United States. English wasn't the primary language spoken. Acting frustrated or angry about this was rude and obnoxious! I needed to be mindful of the practices of a culture different from my own.

For the nine summers I spent in Japan as well as visiting other countries, including China, South Korea, and Thailand, I gained a deep respect and admiration for the various cultures to which I was exposed. They were certainly in stark contrast to my midwestern hometown. Probably the most valuable lesson I learned in my travels was that my own culture, values, and country were an incredibly tiny part of the world. Living abroad forced to me to peek outside of my ethnocentric blinders and challenge my cultural encapsulation. My exposure also sparked my passion for learning about other people and how they define themselves.

I believe these experiences drove me to start questioning all of the "isms" early in my life. However, it was not until my early 30s that I began to understand my own cultural identity and "isms." As a kid, I truly felt that I was "color-blind" and "we are all the same," unaware that this was a very immature and simplistic conceptualization of human beings. Although well-intentioned, I spent many years operating under what Edwards (2006) calls the "Aspiring Ally for Altruism," an identity development phase (which will be detailed later in this chapter) in which I utilized strong verbal "attacks" on people whom I felt were victimizing a nondominant group. I had yet to start to understand my own role in the system of oppression. My attempts to bring about change through spraying people with "bullets" of knowledge, anger, and shame were certainly not a helpful way to open or maintain a meaningful conversation. Instead, it served to isolate me from those I wished to defend, as well as the dominant group that I was attempting to engage.

Finally, in graduate school for my MA in Counseling, I was required to take a thorough and honest look at myself to assess who I really was when I entered a room with a client and interacted with the world. It was brutal, wonderful, painful, and amazing. I had always defined myself as a female Caucasian "spiritual mutt," meaning that I wasn't attached to an organized religion and I was a mix of Alsatian, Irish, Native American, Scottish, Swedish, and "unknown," since my maternal grandmother was adopted. But this definition was clearly just the tip of the iceberg. The examination of my value system, my privileges, and my assumptions was a complex process, and up until that moment, I had not been keenly aware of how they were operating on a conscious level. I had so many intense emotions when I began to deeply assess myself on the power/privilege spectrum and my role in perpetuating the system, as well as my own marginalization by the same system. This was a true turning point in my life, in my work, and began the shift in my aspiring ally identity and actions.

And yet—

I am nowhere near a social justice ally expert. Not even close. I, like all of us, am just a work in progress. I make mistakes all the time, sometimes big mistakes. I apologize. I ask for feedback. I learn. I grow.

It can be overwhelming and distressing to focus on all that we don't *know*, or the magnitude of what we need to do in order to effect change. The fear of making mistakes can sometimes stop us from moving forward in the process of self-discovery. Sometimes it is fear of the sheer enormity of the tasks that stops us in our tracks. I invite you to make mistakes with me and with all of us who aspire to align with ally thoughts/behaviors/actions. It's my hope that this chapter will help to foster your expansion of self, both professionally and personally, no matter where you are in your journey from Ugly American to an aspiring ally.

Amy: *Was I born an ally? Did my inclinations toward being an ally arise from nature or nurture or a combination of both?* I do not have a definitive answer for these questions, but as long as I can remember, I have felt like an ally and an advocate. From an early age, it seemed to me that there were groups of people who need allies.

As a seven-year-old, I had a strong desire to be an ally for an elderly neighbor whose family rarely came to visit her. I remember thinking that just because she was in her late 70s did not mean that her life was meaningless. I asked myself and my parents, "Why does she seem so lonely, abandoned, and forgotten?" Since her family went months without visiting her, I listened to her stories, performed simple chores, and read to her. My ally passion for the elderly also manifested itself in summer vacations to see relatives. I felt strongly that the nursing homes we visited were not doing a sufficient job in taking care of their residents. I believed that the residents needed someone to speak up for their dignities and rights.

In junior and senior high, I joined service clubs that focused on reaching out to help the less fortunate in our community. Providing homeless people with basic needs and services was something I thought critically important for our society.

My advocacy for the gay community had its roots in high school, when a close friend came out to me. He shared that many of our peers ahd told him he was disgusting, gross, and disturbed. A number of our classmates stated that they did not want to hear about his same-sex relationships. I began to realize that homophobic gestures and comments were common occurrences at school, in my community, and on television. During undergraduate school, several more friends came out to me. I continued to witness frequent homophobic actions and remarks in my community and in the media. It hurt me deeply. A lesbian friend in graduate school taught me a lot about the persecutions of the LGBTQ community. She opened my eyes and helped me to truly understand how much I had to learn about my own privilege. I am very grateful for my friend's candor, our relationship, and her patience. To this day, she is a resource and a help to me as I seek to continually improve as an ally.

When I started my career as a music therapist, I quickly realized the importance of advocacy for our clients and patients. I facilitated cancer support groups and became an ally and advocate for people with cancer as they negotiated so many life-changing situations and difficulties. I also began working in private and state mental health facilities. I was shocked and saddened by the misunderstandings and stereotypes that exist for individuals who are experiencing varying degrees of mental illnesses. This started my journey as a staunch ally and advocate for individuals and their families experiencing mental health issues.

My 10-year work with at-risk youth in a large metropolitan city was profound and life-changing. I became a deeply invested ally and advocate for inner-city disadvantaged youth. I found a passion for speaking and standing up for, supporting, and encouraging young people who are born into utter chaos, lack of supervision, and difficult circumstances beyond their control. These amazing young people took me on a journey that transformed my life in ways that I never imagined.

Opportunities to be allies and advocates are all around us. Join us as we seek to motivate and encourage others to support, learn from, and speak up for those who are oppressed and marginalized.

What Is an Ally?

What makes someone an ally? The word "ally" can be used as either a noun or a verb. The Oxford Dictionary (2014) defines the noun form of "ally" as a state officially collaborating with another for armed services or other purposes, usually by contract. The verb use of "ally" is to bond or chain together a product or resource with another for shared value. According to Merriam-Webster (2014), the history and origin of the word "ally" dates back to c. 1300, from the Middle English allien, from the Anglo-French word alier, and from the Latin alligare, which means "to bind to." Synonyms for "ally" include accomplice, accessory, aide, associate, assistant, collaborator, colleague, coadjutor, confederate, coworker, friend, helper, and partner. Antonyms include antagonist, detractor, enemy, foe, and opponent.

Definitions for social justice allies do not hold the same militaristic connotations. Within social justice movements, a critical part of being an ally with another person or group of people is examining issues of oppression and privilege and working toward equality. Green (1998) and Vaillancourt (2012) describe social justice in the context of equality within societal members: equal access to life opportunities, goods, and resources, as well as the fact that every member has equal control of and participation in the societal decision-making process. Bishop (2002) defines an ally as a member of an oppressor group who acts to end a system of repression, which gives her or him privilege. Examples of this definition include a man who works to end sexism and a heterosexual who works to end homophobia.

Along the same lines, Ayvazian (2010) says that an ally is a part of a dominant group in our society who works to disassemble any form of persecution from which she or he gets the advantage. She shares that ally behavior involves taking personal accountability for the alterations we know are needed in our society but are often disregarded or left to be allocated to others. Ayvazian (2010) acknowledges that the work of an ally is challenging, difficult, and exhausting, both personally and professionally. She reminds us that it is crucial for allies to take care of themselves in order to maintain their drive and passion for constant challenges.

Hardiman, Jackson, and Griffin (2010) similarly define allies as agents of change who are participants of the privileged group acting in contradiction of the oppression(s) from which they derive approval, authority, and license. Additionally, they discuss several reasons as to how people are motivated to become allies, affirming that some may be motivated by their own self-interest because of feeling that one day *they* will be part of an oppressed group, such as those who experience ageism. Others may be motivated by spiritual beliefs, ethics, or by altruism. Some may be driven by their association with those who are currently experiencing oppression, such as having a family member or close friend who is part of an oppressed, targeted group.

Throughout the ages, the oppressed, along with their allies, have used music to empower their messages of building hope, strength, progress, and change. Much can be said about the music of various social justice movements and how it affected and influenced those who experienced that particular time in history. Various artists from diverse backgrounds have written, produced, and performed social justice music in a wide variety of styles, including but not limited to folk, rock, gospel, country, blues, jazz, pop, and rap. Not surprisingly, music continues to be a driving force and inspiration in contemporary social justice movements. Living in an ever-changing world challenges us to stay informed and use an assortment of resources to best understand the cultural shifts and their impact on those who are oppressed. As music therapists, it is essential that we consider the role of social justice music and how it impacts the people we serve.

Ally and Music Therapist

Why are you, or do you want to become, a music therapist? What brought you to the field? Personal qualifications listed in the American Music Therapy Association's (AMTA) brochure *A Career In Music Therapy* include an "interest in people and a desire to help others empower themselves" (2014a, p. 2). Clearly, our work is not fundamentally about just "helping." There are layers upon intricate layers of processes that occur within music therapy, but the underlying motivator for many of us is a desire to connect and empower human beings through music. As music therapists, we are not automatically given the title of "ally" nor do we display ally behaviors and actions unless we have undertaken considerable time working on self-awareness, education/training, and direct-action practice. However, many of us do have the central drive or interest in the attributes and actions of an ally. Consider section 2.3.2 in the AMTA Code of Ethics:

> The MT refuses to participate in activities that are illegal or inhumane, that violate the civil rights of others, or that discriminate against individuals based upon race, ethnicity, language, religion, marital status, gender, gender identity or expression, sexual orientation, age, ability, socioeconomic status, or political affiliation. In addition, the MT works to eliminate the effect of biases based on these factors on his or her work. (2014b, n.d.)

With this in mind, we understand that the development and practice of an ally is not optional as a music therapist, but an ethical requirement.

Although there is not one specific body of work on social justice/ally development in music therapy, Curtis (2012) highlights: "In each area, as in social justice work, music therapists have been informally integrating these concepts into their work, doing so independently and for a considerable time prior to any formal representation in the music therapy literature" (p. 209). Community music therapy, feminist music therapy, culture-centered music therapy theory, and other multicultural and empowerment approaches which integrate social justice issues and ally behaviors within music therapy have been detailed in our literature and continue to gain momentum in our field (Curtis, 2006, 2012, 2015; Faire & Langon, 2004; Hadley, 2006, 2013a, 2013b; Kenny, 2006; Kenny & Stige, 2002; Kim & Whitehead-Pleaux, 2015; Pavlicevik & Ansdell, 2004; Stige, 2002; Vaillancourt, 2010, 2012; Whitehead-Pleaux et al., 2012). Throughout this chapter, you will gain a greater understanding of the imperative need for both individual and systemic ally development, personally and professionally, in order to serve our clients and communities in an ethical and empowered approach. Bishop (2002) outlines a number of critical attributes and distinguishing characteristics of allies, which are easily translatable to music therapy clinical practice:

Allies Have a Sense of History and Knowledge. As part of the AMTA Professional Competencies (AMTA, 2013a), music therapists are required to have a strong grasp of music therapy historical principles and practices which have been firmly grounded in European and American psychological constructs (Estrella, 2001). The AMTA Standards of Clinical Practice (AMTA, 2013b) establish that, at the bare minimum, we keep current with trends and developments within our field, which includes examining, and adjusting accordingly, our current practices to reflect diversity and inclusivity. Music therapists who identify as allies work to translate their actions/thoughts/behaviors beyond their professional selves and into their personal lives and communities. Beyond this, music therapy allies are knowledgeable about their personal history, the histories of the different groups of which they are a part, and how these histories intersect with the histories of other groups. Music therapists who learn from our past and grow into our future are better equipped to help others.

Allies Possess an Understanding of Their Own Roots. As part of the clinical assessment process, music therapists work to understand and clarify the musical background and identity markers of our clients and ourselves. In turn, our identification with the origins of our own musical and personal identities aids us in the appreciation, understanding, and consideration of those whom we strive to support. Without the exploration of our own identity markers, we will be unable to fully connect with our clients on a therapeutic level and may unknowingly engage in damaging practices in music therapy.

Allies Accept Struggle. Music therapy principles and practices do not involve the use of scientific formulas that produce the exact results each time they are applied. We recognize that part of our work involves a concerted effort to assess, plan, implement, reassess, and adjust as needed. Music therapists understand and grasp that part of the individual and/or group process involves effort and exertion. We understand that there is struggle on the road to self-awareness and that social justice ally actions/thoughts/behaviors involve inherent struggles. Music therapists who are allies understand the systems of power and privilege and the inherent reality of struggle that a nondominant group or person has.

Allies Have an Accurate Wisdom of Their Own Influence and a Mindfulness Regarding Their Own Process of Learning. Music therapists assess the impact we have upon others in our therapeutic and professional relationships. We thoughtfully measure our influence, privilege, and identity markers and proceed to practice with objectivity, reliability, trustworthiness, and respect for others. With attentiveness, we strive to understand the development of our knowledge and how it relates to our professional contacts and relationships.

Allies Have a Solid Understanding of Self and an Absence of an Ego-Driven Stance on Matters. Music therapists have a twofold commitment to our personal growth and our professional growth. Our own self-knowledge and consideration aids us in helping and advocating with our clients. When we find ourselves getting attached to a specific stance, it is important that we take a step back and continually assess all facets of our experiences and ourselves in order to grow in our ally behaviors/thoughts/actions.

Allies View Their Own Limitations with Honesty, Sincerity, and a Lack of Embarrassment. In the Professional Competencies and Responsibilities section of the AMTA Code of Ethics (2014), it is stated that music therapists will be "cognizant of their own limitations" (n.d.). We are charged to do whatever is essential to guarantee that services to our clients are not affected by our shortcomings. This may necessitate us seeking supervision or professional guidance or limiting or discontinuing services with our clients.

Allies Possess Knowledge of Social Structure Concepts and Shared Responsibilities. As music therapists, we are entrusted to understand the social and moral expectations of the communities in which we work and those of our clients. We strive to study, understand, and appreciate differences in community groups and organizations. We work cooperatively with other professionals to reach similar goals and objectives.

Allies Have a Sense of Process and Change. Music therapists have an appreciation for what it means to understand methodology and modifications. We know that our work is a series of progressions, adjustments, and transformations. Our evaluative practices aid our ability to work toward the most effective music therapy experiences to achieve the goals of our clients. We understand that process and change are the heart of self-awareness and actualization.

Allies Have a Sense of Connection with All Other People. In our commitment to the music therapy profession, the welfare of others is foremost in our relationships. Our code of ethics guides and informs us in our interactions with our clients, students, research subjects, colleagues, employers, and the community/public. The AMTA Scope of Music Therapy Practice (2015) guides us to work with people of all ages and ability levels.

Allies Comprehend the Concept of Standing with Others Versus Standing over Others. Our role as music therapists never includes holding power or control over others. As outlined in the AMTA Scope of Music Therapy Practice (2015), we position ourselves to perform our duties ethically with professional integrity, respect, and diversity. We work to learn about power, privilege, and identity markers within ourselves and others to ensure that we are standing with others and not over them.

Allies Understand that Good Intentions Have No Value If There Is No Action Against Oppression. Section 3.2 of the AMTA Code of Ethics (2014b) states that a "music therapist will protect the rights of the individuals with whom he/she works, including, but not limited to: safety, dignity, legal and civil rights, treatment, self-determination, respect, and participation in treatment decisions" (n.d.). Allies extend these protections beyond our clients and to all people. We are charged to speak up against persecution even when no targeted person/group is present.

What comes through in all of these descriptions and definitions is that allies are valuable members of society who face the challenges of breaking the cycle of oppression. People who are the target of oppression and prejudice are not the only ones who benefit when allies speak up against discrimination. All of us gain an advantage when any of us make efforts toward removing judgment and bigotry in our society. *Being* an ally is beyond believing in equanimity. *Acting* as an ally means that we foster support from other allies. *Living* as an ally requires that we act with and for others in a quest to end repression and generate equality. *Representing* as an ally is more than being sympathetic toward those who consistently encounter suppression. Allies strive to create a time, space, and place that is filled with empowerment, deliverance, justice, and equality for those who have historically been targeted by methodical repression. As music therapists, we have a duty to our clients and society to abide by the principles and actions of allies.

Individual and Systemic Allies

Another way to view allies and the type of advocating they do is to look at the efforts of individual allies and systemic allies. Individual allies are those who make consistent efforts to speak up against discrimination, regardless of opposition from others. An individual ally works alone and will confront oppression even when a targeted person or group is not present. Without diminishing, stereotyping, or weakening the encounters of marginalized persons, individual allies pay attention to and accept as true the experiences of people who are under attack. Part of the individual ally growth experience is realizing that working alone is not enough. Bishop (2002) asserts that systems are more than the totality of their parts and that their configurations go past those of the individuals who contribute to them. Without joining together, we will be unable to truly make movement in the dismantling of the oppressive systems. This realization inspires individual allies to join together with others to form systemic ally networks. Systemic allies work within various groups toward breaking down barriers of persecution and harassment. The work of systemic allies takes determination, perseverance, and a firm belief that changes within oppressive systems are possible. Outlined below are individual and systemic ally approaches in music therapy practices.

In our efforts to grow as allies in our music therapy practice, we begin to understand that our individual actions are important. These actions can include talking to and educating someone you overhear making false statements about marginalized people; telling a person who uses oppressive words that it is offensive and unacceptable; and refusing to participate in activities that are demeaning to others. Each time music therapists speak up in various situations, we let others know that we are a voice for groups who are consistently experiencing oppression. For example, when a music therapist over hears (overhears) a coworker tell a gay male client, "You need to stop acting like a drama queen and man up," it is important for the music therapist to draw the coworker aside and explain that these remarks are offensive and unacceptable. In group music therapy, another example is one client saying to another, "It's a Black thing and you are a Mexican, so you won't get it." This situation provides an opportunity for the music therapist to facilitate an open conversation about stereotypes and cultural misinformation. Another example is when a client is told that he or she cannot listen to or sing a pagan chant because it may offend Christians who are in the group. The music therapist who seizes this chance to offer feedback about respecting differences and reminding group members that we can all learn and grow from each other even when our belief systems are dissimilar is an individual ally.

In addition to the opportunities to be individual allies, music therapists have a variety of options to become part of a systemic ally network. There are numerous opportunities for music therapists to become involved in groups that work to end discrimination related to age, race, ethnicity, ability, gender, sexual orientation, gender identity or expression, marital status, religion, language, socioeconomic status, or political affiliation. Within our own profession, one such group was formed in 2009 by a group of music therapists from around the country seeking to design a music therapy best practices document for the lesbian, gay, bisexual, transgender, and questioning community (LGBTQ). This group has presented at national conferences, published several articles, and conducted an international survey. Whitehead-Pleaux et al. (2012, 2013) foresee that the music therapy best practices for LGBTQ individuals will begin conversations between music therapists that can press forward to the equitable care of all people.

Another systemic ally group within our profession is the American Music Therapy Association's (AMTA) Diversity Task Force. Formed in 2010, this group was created to assess the diversity of our membership, examine effective models from other groups to increase diversity, and uncover proposed ways to increase diversity in the leadership and membership of the organization. There are several Facebook groups started by music therapists to share/discuss diversity topics, including an LGBTQ group and a group for Latin American music therapists and/or for resources with those working with Latin American clients.

Thankfully, there are many opportunities for working toward individual and systemic change in a variety of ways and places. Individual and systemic ally work can be done at various levels, including local, regional, state, national, and global networks. There are legal groups, advocacy coalitions, educational networks, support groups, civil rights groups, and many other forums where allies can join with others to bring about individual and systemic changes. Outside the community of music therapy, many organizations in United States and Canada support systemic ally work. A list of these groups is outlined the appendix. These organizations are offered as resources for music therapists to use to become involved in systemic ally efforts and as examples of work that we can do within our field. In our efforts to improve, develop, and move forward our profession, it is critical that we seek involvement in these various groups.

Ally as a Member of a Nondominant Group

Can you be an ally to a nondominant group if you are part of another nondominant group? Yes, but the issue is complex and multifaceted. Suyemoto and Fox Tree (2006) discuss challenges specific to allies across minority groups where most dialogs about racism are in reference to White people/privilege and people of color, assuming a shared experience of racial oppression. Conversations about discrimination/ marginalization among and within minority groups can be much more difficult because they risk destroying solidarity and support against shared global racial oppression. Yet, *not* highlighting the divisions may inadvertently collude with the privileged "divide and conquer" strategy by fragmenting efforts: "[I]f we cannot talk about our differences, we cannot be truly inclusive and we will inevitably lose the possibility of true solidarity as those who feel silenced or marginalized seek their support and validation elsewhere" (Suyemoto & Fox Tree, 2006, p. 237). It can be painful and difficult to assess levels of relative privilege in relation to other oppressed groups because (1) it can feel invalidating to consider how we might have race privilege or ethnic privilege in relation to another minority group, when the pain of not having privilege in relation to the dominant group is so overwhelming, and (2) frequently, the relative privilege that we have is afforded to us by the dominant group in order to keep all oppressed groups in their place, so in many ways it is not really privilege at all. And yet, there are certainly differences in the ways in which we are racially and culturally oppressed, and some experiences are easier for some than others (Suyemoto & Fox Tree, 2006, p. 245).

Although Suyemoto and Fox Tree (2006) were focused on the challenges in the creation of allies among People of Color, this discussion can be applied across all members of nondominant groups. There are multiple identity markers that constitute membership in nondominant groups (sexual orientation, gender, disabilities, etc.) and which uniquely alter our privilege relative to the dominant group. Awareness of these multiple identity markers in ourselves and others allows for an open dialog to take place. Without awareness, there will be no hope of developing competency in becoming an effective ally.

Models of Ally Development

Although there has been documentation of the struggle to end oppression by dominant social groups throughout history (Andrews, 2001; Blumberg, 1990; Fogleman, 1994; Schultz, 1995), there is not a large body of literature on the different ways that individuals aspire to be allies (Edwards, 2006). Many people have good intentions in ending oppression and the desire to "do something" about social justice issues, but there is sometimes a disconnect between intention and direct practice. Edwards (2006) and Kendall (2014) both highlight the problem with individuals who are supportive of social justice issues but may not be effective in anti-oppression strategies due to lack of education and self-awareness. A manifestation of misguided ally behavior might be a music therapist who becomes a "personal champion" for a particular client, treating the client as a victim that needs protection from "others," without acknowledging and exploring their own role in the system of oppression and privilege. An ally acknowledges that we are *all* victims, but we are victimized in *different* and *unequal* ways (Edwards, 2006). The following are three models of ally development, including LGBTQ, racial justice, and social justice in higher education frameworks, which may be broadly applicable to conceptualizing all social justice ally development.

Washington and Evans

Washington and Evans (1991) describe four basic levels of becoming an ally to lesbian, gay, and bisexual persons (LGB): Awareness, Knowledge/Education, Skills, and Action. Despite being created for LGB allies, these levels are applicable to becoming an ally for any target group. As has been mentioned in several points in this text, the first level for multicultural competency and ally development is the ongoing process of awareness.

Awareness as a music therapist includes not only your own personal identity markers, history, and examination of bias, but also your levels of privilege. The continuous awareness of self is critical for being able to enter into later levels successfully. Despite the progress on social justice issues from people who have limited self-awareness, effective and sustainable ally behavior requires a strong foundation of self-understanding (Reason & Broido, 2005).

The next level is Knowledge/Education, which can be achieved through formal schooling, Continuing Music Therapy Education credits (CMTEs), self-study/exploration, community organizations, and/or attending relevant concerts or musical experiences and may include studies on laws, policies, practices, music, and cultural history.

The third level, Skills, is the area where people often become fearful or lack the resources or support to be effective (Washington & Evans, 1991). Skills can be acquired through a myriad of ways, including role-playing, attending workshops with chances for direct practice, forming connections, and obtaining supervision.

The final and most important level is Action, which is often the most frightening due to the potential conflict (Washington & Evans, 1991). It is the synthesis of all of the above levels into taking direct advocacy actions. The Action level can be intimidating and challenging, as this level is where there will undoubtedly be conflict and discomfort as you take direct action. Here a music therapist may use a "safe sticker" in their offices/spaces or on instruments, become involved in any

law/policy changes at their facilities (and in their personal lives), and directly challenge oppression when discovered both on an individual and systemic level. We get involved not just for our specific clients, but also on a global level for us all.

Bishop

Bishop (2002) delivers a six-step cognitive and behavioral framework to conceptualize the development of racial justice allies that begins with education and moves to self-awareness. The first step is to understand the origins and self-sustaining mechanisms of oppression on an individual and group level. Step two revolves around the understanding of different oppressions, both similar and different. As Bishop (2002) states: "[A]ll oppressions are interdependent, they all come from the same worldview, and none can be solved in isolation" (p. 20). A suggestion from Bishop (2002) which can aid in education is to keep a list of your privileges and to help others see them, which in turns breaks the invisibility of privilege. Self-awareness through consciousness and healing your own pain is step three. The fourth step involves becoming an active advocate for ourselves in areas of oppression in our lives. This is a critical step in moving from being an aspiring ally to being an ally, because the acknowledgment and advocacy of our own oppressed areas indicates the development of working toward justice for *all*, rather than justice for *them* (Edwards, 2006). Step five is becoming an ally and confronting your own role as an oppressor. According to Bishop (2002), your action as an ally must lie within your own dominant group. The emphasis should be on support rather than leadership when working with an effort by a dominant group. The last step of the framework focuses on the need to maintain hope while working within a social justice movement, acknowledging that the long-term work can be difficult.

Edwards

Edwards (2006) provides a nonlinear three-identity conceptual model for the development of aspiring social justice allies. The model is intended as a helpful self-reflection tool for aspiring allies seeking to further develop their efficacy in social justice work.

The first identity is Aspiring Ally for Self-Interest. Here the prime motivation is to protect from perpetrators people with whom they have a personal connection. They often see themselves as defenders and are generally not interested in (or are blinded to) the underlying systems of oppression. Interest lies in stopping individual bad people from harming loved ones, but otherwise maintaining the status quo. Aspiring allies in this identity have a general worldview of fairness and equality and can often be stunned and angry when they hear of an injustice (Edwards, 2006). Music therapists in this identity are working *over* their clients, as powerful *protectors* rather than on an equal footing.

The second identity is Aspiring Ally for Altruism. In this

identity, the music therapist would be working *for* the members of the victimized target group, as *helpers* who are doing the *right* thing. Because there has been exploration into privilege, unconscious guilt may often be a primary motivator for their actions. They have a conception of the system of oppression, but their aim is to be distanced from the system and their privilege as an exceptional member of the dominant group rather than challenge the system directly. Aspiring Allies for Altruism may be defensive and have difficulty admitting mistakes, not only with members of the dominant group but also with the target as well. In this status, aspiring allies see the system intellectually but focus on other members of the dominant group as the real perpetrators. By vilifying other members of their dominant group, aspiring allies distance themselves from others in the agent group in an attempt to minimize the guilt stemming from their increasing awareness of unearned privilege (Edwards, 2006, p. 50).

The third identity is Ally for Social Justice. The target of this identity lies in the collectivist understanding of oppression that we must work in partnership to end the system of oppression. Music therapists working from this identity recognize that it is not a matter of *us and them,* but a matter of seeking justice for *all*. In this identity, the ally actively seeks to uncover their own *isms* and redefine the system. Allies for Social Justice seek to be allies of issues rather than individuals. There is a full acceptance of privilege and interest in dismantling systems of oppression for the liberation of all peoples (Edwards, 2006).

Becoming an Effective Ally

Where to begin? As detailed above, there are various paths that can be taken to become an effective ally. The first critical step in any path is to increase your self-awareness through exploring your privileges, recognizing your own cultural lens, and educating yourself in the areas of varying values, power, privilege, oppression, and other social justice topics. Part of becoming an effective ally includes the ongoing acquisition of knowledge and skills in the above areas through formal and informal study as well as ongoing supervision. *There is no endpoint in the process.*

Bennett Developmental Model of Intercultural Sensitivity (DMIS)

It is an imperative starting point, both for dominant and nondominant group members, to initiate development of intercultural competency in order to be an effective ally to other nondominant groups. This model of intercultural sensitivity can easily be expanded to assist you in developing sensitivity for all of the multiple identity markers that align to create a person's identity.

Bennett (1993) developed the Developmental Model of Intercultural Sensitivity (DMIS) as an intercultural training model relevant to both dominant and nondominant group members. This model has the goal of guiding people from an ethnocentric to ethnorelative worldview, consequently creating greater intercultural sensitivity and the potential for increased intercultural competence. The DMIS includes six distinct stages: Denial, Defense, Minimization, Acceptance, Adaptation, and Integration. The first three stages are ethnocentric, that is, the experience of one's own culture as the center of reality, and the final three stages are ethnorelative, in other words, the experience of one's own beliefs and culture is just one reality in the myriad of possibilities (Bennett, 2004).

The first stage, Denial, occurs when the individual has an overall incapability to perceive the distinctions between cultural facts. A classic example of Denial is the "we are all the same" or "color-blind" mind-set, where there is a distinct avoidance of acknowledging cultural differences. In this stage, a music therapist would engage clients with no regard, awareness, or thought given to the cultural facts (or dominant/nondominant framework) of anyone but themselves. The main issue to be resolved within this stage is the avoidance of both noticing and confronting cultural differences, both globally and domestically (Bennett, 2004).

Defense, stage two, is the experience that one's own culture is the only viable one. In this stage, people are better able to discriminate cultural differences, but are also more threatened by those differences than they were in the Denial stage. In music therapy, the therapist would have a limited awareness of a difference in cultural facts, but would choose to ignore those facts and implement therapy based on only the therapists' cultural background. In nondominant groups, it is important to note that Defense may be an important process in the development of an unconnected cultural identity with the dominant group. For example, the Immersion/Emersion stage of Cross's (1971, 1991) Racial Identity Scale, originally developed primarily to understand the Black experience in the United States, describes an Intense Black Involvement identity and an Anti-White identity, which may be experienced individually or concurrently. It is from this developmental stage that the emersion to the next stage, Internalization, occurs, where an individual has both an emotional and intellectual integration of being Black (Cross 1971, 1991). The main resolution for the Defense stage is the recognition of cross-cultural commonalities.

Stage three of the Bennett (1993) model is Minimization. In this stage, people may be generally tolerant of other cultures, but expect similarities in the assumed universalism of their *own* cultural worldview/belief system. A Minimization example that appears commonly in the United States is the assumption that other cultures really want to be more "like us" if offered the opportunity. A music therapist in this stage might have awareness of music from a client's culture/identity markers and a base awareness of cultural facts, but still chooses to use popular music from the United States, assuming that it's the ideal music for effective therapy and that the client would want to utilize the music from the dominant culture. The resolution of this stage is the development of cultural self-awareness. As Bennett (2004) points out, "Only when you see that all your beliefs, behaviors, and values are at least influenced by the particular context in which you were socialized can you fully imagine alternatives to them" (p. 68).

In stage four, Acceptance, resolution is focused on accepting the relative values of each cultural context. It is in this stage that individuals are able to keep their own perspective, while simultaneously taking the perspective of another culture. Often, people in the Acceptance phase are eager to learn by asking questions of others to become more informed, but not as a way to generate further divisions. There is acceptance of the cultural differences. The music therapist in Acceptance may seek to learn as much as possible about their clients' culture, identity markers, and music. They acknowledge the differences without placing value on one over another, but are often still unable to behave in culturally appropriate ways. The main resolution in this stage relies on the issue of value relativity and the commitment that enables you to not lose your own perspective while taking other cultural perspectives into consideration (Bennett, 2004).

Progressing further into the ethnorelative worldview, stage five is Adaptation. Not to be confused with assimilation, which implies that you give up your culture for the dominant culture, adaptation is the process of mutual adjustment (Bennett, 2004). A music therapist in Adaptation is able to join musically and otherwise with their clients within the clients' cultural/identity marker context without losing their own identity. In Adaptation, the resolution is based on how to be authentic in your own experience of self while being able to perceive, and behave in, culturally different ways.

The final stage is Integration. It is here that the individual moves in and out of different cultural world views, with the resolution being cultural marginality; in essence, adopting a multicultural perspective which uses multiple cultural frames of reference (Bennett, 1993). In this stage, a music therapist is truly multicultural, moving in and out of different cultural experiences comfortably with clients while still being their authentic selves.

In order to progress to the final stage of Integration, there needs to be a resolution for each previous stage. Many of us who have largely experienced monocultural socialization will start at the beginning of the DMIS in Denial. The resolution of the relevant issues in each stage creates the unfolding of the next orientation, and with each stage, the complexity of the target issues becomes more sophisticated, with the final manifestation being changes in the underlying worldview (Bennett, 2004). With each change in the underlying worldview, therapists will see shifts in their attitudes, skills, and knowledge, both musically and interpersonally.

After reading this section, you may think: *This is crazy!? There is no way that I could ever reach Integration as a therapist, considering that there are a myriad of people I encounter in my work! It would be impossible, with just the music alone, to imply that I could ever learn all the cultural complexities/identity markers and be able to move in and out of them with ease!*

While it is certainly true that none of us can be a cultural expert on *all* people, the importance lies in the *intent to strive* toward Integration, not only in our clinical work, but also as human beings in the world. We may sit in Integration in certain cultural contexts and in Acceptance in others. The important shift, particularly for therapists, becomes when we are consistently operating in the final three ethnorelative stages, rather than the first three.

Awareness of Identity Markers, Values, and Privilege

As music therapists, we have the assumption that we constantly strive toward self-awareness and have been trained in some form of multicultural competency. But are we really in touch with this complex and multifaceted experience of personal identity markers, values, and privilege on a comprehensive level? Due to the differing theoretical foundations in music therapy training programs, there is a wide variety in the acquisition of formal education in this area. Hadley (2013) points out that creative art therapists are not immune to the dominant/subjugating societal narratives of heterosexism, patriarchy, capitalism, medical science, Eurocentrism, and psychology and that we are responsible for both critically examining how these narratives are communicated through the therapeutic process and remaining vigilant against them.

An important consideration in becoming an effective ally and music therapist is the acknowledgement of the strengths and limitations of the Western ethnocentric theories on which our field and other related fields such as traditional psychology and counseling are founded. Oriented toward European-Americans, these theories place prime importance on values such as autonomy, assertiveness, verbal articulation, and separation-individuation (Kim & Whitehead-Pleaux, 2015). Only when we are aware of our *own* value systems operating on a personal and professional level are we able to recognize that value systems may differ in our clients and that we need to adjust our practice accordingly.

Intersectionality

One key to broadening our self-awareness is to personally explore the sociological concept of intersectionality. The term *intersectionality*, coined by Kimberle Crenshaw in 1989 and later elaborated on by Patricia Hill Collins, examines the simultaneous experience of hierarchical and categorical classifications, including, but not limited to, class, gender, nationality, age, and race (McCall, 2005). It highlights the fact that all forms of oppression, such as ableism, racism, sexism, and so forth, are intersecting and mutually dependent in nature manifesting into a "matrix of domination" (Collins, 2000). Use of this concept challenges us to view ourselves outside of the typical oversimplified binary categories. Once we can accurately conceptualize ourselves by finding our positions on the simultaneous intersecting axes of privilege, domination, and oppression, we are more likely able to recognize and view our clients from an integrated, yet distinctly individual perspective. An example of these intersecting axes can be found in Figure 1.

Note all of your different identity markers on the diagram. Notice the line that divides privilege (upper half) with oppression/resistance (lower half). Where are you oppressed, and where are you privileged? What does this mean to you? Consider this diagram when assessing a client and when interacting with others in the world. Examine how our differences matter in the way we move in and through our lives and introduce us to the concepts of situational and relative privileges. This process of assessment is similar to the feminist therapy techniques of Power Analysis and Gender-Role Analysis, where the goal is to increase the clients' understanding of the relative societal powerlessness of women and the inquitable socialization processes of both men and women (Curtis, 2006). Through the increase in understanding, the final aim is not used to identify as helpless, powerless victims of society, but to identify the sources of the problems and both societal and personal solutions (Curtis, 2006; Hall, 1992; Laidlaw & Malmo, 1990; Lerman & Porter, 1990).

Situational and Relative Privilege

Privileges are a system, not a gift. They are received whether you want them or not, as well as whether you are aware of them or not (Goodman, 2001). Privilege can be situational or relative. Situational privilege refers to the experience of the marginalized parts of your identity being a privilege in a specific situation. An example of situational privilege would be the hiring of a White female applicant over a White male applicant for a preschool music therapy position because of a perceived set of gender assumptions. Relative privilege is the experience of the privileged part of one's identity giving someone privilege even in a marginalized population. An example of relative privilege would be the hiring of a White

Figure 1. *Intersecting Axes of Privilege, Domination, and Oppression (adapted from Morgan, 1996)*

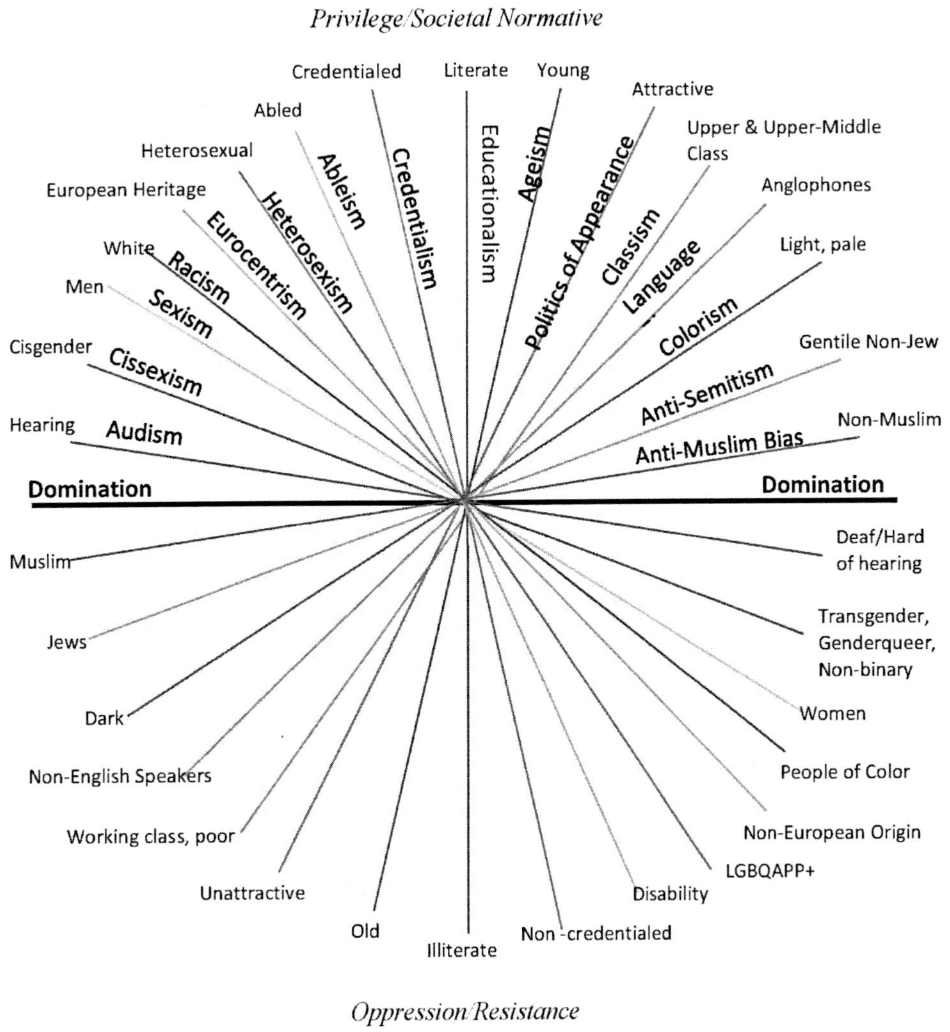

female applicant over a female applicant of color because of a perceived set of racial assumptions.

Why is it important to examine these facets of ourselves to be an effective ally and competent music therapist? It is a matter of exposing the unknown and acknowledging disparities between us, and others, in order to authentically engage with other people. The damage of not identifying and acknowledging our differences not only damages our clients, but also creates a hindrance to building an authentic therapeutic relationship. Imagine that you approach a client with the verbal and physical message of "I don't see color—we are the same," but you are a Caucasian, credentialed, heterosexual female and your client is an African-American, credentialed, heterosexual female. Although you are both female and may have shared experiences of oppression because of your gender, as well as levels of privilege from being credentialed and having a heterosexual status, your experiences in moving through life are not at all the same. Your levels of relative privilege are not the same. Although often originally stemming from good intentions, giving this client the message that you "don't see" all the pieces that make them who they are only continues to reinforce the cycle of oppression instead of dismantling it.

Whether this is your first experience in examining yourself on this level or you're practiced in this work, you may experience feelings of anxiety, anger, confusion, or guilt when identifying your situational and relative privilege. These difficult emotions are a normal part of the process of identifying and unlearning our privilege (Johnson, 2006). In her Privileged Identity Exploration (PIE) model, Watt (2007) identifies eight defensive reactions which can occur when one is being encouraged to reflect on their social, political, or economic position in society: Denial, Deflection, Rationalization, Intellectualization, Principium, False Envy, Benevolence, and Minimization.

In Denial, a person argues against the statement with belief that it doesn't exist, such as "racism doesn't exist anymore; I am where I am not because I am Caucasian, but because I worked really hard to get here."

In Deflection, a person might shift the focus off of the reality and onto a larger target: "I blame my schooling for not teaching me about LGBTQ rights. How was I to know if no one mentioned it?"

Rationalization includes when a person tries to apply logic to why oppressions happen, without having to explore the injustice: "If minority people in poverty worked hard, they would be able to get their families out of that environment and make a better life for themselves."

In Intellectualization, a person identifies intellectual components to avoid discomfort: "I know that sexism exists for women, but it's improved from what it was, so we are making progress."

Principium involves the avoidance of examination based on personal or religious principles: "Discrimination against LGBTQ people is wrong, but I don't agree with equal marriage because it goes against my religious beliefs."

False Envy is the experience of displaying affection as a means of avoidance of the larger issue: "I often wish I was Asian because Asian people are often viewed as more intelligent and hardworking than Caucasian people."

Benevolence is the attempt at well-meaning acts without the acknowledgement of the dominant society structure: "I became a music therapist so that I could help people who are less fortunate than I am."

And finally, Minimization is the process of reducing a macro issue down to simple facts: "If I learn songs from my client's culture, I am providing multicultural music therapy."

All of these defensive reactions can be seen in the aforementioned Bennett (1993) Developmental Model of Intercultural Sensitivity (DMIS) during the ethnocentric stages of development. The PIE model is based upon six assumptions, including the exploration of privilege being ongoing, no final level of privileged identity consciousness, that difficult dialogs are imperative, and that defense modes are normal human reactions, expressed in identifiable behaviors, that vary by situation (Watt, 2007). Working through these normal defenses via continuing education, supervision, specialized training, or therapy enables us to take a step closer to a higher level of functioning within our personal and professional relationships.

Ally Actions

As we seek to describe the many aspects of what it means to be a social justice ally, it is important to define and discuss different types of allies, explain ally development, and explain what it means to become an effective ally. It is also essential to include how allies put theories into action. Ally definitions and theories can be studied and reviewed, but actions are the impetus for putting transformation and changes for social justice into motion. Covering the actions of allies includes dispelling myths as well as presenting a continuum of ally work.

Historical Realities Versus Popular Myths

People sometimes hold beliefs and ideas about groups of people who share common interests and purposes, for example, "Ku Klux Klan members are cowards." Some of these ideas and beliefs are accurate and some are untrue. In our music therapy practices, we advocate for our clients in a variety of ways and strive to provide the most effective treatments available. As we work toward being productive advocates and allies, it is crucial to examine and understand false beliefs versus the accurate realities.

There is a *myth* that using guilt will encourage others to become allies. "You have to join this diversity support group, or people will think that you don't really care" and other such accusations can backfire and actually steer some people away from advocacy participation. The *reality* is that blaming and shaming does not work to motivate people. Making people feel badly typically does not empower changes in beliefs or behaviors, but it often discourages self-confidence and involvement. Instead, people are more likely to respond and act with change and transformation if they feel appreciated and liked.

Making desperate pleas so that others will respond is another *myth* of ally behavior. Statements such as "We have to do this, or else we are doomed" are not instrumental in motivating others to step forward, participate, and act. Hope is a critical factor for inspiring others, and thus the *reality* is that tough issues are more readily accepted when they are presented with an attitude of hope.

The belief that "treating everyone equally or the same" makes you a good ally is another *myth*. The *reality* is that our efforts to be equitable may be unintentionally oppressive. For some, there is a fear that being aware of differences will separate people from one another. In *reality*, learning about dissimilarities and honoring them can effectively draw people to closer relationships because it can bring forth relevant portions of those same experiences in people's lives regardless of differences.

People may have the idea that going to a few classes about inequality and/or reading a book or two about oppression can make a person automatically an informed and prepared ally. The *myth* is that a little bit of knowledge or desire will make someone a good ally. The *reality* is that people may seemingly present as open-minded and accepting, yet some people have not yet truly learned the concepts involved in acting as an ally. Well-intentioned behaviors can be damaging, such as a music therapist who attends one conference session and reports being competent in the topic. Picking up one or two worthwhile expressions in a class or training session without grasping complex ally theories does not necessarily erase the façade that allows someone to pass off as accepting and unprejudiced (Bishop, 2002). Effective allies commit to long-term and on-going training and education in an effort to thoroughly grasp the concepts of oppression and demonstrate ally actions in their own behaviors.

The belief that some forms of oppression are worse than others is a *myth*. The *reality* is that all forms of oppression are interconnected and damaging to humanity. Different forms of oppression can have similarities and differences. Hardiman, Jackson, and Griffin (2010) remind us that it is not helpful to argue about a hierarchy of oppressions. They add that even if one form of oppression is deleted, the continuance of other forms would still have an effect on us all.

Another *myth* of allies is thinking that we can learn and grow as an ally solely based on stories learned from others. In *reality*, it is pertinent for allies to associate with their situations of being oppressed in such a way that they can relate to their position in society as oppressors. Bishop (2002) maintains that developing into an ally is a liberating occurrence because eventually you become an operative for your own emancipation.

Although less a myth than misconception, people wanting to be allies who work exclusively in a homogenous group can sometimes lead the group to become too comfortable. Without having a member of the oppressed group to offer feedback and challenges, a homogenous group can develop blind spots. Bishop (2002) states that it is difficult for us to see our own biases and privileges, regardless of the amount of time we have been working at deprogramming them.

An additional misconception is that we as allies will ultimately see the results of our efforts. Examples from historical social justice movements remind us that even though great time and energy was exerted, allies did not always see the fruits of their labors. This can be frustrating and discouraging, yet when allies support one another, the outcomes are multiplied toward the betterment of our communities and our entire society.

The *reality* for allies is that all oppressions are interrelated and cannot be discussed separately. A further *reality* for allies is the importance of understanding oppression, its history, how it is perpetuated, and how individuals, groups, and organizations can work toward liberation, hope, healing, and awareness. Whatever the form of social injustice being addressed, allies have the guiding goals of being courageous, consistent, and conscious.

In order to dispel social justice myths, misinformation, and untruths, it is important for music therapists to seek relevant education, training, and excellent supervision. This can include taking coursework at a college/university; attending in-services or trainings and conferences; reading books, journals, and periodicals; and exploring diverse media sources and organizations that are outside of their own culture (see Appendix). As we continually pursue fair, respectful, honest, and valuable ways to practice music therapy, we can engage in meaningful conversations by listening to and learning with others outside of our culture.

The Work of an Ally

As developed by Broido (2000b), ally work can be conceptualized as three concurrent processes: inspiring and educating dominant group members, creating institutional and cultural change, and supporting target group members. The following are several personal and professional suggestions for music therapists, adapted from Reason & Broido (2005).

Inspire and Educate Dominant Group Members in School, Workplace, and Home: Confront inappropriate comments and behaviors in a respectful manner; discuss power, privilege, and oppressions of all types and incorporate into your work; raise awareness of power and privilege differentials—don't be afraid to have the difficult discussions; challenge myths that dominant group members cannot effect change; study the history of the social justice movement and share what you learn; study works such as *White Privilege: Unpacking the Invisible Knapsack* by Peggy McIntosh; participate in providing resources, both formally and informally, to educate your peers, family, friends, and coworkers; encourage discussion of power, privilege, and oppressions of all types of professional and peer supervision; and persevere through potential defensiveness, which will be encountered.

Create Institutional and Cultural Change: Advocate for social justice coursework to be included in AMTA's Standards for Education and Clinical Training; study and improve your workplace environment(s) to promote safety and inclusion; support the recruitment and retention of diverse staff and clients in your workplace and in your professional organization(s); work to change unjust policies, laws, and practices both in your workplace and beyond to local, state, and federal governments; boycott institutions that do not support justice on all levels; participate in social justice movements, including marches, rallies, and other public small- or large-scale events; persevere through potential slow institutional change(s); advocate for inclusion of social justice issues/awareness in every facet of your professional career; donate money to organizations that support social justice causes; and join organizations that advance social justice causes.

Support Target Group Members: Listen; be careful of assumptions; apologize when you make mistakes and learn from your mistakes; continue to educate yourself so that you can effectively provide support; be visible with your support in conjunction with target members; create diversity within your group of friends; understand that target group members may be ambivalent about your support at first (Bishop, 2002); and persevere through difficult or painful situations.

Conclusion

After reading this chapter, we hope that you have an interest in becoming an effective ally. We acknowledge that the information can potentially be overwhelming, given its depth, complexities, and the need to confront both our privileged and oppressed identity markers. You might feel angry and immobile with the sheer amount of injustice that exists in the United States, Canada, and worldwide. You may also feel frightened to assess your active or passive role in present systems of oppression or for the inevitable mistakes that you will make along the journey. But allowing the immobilizing feelings to take hold continues to perpetuate the cycle. We must start somewhere to effect change. As Martin Luther King, Jr., so eloquently stated in his 1967 book, *Where Do We Go from Here: Chaos or Community?:*

> Returning violence for violence multiplies violence, adding deeper darkness to a night already devoid of stars. Darkness cannot drive out darkness: Only light can do that. Hate cannot drive out hate: Only love can do that. The beauty of nonviolence is that in its own way and in its own time it seeks to break the chain reaction of evil. (pp. 62–63)

The feeling of darkness and despair is understandable and certainly appropriate when faced with the magnitude of suffering and inequality in the world. It is our hope that this chapter sparks the light to shine through as well. By choosing

to be in the profession of music therapy, we have made the commitment to stand side by side with our clients within the human experience. Through continued education, exploration of self, and implementing direct practices of effective ally actions, we can all chip away at the chain reaction of oppression and social injustice in order to eventually liberate us *all.*

References

Ally (Def. 1). (n.d.). Oxford Dictionary Online. Retrieved from http://www.oxforddictionary.com/dictionary/us/definition/american_english/ally.

Ally (Def. 2). (n.d.). Merriam-Webster. Retrieved from http://merriam-webster.com/dictionary/ally.

American Music Therapy Association. (2015). *Scope of music therapy practice.* Retrieved from http://www.musictherapy.org/scopeofmusictherapypractice.html

American Music Therapy Association. (2014a). *A career in music therapy* (Brochure). Silver Spring, MD: AMTA.

American Music Therapy Association. (2014b). *Code of ethics.* Retrieved from http://www.musictherapy.org/ethics.html

American Music Therapy Association. (2013a). *AMTA professional competencies.* Retrieved from http://www.musictherapy.org/about/competencies/

American Music Therapy Association. (2013b). *AMTA standards of clinical practice.* Retrieved from http://www.musictherapy.org/standards.html

Andrews, K. T. (2001). Social movements and policy implementation: The Mississippi civil rights movements and the war on poverty, 1965 to 1971. *American Sociological Review, 66*(1), 71–95.

Ayvazian, A. (2010). Interrupting the cycle of oppression: The role of allies as agents of change. In M. Adams, W. J. Blumenfeld, C. Castaneda, H. W. Hackman, M. L. Peters, & X. Zuniga. (Eds.), *Readings for diversity and social justice* (2nd ed., pp. 625–628). New York, NY: Routledge.

Bennett, M. (2004). Becoming interculturally competent. In J. Wurzel (Ed.), *Toward multiculturalism: A reader in multicultural education* (2nd ed., pp. 62–77). Newton, MA: Intercultural Resource Corporation.

Bennett, M. J. (1993). Towards ethnorelativism: A developmental model of intercultural sensitivity. In R. M. Paige (Ed.), *Education for theintercultural experience* (2nd ed., pp. 21–71). Yarmouth, ME: Intercultural Press.

Bishop, A. (2002). *Becoming an ally: Breaking the cycle of oppression—in people* (2nd ed.). Halifax, NS: Fernwood.

Blumberg, R. L. (1990). White mothers as civil rights activists: The interweave of family and movement roles. In G. West & R. L. Blumberg (Eds.), *Women and social protest* (pp. 166–179). New York, NY: Oxford University Press.

Broido, E. M. (2000a). The development of social justice allies during college: A phenomenological investigation. *Journal of College Student Development, 41,* 3–17.

Broido, E. M. (2000b). Ways of being an ally to lesbian, gay, and bisexual students. In V. A. Wall & N. J. Evans (Eds.), *Toward acceptance: Sexual orientation issues on campus.* Lanham, MD: University Press of America.

Broido, E. M., & Reason, R. D. (2005). The development of social justice attitudes and actions: An overview of current understandings. In R. D. Reason, E. M. Broido, T. L. Davis, & N. J. Evans (Eds.), *Developing social justice allies (New Directions for Student Services, n. 110)* (pp. 17–28). San Francisco, CA: Jossey-Bass.

Collins, P. H. (2000). *Black feminist thought: Knowledge, consciousness, and the politics of empowerment.* (2nd ed.). New York, NY & London, UK: Routledge.

Cross, W. E., Jr. (1971). The Negro-to-Black conversion experience. *Black World, 20,* 13–27.

Cross, W. E., Jr. (1991). *Shades of Black: Diversity in African-American identity.* Philadelphia, PA: Temple University Press.

Curtis, S. L. (2006). Feminist music therapy: Transforming theory, transforming lives. In S. Hadley (Ed.), *Feminist perspectives in music therapy: Empowering women's voices* (pp. 227–244). Philadelphia, PA: Barcelona Publishers.

Curtis, S. L. (2012). Music therapy and social justice: A personal journey. *The Arts in Psychotherapy, 39,* 209–213.

Curtis, S. L. (2015). Profile of community music therapists in North America: A Survey. *Voices: A World Forum for Music Therapy, 1*(1). doi:10.15845/voices.v1i1.811

Edwards, K. E. (2006). Aspiring social justice ally development. *NASPA Journal, 43*(4), 39–60.

Estrella, K. (2001). Multicultural approaches to music therapy supervision. In M. Forisnash (Ed.), *Music Therapy Supervision* (pp. 39–66). Gilsum, NH: Barcelona Publishers.

Faire, R., & Langan, D. (2004). Expressive music therapy: Empowering engaged citizens and communities. *Voices: A World Forum for Music Therapy.* Retrieved from http://www.voices.no/mainissues/mi40004000159.html

Fogleman, E. (1994). *Conscience and courage: Rescuers of Jews during the Holocaust.* New York, NY: Anchor Books.

Goodman, D. (2001). *Promoting diversity and social justice: Educating people from privileged groups.* Thousand Oaks, CA: SAGE Press.

Green, P. (1998). *Equality and democracy.* New York, NY: A New Press Back-to-Basics Book.

Hadley, S. (2013a). Dominant narratives: Complicity and the need for vigilance in the creative arts therapies. *Arts in Psychotherapy, 40*(4), 373–381. doi:10.1016/j.aip.2013.05.007

Hadley, S. (2013b). *Experiencing race as a music therapist: Personal narratives.* Gilsum, NH: Barcelona Publishers.

Hadley, S., & Norris, M. (2015). Musical multicultural competency in music therapy: The first step. *Music Therapy Perspectives. 34*(2), 129-137. doi:10.1093/mtp/miv045

Hall, C. M. (1992). *Women and empowerment: Strategies for increasing autonomy.* Washington, DC: Hemisphere Publishing Corporation.

Hardiman, R., Jackson, B. W., & Griffin, P. (2010). Conceptual foundations. In M. Adams, W. J. Blumenfeld, C. Castaneda, H. W. Hackman, M. L. Peters, & X. Zuniga (Eds.), *Readings for diversity and social justice* (2nd ed., pp. 26–35). New York, NY: Routledge.

Johnson, A. G. (2006). *Privilege, power, and difference* (2nd ed.). Mountain View, CA: Mayfield.

Kendall, F. E. (2014). *Examples of speeches, workshops, and consultation topics: How to be an ally if you are a person of privilege.* Retrieved from http://franceskendall.com/workshops.html

Kenny, C. (2006). *Music & life in the field of play: An anthology.* Gilsum, NH: Barcelona Publishers.

Kenny, C. B., & Stige, B. (Eds.). (2002). *Contemporary voices in music therapy: Communication, culture, and community.* Oslo, Norway: Unipub Forlag.

King, M. L., Jr. (1967). *Where do we go from here: Chaos or community?* New York, NY: Harper & Row.

Kim, S. A., & Whitehead-Pleaux, A. (2015). Music therapy and cultural diversity. In B. Wheeler (Ed.), *Music therapy handbook* (pp. 51–63). New York, NY: Guilford Press.

Laidlaw, T. A., & Malmo, C. (Eds.). (1990). *Healing voices: Feminist approaches to therapy with women.* San Francisco, CA: Jossey-Bass.

Lerman, H., & Porter, N. (1990). *Feminist ethics in psychotherapy.* New York, NY: Springer.

Maloney, R. P. (2014). *Systemic change, an introduction.* Retrieved from http://famvin.org/wiki/Systemic_Change,_an_Introduction

McCall, L. (2005). The complexity of intersectionality. *SIGNS: Journal of Women in Culture and Society 30*(31), 771–802.

McIntosh, P. (1988). White privilege: Unpacking the invisible knapsack. In P. S. Rothenberg, *Race, class, gender in the United States: An integrated study.* (2004, pp. 188–192). New York, NY: Worth Publishing.

Morgan, K. P. (1996). Describing the emperor's new clothes. Three myths of educational (in)equality. In A. Diller, B. Houston, K. P. Morgan, & M. Ayim (Eds.), *The gender question in education: Theory, pedagogy, and politics.* Boulder, CO: Westview Press.

Pavlicevic, M., & Ansdell, G. (2004). *Community music therapy.* London, UK: Jessica Kingley.

Reason, R. D., & Broido, E. M. (2005). Issues and strategies for social justice allies (and the student affairs professionals who hope to encourage them). In R. D. Reason, E. M. Broido, T. L. Davis, & N. J. Evans (Eds.), *Developing social justice allies (New Directions for Student Services, n. 110)* (pp. 81–89). San Francisco, CA: Jossey-Bass.

Shultz, D. L. (1995). "We didn't think in those terms then": Narratives of Jewish women in the southern civil rights movement, 1960–1966 (Doctoral dissertation, The Union Institute). *Dissertation Abstracts International, 56*(07), 2843.

Stige, B. (2002). *Culture-centered music therapy.* Gilsum, NH: Barcelona Publishers.

Suyemoto, K. L., & Fox Tree, C. A. (2006). Building bridges across differences to meet social action goals: Being and creating allies among people of color. *American Journal of Community Psychology, 37,* 237–246. doi:10.1007/s10464-006-9048-1

Thompson, V. (2005). *What is a multicultural ally? Curricular material developed for multicultural awareness course.* Berkeley, CA: The Wright Institute.

Vaillancourt, G. (2010). Mentoring apprentice music therapists for peace and social justice through community music therapy: An arts-based study (Doctoral dissertation, Antioch University, 2009). UMI Dissertation Publishing.

Vaillancourt, G. (2012). Music therapy: A community approach to social justice. *The Arts in Psychotherapy, 39,* 173–178.

Washington, J., & Evans, N. J. (1991). Becoming an ally. In N. J. Evans & V. A. Wall (Eds.), *Beyond tolerance: Gays, lesbians, and bisexuals on campus* (pp. 195–204). Washington, DC: American College Personnel Association.

Watt, S. K. (2007). Difficult dialogues and social justice: Uses of the privileged identity exploration (PIE) model in student affairs practice. *College Student Affairs Journal 26*(2), 114–126.

Whitehead-Pleaux, A., Donnenwerth, A., Robinson, B., Hardy, S., Oswanski, L., Forinash, M., Hearns, M., Anderson, N., & Tan, X. (2013). Music therapists' attitudes and actions regarding the LGBTQ community: A preliminary report. *The Arts in Psychotherapy, 40,* 409–414.

Whitehead-Pleaux, A., Donnenwerth, A., Robinson, B., Hardy, S., Oswanski, L., Forinash, M., Hearns, M., Anderson, N., & York, B. (2012). Lesbian, gay, bisexual, transgender, and questioning: Best practices in music therapy. *Music Therapy Perspectives, 30*(2), 158–166.

Appendix A

Social Justice–Related Organizations

American Association of People with Disabilities: promotes equal opportunity, economic power, independent living, and political participation for people with disabilities. (www.aapd.com)

Amnesty International: a global movement of more than 3 million supporters, members, and activists in over 150 countries and territories who campaign to end grave abuses of human rights. (www.amnesty.org)

Council on American-Islamic Relations: strives to enhance the understanding of Islam, encourage dialogue, protect civil liberties, empower American Muslims, and build coalitions. (www.cair.com)

Creative Arts Therapists (CATs) of Color: A network of creative arts therapists composed of people of color who come together for the common purpose of promoting professional and educational development, sharing culturally relevant practices, providing mutual support, and encouraging cultural competence. (www.catsofcolor.com)

Parents, Families, and Friends of Lesbian and Gays: a national support, education, and advocacy organization for lesbian, gay, bisexual, and transgender (LGBT) people and their families, friends, and allies. (www.pflag.org)

National Alliance on Mental Illness: dedicated to building better lives for the millions of Americans affected by mental illness. (www.nami.org)

National Congress of American Indians: serves the interests of tribal governments and communities for American Indians and Alaska Native organizations. (www.ncai.org)

National Council on Aging: works to improve the health and economic security of millions of older adults. (www.ncoa.org)

National Council of Asian Pacific Americans: a coalition of 33 national Asian Pacific American organizations around the country. (www.ncapaonlin.org)

National Council of La Raza: civil rights and advocacy organization that works to improve opportunities for Hispanic Americans. (www.nclr.org)

The Jewish Federation of North America: represents 153 Jewish federations and over 300 network communities for social welfare, social services, and educational needs. (www.jewishfederations.org)

The National Association for the Advancement of Colored People: an organization whose vision is to ensure a society in which all individuals have equal rights without discrimination based on race. (www.naacp.org)

The National Organization for Women: an organization dedicated to a multi-issue and multistrategy approach to women's rights. (www.now.org)

The People's Institute for Survival and Beyond: a national and international collective of antiracist, multicultural community organizers and educators dedicated to building an effective movement for social transformation. (www.pisab.org)

Training for Change: an organization that teaches the skills of nonviolent social change. (www.trainingforchange.org)

Chapter 19

CULTURALLY COMPETENT MUSIC THERAPY ASSESSMENTS

Annette Whitehead-Pleaux, Stephanie L. Brink, & Xueli Tan

Annette: *I was in the office, writing an email, when a child life specialist came in and referred me to a new five-year-old patient. He was frightened and crying, having just arrived after a 36-hour journey to Boston. The child life specialist thought that music therapy might be the best treatment, as he was so upset and not responding to anyone talking. The child was from Senegal, a country in Africa, and spoke Wolof. I knew nothing about Senegalese culture, music, or customs, so I grabbed my guitar and a small array of hand percussion and headed to his room.*

In his room, his father and the interpreter stood next to the bed that held the small child who was crying. The child and father did not speak or understand English. I quickly introduced myself through the interpreter and played "Twinkle, Twinkle, Little Star." The child stopped crying and started playing a maraca with me. We played for a few minutes. When we completed the song, I started speaking with his father through the interpreter again. I explained how I work with music to help kids feel less scared and more comfortable in the hospital. I then told him quite honestly that I did not know anything about Senegalese culture, music, and customs, but I wanted to learn so that I could better help his child. I asked for his help, and together with the interpreter, we found common ground and ways in which I could work with his child through his admission.

This case is very similar to so many I have worked with in my tenure at the hospital. Many of the children live in different countries and come to the United States for medical care. Over the years, I have seen just how very important it is not just to understand a patient's physical and emotional needs, but also to work with the patient within the culture(s) with which he/she/ze identifies. Not only incorporating the music and instruments of the culture(s) into the music therapy interventions, but also understanding how these culture(s) impact the child's and family's beliefs about the roles of music in their lives, the societal norms and rules around music, and whether there is a connection between the creative arts and health. It is vital, then, to find out how the individual patient's personal relationship to music and how she/he/ze understands it to fit into this hospital experience.

Stephanie: *The hospital had just accepted several patients from the Middle East, all of whom had acute care needs. One of the children among those who had arrived was a 14-month-old baby girl who had suffered a severe facial burn from a roadside bomb. When I arrived at the patient's room, she was inconsolably crying in her mother's arms. The patient's mother looked unsure and utterly exhausted. With the help of the interpreter, I introduced myself and music therapy services. From working with a handful of other children and families*

from Middle Eastern countries, I had some knowledge that music was not always acceptable in the Muslim religion. I explained to the mother that music can sometimes help children to calm down when they are distressed, but if that was against her beliefs, then she could certainly refuse the service with no negative consequence. The patient's mother responded by saying, "I don't know if it will help, but I will try anything that might stop my daughter's crying." I began to improvise with voice and guitar. Having no Arabic vocabulary, I went back and forth between humming and singing common Western language syllables, the most prominent of which being "la" in this particular incidence. I played and sang throughout the child's bandage change. She appeared to respond positively to music therapy intervention, as evidenced by calming.

Later, I came to discover that the syllable "la" directly translated to the word "no" in Arabic. Through perhaps only a happy coincidence, I'd like to believe that the word "la," or "no," may have resonated with the child's feeling at the moment. I may never know this to be true, but in the end, the goal of soothing the child in a moment of acute distress was achieved, and the expression on the patient's mother's face was one of relief and gratitude.

One of the most remarkable things about the environment in which I work is the incredible diversity of our patient population. I have learned a great deal about myself and about myriad diverse cultures throughout my experience working in this setting. Along my path, there have been some missteps and some happy coincidences. Each lesson gleaned from these experiences has proven invaluable.

It has been through my clinical work that I have learned the importance of seeking to educate myself about culturally competent music therapy. I continue to grow in learning of my own personal biases, seeking to understand the broader culture of a client, not making blanket assumptions about specific groups, exploring how Western cultural bias can impact music therapy treatment/interventions, and, above all, acknowledging that the greatest strength in working with culturally diverse populations comes from being forthright about what you, the therapist, do not know about another person's culture. This is truly how, I believe, music therapists can initiate building a bridge to the creation of a cross-cultural therapeutic relationship.

Xueli: *While Annette and Stephanie had given clinical vignettes to illustrate the increasingly pluralistic music therapy workplace, I, on the other hand, will present some vignettes from the perpective of one who had been the recipient of less culturally conscious health practices. I am allergic to a lot of medications. The wrong medications or even the wrong dosage* can send me to the emergency room with complaints of nausea, vomiting, and oversize patches of rashes all over my body. After one such unpleasant episode, I returned to the doctor's office to request a different medication. The doctor's dismay was apparent: "But that (side effect) happens only 3% of the time!" My brain was screaming back at her, "But I am that 3%!" Clinical trials are often conducted with people from the majority culture. For example, the racial makeup in a study carried out by the National Cancer Institute consisted of 8% Blacks/African-Americans, 2.8% Asian/Pacific Islander, 0.5% Native American/ Alaskan Native, a small number of people who identified as mixed race, and more than 85% White (EMPACT Consortium, 2012). Thus, I am the covariate in the statistical equation because of the color of my skin and my genetic makeup. If my race and ethnic background creates "noise" in the research study, then I become a confounding variable, waiting on the sidelines until there is enough mass (sample size) to be included into the equation. I switched to a new doctor and took it as my responsibility to have a discussion about such racial genetic differences and how they might affect assessment, diagnosis, and prescription of treatments for me.

My case is not an isolated incidence. I have a friend, originally from Asia but now living in the United States, who was diagnosed with "some eye disease you caught when you went back to Asia last month." After several unnecessary eye exams, it turned out that she has presbyopia and all she needed was a pair of reading glasses!

In a more serious case, a friend was diagnosed with Asperger's syndrome because she withdrew from the community around her and prefers to have no social contact with anyone. For two years, she lived under the shadows of that diagnosis. When she finally had the opportunity to move away from the community, she realized that she did not have Asperger's syndrome. As one of the very few persons of color in that previous community, she had found that the instances of microinvalidation and discrimination were frequent. These daily stressors dissuaded any wish to socialize and connect with others in the community. In hindsight, it was not difficult to see why her behaviors might have resembled someone diagnosed with Asperger's syndrome. But once we include the cultural context to frame the behaviors, the understanding of her predicament is much more poignant.

Introduction

Assessment is the start of music therapy with a client. It is the point in time when we gather information from and about the potential client to gauge whether music therapy is appropriate for she/he/ze. From it, music therapists set the direction for the course of treatment, including setting goals and objectives as well as often designing interventions. In addition, it can give the client insight into how the music therapist practices, both through the interventions the music therapist uses to assess the client and also through the questions the music therapist asks and the way the music

therapist asks these questions. As our communities continue to become more diverse, the incorporation of culturally competent music therapy practices is vital for us to meet our clients where they are.

This chapter will explore culturally competent music therapy assessment practices. The authors start with an examination of what constitutes cultural competence. To understand why cultural competence is important for music therapists in North America, the authors explore the changing demographics of Canada and the United States. Next, we will investigate documents of the three North American music therapy associations, looking for culturally competent language and practices described therein. Fourth, the authors investigate education modes and meeting the education needs of new and practicing music therapists. This will lead to an examination of the existing music therapy assessments, looking for evidence of cultural competency. Finally, the authors present their model for culturally competent music therapy assessment.

What Is Cultural Competence?

Becoming culturally competent is by no means automatic. It is a dynamic process that occurs over the course of time and through experience and training (Sue et al., 1998). The journey begins with exploration of one's own personal bias and cultural influences and proceeds to cultural awareness, the insight that our clients are innately impacted by their own biases/cultural influences. This step is then followed by cultural sensitivity, the curiosity and desire to truly understand the implications of another individual's cultural influences. From cultural sensitivity, we move to cultural competence, or the integration of acquired knowledge from increasing cultural sensitivity into the therapist's assessment and treatment planning process. This process is beautifully outlined in Sue et al. (1998). Sue went beyond looking at the clinician's development of cultural competence to explore a broader view from the organizational perspective. Although Sue speaks from experience in the world of counseling, what he refers to as the dimensions of multicultural counseling competencies lend themselves well to the practice of music therapists.

Sue et al. (1998) stressed the importance of having a clear concept of the meaning of the term "multiculturalism" before moving on to cultural or multicultural competence. He stated that "it is important to note that the precise definition of multiculturalism is continually evolving, and the language used to describe its characteristics and process also continues to change" (Sue et al., 1998, p. 5). Having said this, the authors go on to provide a working definition for multicultural competence into characteristics of multiculturalism from the vantage point of a clinical counselor. Some of these concepts include the idea that diverse worldviews are neither positive nor negative; they just are and are to be appreciated and embraced. They emphasized that instead of viewing the convergence of the many different cultures that we encounter in our communities as a challenge or as something merely to be endured, we are better off viewing this convergence as a gift. It is important for the clinical to integrate into their understanding that …

> multiculturalism is reflected in more than just race, class, gender, and ethnicity. It also includes diversity in religion, national origin, sexual orientation, ability and disability, age, geographic origin, and so forth. Each of these characteristics contributes to our individual and collective diversity. (Sue et al., 1998, p. 5)

Multiculturalism is cultivating respect for values that may not only differ, but also be in direct conflict with our own. It is about dialogue and openness and a willingness to learn from and about each other. For music therapists, multiculturalism is providing with compassion and competence appropriate music therapy services for those clients whose worldviews may be dramatically different from our own.

While the vast majority of music therapists agree that multiculturalism ought to be a highly valued concept in terms of music therapy education and practice, many misunderstand the meaning behind the terms "culture," "cultural sensitivity," and "cultural competence." Without specific training, many music therapists may subscribe to the idea that the struggles and subsequent growth of their clients are comparable across cultures. This is just not so and has been shown through studies to be a somewhat naïve way of thinking (Topozada, 1995). Many music therapists who work with multicultural populations state that they have learned to be culturally competent through their clinical experience. While that may be a great start, music therapists, much like our counseling and art therapy peers, must find a path to engage in formalized education around multiculturalism and cultural competence in music therapy practice. Although the AMTA competencies vaguely suggest that cultural competence is important, as previously noted, there is no explanation as to how we give evidence to what culturally competent music therapy looks like from a practical or measurable standpoint.

Cultural competence is about far more than a list of stereotypes or assumptions made about a particular group of people. Cultural competence comes from a place of humility, genuine interest, and seeking to understand how another person's culture influences their worldview and the way in which they live their lives. It allows space for disagreement and acceptance of differences. It allows not for mere tolerance but for working toward mutual respect and the admiration of differences. Having a complete understanding of the significance of multiculturalism and cultural competence is essential to our evolving globalist society and, in turn, invaluable to clinicians in our pursuit of providing comprehensive and effective services to our multicultural/culturally diverse client populations.

Changing Demographics

Culturally competent music therapy is a necessity in North America because over the past several decades, the demographics of Canada and the United States have changed greatly. Both countries have had an increase in the numbers and diversity of their minority populations.

Canada's population has tripled since 1940 (Canadian Council on Social Development, n.d.). Much of this growth has been from immigration. With nearly 21% of Canada's population being foreign-born, Canada has a higher percentage of immigrant residents than any other G8 country (Canadian Council on Social Development, n.d.). Within Canada, the top countries of origin for these foreign-born residents are the Philippines, China, India, United States, Pakistan, United Kingdom, Iran, South Korea, Colombia, and Mexico.

The Canadian population had a marked increase in the number of people who identify themselves as members of visible minorities (Canadian Council on Social Development, n.d.). According to the 2001 Canadian Census, 13.4% of citizens identified as members of visible minorities; by 2006, that number had increased to 16.2%. Most recently, in 2011, the census found 19.1% of residents were visible minorities. This marks significant growth in the racial and ethnic diversity of Canada. In 2001, the visible minority populations were 3.5% Chinese, 3.2% Aboriginal, 3.1% South Asian, 2.2% Black, and 1% Filipino. In between 2001 and 2011, there was a change in the data that was collected. In 2011, the ethnicity of origin data shows the population of Canada to be 77% European, 14% Asian, 4% Aboriginal, 3% Black, 1% Latina/o, and 0.5% multiracial. From 1996 to 2001, the Aboriginal residents of Canada increased in numbers by 22%.

In the United States, the demographics continue to change and evolve. According to data from the last three U.S. Censuses, there have been steady changes to the racial and ethnic makeup of the country.

Table 1

Distribution of U.S. Population by Race and Ethnicity
(US Census Bureau, 2001; US Census Bureau, 2011)

	1990	2000	2010
White	80.3%	75.1%	72.4%
Black	12.1%	12.3%	12.6%
Hispanic	9.0%	12.5%	16.3%
2 or more races		2.4%	2.9%
Asian or Pacific Islander	2.9%	3.8%	5.0%
American Indian & Alaska Native	0.8%	0.9%	0.9%

As demonstrated in Table 1, it is evident that the population of the United States is changing significantly. In 2000, the percentage of people who identified as being of Hispanic ethnicity surpassed in size of the percentage of people who identified as Black (U.S. Census, 2001). It is significant to note that all categories of people of color have grown in percentage, while the White population has decreased.

Another marker of the way the population of the United States has changed is seen by looking at the categories the U.S. Census uses and how they have changed from 1990 to 2000. In 1990, there were six race and ethnicity categories: White, Black, Native American and Alaska Native, Asian or Pacific Islander, Hispanic Origin, and Other Race. In contrast, the 2000 Census had eight categories, with several having definitions: White, Black or African-American, Native American or Alaska Native, Asian (Asian Indian, Chinese, Filipino, Japanese, Korean, Vietnamese, Other Asian), Native Hawaiian and Pacific Islander (Guamanian or Chamorro, Samoan, Other), Some Other Race, Two or More Races, and Hispanic or Latino origin (Mexican, Puerto Rican, Cuban, Other Hispanic or Latino). Racial/ethnic groups that were lumped together in 1990 were separated and counted. Similarly, people of two or more races were finally given a box to check that embraced their racial/ethnic heritage; in previous censuses, they had had to choose one race/ethnicity or another, denying their true dual or multiple heritage(s).

In 2010, the categories of the U.S. Census were expanded again. Hispanic ethnicity was modified to Hispanic, Latino, and Spanish Origin. Within Hispanic, Latino, and Spanish Origin, individuals were asked to identify whether they were one or more of these four ethnicities: (1) Mexican, Mexican-American, Chicano; (2) Puerto Rican; (3) Cuban; or (4) Other Hispanic, Latino, and Spanish. When individuals check Other, they are asked to identify their country of origin/heritage. Race categories have also changed drastically. People are given the option to check off one or more races. The list of races is (1) White; (2) Black, African-American, Negro; (3) American Indian and Alaska Native (space is provided to identify primary tribal affiliation); (4) Asian Indian; (5) Chinese; (6) Filipino; (7) Japanese; (8) Korean; (9) Vietnamese; (10) Other Asian (space is provided to identify country of origin/heritage); (11) Native Hawaiian; (12) Guamanian or Chamorro; (13) Samoan; (14) Other Pacific Islander (space is provide to identify country or origin/heritage; and (15) Some Other Race (space is provided to identify their country of origin/heritage). In 20 years, the U.S. Census went from six categories of race/ethnicity to 14. This shift in 20 years demonstrates just how the diversity of culture in the United States has grown and the awareness of different cultures has greatly increased. These are just changes with race and ethnicity within our countries. These changes are an indication of the how the population of the United States has continued to become more diverse.

The religious demographics of Canada and the United States have also changed dynamically over the past few decades. The Pew Research Center (2013) conducted research into the Canadian population in 1971 and 2011. The researchers saw dramatic reductions in percentage of Protestants (41% to 27%) and Catholics (47% to 39%) in that forty-year timespan. While Christian based faiths decrease, there were increases in other religions (4% to 11%) and unaffiliated (4% to 24%).

In looking at religious demographics of the United States, there are interesting trends noticed from 2007 to 2014. The Pew

Research Center sees a decline in Christian-based faiths from 78.4% of Americans in 2007 to 70.6% in 2014, a loss of 7.8% (Pew Research Center, 2014). The researchers saw an increase in non-Christian faiths from 4.7% to 5.9% from 2007 to 2014. Within the non-Christian faiths, Islam increased by 0.5% and Sanatana Dharma by 0.3%. Interestingly, the numbers of people who are unaffiliated (including agnostic and atheist) increased from 16.1% to 22.8% in that same seven-year time period.

When looking to the future demographics of North America, it is reasonable to assume the diversity of our nations will continue to increase. As the population around us diversifies, it is also reasonable to assume that our client populations will continue to become more and more diverse, which increases the need for music therapists to adopt culturally competent music therapy practices.

Documents of the Associations

There are three major music therapy associations in Canada and the United States, the Canadian Association of Music Therapy (CAMT), the American Music Therapy Association (AMTA), and the Certifying Board of Music Therapists (CBMT). Each organization has documents that serve to guide its members in a variety of areas. The organizations have codes of ethics available through Internet search. In addition, AMTA has their clinical standards, competencies, and educational standards available to Internet search. While many of these documents discuss culturally competent practices, clear guidelines do not exist.

Both CAMT and AMTA have codes of ethics. These codes are set in place to offer guidance and regulation for our field in each respective country. The Code of Ethics (2002) of the CAMT discusses elements of culture in two sections: Principles and Values Respect for Society. The Principles and Values section requires the music therapist to uphold ...

> the fundamental rights of each person, and accept that an individual should be treated primarily as a person, not as an object or a means to an end. Music therapists acknowledge that all persons have a right to their innate worth as human beings, and that this worth is not enhanced or reduced by their culture, nationality, ethnicity, colour, race, religion, gender, marital status, sexual orientation, physical or mental abilities, age, socioeconomic status, and/or any other preference or personal characteristic, condition, or status. (p. 2)

This section of the Canadian Code of Ethics continues by stating that music therapists are to respect the dignity and rights of people by acknowledging self-determination and autonomy, using verbal and written communication that is respectful, refraining from participating in or condoning discrimination, and not infringing "in service or research activities, on the personally, legally, or culturally defined private space of individuals or groups unless explicit permission is granted to do so" (CAMT, 2002, p. 6).

The Respect for Society section focuses on the ethical guiding principles for the music therapist to follow in society at large. Music therapists are to express "respect for and abide by prevailing community mores, social customs, and cultural expectations in all activities" (CAMT, 2002, p. 19). In addition to this, music therapists are to "acquire adequate knowledge of the culture, social structure, and customs of a community before beginning any major work there" (CAMT, 2002, p. 19)

The AMTA Code of Ethics directs its members to not engage in discrimination against people who are clients, subjects, students, colleagues, or organizations "based upon race, ethnicity, language, religion, marital status, gender, gender identity or expression, sexual orientation, age, ability, socioeconomic status, or political affiliation" (AMTA, 2015a, 2.3.2). Like the Canadian Code of Ethics, AMTA's Code of Ethics is very clear about not engaging in discrimination. However, AMTA's does not expand into further intersections of cultural competence and ethics as does the Canadian document, including respect for cultures.

The AMTA Professional Competencies is a document that lists the skills that each student of music therapy must obtain to be considered a full-fledged music therapist. This document lists a myriad of competencies. One competency that discusses culturally competent music therapy states that the music therapist will "identify the elemental, structural, and stylistic characteristics of music from various periods and cultures" (AMTA, 2013, 1.2). In the section titled Professional Role/Ethics, three competencies focus on culturally competent music therapy practices. In 17.9, the music therapist is expected to "demonstrate knowledge of and respect for diverse cultural backgrounds" (AMTA, 2013, 17.9). There is no guidance as to the nature of the knowledge the music therapist is to demonstrate. Similarly vague, 17.11 states that a music therapist must "demonstrate skill in working with culturally diverse populations" (AMTA, 2013, 17.11). The competency marked 17.10 clearly states that music therapists will "treat all persons with dignity and respect, regardless of differences in race, ethnicity, language, religion, marital status, gender, gender identity or expression, sexual orientation, age, ability, socioeconomic status, or political affiliation" (AMTA, 2013, 17.10). AMTA's professional competencies do not delineate clear competencies for culturally competent practices.

The Standards of Clinical Practice (AMTA, 2015b) is a document that delineates the bare minimum that each music therapist must do to practice music therapy. The standards state that each "music therapy assessment will explore the client's culture" (AMTA, 2015b, 2.2). This exploration is described as one that "can include but is not limited to race, ethnicity, language, religion/spirituality, socioeconomic status, family experiences, sexual orientation, gender identity or expression, and social organizations" and is appropriate for the client's culture(s) (AMTA, 2015b, 2.2). When looking at the

standards, we find few that deal directly with culturally competent music therapy practices. Music therapists are expected to "include music, instruments, and musical elements, from the client's culture as appropriate" (AMTA, 2015b, 3.6.1). These standards do not require a thorough set of skills/behaviors that reflect cultural competence.

Unfortunately, the AMTA Standards of Education and Clinical training do not reference any direct focus of study on culturally competent music therapy practices (AMTA, n.d.). The authors find it concerning that the documents that lay out what skills and behavior a music therapist must have to practice are not supported in the educational and clinical training standards.

CBMT is the third organization within North America that defines music therapy practice. Within its document, Board Certification Domains (2015), CBMT addresses some culturally competent behavior. Like CAMT and AMTA, CBMT states that culture and spirituality need to be identified in the music therapy assessment of each client. In addition, the client's culture(s), among other factors, is/are to be considered in the design of music therapy treatment plans. However, unlike the other documents examined here, those of CBMT go further into the individual therapist's role by stating that the music therapist must acknowledge their "bias and limitations in interpreting assessment information (e.g., cultural differences, clinical orientation)" (CBMT, 2015, p. 1).

Individual music therapists and groups of music therapists have explored cultural competence. Whitehead-Pleaux et al. (2012) were the first within the field of music therapy in the United States and Canada to propose a set of best practices in regard to lesbian, gay, bisexual, transgender, queer/questioning (LGBTQ) individuals. Focusing on clinical practice, work environment, and education and clinical training, Whitehead-Pleaux et al. (2012) described culturally competent practices. The authors point out that best practices for other diverse groups are needed to advance culturally competent practices in music therapy.

The professional organizations within Canada and the United States offer some guidance toward culturally competent expectations, skills, and proficiencies. Individual music therapists have begun to define these practices for specific populations. However, these do not encompass the depth and breadth of culturally competent music therapy practice.

Existing Music Therapy Assessments

Bruscia (1988) summarized the sentiments of creative arts therapists in regard to the accessibility and uniqueness of utilizing the arts in the assessment process. Because creative arts, especially in the form of music, are so easily accessible and valued, patients or clients are motivated to engage in the process with the therapists. In addition, because arts tend to be symbolic and nonverbal, they offers inimitable perspectives and insights about the individuals' issues and concerns (Bruscia, 1988). Although assessment has been a part of music therapy practice since the early 1960s, the emphasis on the importance of assessment has been limited because the profession of music therapy has emerged from empirical practice rather than from theoretical frameworks (Wheeler, 2013; Wigram, Pedersen, & Bonde, 2002). Indeed, Lipe (2015) commented that the literature on music therapy assessments dated prior to 1992 is scarce. Because standardized music therapy assessments are limited, Lipe (2015) relied on her own expertise and literature from allied health professionals to highlight a four-step process in developing music therapy assessments. The four steps, in sequential order, are Step 1: Specify the purpose of the assessment; Step 2: Content validation; Step 3: Quantitative evaluation; and Step 4: Validation phase (Lipe, 2015, p. 86).

Relating to identifying the specific purpose of the assessment, Wigram et al. (2002, p. 247) listed five forms of assessment models and evaluations: (1) Diagnostic assessment: To obtain evidence to support a diagnostic hypothesis; (2) General assessment: To obtain information on general needs, strengths and weaknesses; (3) Music therapy assessment: To obtain evidence supporting the value of music therapy as an intervention; (4) Initial period of clinical assessment in music therapy: To determine in the first two to three sessions a therapeutic approach relevant to the client; and (5) Long-term music therapy assessment: To evaluate over time the effectiveness of music therapy.

The following sections illustrate some examples of music therapy assessment tools that have surfaced within the past 15 years.

The Individualized Music Therapy Assessment Profile (IMTAP)

The IMTAP functions as a general assessment, initial period of clinical assessment, and long-term assessment (Baxter, Berghofer, MacEwan, Nelson, Peters, & Roberts, 2007; Wigram et al., 2002). This assessment tool was intended for use in pediatric and adolescent clinical settings. The many components of IMTAP allow the music therapist to use each independently or to map out the entire patient progress from the initial session to termination. A team of six music therapists in clinic developed the test items by drawing from their own expertise in working with children and adolescents with a variety of diagnoses. They complemented this initial effort with a literature review of test instruments and assessments from related fields.

Special Education Music Therapy Assessment Process (SEMTAP)

The SEMTAP emerged from the expertise and experiences of music therapists over a period of 18 years in more than 20 public school districts in Texas (Coleman & Brunk, 2003). SEMTAP is a criterion-referenced test, that is, the objective of the assessment is to show how students with special needs perform specific skills related to their Individualized Education Plan (Coleman & Brunk, 2003).

Music Therapy Assessment for Developmental Disabilities (MTADD)

The MTADD assessment is applicable to individuals of all ages and with diverse disabilities (Boxill & Chase, 2007). The recommendation is that an assessment take place over several sessions lasting a few weeks. This assessment evaluates individuals using a checklist of items grouped under various domains such as eye contact, attention span, motor skills, communication, and cognitive and social skills.

Psychiatric Music Therapy Questionnaire (PMTQ)

There are three versions of PMTQ to cater to children, adolescent, and adult populations (Cassity & Cassity, 2006). The PMTQ captures intake information related to issues most frequently addressed by music therapists working in psychiatric settings. Cassity and Cassity (2006) regarded the PMTQ as a "behavioral interview questionnaire" (p. 40) in which patients utilize Likert scales to rate themselves.

Music Therapy Assessment Tool for Awareness in Disorders of Consciousness (MATADOC)

The MATADOC, a standardized measure for assessing patients with disorders of consciousness, emerged from a clinically derived assessment that was developed and refined over a period of 17 years (Magee, Siegert, Taylor, Daveson, & Lenton-Smith, 2016). The assessment entails 14 items categorized under three subscales. The principal subscale evaluates the patients' responses to visual and auditory stimuli, responses to verbal commands, and arousal; the second subscale measures behavioral response to music and musical response; and the third subscale assesses motor, communication, and emotional behaviors (Magee et al., 2016).

Rothwell (2005) made a recommendation (p. 91) that journal editors of research publications require a section titled "To Whom Do These Results Apply?" External validity is compromised when the trial sample is not an accurate or adequate representation of the clinical population (Rothwell, 2005). The descriptions of test participants rarely extend beyond their age, gender, and current status, for example, "20 university students (12 males, 8 females)." Discussions about the participants' cultural, racial, and ethic backgrounds are not discussed. A systematic review of approximately 20 years of the measures of cultural competence most frequently used in medicine and in health professions raised several concerns (Kumas-Tan, Beagan, Loppie, Maclead, & Frank, 2007). One issue was that these measures were "normed on predominantly White, middle-class, highly educated populations" (Kumas-Tan et al., 2007, p. 548), thereby invalidating the ability to project such measures to the ever-increasing diverse population. In addition, the researchers found that many assessment measures oversimplify culture and cultural competence. These measures tended to classify culture as relating to only ethnicity and race (Kumas-Tan et al., 2007). Thus, the individuals' other identity markers, such as age, gender, sexual orientation, religious preference, social class, and geographical location, were not considered. By oversimplifying, clinicians risk running out-of-context assessments by removing the individuals from their cultural frameworks. For example, the meaning of silence in therapy sessions can be interpreted in many ways, depending on the age and gender of the client and therapist and/or their similar or dissimilar ethnic backgrounds or socioeconomic statuses.

Evidence-Based Practice (EBP) calls for clinicians to consider not only the best research evidence, but also the expertise of their own clinical work as well as the goals and preferences of their patients or clients (Gilgun, 2004). To answer the call to demonstrate efficacy and evidence-based practice, standardized assessment tools are likely to become increasingly central and pertinent in the music therapy field (Boxill & Chase, 2007; Wigram et al., 2002). The shifting trend toward short-term treatment in our health care system and the exponential increase in the number of individuals with minority identity markers would significantly affect how clinicians and researchers construct music therapy assessments.

Cultural Paradigm

From our experience in working with children and families from around the world for 25 combined years, we started to conceptualized our practice with culturally diverse children and families as this simple Cultural Paradigm.

Figure 1. *Cultural Paradigm*

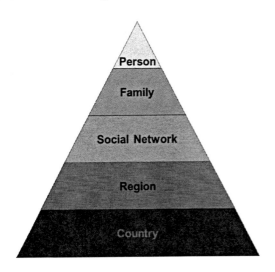

We chose a pyramid shape to illustrate the hierarchy from the most global cultural factors up through the individual client that impact a client's worldview, relationship to music, and perceptions around the concept of therapy. From this paradigm, we continued to expand on our ideas of how to incorporate a client's culture(s) into our music therapy assessment. As each of us implemented our beginning

conceptualized ideas of multicultural assessment, we found that our original model needed expansion to include more cultures. This paradigm was expanded to show the multiple cultural influences upon each of our clients. In the following section, we share our expanded model and how it applies in music therapy cultural assessment and treatment planning.

Client Cultural Assessment and Treatment Planning

As we considered the influence of cultures on individuals and the intersectionality of these cultures within the individual, we struggled with how best to conceptualize this. From working with people for many years, each of us knew that our clients, as well as we, ourselves, have a multitude of identities influenced by cultures that we step into and out of. To capture this dynamic influence upon the individual, we conceptualized it in this diagram.

Figure 2. *Cultural Influences on Identity*

In the center of our model is the "person" or, for the sake of this chapter, the client. The client is surrounded by a variety of circles of culture types to which the client is connected. These types include culture(s) of heritage; culture(s) of religion; culture(s) of gender, identity, and orientation; socioeconomic culture(s); generational culture(s); culture(s) of location; survivor culture(s); culture(s) of disability; and culture(s) of identification. Each of these cultures influences and informs the client. Ways to explore these cultures within the music therapy assessment will be explored.

Culture(s) of heritage includes racial and ethnic cultures. Throughout the book, many authors have explored several of these cultures and the intersection between the culture, music, health, and individual. In considering culture(s) of heritage, there are several questions we must ask while conducting a music therapy assessment.

(1) What is the client's musical heritage?
(2) What role do music and the arts play in the culture of heritage?
(3) What are the norms and mores of the culture regarding music?
   a. What instruments are permissible?
   b. What genres of music are permissible?
(4) What role does this/these heritage(s) play in the client's life?
(5) How do the client's culture(s) of heritage influence thoughts, attitudes, and beliefs about music, therapy, and wellness?
(6) What role do the music(s) from the culture(s) of heritage play in the client's life?
(7) Is there a genre/artist from her/his/zer culture(s) of heritage that she/he/ze listens to/plays/resonates with?
   a. Why?
(8) Are there genres/artists from her/his/zer culture(s) of heritage that he/she/ze dislikes?
   a. Why?
(9) Is the client involved in music/dance groups that are related to her/his/zer culture(s) of heritage?
   a. If so, what?
(10) How does this/these culture(s) influence the client's presentation, beliefs, and actions?

Religion can be based both in spiritual/faith beliefs as well as in social customs. Examples of this are two people, George and Lucy. Both are Catholic. George goes to worship at church every Sunday, prays daily, and abstains from eating red meat on Fridays during Lent because it is a form of penitence. Lucy rarely goes to church but also abstains from eating red meat on Fridays of Lent because it is what Catholics do. It is important to ascertain in what ways our clients are involved in their religion.

(1) What role does religion play in the client's life?
   a Is it cultural or spiritual or both?
(2) What are the norms and mores of the religion regarding music?
   a What instruments are permissible?
   b What genres of music are permissible?
(3) How do the culture(s) of religion influence the client's thoughts, attitudes, and beliefs about music, therapy, and wellness?
(4) What role does music from the client's religion play in her/his/zer life?
(5) Is the client involved in some aspect of music during the religious ceremonies?
   a. If so, what?
(6) How do this/these culture(s) influence the client's presentation, beliefs, and actions?

Socioeconomic status and the cultures that surround that status have a deep influence upon most people. If a person grew up in poverty without having enough to eat, she/he/ze may maintain the cultural value learned when young of never wasting food. When considering the influence of socioeconomic status/culture on a client's experiences with music, it is important to consider how accessible things like instruments, lessons, concerts, music files/albums/CDs, electronic music technologies, and so forth are to the client.

Within socioeconomic status and cultures, there are status symbols that signify one's place within society. These are often brands of clothing, accessories, cars, phones, computers/tablets, and so on. They extend into music, with brands, instruments and electronic music technologies, genres of music, and accessibility to concerts. It is not uncommon for clients to make assumptions about the music therapist's socioeconomic status/culture based on the instruments and electronic music technologies used in sessions.

(1) What are the financial limitations the client faces?
   a. Does this affect the client's access to listening to music, recorded and/or live?
   b. Does this affect the client's access to instruments or music technology?
   c. Does this affect the client's access to music education?
(2) What are the values and norms associated with the client's socioeconomic status/culture?
   a. What are music values and norms associated with the client's socioeconomic status/culture?
(3) How does this/these culture(s) influence the client's presentation, beliefs, and actions?

There are several types of generational cultures to consider with clients. First, if a client is a first-, second-, or third-generation immigrant, there are differences between the cultures of each generation. These differences relate to the degree that the culture of heritage is integrated with the culture of the country of residence. As is discussed in several chapters, the differences between the first, second, and third generations are great and can cause stress between family members.

Another type of generational culture to consider is that based on birth dates. Examples of these include the baby boomers, slacker generation, generation X, and millennials. Each has its own values, customs, ideas, arts, and symbols. The music of each generation is different from that of the previous and often the music that music therapists go to when working with a new client. When assessing a new client, it is important to note their generation and how it influences their music interests, likes, and dislikes. The different generations may also influence the types of instruments the client will be interested in using or not using. Generational differences are seen with technology. Although there are many music therapists who are digital immigrants and quite savvy with technology, the younger generations (digital natives), who have grown up with smart devices and computers, are quite adept at interfacing with technology. Below are some questions to incorporate into a music therapy assessment.

(1) If the client has an immigrant heritage, what generation is she/he/ze?
   a. How does this generational heritage culture influence thoughts, attitudes, and beliefs about music, therapy, and wellness?
(2) Are there generational musical considerations?
(3) What is the client's familiarity and comfort with technology?
   a. How does the client access music through technology?
   b. Is the technology up to date? (important when using homework or teaching independent coping strategies)
(4) How does this/these culture(s) influence the client's presentation and actions?

Within North American societies, there are cultures for gender identity, gender expression, and sexual orientation. These cultures have norms and rules that impact our interactions with music, whether through playing, listening, or creating. When administrating an assessment, it is important to consider several questions about the intersections of gender identity, gender expression, and sexual orientation.

(1) What are the societal norms of the client's gender, and does the client follow these norms?
(2) How does the client identify their gender, or does she/he/ze choose to not identify?
   a. What name does the client prefer you to use for them?
   b. What pronouns does she/he/ze prefer?
   c. What terms does the client feel comfortable with you (the music therapist) using to refer to their gender?
   d. Are there musical limitations or interests related to the client's gender?
   e. If the client identifies as a sexual orientation other than male or female, does she/he/ze listen to music by artists who identify similarly or genres associated with one or more LGBTQI+ communities?
   f. If so, who or which?
   g. Is the client open about her/his/zer gender identity?
(3) What is the client's gender expression?
   a. Is she/he/ze cis gendered?
   b. How would the client prefer to appear if their gender expression is being limited?
   c. Are there musical limitations or interests related to the client's gender expression?
   d. If so, what?

(4) How does the client define her/his/zer sexual orientation?
   a. What terms do they feel comfortable with you (the music therapist) using to refer to their sexual orientation?
   b. Are there musical limitations or interests related to the client's sexual orientation?
   c. If the client identifies as a sexual orientation other than straight/heterosexual, does she/he/ze listen to music by artists who are from the LGBTQI+ community or genres associated with one or more LGBTQI+ communities?
   d. If so, who or which?
   e. Is the client involved in a LGBTQI+ music group (choir, band, or orchestra)?
   f. Is the client out?

The diversity in culture that is based on regions is true not just for the United States and Canada, but for every country. There are regional cultures which include specific genres of music, customs, beliefs, religions, and so forth. The regional cultures within a country can have opposing norms and beliefs. This knowledge will influence your approach and music therapy interventions. When assessing clients, it is important to consider the cultures of the location—not only where she/he/zer resides now, but also the cultures of location where she/he/zer has lived prior to the time of the assessment.

(1) What role does the culture where the client lives play in the client's identity?
(2) What are the norms and mores of this culture regarding music?
(3) What are the music genres associated with that location?
   a. Does the client engage in music within the locational genres?
(4) What other locational/regional cultures has the client lived in?
   a. What influence do these cultures have on the client?

Cultures of disability often center on the specific disability(ies) that the client or person closely associated with the client has. These can range from developmental and intellectual disabilities to substance abuse, physical disabilities, mental illness, and beyond. When assessing a client, it is important to learn about their involvement or noninvolvement in the associated culture. This can impact greatly the direction that is taken in music therapy as well as any referrals the music therapist makes to outside organizations or treaters. Below are some questions that can help to facilitate learning more about the client in relation to disability cultures.

(1) What role do disability cultures play in the client's life and identity?
(2) Is the client/family/caretaker a member of an

organization associated with the disability?
   a. If so, to what degree to they subscribe to the culture associated with the organization?
   b. If not, why?
(3) What are the norms and mores of this culture regarding music?
(4) Are there songs, musicians, or concerts associated with this culture?
   a. Is the client/family/caregiver aware of these?
   b. Is this music which the client enjoys/has interest in?
   c. If not, why?

Survivor cultures do not apply to all clients. Some clients may reveal their survivorship within the assessment, while others may reveal it later. Some may never reveal this information within their music therapy session. If the client reveals that they are a survivor or if this information is in the client's record, it is important for the music therapist to assess the client's involvement with the cultures associated with the type of trauma the client has survived (cancer, sexual abuse, domestic violence, war, amputation, burn, etc.). The cultures associated with each type of survivorship vary, as does the music associated. Below are some questions to consider as you conduct your assessment. If the client has not revealed their survivor status but it is listed in the client's record, care must be taken when asking these questions.

(1) What role do survivor cultures play in the client's life and identity?
(2) Is the client/family/caretaker a member of an organization associated with the type of trauma or survivorship?
   a. If so, to what degree do they subscribe to the culture associated with the organization?
   b. If not, why?
(3) What are the norms and mores of this culture regarding music?
(4) Are there songs, musicians, or concerts associated with this culture?
   a. Is the client/family/caregiver aware of these?
   b. Is this music which the client enjoys/has interest in?
   c. If not, why?

The final culture(s) to assess are the one(s) with which the client identifies. Often, people will identify with a culture that is not one they grew up in, lived in, or experienced. This is definitely a phenomenon seen with adolescents who are exploring who they are by "trying on" different identities. Within music, this is seen when someone's preferred music is from a culture that is counter to the culture(s) that she/he/ze lives in. An example is a White affluent male who listens to and embraces the cultural stylings of gangster rap. This male is not from the culture where gangster rap developed yet not only listens to the music but has adapted its language, clothing, and presentation to resemble the inner city Black culture(s). As

music therapists, an understanding of what culture(s) the client identifies with is the final portion to the cultural assessment. There are several questions that help us to explore this cultural identity.

(1) With what culture(s) does the client identify?
   a. Why?
   b. Does the client listen to the music of that culture?
   c. Why?
   d. Which artists/bands/genres?
   e. How does this culture influence the client's presentation and actions?

These questions are really just starting points for music therapists to consider incorporating into their music therapy assessments. This information is necessary to truly meet and support your client where they are and to avoid gross missteps based on a lack of knowledge or bias. The key concept when assessing cultural influences on music is simply determining the client's personal relationship to the music of the cultures that play a role in her/his/zer life. Knowing this information is key to goal-setting, treatment planning, and implementation. It is essential to integrate the client's culture(s) and music into the music therapy goals and interventions.

To this end, it falls on the music therapist to learn about the cultures that influence the clients with whom she/he/ze works. There are a variety of avenues available to music therapists in this task. The first is to research the culture and music associated with it. The information highway has made this task much easier than it was just 10 years ago. The availability of many genres of music from across the globe has grown exponentially. This increased availability of music and information about music has made learning more accessible to all music therapists.

Another resource that can be available to music therapists when working with people from other cultures of heritage is interpreters. It is important for music therapists to know how to use an interpreter correctly. Talk with the interpreter prior to the session to explain what you want to cover, as well as ask questions of how best to present the concepts to be covered in the session. The interpreter is not only a language translator, but also a cultural ambassador, available to providers to help bridge the gulfs between cultures. When working with an interpreter, look at the client when you are talking to them, not at the interpreter. Use first-person language and not third-person language. An example is, instead of saying, "Ask them if they play instruments," say, "What instruments you play?" The communication is between the client and the music therapist. The interpreter holds the skills to make that communication possible but is not the one a music therapist is addressing in the session. To help facilitate the communication between the music therapist and the client, learning key phrases or greetings in the client's language can go a long way in showing the music therapist's genuine interest in knowing the client as an entire person, not just the part with which she/he/ze is working.

Once music therapists learn about the cultures and the

music associated with them, the next step is incorporating the music into sessions as appropriate. This can be accomplished in a variety of ways. Music therapists can incorporate recorded music from that culture in their interventions. They can learn songs from that culture and play them live. Music therapists can incorporate elements of the music styles (melodies, rhythms, harmony, progressions, tempo, etc.) from the culture in improvisations. By incorporating instruments from that culture or ones that approximate the sound/shape/style of playing, the music therapist can validate the client's connection to that culture. Finally, the music therapist can ask the client to teach her/him/zer songs from their culture that have meaning to the client.

The Role of Education in Culturally Competent Music Therapy Assessment

Music therapy is taught from various philosophical perspectives, including behavioral, humanistic, cognitive behavioral, analytic, and transpersonal. Students should carefully consider the educational paradigm of the program into which they choose to enter. Regardless of the underlying program philosophy, each program must include some component of self-reflection on the part of the therapist in training. That self-reflection/self-awareness can be developed through techniques such as musical improvisation (free or specific to an aspect of the therapist's development), reflective journaling, mandala, and supervision, to name a few.

Self-reflection/increase of self-awareness on the part of the developing clinician or seasoned professional is an intrinsically valuable skill as it relates to increasing cultural awareness should this be a direction in which an individual wishes to grow. Self-reflective practices translate well in exploring the topic of personal bias and how biases impact clinical work. To be clear, everyone has some form of implicit bias, whether they are cognizant of it or not. But how do we as clinicians, novice or experienced, know the "why," "when," or "how" of exploring our own personal bias?

If the truth be told, we are still only beginning this discussion in music therapy journals and literature on the topic of cultural competence. Those who have explored the topic have done so with the hope of sparking interest beyond their writings. In the literature, there is an apparent agreement that although the vast majority of music therapists value the concept of providing multicultural music therapy to their clients, clinicians do not feel as though they have received adequate training in their undergraduate curricula in providing multicultural music therapy. It is worthy of mention that these sources are at a minimum of a decade old (Chase, 2003; Toppozada, 1995). Chase (2003) stated, "[R]esearch indicates that music therapy professionals have a strong interest and high level of comfort in providing multicultural music therapy, but feel ill-prepared by their undergraduate training programs. Most professionals gained cultural awareness through clinical experience" (p. 84). The idea of gaining cultural awareness through clinical

experience is a notion that allows for exceedingly broad possibilities of interpretation.

Many clinicians, through no fault of their own, may have a misunderstanding of what multicultural music therapy or culturally competent music therapy looks like, sounds like. or feels like. Toppozada (1995) discussed the importance of formally training music therapists to work with clients of diverse backgrounds. He wrote: "[S]ome in this country (United States) feel that all people are basically the same, and that the best way to effectively help someone is to be culturally, ethnically, and racially 'blind'" (p. 66). Taking a one-size-fits-all approach to providing therapy services is an erroneous tactic. However, without being provided guidance on the topic, it may be difficult to know just how to approach providing culturally competent music therapy services. Toppozada (1995) continued:

> [A]lthough therapists may feel that they are helping their clients by relying solely on good counseling techniques, they may be completely unaware that their cultural ignorance is undermining their efforts … [and that] … majority culture therapists may be unaware of their own biases, while their minority clients may in fact be acutely aware of them. (p. 67)

This statement speaks to the importance of incorporating multicultural education into training programs. Practicing music therapists may not even know what they do not know. In essence, we do not know what we do not know.

Toppozada (1995) surveyed music therapists about multicultural practices, analyzing the responses of many practicing music therapists in regard to how education on multicultural music therapy can be achieved. He found that many of the respondents believed that the undergraduate music therapy curriculum needs to incorporate an additional course on ethnomusicology, multicultural counseling, or ethnic studies, while others disagreed based on the already heavy course work demands placed on undergraduate music therapy students.

In addition, the Toppozada (1995) survey explored integrating multicultural awareness and competency into already existing facets of music therapy undergraduate training. For example, in our assessment processes, we learn that our treatment plans must be individualized. We are trained to assess our clients by population and through musical, developmental, cognitive, social/emotional, and physical domains. Why not add the domain of culture?

As previously noted, there is certainly room to take a closer look at the clinical competencies for music therapists regarding what it means to provide culturally competent music therapy services. Simply stating that entry-level music therapists must be able to "demonstrate knowledge" or "demonstrate skill" in regard to working with diverse cultures or in having a knowledge base for music of a given culture does not provide much of a scaffold for fledgling or even seasoned professionals. Many music therapists incorporate culture into their assessments. Those who work with a specific type of assessment, perhaps set up through their employer, may be limited by the documentation they must use. There is no consistent road map for cultural assessment taught in music therapy undergraduate training. Speaking from our own experience, it may be very challenging to meet an expectation when that expectation has not been made clear.

Another perhaps more approachable method of increasing the multicultural education of music therapists beyond the classroom might be the addition of multicultural continuing education for professionals following a model similar to that recently instituted on the topic of ethics in music therapy practice. The expectations for ethics continuing education are very clearly laid out by CBMT, and clinicians have managed to adapt quite well in meeting this new and very important expectation.

Counseling, education, and our allied health profession peers have all begun earnest efforts to increase the development of education and policy regarding multicultural competence in their respective fields. These efforts have resulted in the increased accountability of providers to culturally diverse populations. The progress that our allied professions have made in this area suggests that there are many possible approaches to meeting the multicultural educational needs of new and practicing music therapists. Music therapists themselves have expressed the desire for more education in this area. The changing demographics of the United States, Canada, and beyond would suggest that it is past time that the field of music therapy begin to strategize formal steps for achieving this goal of incorporating/increasing multicultural education for the benefit of music therapy professionals and, moreover, for the benefit of the culturally diverse clients whom we serve.

Conclusion

The approach to cultural music therapy assessment that we have presented here has been developed over 25 collective years in working with children and families from across the globe in the microcosm of the international hospital environment. We share our approach not as experts but as two clinicians who are continually learning. We have both struggled along our paths to providing culturally competent music therapy services for our clients. We have grappled with finding the best approaches to incorporate the client's culture into our assessment and treatment practices. We have both made mistakes in our work and have garnered much of value from each misstep. We have also been able to meet our clients and successfully incorporate culturally competent music therapy practices.

The best practice we will leave you with is humility. It is not an easy thing to embody, but it is essential when we interact with people from a culture(s) other than our own. We have learned that simply saying that we do not know but are willing to learn bridges the chasm between the worlds of our clients and ourselves. When we make a misstep or

mistake, we have learned that saying we are sorry with authenticity bridges any divides created by our own ethnocentrisism. This humility is based in our sincere desire to really know the client so that we can truly accompany them with our music on their path to wellness.

References

American Music Therapy Association. (n.d.). *Standards of education and clinical training*. Retrieved from http://www.musictherapy.org/members/edctstan/

American Music Therapy Association. (2013). *Professional competencies*. Retrieved from http://www.musictherapy.org/about/competencies/

American Music Therapy Association. (2015a). *Code of ethics*. Retrieved from http://www.musictherapy.org/about/ethics/

American Music Therapy Association. (2015b). *Standards of clinical practice*. Retrieved from http://www.musictherapy.org/about/standards/

Baxter, H. T., Berghofer, J. A., MacEwan, L., Nelson, J., Peters, K., & Roberts, P. (2007). *The individualized music therapy assessment profile*. London, UK, & Philadelphia, PA: Jessica Kingsley.

Boxill, E. H., & Chase, K. M. (2007). *Music therapy for developmental disabilities*. Austin, TX: Pro-Ed.

Bruscia, K. E. (1988). Standards for clinical assessment in the arts therapies. *Arts in Psychotherapy, 13*, 5–10.

Canadian Association for Music Therapy. (2002). *Code of ethics*. Retrieved from http://www.musictherapy.ca/documents/official/codeofethics99.pdf

Canadian Council on Social Development. (n.d.). *CCDS's stats & facts demographic profile for Canada*. Retrieved from http://www.ccsd.ca/factsheets/demographics

Cassity, M. D., & Cassity, J. E. (2006). *Multimodal psychiatric music therapy for adults, adolescents, and children: A clinical manual* (3rd ed.). London, UK, & Philadelphia, PA: Jessica Kingsley.

Chase, K. M. (2003). Multicultural music therapy: A review of literature. *Music Therapy Perspectives, 21*(2), 84–88.

Coleman, K. A., & Brunk, B. K. (2003). *SEMTAP Handbook: Special education music therapy assessment process*. Grapevine, TX: Prelude Music Therapy.

EMPACT Consortium. (2012, October 31). *How cultural factors affect minority recruitment to clinical trials*. Retrieved from http://empactconsortium.com/wp-content/uploads/2012/05/Cultural_Factors_508.pdf

Gilgun, J. F. (2004). Qualitative methods and the development of clinical assessment tools. *Qualitative Health Research, 14*(7), 1008–1019.

Kalback, W. E., Trovato, F., & James-Abba, E. (2015). Population. *The Canadian Encyclopedia*. Retrieved from http://www.thecanadianencyclopedia.ca/en/article/population/#h3_jump_3

Kumas-Tan, Z., Beagan, B., Loppie, C., Macleod, A., & Frank, B. (2007). Measures of cultural competence: Examining hidden assumptions. *Academic Medicine, 82*(6), 548–557.

Lipe, A. (2015). Music therapy assessment. In B. L. Wheeler (Ed.), *Music therapy handbook* (pp. 76–90). New York, NY: The Guilford Press.

Magee, W. L., Siegert, R. J., Taylor, S. M., Daveson, B. A., & Lenton-Smith, G. (2016). Music Therapy Assessment Tool for Awareness in Disorders of Consciousness (MATADOC): Reliability and validity of a measure to assess awareness in patients with disorders of consciousness. *Journal of Music Therapy, 53*(1), 1–26. doi:10.1093/jmt/thv017

Pew Research Center. (2013). *Canada's changing religious landscape*. Retrieved from http://www.pewforum.org/2013/06/27/canadas-changing-religious-landscape/

Pew Research Center. (2015). *America's changing religious landscape*. Retrieved from http://www.pewforum.org/2015/05/12/americas-changing-religious-landscape/

Rothwell, P. M. (2005). External validity of randomized controlled trials: "To whom do the results of this trial apply?" *Lancet, 364,* 82–93.

Sue, D. W., Kim, R. H., Casas, M. J., Carter, R. T., Fouad, N. A., Ivey, A. E., … & Vazquez-Nuttall, E. (1998). *Multicultural counseling competencies: Individual and organizational development*. Thousand Oaks, CA: SAGE.

Toppozada, M. R. (1995). Multicultural training for music therapists: An examination of current issues based on a national survey of professional music therapists. *Journal of Music Therapy, 32*(2), 65–90.

U.S. Census Bureau. (2000). *U.S. Census 2000: Demographic profiles*. Retrieved from http://www.census.gov/census2000/demoprofiles.html

U.S. Census Bureau. (2001). *Population by race and Hispanic or Latino origin for the United States: 1990 and 2000 (PHC-T-1)*. Retrieved from http://www.census.gov/population/www/cen2000/briefs/phc-t1/index.html

U.S. Census Bureau. (2011). *Overview of race and Hispanic origin: 2010*. Retrieved from http://www.census.gov/prod/cen2010/briefs/c2010br-02.pdf

Wheeler, B. L. (2013). Music therapy assessment. In R. Cruz & B. Feder (Eds.), *Feder's the art and science of evaluation in the arts therapies* (2nd ed., pp. 344–382). Springfield, IL: Charles C. Thomas.

Whitehead-Pleaux, A., Donnenwerth, A., Robinson, B., Hardy, S., Oswanski, L., Forinash, M., … & York, E. (2012). Lesbian, gay, bisexual, transgender, and questioning: Best practices in music therapy. *Music Therapy Perspectives, 30*(2), 158–166.

Wigram, T., Pedersen, I. N., & Bonde, L. O. (2002). *A comprehensive guide to music therapy: Theory, clinical practice, research and training*. London, UK: Jessica Kingsley.

Chapter 20

TECHNOLOGY AND CULTURALLY COMPETENT MUSIC THERAPY PRACTICE

Annette Whitehead-Pleaux

As we examine culturally competent music therapy practices, it is impossible to not include technology in the conversation. Electronic music technologies (EMTs) have brought one of the biggest changes to our field since music therapy began. EMTs will continue to modify and expand the interventions possible in music therapy. EMTs increase music therapists' access to music and instruments from across the globe as well as create new and expanded opportunities for our clients to engage in music through creation, improvisation, singing, performance, and listening. As we ponder how to better meet the cultural needs of our clients, EMTs may be one of the many tools that music therapists employ.

Electronic Music Technologies 101

Within the broad label of EMTs, there are many types of technologies. These include computers, handheld devices, video game systems, adaptive devices, and electronic instruments.

The first to consider is computers. Computers offer both programs and access to the Internet, which has a variety of sites that pertain to music. Computers include desktops and laptops. Laptops are portable and more often incorporated in music therapy clinical sessions. Computers run a variety of programs or apps, which are digital programs that have one specific function.

Next, handheld devices such as tablets, smartphones, and MP3 players offer a variety of applications (apps) which are similar to computer programs or games. A tablet (tablet computer) is a mobile device, larger than a mobile phone, that has a touch screen. Many tablets use an accelerometer, a device that detects the physical movements of the tablet. Using apps rather than programs, tablets offer a variety of functions, from work-related activities to games, to music listening. One type of tablet often used in music therapy clinical practice is the iPad, which is a tablet computer designed by Apple that has a touch screen and utilizes the same operating system as an iPod Touch or iPhone. A smartphone is a mobile phone that is built on a mobile computing system. Smartphones use apps to provide a variety of functions, similar to those of a tablet. There are various platforms that smartphones employ that allow the phone to run apps as well as play and store media on top of the phone functions. An MP3 or MP4 player is an electronics device that is capable of storing and playing digital media such as audio, images, video, documents, and so forth.

Video game systems represent a third technology category. These systems offer a variety of music-based video games that can focus on playing instruments, composing music, and dancing to music. They vary in the way they are played. Some use a handheld controller that is manipulated through touching buttons. Others use handheld controllers that employ a combination of buttons and accelerometer technology. These require both button play as well as physical movement that often matchs the movement by the avatar within the game. A third type of video game system uses video input of the player's movement to manipulate the avatar within the game. Finally, some video games have specialized controllers that look like the instrument within the game. An example of this is RockBand, which incorporates guitar and drum controllers.

The fourth type of EMTs is adaptive devices, including switches and adaptive communication devices. These have been used by music therapists who work with individuals with intellectual and developmental disabilities, as well as individuals with neurologic dysfunctions, to allow them to communicate and participate in music therapy sessions.

Similarly used for many years by music therapists is the fifth type of EMTs, electronic instruments. These include electronic instruments such as keyboards, Q-chords, DJ scratch pads, and so on. This type of EMTs continues to adapt and expand with each year. These technologies and more fall under the term "EMTs" and are used in music therapy practice.

A final type of technology that has been incorporated into music therapy practice is Bluetooth speakers. These speakers are the same as traditional speakers except for the way in which the Bluetooth speaker connects to the music-producing device. While traditional speakers connect through a cord or wire, Bluetooth uses technology similar to cellular technology that beams a signal from the music device to the speaker. These speakers are often small and portable, perfect for a music therapy session.

As with all music therapy interventions, we do not use EMTs in our sessions without careful consideration in each intervention. When looking at EMTs through a culturally competent msuic therapy practice lens, we see a variety of benefits and limitations that present themselves. As this chapter continues, we explore the benefits and limitations, knowing that this chapter serves only as a starting place for this dialogue. It is hoped that this dialogue will continue within the field of music therapy.

Benefits and Limitations of EMTs

There are a variety of benefits and limitations when using different EMTs within music therapy practice. The benefits can be broken down into the categories of internet marketplaces, music streaming, apps and computer programs, and the internet as a research tool. The limitations include the cultural meaning of technology and cultural rules with technology.

The first and one of the most significant benefits that technology brings to culturally competent music therapy is the internet marketplace, which give us the ability to purchase or download music from nearly every culture. Over the past 10 years, there has been an enormous shift in the availability of music from other cultures through technology. Internet stores such as iTunes and Amazon have begun to expand their offerings to include music from the non-Western and nondominant cultures of the world. Through the Internet, products from smaller music companies, recording labels, and businesses that cater to a specific culture have been accessible for purchase or download. These changes aid music therapists in their quest to find and provide music in our sessions that is from our client's cultures.

Another benefit of the internet marketplace, similar to the first, is the availability of authentic music instruments from across the world. Through the internet, one can purchase nearly any type of instrument and have it delivered to their workplace in a matter of a few days. In addition, many United States–based music companies are creating instruments that have features and sounds similar to those of instruments used in nondominant cultures. Again, via the internet, a music therapist has easy access to these instruments, thus increasing the opportunities to incorporate elements of the client's culture(s) into the music therapy sessions.

The second benefit of EMTs is the increased ways to bring music of the client's culture to the session through Internet sites that allow music streaming. The different types of sites can include internet radio, automated music recommendation services, podcasts, and video-sharing websites. These sites vary with content and in the ways one accesses music on themt. With internet radio sites, the user needs only to go to the site to hear the music. However, the user has little to no control over the content, as the songs are chosen by an internet DJ, not the user. However, these sites allow clients to tune in to radio stations that come from her/his home or the culture with which s/he identifies. Automated music recommendation services (e.g., Pandora, Amazon Prime Music Stations, or Apple Music) require the user to enter a song title, artist, or genre of music. A personalized song list is generated by the website, based on the information the user provides. The user has some control and can often say whether s/he likes or dislikes a song. These likes and dislikes will further refine the music played to fit the individual user's desires. Podcasts are prerecorded shows, often episodic. The user may have to subscribe to the podcast and then can download them to a computer, tablet, smartphone, or MP3 player. Finally, video-sharing websites offer a variety of videos with music content. A user can search for a specific song or artist and can find a variety of videos. Often the user may find the official video from the artist, a variety of unofficial videos created by fans, and official or unofficial video from live performances. It is important for the music therapist to know that the content on all of these sites is not well controlled, especially that from the video-sharing sites, and should be previewed if possible prior to a session. Teaching the client how to access these sites can be an important tool in learning self-care and recreation.

A fourth benefit to using EMTs in culturally competent music therapy practice is apps. Over the past several years, the types, variety, and number of apps available have expanded exponentially. There are a variety of music-based apps available that are applicable to music therapy interventions. These apps can include those that resemble acoustic instruments, songwriting apps, and music-based games. This chapter will focus on the cultural aspects of two types of music-based apps, instrument apps and songwriting apps. At this point in time, the music apps for Apple products far exceed the apps available for Android devices. At the current rates of development and changes in the electronic technology field, it is possible that this may change. Based on the superior quality of the Apple apps, the author will focus on apps for the iPad and iPod Touch/iPhone.

With the explosion of app development over the past years, it is possible to find a music instrument app that simulates the sound of many instruments from across the world. The apps sometimes show a photo or drawing of the instrument. The action required to "play" the instrument can be similar to the action needed to play the real instrument. Some examples of these apps to further illustrate this point include a tabla app requires the user to strike the drum head and an ocarina app that requires the user to blow in the microphone and finger the notes. Other apps do not resemble the instrument or the actions necessary to play it but produce the sound of the instrument. An example of this type of app is ThumbJam, which has a variety of instruments from Western and other cultures, including instruments like the darabukka, cittern, and Scottish smallpipes. Apps like this one feature a screen that denotes the notes or different sounds for the user to touch to "play," but the screen does not resemble the musical instrument at all. It may be a screen with a variety of buttons to touch that will play the different sounds or notes of the instrument. Through the use of apps, music therapists can bring "instruments" of the client's culture to be used in the music therapy interventions.

In addition to apps that feature instruments from a variety of cultures, many instrument apps feature a variety of scales and modes from across the globe. Apps with real instruments, like ThumbJam, feature a variety of acoustic and electronic instrument sounds in which a myriad of different scales can be applied. For example, the user can "play" the Adonai Maiakh scale from Israel on the trumpet or the Arbhi Descending scale from India on the MegaSaw. Other apps that feature electronic instrument sounds, like Bebot and Cosmovox, also have a variety of scales from across the globe. Although these instruments may not have sounds that reflect the traditional or even popular music with which the client may be familiar, having access to scales that are familiar to

Table 1
A Selection of Instrument Apps

App Name	Instruments Contained
Bagpipes	Bagpipes, needs microphone
Bebot	Electronic robot who "sings" in a variety of scales from many cultures
Bongos and Congas	Both types of drums
Celtic Harp	Chord harp sounds; able to change keys
Cosmovox	Electronic instrument that plays a variety of scales from many cultures (many from India)
Darbuka Doumbek Classic	Doumbek
Guqin	A seven-string Chinese instrument; a variety of scales and keys
iKoto	A Japanese harp; a variety of scales
Kalimba Free	Kalimba
Korean Traditional Percussion	A variety of Korean percussion instruments
Pocket Bhangra	A variety of instruments from India
Pocket Shaker	A variety of percussion from aroundcross the world
Shiny Drum	A variety of drums and percussion from many cultures
Thumb Jam	A variety of instruments, real and electronic, from across many cultures; able to change keys
Tingalin	An Albanian lute; a variety of scales.
UD HD	Arabic and Turkish traditional lute; a variety of scales and keys
Zampona	Andean pan flute; able to change scales and notes

the client increase their accessibility and relevance to the client's cultural music home.

Songwriting apps have also changed, expanding to include genres of music from nondominant cultures and loops from instruments from nondominant cultures, as well as varying levels of skill needed to create a quality music product. Apps may incorporate a variety of loops from the dominant cultures as well as nondominant cultures. An example of this is GarageBand. Other apps focus on one specific genre of music from either the dominant or nondominant cultures. An example of this is GrooveMaster, which allows the user to purchase different packs that focus on specific genres, which include heavy metal, hip-hop, reggaeton, reggae, and house, among others. When using a specific genre, like reggaeton, the loops available are from only that genre. Thus the user can create a song that is specific to that genre of music. Another app that is similar and has a variety of genres of music contained within in it is ZoozBeats. The end product usually sounds very similar to the music to which the client likes to listen. By using songwriting apps such as these and others, music therapists can explore ways to further incorporate the

client's culture(s) into the sessions in ways beyond what is accomplishable via traditional acoustic instruments.

Table 2
A Selection of Songwriting Apps

App Name	Culture/Genre of Music
Dubselector	Preselected reggae loops
GarageBand	A variety of loops and instruments from different cultures
GrooveMaker	Reggaeton, reggae, house, hip-hop, techno, club, trance, D 'n' B, electro, and rock
Looptastic	A variety of loops containing genres and instruments from different cultures
Pattern Music	A variety of instruments from different cultures with which the user can compose (pitch, tempo, and note length control)
ZoozBeat	Techno, rock, glitch, salsa, Tejano, etc.; each genre has typical instrumentation with which the user can compose, controlling pitch, tempo, and note length

As with the songwriting apps, there are many different computer software programs that allow the user to create songs. There is songwriting software for both the PC and Apple platforms, and the software varies much as apps do. Some programs contain loops from many different cultures. Examples of these software programs are GarageBand (which is available on Apple products) and Fruity Loops Studio (available for PC products). Other programs focus on a specific genre or a few genres of music, often hip-hop, house, or trance. Many of these software programs allow the user to import samples and create loops from these samples. Thus a music therapist could essentially create samples from portions of music from the client's culture(s) to then incorporate into the song. The client could bring in music files for this use to work with their cultural identity within the music therapy session. In addition to importing samples from music files, these programs often allow for importing sound files by microphone or connection to an electronic instrument or pickup. Finally, many of these programs allow the user to modify any of the samples (pre-existing in the program, imported from a music file, or recorded) through different settings and sound modulators. All of these features allow the music therapist to further cultural expression from the client in ways that acoustic instruments could never allow.

Access to the information highway, the internet, is another huge benefit when working with clients from cultures other than that of the music therapist. No longer does a music therapist need to go to a library or community center to learn about a culture. The internet allows us to research a variety of aspects of the culture: the norms, music, instruments, language, foods, customs, holidays, and so on. With a few keystrokes, we can learn about quite a variety of cultures. However, it is important for music therapists to be wary of internet content, as it is not controlled for quality. There are sites with incorrect information about cultures or the music of a culture. Judicious use of the information available will be of benefit to music therapists as they research cultures. Some important points to keep in mind when researching a culture are, first, to contact agencies or organizations that are for the specific culture you are researching. These agencies and organizations have content control, and the content is often created by members of that culture. Other quality resources to use are universities or colleges that have a specific program on that culture. These programs often have websites about the culture and/or have emails for the researchers who study that culture. Of special interest to music therapists are ethno-musicology programs that focus on specific cultures. These can be of great benefit to a music therapist's journey in understanding more and incorporating elements of the client's culture(s) into the music therapy sessions.

The limitations to using EMTs within culturally competent music therapy practice are fewer than the benefits but no less important to consider.

The first, which has already been stated once, is that the internet does contain incorrect information. Music therapists need to be careful in trusting all they read or hear on an internet website.

Another limitation to consider is a client's unfamiliarity with EMTs or reluctance to engage in the technology, as it may represent much more than the tool that it is to a music therapist. Some of our clients may come from areas where tablet, computer, MP3/MP4 players, or smartphones are not available or available only for the very rich. Clients may not have internet access or even know much about the internet. These technologies may serve to widen the differences between the music therapist and the client, as the technology may represent a higher socioeconomic class, the dominant Western cultures of the United States or Europe, a Western lifestyle, or acculturation.

In addition, different generations have varying levels of comfort, interest, and competence in using technology. Younger generations who have grown up using technology from an early age are known as digital natives. These generations interact with technology with ease and comfort. Their use of technology appears intuitive. However, there are many generations that were not raised with technology but use it. These generations are called digital immigrants. Digital immigrants have learned these technologies with varying levels of proficiency. It is important to be aware of these generational differences but, as with all cultures, to assess each client's comfort with technology individually.

A fourth limitation to EMTs is that some cultures have specific rules about the music, instruments, and levels of technology that an individual may use. Some of these rules are covered in other chapters within this book. Prior to offering a client a drum app, it is important for the music therapist to know if playing an electronic drum is equal to playing the actual drum and whether it is allowed for this client to do so in

her/his/zer culture. It is vital for us to be aware of these rules and, when in doubt, to ask the client or, if the client is a child, ask the client's parent/guardian. Although tedious at times, these questions keep the therapeutic space safe for the client and open up opportunities for the music therapist to better understand and know her/his client.

Giving each client the space to decide whether to explore this new technology within the session can help us to provide the best music therapy interventions to address the client's goals and objectives. If the client decides to not engage in using EMTs, it is OK for the music therapist at some point to explore why.

Finally, as with all culturally competent music therapy interventions, it is important for the us to learn what culture(s) the client identifies with prior to bringing in any culturally competent music therapy interventions. As discussed in other chapters, it is vital for music therapists to learn each client's cultural identity and not make assumptions based on race, religion, nationality, ability, ethnicity, age, gender, sexual orientation, and so on. If the client is unable to answer questions about her/his musical cultural preferences, it is important to talk with others who may be able to give the music therapist an indication of the client's preferences.

Conclusion

Technology, including EMTs and the internet, will continue to change our practice of music therapy over the foreseeable future. These changes are felt strongly in the practice of culturally competent music therapy. Careful application of these technologies can greatly enhance music therapy interventions and client outcomes. As with all culturally competent music therapy, bringing technology to the session and the client requires an approach filled with humility and respect that will create the communication lines to facilitate the best possible outcomes within the music therapy treatment.

References

Burland K., & Magee W. L. (2014). Developing identities using music technology in therapeutic settings. *Psychology of Music, 42*(2), 177–189.

Cevasco A. M., & Hong A. (2011). Utilizing technology in clinical practice: A comparison of board-certified music therapists and music therapy students. *Music Therapy Perspectives, 29,* 65–73.

Cevasco, A. M. (2012). Music technology in the neonatal intensive care unit. In W. Magee (Ed.), *Music technology in therapeutic and health settings* (pp. 111-132). London: Jessica Kingsley.

Crowe B., & Rio R. (2004). Implications of technology in music therapy practice and research for music therapy education: A review of literature. *Journal of Music Therapy, 41,* 282–320.

Egelbrecht R., & Shoemark H. (2015). The acceptability and efficacy of using iPads in music therapy to support wellbeing with older adults: A pilot study. *Australian Journal of Music Therapy, 26,* 52–73.

Hahna N. D. Hadley S. Miller V. H., & Bonaventura M. (2012). Music technology usage in music therapy: A survey of practice. *The Arts in Psychotherapy, 39*(5), 456–464.

Knight A. (2013). Uses of iPad applications in music therapy. *Music Therapy Perspectives, 31*(2), 189–196.

Knight A., & LaGasse A. B. (2012). Re-connecting to music technology: Looking back and looking forward. *Music Therapy Perspectives, 30*(2), 188–195.

Knight, A., & Krout, R. E, (2016). Making sense of today's electronic music technology resources for music therapy. *Music Therapy Perspectives, 34*(2), 1-7.

Krout R. E. (1990). Integrating technology. *Music Therapy Perspectives, 8*(1), 8–9.

Krout R. E. (2008). Assessing and using emerging adaptive electronic music technology to facilitate creative client expression in music therapy. *New Zealand Journal of Music Therapy, 6,* 27–46.

Krout R. E. (2014). Engaging iPad applications with young people with Autism Spectrum Disorders. In W. Magee (Ed.), *Music technology in therapeutic and health settings* (pp. 181–197). London: Jessica Kingsley.

Krout R. E. (2015). *Evaluating and integrating electronic music technology in music therapy.* New Braunfels, TX: Barcelona Publishers.

Kubicek, L. (2014). Creative adaptions of music technology in adult cancer care. In W. Magee (Ed.), *Music technology in therapeutic and health settings* (pp. 165–179). London: Jessica Kingsley.

Lindeck, J. (2014). Applications of music technology in a children's hospice setting. In W. Magee (Ed.), *Music technology in therapeutic and health settings* (pp. 165–179). London: Jessica Kingsley.

Magee W. L. (2006). Electronic technologies in clinical music therapy: A survey of practice and attitudes. Technology and Disability, 18(3), 139–146.

Magee W. L., & Burland K. (2008). Using electronic music technologies in music therapy: Opportunities, limitations and clinical indicators. *British Journal of Music Therapy, 22*(1), 3–15.

Magee, W. L. (2014). Indications and countraindication for using music technology with clinical population: When to use and when not to use. In W. Magee (Ed.), *Music technology in therapeutic and health settings* (pp. 83-110). London: Jessica Kingsley.

Magee, W. L., & Wimberly, D. (2014). Gender-technology relations in the training and practice of music technology in therapeutic settings. In W. Magee (Ed.), *Music technology in therapeutic and health settings* (pp. 311-326). London: Jessica Kingsley.

Martino L., & Bertolami, M. (2014). Using music technology with children and adolescents with visual impairments and additional disabilities. In W. Magee (Ed.), *Music technology in therapeutic and health settings* (pp. 165–179). London: Jessica Kingsley.

Roth E. A. (2014). Music technology for neurologic music therapy. In M. H. Thaut V. Hoemberg (Eds.), *Handbook of neurologic music therapy* (pp. 12–23). New York: Oxford University Press.

Sandnovik, N. (2014). The birth of a therapeutic recording studio: Addressing the needs of the hip-hop generation on an adult inpatient psychiatric unit. In W. Magee (Ed.), *Music technology in therapeutic and health settings* (pp. 247-262). London: Jessica Kingsley.

Street, A. (2014). Using GarageBand music software wit adults with acquired brain injury at Headway East London: Identify, communication, and executive function. In W. Magee (Ed.), *Music technology in therapeutic and health settings* (pp. 217-234). London: Jessica Kingsley.

Weissberger A. (2014). GarageBand as a digital co-facilitator: Creating and capturing moments with adults and elderly with chronic health conditions. In W. Magee (Ed.), *Music technology in therapeutic and health settings* (pp. 279–291). London: Jessica Kingsley.

Whitehead-Pleaux A. P. Clark S. L., & Spall L. E . (2011). Indications and counterindications for electronic music technologies in a pediatric medical setting. *Music and Medicine, 3*(3), 154–162.

Whitehead-Pleaux, A., & Spall, L. (2014). Innovations in medical music therapy: The use of electronic music technologies in a pediatric burn hospital. In W. Magee (Ed.), *Music technology in therapeutic and health settings* (pp. 133-148). London: Jessica Kingsley.

CONCLUSION

Annette Whitehead-Pleaux & Xueli Tan

Are You Ready to Interrupt the Usual?

Together now, we have traveled through theories, facts, research, ideas, and the personal stories of the authors. We have learned why oppression and microaggression exist, as well as our biases and our roles within these systems. We have heard the voices of those who have been oppressed. We also have heard from social justice allies, and they illuminated the paths toward becoming just that. We have learned practical ways to integrate culturally competent practices into our music therapy assessments and interventions. What else is there to consider?

The work of becoming a culturally competent music therapist starts with awareness, with learning, and with listening. But it does not end there. The path then must turn inward. Each of us must keep looking into ourselves. We must turn on all the lights and see even into the dark crevices that we wish not to see. We must learn who we are, how we are with others, where we have biases, where we are oppressed, where we are the oppressor, and where we act in resistance to oppression. After looking deeply at ourselves, we have a choice. Do we want to continue on in this fashion? Or do we decide that we want affect real changes?

While this book brings forth questions for each reader about our own cultural competence, it also brings forth questions about the field of music therapy. We are at a juncture as a field. Are we ready to recognize and honor the voices of the minorities? Are we ready to see below the surface and acknowledge the impact of power and privilege on not only our own lives, but on how we navigate the professional arena? This book is the first to discuss culturally competent music therapy practice in North American in this format. This is a new way to look at culture for many of us.

This book contains many words from our authors that are penned with sincerity, kindness, and courage. At times, the narratives emerged from a place of exhaustion; after all, speaking the language of power, privilege, and oppression takes tremendous strength, resilience, and audacity. Like learning a new language, we are still learning this new vocabulary. At times, we get frustrated because people cannot understand what we are trying to say. At times, we stammer as we try to find the words to explain justice, equity, and inclusion. We get exasperated because our levels of consciousness are misaligned and we are not yet attuned to a common prosody, intonation, and accent. Nevertheless, we must speak.

Our lives begin to end the day we become
silent about things that matter.
—Dr. Martin Luther King, Jr.

Reading this book is not the real work. Changing yourself and speaking your truth—that's the real work.

INDEX